Course   Nutrition
            Vol. 1
            Cabrillo College/West Valley College

http://create.mheducation.com

ISBN-10: 1308106858   ISBN-13: 9781308106854

Contents

Credits

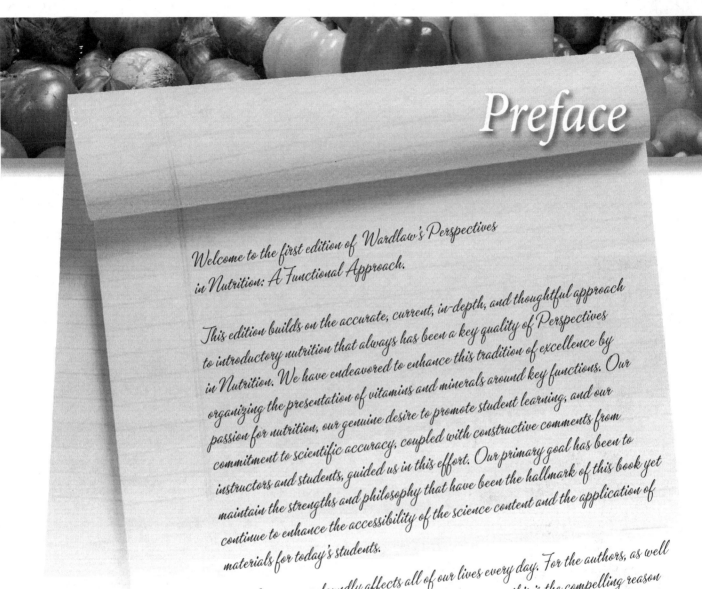

Preface

Welcome to the first edition of Wardlaw's Perspectives in Nutrition: A Functional Approach.

This edition builds on the accurate, current, in-depth, and thoughtful approach to introductory nutrition that always has been a key quality of Perspectives in Nutrition. We have endeavored to enhance this tradition of excellence by organizing the presentation of vitamins and minerals around key functions. Our passion for nutrition, our genuine desire to promote student learning, and our commitment to scientific accuracy, coupled with constructive comments from instructors and students, guided us in this effort. Our primary goal has been to maintain the strengths and philosophy that have been the hallmark of this book yet continue to enhance the accessibility of the science content and the application of materials for today's students.

Nutrition profoundly affects all of our lives every day. For the authors, as well as many other educators, researchers, and clinicians, this is the compelling reason for devoting our careers to this dynamic field. The rapid pace of nutrition research and provocative (and sometimes controversial) findings challenge us all to stay abreast of the latest research and understand its implications for health. We invite you to share with us topics that you believe deserve greater or less attention in the next edition.

To your health!

Carol Byrd-Bredbenner
Gaile Moe
Donna Beshgetoor
Jacqueline Berning
Danita Kelley

Nutrition Basics

A nutritious diet is key to good health and longevity. To learn more, carefully study this text and visit **nutrition.gov.**

PART 1 Nutrition Basics

1 *The Science of Nutrition*

Chapter Outline

1.1 Nutrition Overview

Expert Perspective from the Field: Functional Foods

1.2 Energy Sources and Uses

1.3 The North American Diet

1.4 Nutritional Health Status

1.5 Genetics and Nutrition

1.6 Using Scientific Research to Determine Nutrient Needs

1.7 Evaluating Nutrition Claims, Products, and Advice

Student Learning Outcomes

After studying this chapter, you will be able to

1. Define the terms nutrition, carbohydrates, proteins, lipids (fats and oils), vitamins, minerals, water, and calories.

2. Use the physiological fuel values of energy-yielding nutrients to determine the total energy content (calories) in a food or diet.

3. Describe the major characteristics of the North American diet and the food behaviors that often need improvement.

4. Describe the factors that affect our food choices.

5. Discuss the components and limitations of nutritional assessment.

6. List the attributes of a healthful lifestyle that are consistent with the *Healthy People 2020* goals.

7. Identify diet and lifestyle factors that contribute to the leading causes of death in North America.

8. Describe the role of genetics in the development of nutrition-related diseases.

9. Explain how the scientific method is used in developing hypotheses and theories in the field of nutrition.

10. Identify reliable sources of nutrition information.

IN OUR LIFETIMES, WE WILL eat about 60 tons of food served at 70,000 meals and countless snacks. Research over the last 50 years has shown that the foods we eat have a profound impact on our health and longevity. A healthy diet—especially one rich in fruits and vegetables—coupled with frequent exercise can prevent *and* treat many age-related diseases.[1] In contrast, eating a poor diet and getting too little exercise are **risk factors** for many common life-threatening chronic diseases, such as cardiovascular (heart) disease, diabetes, and certain forms of cancer.[2, 3] Another diet-related problem, drinking too much alcohol, can impair nutritional status and is associated with liver disease, some forms of cancer, accidents, and suicides. As you can see in the chart (Fig. 1-1), diet plays a role in the development of most of the leading causes of death in the U.S. The combination of poor diet and too little physical activity is indirectly the second leading cause of death. In addition, obesity is considered the second leading cause of preventable death (smoking is the first).[4]

We live longer than our ancestors did, so preventing age-related diseases is more important now than ever before. Today, many people want to know more about how nutritious dietary choices can bring the goal of a long, healthy life within reach.[5] They may wonder what the best dietary choices are, how nutrients contribute to health, or if multivitamin and mineral supplements are needed. How can people know if they are eating too much saturated fat, *trans* fat, or cholesterol? Why are carbohydrates important? Is it possible to get too much protein?

4   **PART 1**   Nutrition Basics

Figure 1-1 Leading causes of death in the U.S. The major health problems in North America are largely caused by a poor diet, excessive energy intake, and not enough physical activity.

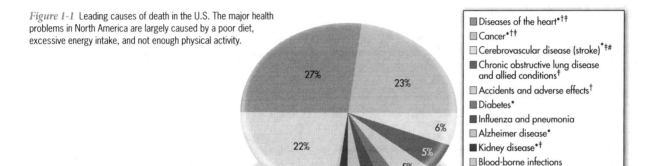

- ▉ Diseases of the heart$^{\bullet\dagger\ddagger}$
- ☐ Cancer$^{\bullet\dagger\ddagger}$
- ☐ Cerebrovascular disease (stroke)$^{\bullet\ddagger\#}$
- ▉ Chronic obstructive lung disease and allied conditions†
- ☐ Accidents and adverse effects†
- ▉ Diabetes$^{\bullet}$
- ▉ Influenza and pneumonia
- ▉ Alzheimer disease$^{\bullet}$
- ▉ Kidney disease$^{\bullet\dagger}$
- ☐ Blood-borne infections
- ☐ All other causes

From Centers for Disease Control and Prevention, National Vital Statistics Report. Canadian statistics are quite similar.

$^{\bullet}$ Causes of death in which diet plays a part
† Causes of death in which excessive alcohol consumption plays a part
‡ Causes of death in which tobacco use plays a part
$^{\#}$ Diseases of the heart and cerebrovascular disease are included in the more global term *cardiovascular disease.*

Is the food supply safe to eat? Would a vegetarian diet lead to better health? This book, beginning with this chapter, will help you build the nutrition knowledge base needed to answer these questions (and many more!) and apply this knowledge to safeguard your health, as well as the health of others.

As you begin your study of nutrition, keep in mind that this field of study draws heavily on chemistry, biology, and other sciences. For the greatest understanding of nutrition principles, you may want to review human physiology (Appendix A), basic chemistry concepts (Appendix B), and the metric system (Appendix H).

 1.1 Nutrition Overview

▶ Bold terms in the book are defined in the Glossary. Bold terms also are defined in the text and/or chapter margin when first presented.

The American Medical Association defines **nutrition** as the "science of food; the nutrients and the substances therein; their action, interaction, and balance in relation to health and disease; and the process by which the organism (e.g., human body) ingests, digests, absorbs, transports, utilizes, and excretes food substances." Food provides the nutrients needed to fuel, build, and maintain all body cells.

Nutrients

You probably are already familiar with the terms *carbohydrates, lipids (fats and oils), proteins, vitamins,* and *minerals* (Table 1-1). These, plus water, make up the 6 classes of nutrients in food. **Nutrients** are substances essential for health that the body cannot make or makes in quantities too small to support health.

To be considered an essential nutrient, a substance must have these characteristics:

- It has a specific biological function.
- Removing it from the diet leads to a decline in human biological function, such as the normal functions of the blood cells or nervous system.
- Adding the omitted substance back to the diet before permanent damage occurs restores to normal those aspects of human biological function impaired by its absence.

Table 1-1 Essential Nutrients in the Human Diet*

Energy-Yielding Nutrients

Carbohydrate	Lipids (Fats and Oils)		Protein (Amino Acids)		
Glucose (or a carbohydrate that yields glucose)	Linoleic acid (omega-6) a-Linolenic acid (omega-3)	Histidine Isoleucine Leucine	Lysine Methionine Phenylalanine	Threonine Tryptophan Valine

Non-Energy-Yielding Nutrients

Vitamins		Minerals			
Water-Soluble	**Fat-Soluble**	**Major**	**Trace**	**Some Questionable Minerals**	**Water**
Thiamin	A	Calcium	Chromium	Arsenic	Water
Riboflavin	D	Chloride	Copper	Boron	
Niacin	E	Magnesium	Fluoride	Nickel	
Pantothenic acid	K	Phosphorus	Iodide	Silicon	
Biotin		Potassium	Iron	Vanadium	
B-6		Sodium	Manganese		
B-12		Sulfur	Molybdenum		
Folate			Selenium		
C			Zinc		

*This table includes nutrients that the current *Dietary Reference Intakes* and related publications list for humans. There is some disagreement about whether the questionable minerals and certain other minerals not listed in the table are essential. Fiber could be added to the list of essential substances, but it is not a nutrient (see Chapter 5). The vitamin-like compound choline plays essential roles in the body but is not listed under the vitamin category at this time. Alcohol is a source of energy, but it is not an essential nutrient.

Nutrients can be assigned to 3 functional categories:

1. Those that primarily provide energy (typically expressed in kilocalories [kcal]).
2. Those that are important for growth and development (and later maintenance).
3. Those that keep body functions running smoothly. Some overlap exists among these groupings. The energy-yielding nutrients and water make up a major portion of most foods.[6]

Because carbohydrates, proteins, lipids, and water are needed in large amounts, they are called **macronutrients.** In contrast, vitamins and minerals are needed in such small amounts in the diet that they are called **micronutrients.** Let's now look more closely at the classes of nutrients.

Provide Energy	Promote Growth and Development	Regulate Body Processes
Most carbohydrates	Proteins	Proteins
Proteins	Lipids	Some lipids
Most lipids (fats and oils)	Some vitamins	Some vitamins
	Some minerals	Some minerals
	Water	Water

Alcoholic beverages are rich in energy (calories), but alcohol is not an essential nutrient.

6 **PART 1** Nutrition Basics

Many foods are rich sources of nutrients that we recognize today as essential for health.

Carbohydrates

Carbohydrates are composed mainly of the **elements** carbon, hydrogen, and oxygen. Fruits, vegetables, grains, and beans are the primary dietary sources of carbohydrate. The main types of carbohydrates are simple and complex. Small carbohydrate structures are called sugars or simple carbohydrates—table sugar (sucrose) and blood sugar (glucose) are examples. Some sugars, such as glucose, can chemically bond together to form large carbohydrates, called polysaccharides or complex carbohydrates (Fig. 1-2). Examples of complex carbohydrates include the starch in grains and the glycogen stored in our muscles. Fiber is another type of complex carbohydrate that forms the structure of plants.

Glucose, which the body can produce from simple carbohydrates and starch, is a major source of energy in most cells. It and most other carbohydrates provide an average of 4 calories per gram (kcal/g).[7] (Fiber provides little energy because it cannot be broken down by digestive processes.) When too little carbohydrate is eaten to supply sufficient glucose, the body is forced to make glucose from proteins. (Chapter 5 focuses on carbohydrates.)

Lipids

Like carbohydrates, lipids (e.g., fats, oils, and cholesterol) are **compounds** composed mostly of the elements carbon, hydrogen, and oxygen (Fig. 1-3). Note that the term

macronutrient Nutrient needed in gram quantities in the diet.

micronutrient Nutrient needed in milligram or microgram quantities in the diet.

element Substance that cannot be separated into simpler substances by chemical processes. Common elements in nutrition include carbon, oxygen, hydrogen, nitrogen, calcium, phosphorus, and iron.

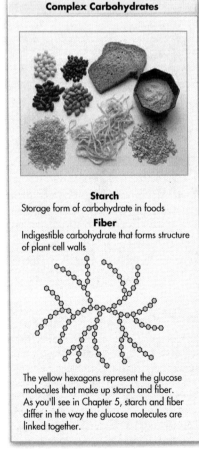

Figure 1-2 Two views of carbohydrates—chemical and dietary perspectives.

fats refers to lipids that are solid at room temperature, whereas oils are those that are liquid at room temperature. Lipids yield more energy per gram than carbohydrates—on average, 9 calories per gram. (See Chapter 9 for details concerning the reason for the high energy yield of lipids.) Lipids are insoluble in water but can dissolve in certain organic solvents (e.g., ether and benzene).

The lipid type called a **triglyceride** is the major form of fat in foods and a key energy source for the body. Triglycerides are also the major form of energy stored in the body. They are composed of 3 fatty acids attached to a glycerol **molecule**. Fatty acids are long chains of carbon flanked by hydrogen with an acid group attached to the end opposite glycerol.

Most lipids can be separated into 2 basic types—saturated and unsaturated—based on the chemical structure of their dominant fatty acids. This difference helps determine whether a lipid is solid or liquid at room temperature, as well as its effect on health. Although almost all foods contain a variety of saturated and unsaturated fatty acids, plant oils tend to contain mostly unsaturated fatty acids, which make them liquid at room temperature. Many animal fats are rich in saturated fatty acids, which make them solid at room temperature. Unsaturated fats tend to be healthier than saturated fats—saturated fat raises blood cholesterol, which can clog arteries and eventually lead to cardiovascular disease.

Two specific unsaturated fatty acids—linoleic acid and alpha-linolenic acid—are essential nutrients. They must be supplied by our diets. These essential fatty acids have many roles, including being structural components of cell walls and helping regulate blood pressure and nerve transmissions. A few tablespoons of vegetable oil daily and eating fish at least twice weekly supply sufficient amounts of essential fatty acids.[7]

Some foods also contain *trans* fatty acids—unsaturated fats that have been processed to change their structure from the more typical *cis* form to the *trans* form (see Chapter 6). These are found primarily in deep-fried foods (e.g., doughnuts and french fries), baked snack foods (e.g., cookies and crackers), and solid fats (e.g., stick margarine and shortening). Large amounts of *trans* fats in the diet pose health risks, so, like saturated fat, their intake should be minimized.[7] (Chapter 6 focuses on lipids.)

Proteins

Proteins, like carbohydrates and fats, are composed of the elements carbon, oxygen, and hydrogen (Fig. 1-4). Proteins also contain another element—nitrogen. Proteins are the main structural material in the body. For example, they are a major part of bone and muscle; they also are important components in blood, cell membranes, **enzymes,** and immune factors.[7] Proteins can provide energy for the body—on average, 4 calories per gram; however, the body typically uses little protein to meet its daily energy needs.

Proteins are formed by the bonding together of amino acids. Twenty common amino acids are found in food; 9 of these are essential nutrients for adults, and 1 additional amino acid is essential for infants. (Chapter 7 focuses on proteins.)

Vitamins

Vitamins have a wide variety of chemical structures and can contain the elements carbon, hydrogen, nitrogen, oxygen, phosphorus, sulfur, and others. The main function of vitamins is to enable many **chemical reactions** to occur in the body. Some of these reactions help release the energy trapped in carbohydrates, lipids, and proteins. Vitamins themselves provide no usable energy for the body.

The 13 vitamins are divided into 2 groups. Fat-soluble vitamins (vitamins A, D, E, and K) dissolve in fat. Vitamin C and the B-vitamins (thiamin, riboflavin, niacin, vitamin B-6, pantothenic acid, biotin, folate, and vitamin B-12) are water-soluble vitamins. The vitamin groups often act quite differently. For example, cooking is more likely to destroy water-soluble vitamins

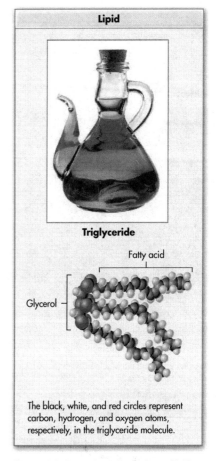

Figure 1-3 Chemical and dietary views of lipids.

atom Smallest unit of an element that still has all of the properties of the element. An atom contains protons, neutrons, and electrons.

compound Atoms of 2 or more elements bonded together in specific proportions.

molecule Atoms linked (bonded) together; the smallest part of a compound that still has all the properties of the compound.

enzyme Compound that speeds the rate of a chemical process but is not altered by the process. Almost all enzymes are proteins.

chemical reaction Interaction between 2 chemicals that changes both chemicals.

Protein

**Hemoglobin
(protein found in red blood cells)**

Amino acids (protein building blocks) are
used to build body proteins like this one.

Figure 1-4 Chemical and dietary views
of protein.

organic compound Substance that
contains carbon atoms bonded to hydrogen
atoms in the chemical structure.

inorganic substance Substance lacking
carbon atoms bonded to hydrogen atoms in
the chemical structure.

metabolism Chemical processes in the
body that provide energy in useful forms and
sustain vital activities.

phytochemicals Physiologically active
compounds found in plants that may provide
health benefits.

zoochemicals Physiologically active
compounds found in foods of animal origin
that may provide health benefits.

than fat-soluble vitamins. Water-soluble vitamins are excreted from the body much more readily than fat-soluble vitamins. As a result, fat-soluble vitamins, especially vitamin A, are much
more likely to accumulate in excessive amounts in the body, which then can cause toxicity.
(Vitamins are the focus of Chapters 12 to 15.)

Minerals

The nutrients discussed so far are all complex organic compounds, whereas minerals are struc-
turally very simple, inorganic substances. The chemical structure of an **organic compound**
contains carbon atoms bonded to hydrogen atoms, whereas an **inorganic substance** generally
does not. In this case, the term *organic* is not related to the farming practices that produce
organic foods (these are described in Chapter 3).

Minerals typically function in the body as groups of one or more of the same atoms
(e.g., sodium or potassium) or as parts of mineral combinations, such as the calcium and
phosphorus-containing compound called hydroxyapatite, found in bones. Because they are
elements, minerals are not destroyed during cooking. (However, they can leak into cooking
water and get discarded if that water is not consumed.) Minerals yield no energy for the body
but are required for normal body function. For instance, minerals play key roles in the nervous system, skeletal system, and water balance.

Minerals are divided into 2 groups: major minerals and trace minerals. Major minerals
are needed daily in gram amounts. Sodium, potassium, chloride, calcium, and phosphorus
are examples of major minerals. Trace minerals are those that we need in amounts of less than
100 mg daily. Examples of trace minerals are iron, zinc, copper, and selenium. (Minerals are
the focus of Chapters 12 to 15.)

Water

Water is the sixth class of nutrients. Although sometimes overlooked as a nutrient, water is
the nutrient needed in the largest quantity. Water (H_2O) has numerous vital functions in the
body. It acts as a solvent and lubricant and is a medium for transporting nutrients to cells.
It also helps regulate body temperature. Beverages, as well as many foods, supply water. The
body even makes some water as a by-product of **metabolism.** (Water is examined in detail
in Chapter 14.)

Phytochemicals and Zoochemicals

Phytochemicals (plant components in fruits, vegetables, legumes, and whole grains)
and **zoochemicals** (components in animals) are physiologically active compounds.
They are not considered essential nutrients in the diet. Still, many of these substances provide
significant health benefits.[8] For instance, numerous studies show reduced cancer risk among
people who regularly consume fruits and veg-
etables. Researchers surmise that some
phytochemicals in fruits and vegetables block the development
of cancer (see Chapter 12).[9, 10]

A tomato contains the phytochemical lycopene;
thus, it can be called a functional food.

Expert Perspective from the Field

Functional Foods

Foods rich in phytochemicals and zoochemicals are sometimes referred to as functional foods. A functional food provides health benefits beyond those supplied by the traditional nutrients it contains—the food offers additional components that may decrease disease risk and/or promote optimal health. According to Dr. Clare Hasler,* **functional foods** fall into four categories.[8]

The phytochemicals and zoochemicals present naturally in unmodified whole foods like fruits and vegetables are thought to provide many health benefits (see Table 1-2). Foods modified by adding nutrients, phytochemicals, zoochemicals, or herbs (see Chapter 18) also may provide health benefits. For instance, margarine fortified with plant stanols may help lower blood cholesterol and prevent cardiovascular disease. Medical foods are designed to help enhance the management of health conditions. An example is phenylalanine-restricted formula fed to infants born with the inborn error of metabolism condition called phenylketonuria (PKU) (see Chapter 9). This formula helps them develop normally. Dr. Hasler indicated that the array of modified foods, medical foods, and special dietary use foods is expanding rapidly. An important trend in the food industry is adding nutrients, phytochemicals, and other components in hopes of boosting the healthfulness of the food supply.

Clare M. Hasler, Ph.D., MBA is an international authority on functional foods. She is the founding executive director of the Robert Mondavi Institute for Wine and Food Science at the University of California, Davis and serves as the university's primary liaison to the wine and food industries. Dr. Hasler also was the founding director of the Functional Foods for Health Program at the University of Illinois and is the lead author on the Academy of Nutrition and Dietetics (formerly American Dietetic Association) Position Paper on Functional Foods.

Functional Food Categories[8]

Conventional Foods: Unmodified Whole Foods

Fruits	Spices	Dairy products
Vegetables	Nuts	Fish
Herbs		

Modified Foods: Fortified, Enriched, or Enhanced Foods

Calcium-fortified orange juice
Omega-3-enriched bread
Breakfast bars enhanced with ginkgo biloba
Cheese made with plant sterols

Medical Foods: Food, Formula, or Supplement Used under Medical Supervision to Manage a Health Condition

Phenylalanine-free formulas for phenylketonuria (PKU)
Limbrel for osteoarthritis
Axona for Alzheimer disease
VSL#3 for ulcerative colitis

Special Dietary Use Foods: Foods That Help Meet a Special Dietary Need

Infant formula for infants
Lactose-free foods for lactose intolerance
Sugar-free foods for weight loss

Some phytochemicals and zoochemicals also have been linked to a reduced risk of cardiovascular disease. It will likely take many years for scientists to unravel the important effects of the many different phytochemicals and zoochemicals in foods. Multivitamin and mineral supplements currently contain few or none of these beneficial chemicals. Thus, nutrition and health experts suggest that a diet rich in fruits, vegetables, legumes, and whole-grain breads and cereals is the most reliable way to obtain the potential benefits of phytochemicals.[11] In addition, foods of animal origin, such as fatty fish, can provide the beneficial zoochemical omega-3 fatty acids (see Chapter 6), and fermented dairy products provide probiotics (see Chapter 4). Table 1-2 lists some phytochemicals under study with their common food sources.

▶ To learn more about bioactive compounds in foods, visit www.sigma-aldrich.com/life-science/nutrition-research/learning-center/bioactive-nutrient-explorer.html.

10 **PART 1** Nutrition Basics

Table 1-2 **Examples of Phytochemicals and Zoochemicals under Study**[6]

Phytochemicals	Food Sources
Allyl sulfides/organosulfides	Garlic, onions, leeks
Saponins	Garlic, onions, licorice, legumes
Carotenoids (e.g., lycopene)	Orange, red, yellow fruits and vegetables (egg yolks are a source as well)
Monoterpenes	Oranges, lemons, grapefruit
Capsaicin	Chili peppers
Lignans	Flaxseed, berries, whole grains
Indoles	Cruciferous vegetables (broccoli, cabbage, kale)
Isothiocyanates	Cruciferous vegetables, especially broccoli
Phytosterols	Soybeans, other legumes, cucumbers, other fruits and vegetables
Flavonoids	Citrus fruit, onions, apples, grapes, red wine, tea, chocolate, tomatoes
Isoflavones	Soybeans, other legumes
Catechins	Tea
Ellagic acid	Strawberries, raspberries, grapes, apples, bananas, nuts
Anthocyanosides	Red, blue, and purple plants (eggplant, blueberries)
Fructooligosaccharides	Onions, bananas, oranges (small amounts)
Stilbenoids (e.g., resveratrol)	Blueberries, grapes, peanuts, red wine
Zoochemicals	**Food Sources**
Sphingolipids	Meat, dairy products
Conjugated linoleic acid	Meat, cheese

Knowledge Check

1. What are the 6 classes of nutrients?
2. What characteristics do the macronutrients share?
3. How are vitamins categorized?
4. How are minerals different from carbohydrates, fat, protein, and vitamins?
5. What are phytochemicals and zoochemicals?

1.2 Energy Sources and Uses

Humans obtain the energy needed to perform body functions and do work from carbohydrates, fats, and proteins. Alcohol is also a source of energy, supplying about 7 calories per gram. It is not considered an essential nutrient, however, because alcohol has no required function. After digesting and absorbing energy-producing nutrients, the body transforms the energy trapped in carbohydrate, protein, fat, and alcohol into other forms of energy in order to do the following:

- Build new compounds
- Perform muscular movements
- Promote nerve transmissions
- Maintain **ion** balance within cells

ion Atom with an unequal number of electrons (negative charges) and protons (positive charges). Negative ions have more electrons than protons; positive ions have more protons than electrons.

Nutrition Facts

Serving Size 1 slice (36g)   Servings Per Container 19

Amount Per Serving

Calories 80   Calories from Fat 10

	% Daily Value*			% Daily Value*
Total Fat 1g	**2%**	**Total Carbohydrate** 15g		**5%**
Saturated Fat 0g	**0%**	Dietary Fiber 2g		**8%**
Trans Fat less than 1g	**			
Cholesterol 0mg	**0%**	Sugars less than 1g		
Sodium 200mg	**8%**	**Protein** 3g		

Vitamin A 0%   Vitamin C 0%   Calcium 0%   Iron 4%

HONEY WHEAT BREAD

*Percent Daily Values (DV) are based on a 2000 calorie diet. Your daily values may be higher or lower depending on your calorie needs:

		Calories:	2000	2500
Total Fat	Less than		65g	80g
Sat Fat	Less than		20g	25g
Cholesterol	Less than		300mg	300mg
Sodium	Less than		2400mg	2400mg
Total Carbohydrate			300g	375g
Dietary Fiber			25g	30g

** Intake of *trans* fat should be as low as possible.

INGREDIENTS: WHOLE WHEAT, WATER, ENRICHED WHEAT FLOUR [FLOUR, MALTED BARLEY, NIACIN, REDUCED IRON, THIAMINE MONONITRATE (VITAMIN B1) AND RIBOFLAVIN (VITAMIN B2)], CORN SYRUP, PARTIALLY HYDROGENATED COTTONSEED OIL, SALT, YEAST.

Figure 1-5 Use the nutrient values on the Nutrition Facts label to calculate the energy content of a food. Based on carbohydrate, fat, and protein content, a serving of this food (honey wheat bread) contains 81 kcal ([15 × 4] [1 × 9] [3 × 4] = 81). The label lists 80 because Nutrition Facts labels round values.

(See Chapter 4 for more on digestion and absorption. Chapter 9 describes how energy is released from chemical bonds and then used by body cells to support the processes just described.)

Calorie is often the term used to express the amount of energy in foods. Technically, a **calorie** is the amount of heat energy it takes to raise the temperature of 1 gram of water 1 degree Celsius (1°C). Because a calorie is such a tiny measure of heat, food energy is more accurately expressed in terms of the kilocalorie (kcal), which equals 1000 calories. (If the *c* in calories is capitalized, this also signifies kilocalories.) A **kilocalorie (kcal)** is the amount of heat energy it takes to raise the temperature of 1000 g (1 liter) of water 1°C. In everyday usage, the word *calorie* (without a capital *c*) also is used to mean kilocalorie. Thus, the term *calorie* and its abbreviation, *kcal,* are used throughout this book. Any values given on food labels in calories are actually in kilocalories (Fig. 1-5).

The calories in food can be measured using a bomb calorimeter (see Chapter 10). Or they can be estimated by multiplying the amount of carbohydrates, proteins, lipids, and alcohol in a food by their physiological fuel values. The physiological fuel values are 4, 9, 4, and 7 for carbohydrate, fat, protein, and alcohol, respectively. These values are adjusted to account for the extent to which foods can be digested and substances (e.g., waxes and fibers) that humans cannot digest. Thus, they should be considered estimates.

Physiological fuel values can be used to determine the calories in food. Consider these foods:

Physiological fuel values.

Carbohydrate
4 kcal per gram

Protein
4 kcal per gram

Energy sources for body functions

Alcohol
7 kcal per gram

Fat
9 kcal per gram

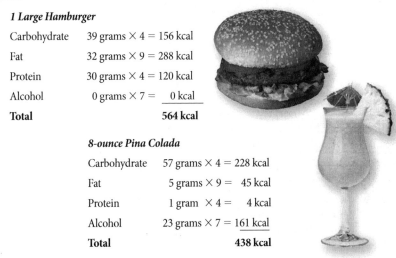

1 Large Hamburger

Carbohydrate	39 grams × 4 = 156 kcal
Fat	32 grams × 9 = 288 kcal
Protein	30 grams × 4 = 120 kcal
Alcohol	0 grams × 7 = 0 kcal
Total	**564 kcal**

8-ounce Pina Colada

Carbohydrate	57 grams × 4 = 228 kcal
Fat	5 grams × 9 = 45 kcal
Protein	1 gram × 4 = 4 kcal
Alcohol	23 grams × 7 = 161 kcal
Total	**438 kcal**

▶ Many scientific journals express energy content of food as kilojoules (kJ), rather than calories. A mass of 1 gram moving at a velocity of 1 meter/second possesses the energy of 1 joule (J); 1000 J = 1 kJ. Heat and work are two forms of energy; thus, measurements expressed in terms of kilocalories (a heat measure) are interchangeable with measurements expressed in terms of kilojoules (a work measure): 1 kcal = 4.18 kJ.

kilocalorie (kcal) Heat energy needed to raise the temperature of 1000 grams of water 1 degree Celsius.

These values also can be used to determine the portion of total energy intake that carbohydrate, fat, protein, and alcohol provide to your diet. Assume that one day you consume 283 g of carbohydrates, 60 g of fat, 75 g of protein, and 9 g of alcohol. This consumption yields a total of 2035 kcal ([283 × 4] + [60 × 9] + [75 × 4] + [9 × 7] = 2035). The percentage of your total energy intake derived from each nutrient can then be determined:

% of energy intake as carbohydrate = (283 × 4) / 2035 = 0.56 × 100 = 56%

% of energy intake as fat = (60 × 9) / 2035 = 0.27 × 100 = 27%

% of energy intake as protein = (75 × 4) / 2035 = 0.15 × 100 = 15%

% of energy intake as alcohol = (9 × 7) / 2035 = 0.03 × 100 = 3%

Knowledge Check

1. What does the term *calorie* mean?
2. How do calories, kilocalories, and kilojoules differ?
3. How many calories are in a food that has 8 g carbohydrate, 2 g alcohol, 4 g fat, and 2 g protein?

1.3 The North American Diet

Large surveys are conducted in the U.S. and Canada to determine what people are eating. The U.S. government uses the National Health and Nutrition Examination Survey (NHANES) administered by the U.S. Department of Health and Human Services. In Canada, this information is gathered by Health Canada in conjunction with Agriculture and Agrifood Canada. Results from these surveys and others show that North American adults consume, on average, 16% of their energy intake as proteins, 50% as carbohydrates, and 33% as fats. These percentages are estimates and vary slightly from year to year and to some extent from person to person. Although these percentages fall within a healthy range[12] (see Chapter 2), many people are eating more than they need to maintain a healthy weight.[12, 13]

Animal sources, such as meat, seafood, dairy products, and eggs, supply about two-thirds of the protein intake for most North Americans; plant sources provide only about a third. In many other parts of the world, it is just the opposite: plant proteins—from rice, beans, corn, and other vegetables—dominate protein intake. About half the carbohydrate in North American diets comes from simple carbohydrates (sugars); the other half comes from starches (e.g., pastas, breads, and potatoes). Most North Americans need to reduce sugar intake and increase intake of starch and fiber. Because approximately 60% of dietary fat comes from animal sources and only 40% from plant sources, many North Americans are consuming far more saturated fat and cholesterol than is recommended.

These surveys also indicate that most of us could improve our diets by focusing on rich food sources of vitamin A, vitamin E, iron, and calcium and reducing our intake of sodium. Nutrient intake varies in some demographic groups, which means these individuals need to pay special attention to certain nutrients. For example, older adults often get too little vitamin D and women of childbearing years frequently have inadequate iron intake.

In terms of food, many North Americans could improve their nutrient intake by moderating intake of sugared soft drinks and fatty foods and eating more fruits, vegetables, whole-grain breads, and reduced-fat dairy products. Vitamin and mineral supplements also can help meet nutrient needs but, as you'll see in Chapter 12, they cannot fully make up for a poor diet in all respects.[14]

Increasing vegetable intake, such as a daily salad, is one strategy to boost intake of important nutrients.

What Influences Our Food Choices?

Although we have to eat to obtain the nutrients needed to survive, many factors other than health and nutrition affect food choices. Daily food intake is a complicated mix of the need to satisfy **hunger** (physical need for food) and social and psychological needs (Fig. 1-6).[15, 16] In areas of the world where food is plentiful and fairly easy to access (e.g., the U.S., Canada, Europe, Australia, and Japan), the food selected to meet our needs is largely guided by **appetite**—the psychological desire to eat certain foods and reject others. Appetite and food choice depend on many factors.

- *Food flavor, texture, and appearance preferences*—for many people, these are the most important factors affecting food choices. Creating more flavorful foods that are both healthy and profitable is a major focus of the food industry.
- *Culture* (knowledge, beliefs, religion, and traditions shared by a group or social network of people) teaches individuals which foods are considered proper or appropriate to eat and which are not. For example, many people in North America believe it is proper to eat beef; however, people in some cultures never consider eating beef. Some cultures savor foods such as blood, mice, and insects—even though these foods are packed with nutrients and safe to eat, few North Americans feel they are proper to eat. Early experiences with people, places, and situations influence lifelong food choices. New immigrants often retain the diet patterns of their country of origin until they

The major health problems in North America are largely caused by a poor diet, excessive energy intake, and not enough physical activity.

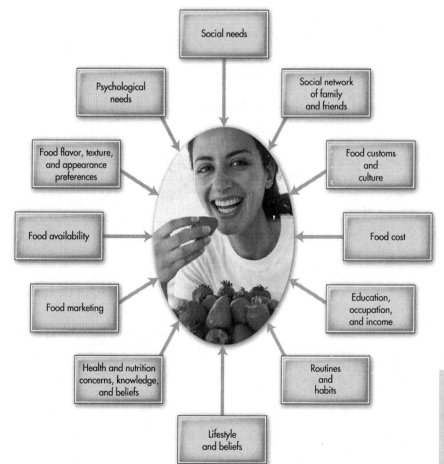

Figure 1-6 Food choices are affected by many factors. Which have the greatest impact on your food choices?

hunger Primarily physiological (internal) drive for food.

appetite Primarily psychological (external) influences that encourage us to find and eat food, often in the absence of obvious hunger.

14 **PART 1** Nutrition Basics

Take Action

Why You Eat What You Do

Choose 1 day of the week that is typical of your eating pattern. List all the foods and drinks you consume for 24 hours. Using the factors that influence food choices discussed in Section 1.3, indicate why you consumed each item. Note that there can be more than one reason for choosing a particular food or drink.

Now ask yourself: What was the most frequent reason for eating or drinking? To what extent are health or nutrition concerns the reason for your food choices? Should you make these reasons higher priorities?

become acculturated (i.e., they have adopted the cultural traits or social patterns of the new country).

- *Lifestyle* includes the way we spend our resources and assign priorities. People with very busy lives often have limited time and energy to buy and prepare foods, so they opt for convenience or fast food. For some, it may be more important to spend extra time working rather than making it a priority to exercise and eat healthfully.

- *Routines and habits* related to food and eating affect what as well as when we eat. Most of us eat primarily from a core group of foods—only about 100 basic items account for 75% of a person's total food intake.

- *Food cost and availability* are important but play only moderate roles in food choices for many of us because food is relatively inexpensive and widely available in North America.[1] In fact, we spend only about 10% of after-tax income on food.

- *Environment* includes your surroundings and experiences. In North America, the environment is filled with opportunities to obtain affordable, delicious, high-calorie food—vending machines, bake sales, food courts in shopping areas, and candy displays in bookstores—and encourages (via marketing) the consumption of these foods. Experiences with friends, family, and others also can influence food choices.

- *Food marketing* is any type of action a company takes to create a desire in consumers to buy its food; *advertising* is one type of food marketing. The food industry in the U.S. spends well over $34 billion annually on advertising. Some of this advertising is helpful, such as when it promotes the importance of calcium and fiber intake. However, the food industry more frequently advertises fast food, highly sweetened cereals, cookies, cakes, and pastries because such products generate the greatest profits.

- *Health and nutrition concerns, knowledge, and beliefs* also can affect food choices. Those most concerned about health and who have the greatest nutrition knowledge tend to be well-educated, middle-income professionals. The same people are generally health-oriented, have active lifestyles, and work hard to keep their bodies at a healthy weight.

Knowledge Check

1. What type of food provides most of the protein in the diets of North Americans?
2. Which types of carbohydrates do most North Americans need to increase in their diets?
3. Which vitamins and minerals do many North Americans need to increase in their diets?
4. What factors affect food choices?

1.4 Nutritional Health Status

In a well-nourished person, the total daily intake of protein, fat, and carbohydrate weighs about 450 g (about 1 pound). In contrast, the typical daily mineral intake weighs about 20 g (about 4 teaspoons) and the daily vitamin intake weighs less than 300 mg (1/15th of a teaspoon). These nutrients can come from a variety of sources—fruits, vegetables, meats, dairy products, or other foods. Our body cells are not concerned with which food supplied a nutrient—what is important, however, is that each nutrient be available in the amounts needed for the body to function normally.

The body's nutritional health is determined by the sum of its status with respect to each nutrient. There are 3 general categories of nutritional status: desirable nutrition, undernutrition, and overnutrition. The common term *malnutrition* can refer to either overnutrition or undernutrition, neither of which is conducive to good health.

Optimal, or **desirable, nutritional status** for a particular nutrient is the state in which the body tissues have enough of the nutrient to support normal functions, as well as to build and maintain surplus stores that can be used in times of increased need.[17] A desirable nutritional status can be achieved by obtaining essential nutrients from a variety of foods.

Undernutrition occurs when nutrient intake does not meet nutrient needs, causing surplus stores to be used. Once nutrient stores are depleted and tissue concentrations of an essential nutrient fall sufficiently low, the body's metabolic processes eventually slow down or even stop. The early stage of a nutrient deficiency is termed **subclinical** because there are no overt signs or symptoms that can be detected or diagnosed. If a deficiency becomes severe, clinical signs and symptoms eventually develop and become outwardly apparent.[17] A **sign** is a feature that can be observed, such as flaky skin. A **symptom** is a change in body function that is not necessarily apparent to a health-care provider, such as feeling tired or achy. Table 1-3 describes the signs and symptoms associated with iron status.

Consumption of more nutrients than the body needs can lead to **overnutrition.** In the short run—for instance, a week or so—overnutrition may cause only a few symptoms, such as intestinal distress from excessive fiber intake. If an excess intake continues, the levels of some nutrients in the body may increase to toxic amounts.[17] For example, too much vitamin A can have negative effects, particularly in children, pregnant women, and older adults. The most common type of overnutrition in industrialized nations—excess intake of energy-yielding nutrients—often leads to obesity. Obesity, in turn, can lead to other serious chronic diseases, such as type 2 diabetes and certain forms of cancer.

Health Objectives for the U.S. for the Year 2020

Health promotion and disease prevention have been public health strategies in the U.S. and Canada since the late 1970s. One part of this strategy is *Healthy People 2020,* a report issued in 2010 by the U.S. Department of Health and Human Services, Public Health Service.[18]

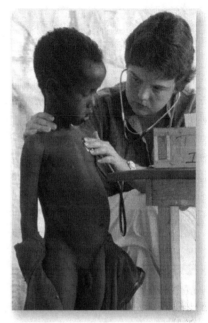

An assessment of this child's nutritional health status indicates stunted growth and edema due to limited protein intake caused by inability to purchase enough protein-rich foods. Learn more about protein deficiency in Chapter 7.

sign Physical attribute that can be observed by others, such as bruises.

symptom Change in physical status that is noted by the individual with the problem, such as stomach pain.

Table 1-3 Nutritional Status Using Iron as an Example	
Condition	**Signs and Symptoms Related to Iron**
Undernutrition: nutrient intake does not meet needs	Decline in iron-related compounds in the blood, which reduces the ability of the red blood cells to carry oxygen to body tissues and, in turn, causes fatigue on exertion, poor body temperature regulation, and eventually pale complexion
Desirable nutrition: nutrient intake supports body function and permits storage of nutrients to be used in times of increased need	Adequate liver stores of iron, adequate blood levels of iron-related compounds, and normal functioning of red blood cells
Overnutrition: nutrient intake exceeds needs	Excess liver stores of iron, which damage liver cells

CRITICAL THINKING

Ying loves to eat hamburgers, fries, and lots of pizza with double amounts of cheese. He rarely eats any vegetables and fruits but, instead, snacks on cookies and ice cream. He insists that he has no problems with his health, is rarely ill, and doesn't see how his diet could cause him any health risks. How would you explain to Ying that, despite his current good health, his diet could predispose him to future health problems?

For suggested answers to the Critical Thinking questions in this and every chapter, see the website for this book: www.mhhe.com/wardlawpers9

Table 1-4 Sample of Nutrition-Related Objectives from *Healthy People 2020*

Increase the proportion of adults who are at a healthy weight

Reduce the proportion of children, adolescents, and adults who are obese

Reduce household food insecurity and in doing so reduce hunger

Increase the contribution of fruits and vegetables to the diets of the population aged 2 years and older

Increase the contribution of whole grains to the diets of the population aged 2 years and older

Reduce consumption of calories from solid fats and added sugars

Reduce consumption of sodium in the population aged 2 years and older

Increase consumption of calcium in the population aged 2 years and older

Reduce iron deficiency among young children, females of childbearing age, and pregnant women

Increase the proportion of adolescents and adults who meet the objectives for aerobic physical activity and for muscle-strengthening activity

Increase the proportion of children and adolescents aged 2 years through 12th grade who view television or videos or who play video games for no more than 2 hours a day

Note: Related objectives include those addressing osteoporosis, various forms of cancer, diabetes, food allergies, cardiovascular disease, low birth weight, nutrition during pregnancy, breastfeeding, eating disorders, physical activity, and alcohol use.

This report provides science-based, 10-year national goals for improving the health of all Americans—many of these goals are nutrition-related (see Table 1-4 for examples). The main objective of *Healthy People 2020* is to help all people attain high-quality, longer lives free of preventable disease, disability, injury, and premature death. Promoting health equity and eliminating health disparities are a particular focus of *Healthy People 2020* because overall health status currently lags in some population groups, especially with respect to hypertension, type 2 diabetes, and obesity. Learn more at healthypeople.gov.

Assessing Nutritional Status

A nutritional assessment can help determine how nutritionally fit you are (Table 1-5). Generally, assessments are performed by a physician, often with the aid of a registered dietitian.[19]

Assessments include an analysis of numerous background factors known to affect health. For example, many diseases have a genetic component, so family history plays an important role in determining nutritional and health status. Another background factor is a person's own medical history, especially any health conditions, diseases, or treatments that could hinder nutrient absorptive processes or the use of a nutrient.

In addition to background factors, parameters that complete the picture of nutritional status are anthropometric, biochemical, clinical, dietary, and environmental assessments. **Anthropometric assessment** involves measuring various aspects of the body, including height, weight (and weight changes), body circumferences (e.g., waist, hips, arm), and skinfold thickness (an indicator of body fatness). Anthropometric measurements are easy to obtain and are generally reliable.

Biochemical assessments include the measurement of the concentrations of nutrients and nutrient by-products in the blood, urine, and feces and of specific blood enzyme activities.[17] For example, the status of the vitamin thiamin is measured, in part, by determining the activity of an enzyme called transketolase used to metabolize glucose (see Chapter 13). To test for this, cells (e.g., red blood cells) are broken open and thiamin is added to see how it affects the rate of the transketolase enzyme activity.

▶ A practical example using the ABCDEs for evaluating nutritional state can be illustrated in a person who chronically abuses alcohol. On evaluation, the physician notes the following:

Anthropometric: Low weight-for-height, recent 10 lb weight loss, muscle wasting in the upper body

Biochemical: Low amounts of the vitamins thiamin and folate in the blood

Clinical: Psychological confusion, skin sores, and uncoordinated movement

Dietary: Consumed mostly alcohol-fortified wine and hamburgers for the last week

Environmental: Currently residing in a homeless shelter, $35.00 in his wallet, unemployed

Assessment: This person needs professional medical attention, including nutrient repletion.

Table 1-5 Conducting an Evaluation of Nutritional Health	
Factors	**Examples**
Background	**Medical history** (e.g., current and past diseases and surgeries, body weight history, current medications) **Family medical history**
Nutritional	**Anthropometric assessment** (e.g., height, weight, skinfold thickness, arm muscle circumference) **Biochemical (laboratory) assessment** (e.g., compounds in blood and urine) **Clinical assessment** (e.g., physical examination of skin, eyes, and tongue; ability to walk) **Dietary assessment** (e.g., usual food intake, food allergies, supplements used) **Environmental assessment** (e.g., education and economic background, marital status, housing condition)

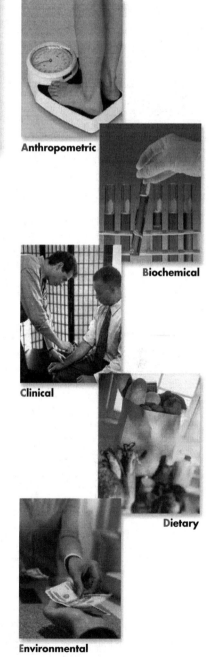

Anthropometric

Biochemical

Clinical

Dietary

Environmental

Figure 1-7 The ABCDEs of nutritional assessment: Anthropometric, Biochemical, Clinical, Dietary, and Environmental status.

During a **clinical assessment,** health-care providers search for any physical evidence of diet-related diseases (e.g., high blood pressure, skin conditions). The healthcare provider tends to focus the clinical assessment on potential problem areas identified from the dietary assessment. **Dietary assessment** examines how often a person eats certain types of foods (called a food frequency); the types of foods eaten over a long period of time, perhaps as far back as childhood (called a food history); and typical intake, such as foods eaten in the last 24 hours or several days (e.g., a 24-hour recall or a 3-day recall). Finally, an **environmental assessment** (based on background data) provides information on the person's education and economic background. This information is important because people who have inadequate education, income, and housing and/or live alone often have a greater risk of poor health. Those with limited education may have a reduced ability to follow instructions given by health-care providers and/or incomes that hinder their ability to purchase, store, and prepare nutritious food. Taken together, these 5 parameters form the ABCDEs of nutritional assessment: anthropometric, biochemical, clinical, dietary, and environmental (Fig. 1-7).

Limitations of Nutritional Assessment

Nutritional assessments can be helpful in improving one's health. However, it is important to recognize the limitations of these assessments. First, many signs and symptoms of nutritional deficiencies—diarrhea, skin conditions, and fatigue—are not very specific. They may be caused by poor nutrition or by other factors unrelated to nutrition. Second, it can take a long time for the signs and symptoms of nutritional deficiencies to develop and, because they can be vague, it is often difficult to establish a link between an individual's current diet and his or her nutritional status.

Third, a long time may elapse between the initial development of poor nutritional health and the first clinical evidence of a problem. For instance, a diet high in saturated fat often increases blood cholesterol, but it does not produce any clinical evidence for years. Nonetheless, the cholesterol is building up in blood vessels and may lead to a heart attack. Another example of a serious nutrition-related health condition with signs and symptoms that often don't appear until later in life is low bone density (osteoporosis) resulting from insufficient calcium intake that may have begun in the teen years. Currently, a great deal of nutrition research is trying to identify better methods for detecting nutrition-related problems early—before they damage the body.

Soft drinks account for about 10% of the energy intake of teenagers in North America and, in turn, contribute to generally poor calcium intakes seen in this age group. Consuming insufficient calcium increases their risk of osteoporosis in future years.

Importance of Being Concerned about Your Nutritional Status

Regardless of the limitations of nutritional assessment, people who focus on maintaining desirable nutritional health are apt to enjoy a long, vigorous life and are less likely to develop health problems, such as those in Figure 1-8. In fact, a recent study found that women who followed a healthy lifestyle experienced an 80% reduction in risk of heart attacks, compared with women without such healthy practices.[4] Here is what these healthy women did:

- Consumed a healthy diet that was varied, rich in fiber, and low in animal fat and *trans* fat and included some fish
- Avoided becoming overweight
- Regularly drank a small amount of alcohol
- Exercised for at least 30 minutes daily
- Did not smoke

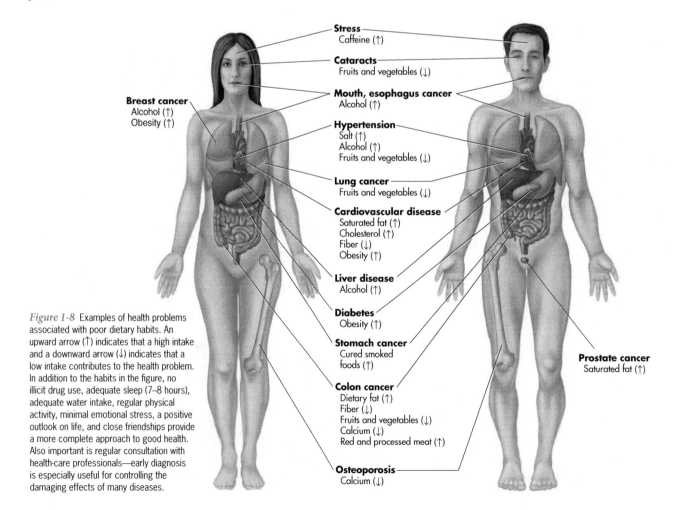

Figure 1-8 Examples of health problems associated with poor dietary habits. An upward arrow (↑) indicates that a high intake and a downward arrow (↓) indicates that a low intake contributes to the health problem. In addition to the habits in the figure, no illicit drug use, adequate sleep (7–8 hours), adequate water intake, regular physical activity, minimal emotional stress, a positive outlook on life, and close friendships provide a more complete approach to good health. Also important is regular consultation with health-care professionals—early diagnosis is especially useful for controlling the damaging effects of many diseases.

Stress
Caffeine (↑)

Cataracts
Fruits and vegetables (↓)

Mouth, esophagus cancer
Alcohol (↑)

Breast cancer
Alcohol (↑)
Obesity (↑)

Hypertension
Salt (↑)
Alcohol (↑)
Fruits and vegetables (↓)

Lung cancer
Fruits and vegetables (↓)

Cardiovascular disease
Saturated fat (↑)
Cholesterol (↑)
Fiber (↓)
Obesity (↑)

Liver disease
Alcohol (↑)

Diabetes
Obesity (↑)

Stomach cancer
Cured smoked foods (↑)

Colon cancer
Dietary fat (↑)
Fiber (↓)
Fruits and vegetables (↓)
Calcium (↓)
Red and processed meat (↑)

Osteoporosis
Calcium (↓)

Prostate cancer
Saturated fat (↑)

While Allen was driving to campus last week, he heard a radio advertisement for a nutrient supplement containing a plant substance that was discovered recently. It supposedly gives people more energy and helps them cope with the stress of daily life. This advertisement caught Allen's attention because he has been feeling run-down lately. He is taking a full course load and has been working 30 hours a week at a local restaurant. Allen doesn't have a lot of extra money to spare. Still, he likes to try new things, and this recent breakthrough sounded almost too good to be true. After searching for more information on the Internet, he discovered that the recommended dose would cost $60 per month. Because Allen is looking for some help with his low energy level, he decides to order a 30-day supply. Does this extra expense make sense to you?

Knowledge Check

1. What is the difference between a sign and a symptom?
2. How does undernutrition differ from overnutrition?
3. What are the ABCDEs of nutritional assessment?
4. What are 3 limitations of nutritional assessment?

 1.5 Genetics and Nutrition

In addition to lifestyle and diet, genetic endowment also affects almost every medical condition. During digestion, the nutrients supplied by food are broken down, absorbed into the bloodstream, and transported to cells. There, genetic material, called **deoxyribonucleic acid (DNA)**, inside the nucleus of the cells directs how the body uses the nutrients consumed. As you can see in Figure 1-9, foods and humans contain the same nutrients, but the proportions differ—**genes** in body cells dictate the type and amount of nutrients in food that will be transformed and reassembled into body structures and compounds.

deoxyribonucleic acid (DNA) Site of hereditary information in cells. DNA directs the synthesis of cell proteins.

genes Hereditary material on chromosomes that makes up DNA. Genes provide the blueprints for the production of cell proteins.

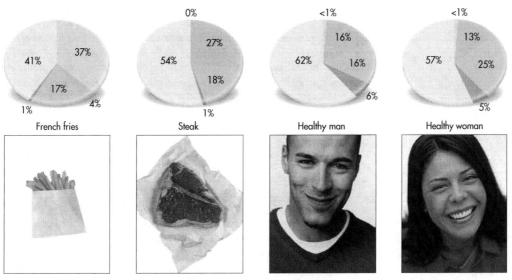

Figure 1-9 Proportions of nutrients in the human body, compared with those in typical foods—animal or vegetable. Note that the amount of vitamins found in the body is extremely small and, so, is not shown.

20   **PART 1** Nutrition Basics

Genes are present on DNA—a double helix. The cell nucleus contains most of the DNA in the body.

mutation Change in the chemistry of a gene that is perpetuated in subsequent divisions of the cell where it occurred; a change in the sequence of the DNA.

risk factor Hereditary characteristic or lifestyle behavior (e.g., dietary habits, smoking) that increases the chances of developing a disease.

Genes direct the growth, development, and maintenance of cells and, ultimately, of the entire organism. Genes contain the codes that control the expression of individual traits, such as height, eye color, and susceptibility to many diseases. An individual's genetic risk of a given disease is an important factor, although often not the only factor, in determining whether he or she develops that disease.

Each year, new links between specific genes and diseases are reported. It is likely that soon it will be relatively easy to screen a person's DNA for genes that increase the risk of disease. Currently, there are about 1000 tests that can determine whether a person has a genetic **mutation** that increases the risk of certain illnesses. For example, a woman can be tested for a mutation in certain genes that elevates her chances of developing breast cancer.

Nutritional Diseases with a Genetic Link

Most chronic nutrition-related diseases (e.g., diabetes, cancer, osteoporosis, cardiovascular disease, hypertension, obesity, and cancer) are influenced by interactions among genetic, nutritional, and other lifestyle factors. Studies of families, including those with twins and adoptees, provide strong support for the effect of genetics in these disorders. In fact, family history is considered one of the most important **risk factors** in the development of many nutrition-related diseases.[20]

For example, both of the common types of diabetes, certain cancers (e.g., colon, prostate, and breast cancer), and osteoporosis have genetic links. In addition, about 1 in every 500 people in North America has a defective gene that greatly delays cholesterol removal from the bloodstream—this defective gene increases the risk of cardiovascular disease. Another example is hypertension (high blood pressure). Numerous North Americans are very sensitive to salt intake. When these salt-sensitive individuals consume too much salt, their blood pressure climbs above the desirable range. The fact that more of these people are African-American than White suggests that at least some cases of hypertension have a genetic component. Obesity also has genetic links. A variety of genes (likely 1000 or more) are involved in the regulation of body weight.

Although some individuals may be genetically predisposed to chronic disease, whether they actually develop the disease depends on lifestyle choices and environmental factors that influence the disease.[21] It's important to realize that predisposition to chronic disease is not the same type of genetic characteristic as being born with blue eyes or larger ears. With chronic disease, heredity is not necessarily destiny—individuals can exert some control over the expression of their genetic potential. For instance, those with a predisposition to premature heart disease can take steps to delay its onset by eating a nutritious diet, getting regular exercise, keeping weight under control, and getting medical treatment to lower blood cholesterol levels and control blood pressure. Likewise, those who did not inherit the potential for heart disease put themselves at risk of this disease by becoming obese, smoking, abusing alcohol, and not getting medical treatment to keep blood cholesterol, blood pressure, and type 2 diabetes under control.

Your Genetic Profile

By recognizing your potential for developing a particular disease, you can avoid behaviors that contribute to it. For example, women with a family history of breast cancer should avoid becoming obese, minimize alcohol use, and get mammograms regularly. In general, the more relatives with a genetically transmitted disease and the more closely they are related to you, the greater your risk. One way to assess your risk is to create a family tree of illnesses and deaths (a genogram) by compiling a few key facts on your primary biological relatives: siblings, parents, aunts, uncles, and grandparents (Fig. 1-10).

High-risk conditions include having more than one first-degree relative (i.e., one's biological parents, siblings, and offspring) with a specific disease, especially if the disease occurred before age 50 to 60 years.[20] In the family in Figure 1-10, prostate cancer killed Jamal's father. Knowing this, his physician likely would recommend that he be tested for

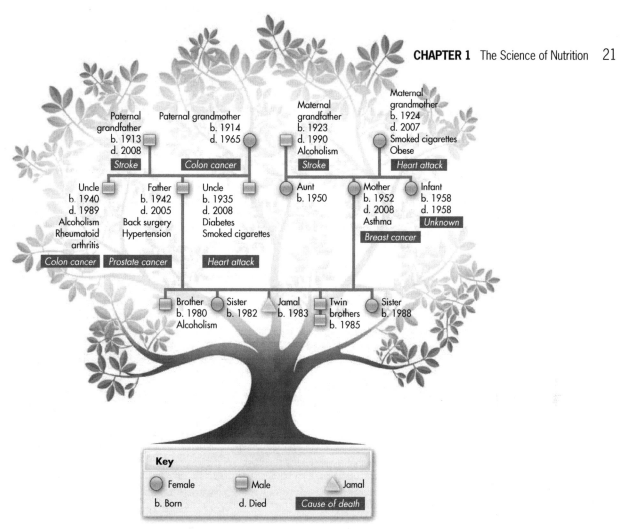

Figure 1-10 Example of a family tree for Jamal. If a person is deceased, the cause of death is shown. In addition to causes of death, medical conditions family members experienced are noted.

prostate cancer more frequently or starting at an earlier age than men without a family history of the disease. Because their mother died of breast cancer, his sisters' doctor may recommend they consider having their first regular mammograms at a younger age than typical, as well as adopting other preventive practices. Heart attack and stroke also are common in the family, so all the children should adopt a lifestyle that minimizes the risk of developing these conditions, such as moderating their intake of animal fat and sodium. Colon cancer is evident in the family, which makes it important for them to have careful screening throughout life.

Gene Therapy

Scientists are currently developing therapies to correct the damaged DNA that causes some genetic disorders. Typically, scientists isolate normal DNA, package it into a molecular delivery vehicle (usually a disabled **virus**), and inject it into the cells affected by the disease—such as liver cells. Inside the cell, the normal genetic material begins functioning and restores the cells to normal. Scientists hope that gene therapy applications can be used in the future to treat many diseases, especially those that are inherited. Although there has been some success with gene therapy, there are still many obstacles to overcome before gene therapy can become an effective treatment. The U.S. Food and Drug Administration (FDA) is actively overseeing human gene therapy research; however, it has not yet approved the sale of any of these therapies. This research could lead to gene-based treatments for cancer, heart disease, cystic fibrosis, and other diseases.

virus Smallest known type of infectious agent, many of which cause disease in humans. They do not metabolize, grow, or move by themselves. They reproduce by the aid of a living cellular host. Viruses are essentially a piece of genetic material surrounded by a coat of protein.

22   PART 1   Nutrition Basics

▶ These websites can help you gather more information about genetic conditions and testing.

www.geneticalliance.org

www.kumc.edu/gec/support

www.genome.gov

www.faseb.org/genetics

www.dnalc.org

genomics.energy.gov

www.ncgr.org

Genetic analysis for disease susceptibility is becoming more common as the genes that increase the risk of developing various diseases are isolated and decoded.

Genetic Testing

Genetic tests analyze a person's genes to determine the likelihood of developing certain diseases. These tests are especially valuable for families afflicted by certain illnesses. In addition, they can help people who are healthy now predict the illnesses they will probably develop.[6] Advance knowledge that a disease is likely to develop may provide opportunities to replace genes that encourage diseases, such as cancer and Alzheimer disease, with those that do not. Advance knowledge also could help couples wanting to have children make more informed choices (e.g., consider alternatives, such as adoption) and help health-care providers develop health and nutrition care plans that delay the onset of the disease. Additionally, this knowledge could help health-care providers diagnose diseases earlier and more accurately and prescribe individualized medical and nutrition therapies, instead of giving the same treatment to all patients with the same disease. It is likely that many medications may be more appropriate in people with certain genetic traits.

Some experts recommend that anyone considering genetic testing first have a genetic counselor analyze his or her family history, evaluate the risk of developing or passing along an inherited disease, and help determine whether testing is worth the time and effort. If you want to know if you are at risk of a specific genetic disease, it is a good idea to ask your physician about the possibility and likely usefulness of testing you. Some consumers opt to purchase at-home genetic test kits directly without involving a doctor or insurance company. Typically, the test kit is mailed to the consumer, who collects the DNA sample (often by swabbing inside the cheek) and returns it to the lab. Results are provided by mail, fax, phone consultation, or web posting.

Genetic testing can help consumers take a more proactive role in protecting their health. However, given the limit on resources allocated to medical care in North America, it is not possible to identify all the people at genetic risk of the major chronic diseases and other health problems. In addition, in many cases, genetic susceptibility does not guarantee development of the disease. And, in almost all cases, there is no way to cure a specific gene alteration—only the health problems that result can be treated. Researchers also are concerned that people who are found to have genetic alterations that increase disease risk may face job and medical insurance discrimination. Testing positive also could lead to unnecessary radical treatment. As well, a seemingly hopeless diagnosis could result in depression when a cure is out of reach.[22, 23] Users of at-home genetic tests may face additional risks, such as receiving misleading results if unproven or invalid tests are used, making unsafe health decisions if they do not receive guidance from a health-care professional, or finding the testing company has not kept their genetic information confidential.

The wisdom of genetic testing is an open question. Perhaps preventive measures and careful scrutiny of the specific genetically linked diseases using one's family tree would suffice. Be aware that, throughout this book, discussions will point out how to avoid "controllable" risk factors that contribute to the development of genetically linked nutrition-related diseases present in your family tree.

> ### Knowledge Check
>
> 1. What is the role of genes?
> 2. What are 3 chronic nutrition-related diseases with a genetic link?
> 3. What is a genogram?

Take Action

Create Your Family Tree for Health-Related Concerns

Adapt this diagram to your own family tree. Under each heading, list year born, year died (if applicable), major diseases that developed during the person's lifetime, and cause of death (if applicable). Figure 1-10 provides an example.

Note that you are likely to be at risk of developing any diseases listed. Creating a plan for preventing such diseases when possible, especially

those that developed in your family members before age 50 to 60 years, is advised. An online version of the family tree is available at www.hhs.gov/familyhistory. Speak with your health-care provider about any concerns arising from this activity.

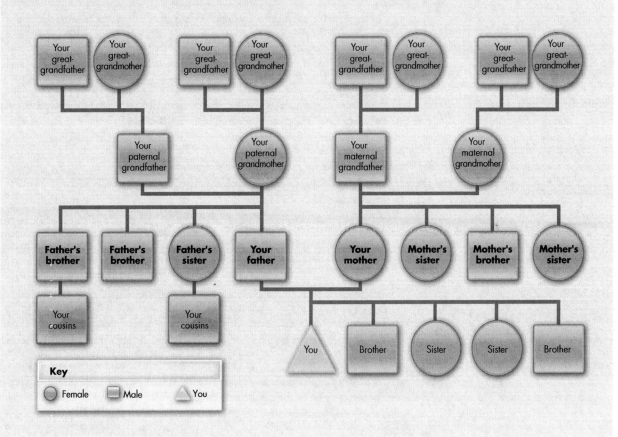

1.6 Using Scientific Research to Determine Nutrient Needs

How do we know what we know about nutrition? How has this knowledge been gained? In a word, research. Like other sciences, the research that sets the foundation for nutrition has developed through the use of the scientific method—a testing procedure designed to uncover facts and detect and eliminate error. The first step is the observation of a natural phenomenon. Scientists then suggest possible explanations, called hypotheses, about the causes of the phenomenon. Distinguishing a true cause-and-effect relationship from mere coincidence can be difficult. For instance, early in the 20th century, many people in orphanages, prisons, and mental hospitals suffered from the disease pellagra, which suggested this disease was caused by germs that spread among people living close together. In time, however, it became clear that this connection was simply coincidental—the real cause of pellagra is a poor diet that contains too little of the B-vitamin niacin (see Chapter 13).

To test hypotheses and eliminate coincidental or erroneous explanations, scientists perform controlled experiments to gather data that either support or refute a hypothesis (Fig. 1-11). Very often, the results of one experiment lead to a new set of questions to be answered. If the results of many well-designed experiments provide valid evidence that supports a hypothesis, the hypothesis becomes generally accepted by scientists as a well-documented explanation for the phenomenon. As valid, extensive evidence about a related set of phenomena accumulate, a scientific theory or scientific law may be proposed. A scientific theory or law is a scientifically acceptable explanation of phenomena and how the phenomena are related to each other.

Sound scientific research requires the following:

1. Phenomena are observed.
2. Questions are asked and hypotheses are generated to explain the phenomena.
3. Research is conducted.
4. Incorrect explanations are rejected and the most likely explanation is used as the basis for a model.
5. Research results are scrutinized and evaluated by other scientists. Research conducted in an unbiased, scientific manner is published in a scientific journal.
6. The results are confirmed by other scientists and by more experiments and studies.

The scientific method requires an open, curious mind and a questioning, skeptical attitude. Scientists (as well as students) must not accept proposed hypotheses until they are supported by considerable evidence, and they must reject hypotheses that fail to pass critical analysis. A recent example of this need for skepticism involves stomach ulcers. For many years, it was generally accepted that stomach ulcers were caused mostly by a stressful lifestyle and a poor diet. Then, in 1983, Australian physicians, Barry Marshall and Robin Warren, reported in a respected medical journal that ulcers usually are caused by a common microorganism called *Helicobacter pylori* and can be cured with antibiotics. At first, other physicians were skeptical about this finding and continued to prescribe medications, such as antacids, that reduce stomach acid. As more studies were published, however, and patients were cured of ulcers using antibiotics, the medical profession eventually accepted the findings. (Marshall and Warren were even given the Nobel Prize for Medicine in 2005 for this discovery.) Scientific theories, laws, and discoveries always should be subjected to challenge and change.

Making Observations and Generating Hypotheses

Historical observations have provided clues to important relationships in nutrition science. In the 15th and 16th centuries, for example, many European sailors on long voyages developed the often fatal disease scurvy. A British naval surgeon, Lind, observed

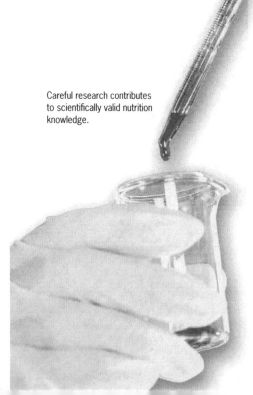

Careful research contributes to scientifically valid nutrition knowledge.

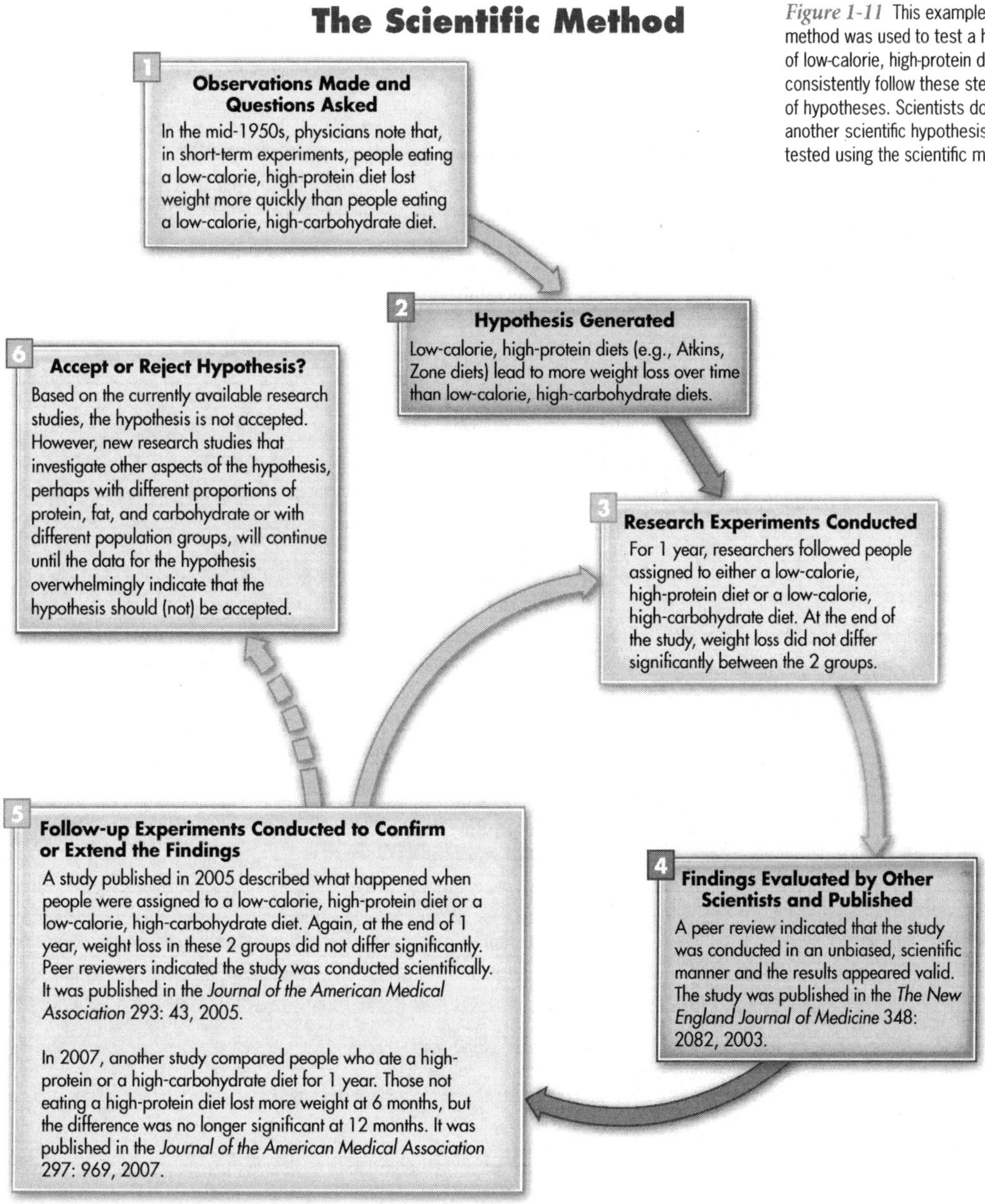

The Scientific Method

Figure 1-11 This example shows how the scientific method was used to test a hypothesis about the effects of low-calorie, high-protein diets on weight loss. Scientists consistently follow these steps when testing all types of hypotheses. Scientists do not accept a nutrition or another scientific hypothesis until it has been thoroughly tested using the scientific method.

1 Observations Made and Questions Asked

In the mid-1950s, physicians note that, in short-term experiments, people eating a low-calorie, high-protein diet lost weight more quickly than people eating a low-calorie, high-carbohydrate diet.

2 Hypothesis Generated

Low-calorie, high-protein diets (e.g., Atkins, Zone diets) lead to more weight loss over time than low-calorie, high-carbohydrate diets.

3 Research Experiments Conducted

For 1 year, researchers followed people assigned to either a low-calorie, high-protein diet or a low-calorie, high-carbohydrate diet. At the end of the study, weight loss did not differ significantly between the 2 groups.

4 Findings Evaluated by Other Scientists and Published

A peer review indicated that the study was conducted in an unbiased, scientific manner and the results appeared valid. The study was published in the *The New England Journal of Medicine* 348: 2082, 2003.

5 Follow-up Experiments Conducted to Confirm or Extend the Findings

A study published in 2005 described what happened when people were assigned to a low-calorie, high-protein diet or a low-calorie, high-carbohydrate diet. Again, at the end of 1 year, weight loss in these 2 groups did not differ significantly. Peer reviewers indicated the study was conducted scientifically. It was published in the *Journal of the American Medical Association* 293: 43, 2005.

In 2007, another study compared people who ate a high-protein or a high-carbohydrate diet for 1 year. Those not eating a high-protein diet lost more weight at 6 months, but the difference was no longer significant at 12 months. It was published in the *Journal of the American Medical Association* 297: 969, 2007.

6 Accept or Reject Hypothesis?

Based on the currently available research studies, the hypothesis is not accepted. However, new research studies that investigate other aspects of the hypothesis, perhaps with different proportions of protein, fat, and carbohydrate or with different population groups, will continue until the data for the hypothesis overwhelmingly indicate that the hypothesis should (not) be accepted.

that the diet eaten while at sea differed from usual diets. In specific, few fruits and vegetables were available while onboard ships. He hypothesized that a missing dietary component caused scurvy. He set up an experiment in which he supplied sailors with a ration of salt water, vinegar, cider, citrus juice, or other liquid. The results of this experiment indicated that citrus (lemons, limes) prevented and cured scurvy. After this, British sailors were given a ration of lime juice, earning them the nickname "limeys." About 200 years later, science had advanced to the point that researchers were able to identify vitamin C as the component in citrus juice that prevents and cures scurvy.

26   **PART 1** Nutrition Basics

Observations of differences in dietary and disease patterns among various populations also have suggested important relationships in nutrition science. If one group tends to develop a certain disease but another group does not, scientists can speculate about how diet causes this difference. The study of diseases in populations, called epidemiology, ultimately forms the basis for many laboratory studies. An example of the use of epidemiology occurred in the 1920s in the U.S., when Goldberger noticed that residents in mental institutions—but not their caretakers—suffered from pellagra. He reasoned that, if pellagra were an infectious disease, both groups would suffer from it. Because they did not, he hypothesized that pellagra was caused by a dietary deficiency. The controlled experiments he conducted found that yeast and high-protein foods can cure pellagra if it is not in its final stage. These research results indicated that pellagra is caused by a deficiency of a component present in these foods. Eventually, this component was found to be niacin.

Laboratory Animal Experiments

Human experiments are the most convincing to scientists; however, when scientists cannot test their hypotheses in experiments with humans, they often use laboratory animals. In fact, much of what is known about human nutritional needs and functions has been generated from laboratory animal experiments.

Experiments may be conducted with laboratory animals when the study would be unethical to conduct with humans. Although some people argue that laboratory animal experiments also are unethical, most believe that the careful, humane use of animals is an acceptable alternative. For example, most people think it is reasonable to feed rats a low-copper diet to study the importance of this mineral in the formation of blood vessels. Almost everyone, however, would object to a similar study in infants.

The use of laboratory animal experiments to study the role of nutrition in human diseases depends on the availability of an **animal model**—a disease in laboratory animals that closely mimics a human disease. For example, in the early 1900s, scientists showed that thiamin (a B-vitamin) cures a beriberi-like disease in chickens. As a result, chickens could be used to study this vitamin deficiency disease. If no animal model is available and human experiments are ruled out, scientific knowledge often cannot advance beyond what can be learned from epidemiological studies. Most human chronic diseases do not occur in laboratory animals.

Research using laboratory animals contributes to knowledge of nutrition.

Human Experiments

Before any research study can be conducted with humans (or laboratory animals), researchers must obtain approval from the research review board at their university, hospital, or company. The review board approves only studies that have a valid experimental protocol, are expected to produce important knowledge, and treat study participants fairly and ethically. The review board also assesses the risks and benefits of the potential treatment to study participants. In human studies, the review board also requires researchers to inform the participants of the study's purpose, procedures, known risks, and benefits, so that they can make informed decisions about whether to participate. This process, called informed consent, is the voluntary, documented confirmation of the participants' agreement to participate in the study.

A variety of experimental approaches are used to test research hypotheses in humans. Migrant studies, for example, look at changes in the health of people who move from one country to another. Cohort studies start with a healthy population and follow it, looking for the development of disease. Other experimental approaches are case-control and double-blind studies.

animal model Laboratory animal useful in medical research because it can develop a health condition (e.g., disease or disorder) that is comparable to one occurring in humans and, thus, can be utilized to learn more about causes of a condition and its diagnosis in humans, as well as assess the usefulness and safety of new treatments or preventive actions.

Case-Control Study

In a case-control study, scientists compare individuals who have the condition in question ("cases"), such as lung cancer, with individuals who do not have the condition ("controls"). The strongest case-control studies compare groups that are matched for other major characteristics (e.g., age, race, and gender) not being studied. You can think of a case-control study as a "mini" epidemiological study. This type of study may identify factors other than the disease being studied, such as fruit and vegetable intake, that differ between the groups, thereby providing researchers with clues about the cause, progression, and prevention of the disease. However, without a controlled experiment, researchers cannot definitely claim cause and effect.[24]

Double-Blind Study

An important approach for more definitive testing of hypotheses is a controlled experiment using a blinded protocol. In a double-blind study, one group of participants—the experimental group—follows a specific protocol (e.g., receives a treatment, such as consuming a certain food or nutrient) while the participants in a corresponding control group follow their usual habits. The control group also usually receives a **placebo** (fake treatment). The placebo camouflages who is in the experimental group and who is in the control group. Study participants are assigned randomly to the control or experimental group, such as by the flip of a coin. Scientists then observe both groups over time to identify any changes that occur in the experimental and the control groups. Sometimes individuals are used as their own control: first they are observed for a period of time while they follow their usual habits. Then, they follow the experimental protocol and their responses are observed.

Two features of a double-blind study help reduce the risk of bias (prejudice), which can easily affect the outcome of an experiment. First, during the course of the experiment, neither the study participants nor the researchers know who is getting the real treatment (experimental group) and who is getting the placebo (control group). An independent third party holds the key to the study group assignment and the data until the study is completed. Second, the expected effects of the experimental protocol are not disclosed to the participants or researchers collecting the data until after the entire study is completed. These features reduce the possibility that the researchers will misperceive or overemphasize changes they hoped to see in the participants to prove a certain hypothesis they believe is true or will unconsciously ignore or minimize the importance of changes that disprove their hypothesis. These features also reduce the chance that study participants begin to feel better simply because they are involved in a research study or are receiving a new treatment, a phenomenon called the **placebo effect.** Double-blind studies improve the chances that any differences observed between the experimental and control groups really are due to the experimental treatment. Sometimes only a single-blind study protocol is possible—in this case, only the study participants are kept uninformed about which participants are assigned to the experimental and control groups. Conducting blinded studies in nutrition is very challenging because it is difficult to create placebo foods and menus.

A recent example illustrates the need to test hypotheses based on epidemiological observations in double-blind studies.[24] Epidemiologists using primarily case-control studies found that smokers who regularly consumed fruits and vegetables had a lower risk of lung cancer than smokers who ate few of these foods. Some scientists proposed that it was the beta-carotene (a yellow-orange pigment that is a precursor to vitamin A) present in many fruits and vegetables that reduced the lung damage caused by tobacco smoke that leads to lung cancer. However, in double-blind studies involving heavy smokers, the risk of lung cancer was found to be higher in those who took beta-carotene supplements

HISTORICAL PERSPECTIVE

War on Pellagra

Early in the 20th century, pellagra killed millions in the U.S. Dr. Joseph Goldberger hypothesized that it was caused by poor diets, not infectious agents. His experiments included feeding healthy people poor diets—they developed pellagra. He fed pellagra patients good diets—they improved. He and his assistant also experimented on themselves. They injected themselves with pellagra patients' blood and took capsules filled with their scabs—they didn't "catch" pellagra. Years after his death, others determined that the specific cause of pellagra is deficiency of niacin (a B-vitamin). Learn more at: history.nih.gov/exhibits/Goldberger/

placebo A fake treatment (such as a sham medicine, supplement, or procedure) that seems like the experimental treatment. It is used to disguise whether a study participant is in the experimental or control group.

placebo effect *Placebo* is derived from a Latin word that means "I shall please." The placebo effect occurs when control group participants experience changes that cannot be explained by the action of the placebo they received. These changes may be linked to a reduction in stress and anxiety, hope that the treatment is working, or a desire to help the researchers achieve their goals. Overall, it is critical for researchers to take the placebo effect into consideration when interpreting research results.

CRITICAL THINKING

For thousands of years, early humans consumed a diet rich in vegetable products and low in animal products. These diets were generally lower in fat and higher in dietary fiber than modern diets. Do the differences in human diets throughout history necessarily tell us which diet is better—that of early humans or of modern humans? If not, what is a more reliable way to pursue this question of potential diet superiority?

▶ For a list of more nutrition- and health-related peer-reviewed journals, see Appendix L.

▶ These are examples of websites that provide reliable health and nutrition information.

www.nutrition.gov
www.eatright.org
www.webmd.com

peer-reviewed journal Journal that publishes research only after researchers who were not part of the study agree that the study was carefully designed and executed and the results are presented in an unbiased, objective manner. Thus, the research has been approved by peers of the research team.

than in those who did not. Some researchers criticized these studies, arguing that the beta-carotene was given too late in the smokers' lives to prevent lung cancer, but even these critics did not suspect that the supplement would increase cancer risk. Soon after these results were reported, the U.S. federal agency supporting other large studies of beta-carotene supplements halted the research, stating that these supplements are ineffective in preventing lung cancer. Although it appears that beta-carotene does not protect against lung cancer, other components in fruits and vegetables might offer protection and may become the focus of future studies.

Overall, health and nutrition advice provided by family, friends, and other well-meaning individuals cannot be accepted as valid until studied in a rigorous, scientific manner.[24] Until that is done, it isn't possible to know whether a substance or procedure is truly effective. When people say, "I get fewer colds now that I take vitamin C," they overlook the facts that many cold symptoms disappear quickly with no treatment, that they want the supplement to work, and that the apparent curative effect of vitamin C or any other remedy is often coincidental rather than causal. Failure to understand the scientific method, as well as the accepted standards of evidence and current limitations of science, leads many people to believe erroneous information about health, nutrition, and disease. Using remedies that are not supported by credible scientific evidence can damage health and delay treatment that could preserve health.

Peer Review of Experimental Results

Once an experiment is complete, scientists summarize the findings and seek to publish the results in scientific journals. Generally, before such results are published in scientific journals, they are critically reviewed by other scientists familiar with the subject. The objective of this peer review is to ensure that only the most unbiased, objective findings from carefully designed and executed research studies are published.

Peer review is an important step because most scientific research is funded by the government, nonprofit foundations, drug companies, and other private industries—all of which have strong expectations about research outcomes. In theory, the scientists conducting research studies will be fair in evaluating their results and will not be influenced by the funding agency. Peer review helps ensure that the researchers are as objective as possible. This then helps ensure that the results published in **peer-reviewed journals,** such as the *American Journal of Clinical Nutrition, New England Journal of Medicine,* and *Academy of Nutrition and Dietetics Journal* (formerly *Journal of the American Dietetic Association*) are much more reliable than those found in popular magazines or promoted on television talk shows.

Press releases from reputable journals and major universities are the main sources for the information presented in the popular media. Unfortunately, these press releases often oversimplify study findings, which may get misinterpreted or overextended in the popular press. Thus, when you hear or see a news report that cites a journal, it is best to review the journal article, so that you can judge for yourself whether the research findings are valid.

Follow-Up Studies

Even when a study has followed a well-designed protocol and the results have been published in a peer-reviewed journal, one experiment is never enough to accept a particular hypothesis or provide a basis for nutrition recommendations. Rather, the results obtained in one laboratory must be confirmed by experiments conducted in other laboratories and possibly under varying circumstances. Only then can we really trust and use the results. The more lines of evidence available to support a hypothesis or an idea, the more likely it is to be true (Fig. 1-12). It is important to avoid rushing to accept new ideas as fact or incorporating them into your health habits until they are proved by several lines of evidence.[25]

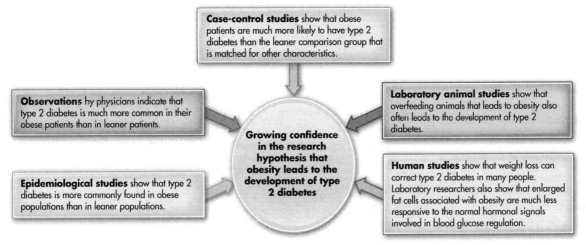

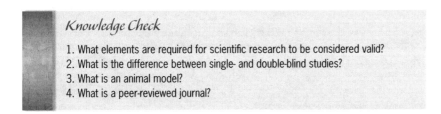

Figure 1-12 Data from a variety of sources can come together to support a research hypothesis. This diagram shows how various types of research data support the hypothesis that obesity leads to the development of type 2 diabetes (see Chapter 5).

Knowledge Check

1. What elements are required for scientific research to be considered valid?
2. What is the difference between single- and double-blind studies?
3. What is an animal model?
4. What is a peer-reviewed journal?

1.7 Evaluating Nutrition Claims, Products, and Advice

Nutrition claims often appear in media stories and in advertisements. Sometimes it is difficult to discern whether the claims are true. The following suggestions can help you make healthful and logical nutrition decisions.[22]

1. Apply the basic principles of nutrition, as outlined in this book, to any nutrition claim. Do you note any inconsistencies?

2. Be wary if the answer is yes to any of the following questions about a health-related nutrition claim:
   - Are only advantages discussed and possible disadvantages ignored?
   - Is this a new or "secret" scientific breakthrough?
   - Are claims made about "curing" disease?
   - Do the claims sound too good to be true?
   - Is extreme bias against the medical community or traditional medical treatments evident? Physicians as a group strive to cure diseases in their patients using proven techniques—they do not ignore reliable cures.

3. Examine the scientific credentials of the individual, organization, or publication making the nutrition claim. Usually, a reputable author is one whose educational background or present employer is affiliated with a nationally recognized university, research institute, or medical center that offers programs or courses in nutrition, medicine, or closely related fields.

▶ These websites can help you evaluate ongoing nutrition and health claims.

www.acsh.org

www.quackwatch.com

ods.od.nih.gov

www.fda.gov

www.eatright.org

Appendix L also lists many reputable sources of nutrition advice for your use.

30   **PART 1** Nutrition Basics

▶ *10 Red Flags That Signal Poor Nutrition Advice*

1. Promise of a quick fix
2. Dire warnings of dangers from a single product or regimen
3. Claims that sound too good to be true
4. Simplistic conclusions drawn from a complex study
5. Recommendations based on a single study
6. Dramatic statements that are refuted by reputable scientific organizations
7. Lists of "good" and "bad" foods
8. Recommendations made to help sell a product
9. Recommendations based on studies published without peer review
10. Recommendations from studies that ignore differences among individuals or groups

4. If research is cited to support a claim, note the size and duration of any study. The larger the study and the longer it went on, the more dependable its findings. Also consider the type of study: epidemiology versus case-control versus blinded. Keep in mind that "contributes to," "is linked to," or "is associated with" does not mean "causes." Do reliable, peer-reviewed journal articles support the claims? Beware of testimonials about personal experience, disreputable publication sources, dramatic results (rarely true), and lack of evidence from supporting studies conducted by other scientists.

5. Be wary of press conferences and other hype regarding the latest findings. Much of this will not survive rigorous scientific evaluation.

Buying Nutrition-Related Products

Popular nutrition-related products claim to increase muscle growth, enhance sexuality, boost energy, reduce body fat, increase strength, supply missing nutrients, increase longevity, and even improve brain function. Although some of us are willing to try these products and believe they can cause the miraculous effects advertised, few of these products have been thoroughly evaluated by reputable scientists. They may not be effective, and the amount and potency of the product may not match what is on the package.

A cautious approach to nutrition-related products is important because of sweeping changes in U.S. law in 1994. The Dietary Supplement Health and Education Act (DSHEA) of 1994 classified vitamins, minerals, amino acids, and herbal remedies as "foods," effectively restraining the U.S. Food and Drug Administration (FDA) from regulating them as rigorously as food additives and drugs. According to this act, rather than the manufacturer having to prove a dietary supplement is safe, the FDA must prove it is unsafe before preventing its sale. In contrast, the safety of food additives and drugs must be rigorously demonstrated before the FDA allows them to be sold (see Chapter 3).

Currently, a product labeled as a dietary supplement (or an herbal product) can be marketed in the U.S. without FDA approval if there is a history of its use or other evidence that it is reasonably safe when used under the conditions indicated in its labeling. (Note that the FDA can act if the product turns out to be dangerous, as with the ban on the sale of the supplement ephedra after numerous deaths.) It is important to note that the "evidence" used to support a claim often is vague or unsubstantiated. Given its budget and regulatory constraints, the FDA is able to challenge only a few of these claims. Some other means for challenging these claims are now emerging. For example, the Federal Trade Commission (FTC), which is responsible for ensuring that advertising is not deceptive, may investigate dubious claims made in advertisements. In addition, the supplement industry itself is trying to develop self-policing procedures.

To protect your health, it is important to scrutinize nutrition-related product labels carefully and check with reputable sources to be certain there is scientific proof that the product is likely to perform as described on the label. Be especially skeptical of using the product for purposes not stated on the label—a product is unlikely to perform a function that is not specifically stated on its label or package insert (legally part of the label). The labels on dietary supplements and herbal products are allowed to claim that general well-being results from consumption of the ingredients, to explain how the product provides a benefit related to a classic nutrient deficiency disease, and to describe how a nutrient affects human body structure or function (called structure/function claims). Structure/function claim examples include "maintains bone health" and "improves blood circulation." The labels of products bearing such claims also must prominently display a disclaimer regarding a lack of FDA review (Fig. 1-13). Despite this warning, many consumers mistakenly assume that the FDA has carefully evaluated the products.

Figure 1-13 The FDA requires the orange highlighted disclaimer to appear on supplement labels.

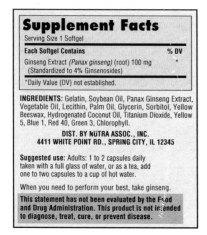

Getting Nutrition-Related Advice: The Nutrition Care Process

For those who feel they need to improve their diet and health, a safe approach is to consult a physician or registered dietitian (R.D.) before purchasing dietary supplements.[19, 23] A person with the credentials "R.D." after his or her name ("R.D.N." also is used in Canada) has completed a rigorous baccalaureate degree program approved by the Academy of Nutrition and Dietetics (formerly the American Dietetic Association), has performed at least 1200 hours of supervised professional practice, and has passed a registration examination. Registered dietitians are trained to provide scientifically valid nutrition advice. To find a registered dietitian, visit the websites of the Academy of Nutrition and Dietetics (www.eatright.org) or Dietitians of Canada (www.dietitians.ca), consult the telephone directory, contact the local dietetic association, or call the dietary department of a local hospital.

When you meet with a nutrition professional, you should expect that he or she will follow the steps in the **Nutrition Care Process.** This process involves the following 4 steps:

- Conduct a nutrition assessment: ask questions about your food and nutrition history and anthropometric, biochemical, clinical, dietary, and environmental assessment data.
- Diagnose nutrition-related problem: use your nutrition history and assessment data to determine your specific nutrition-related problem.
- Create an intervention: formulate a diet plan tailored to your needs, as opposed to simply tearing a form from a tablet that could apply to almost anyone, that addresses the root cause of your nutrition problem with the goal of relieving the signs and symptoms of your diagnosis.
- Monitor and evaluate progress: schedule follow-up visits to track your progress, answer questions, help keep you motivated, and perhaps reassess, rediagnose, and modify your intervention. Family members may be involved in the diet plan, when appropriate. The dietitian will consult directly with your physician and readily refer you back to your physician for those health problems a nutrition professional is not trained to treat.

Be skeptical of health practitioners who prescribe very large doses of vitamin, mineral, or protein supplements for everyone.

Registered dietitians are a reliable source of nutrition advice.

Knowledge Check

1. What are 5 tips for determining whether nutrition claims are true?
2. Why does DSHEA make it wise to be cautious about dietary supplements?
3. What should you expect when you meet with a nutrition professional?

Nutrition Care Process A systematic approach used by Registered Dietitians to ensure patients receive high-quality, individualized nutrition care. This process involves nutrition assessment, diagnosis, intervention, and monitoring and evaluation.

CASE STUDY FOLLOW-UP

Allen should be cautious about taking any supplement, especially one advertised as a "recent breakthrough." There likely have not been enough studies of the supplement to confirm its effectiveness. Also, as you have read, dietary supplements are not closely regulated by the FDA; a general phrase, such as "increases energy," is considered a structure/function claim and such product labeling does not require prior approval by the FDA. Furthermore, the FDA will not have evaluated either the safety or the effectiveness of such a product. Even harmful dietary supplements are difficult for the FDA to recall. There is also a chance that the supplement contains little or none of the advertised ingredient. Unfortunately, Allen will find all this out the hard way and will be out $60. His hard-earned money would be better spent on a nutritious diet and a medical checkup at the student health center. All consumers need to be cautious about nutrition information, especially regarding dietary supplements marketed as cure-alls and breakthroughs— let the buyer beware!

32 **PART 1** Nutrition Basics

Summary

1.1 *Nutrition* is defined as the "science of food; the nutrients and the substances therein; their action, interaction, and balance in relation to health and disease; and the process by which the organism (e.g., human body) ingests, digests, absorbs, transports, utilizes, and excretes food substances." Nutrients are substances essential for health that the body cannot make or makes in quantities too small to support health. Nutrients primarily provide energy, support growth and development, and/or keep body functions running smoothly. Carbohydrates, proteins, lipids, and water are macronutrients. Vitamins and minerals are micronutrients. Phytochemicals are plant components and zoochemicals are components in animals that may provide significant health benefits.

1.2 Humans obtain the energy needed to perform body functions and do work from carbohydrates, fats, and proteins. Alcohol also provides energy but is not considered an essential nutrient. A kilocalorie is the amount of heat energy it takes to raise the temperature of 1000 g (1 liter) of water 1°C. The physiological fuel values are 4, 9, 4, and 7 for carbohydrate, fat, protein, and alcohol, respectively.

1.3 North American adults consume, on average, 16% of their energy intake as proteins, 50% as carbohydrates, and 33% as fats. Animal sources, such as meat, seafood, dairy products, and eggs, are the main protein sources for North Americans. About half the carbohydrate in North American diets comes from simple carbohydrates; the other half comes from starches. Many North Americans are consuming more saturated fat, cholesterol, and sodium and less vitamin A, vitamin E, iron, and calcium than recommended. Daily food intake satisfies hunger (physical need for food) and social and emotional needs. Appetite and food choice depend on many factors.

1.4 Nutritional health is determined by the sum of the status of each nutrient. Optimal, or desirable, nutritional status for a nutrient is the state in which body tissues have enough of the nutrient to support normal functions and to build and maintain surplus stores. Undernutrition occurs when nutrient intake does not meet needs, causing surplus stores to be used. The consumption of more nutrients than needed leads to overnutrition. *Healthy People 2020* set health-promotion and disease-prevention goals, many of which promote desirable nutrition that supports healthful lifestyles and reduces preventable death and disability. A nutritional assessment considers background factors, as well as anthropometric, biochemical, clinical, dietary, and environmental assessments.

1.5 Genetic endowment affects almost every medical condition. Genes direct the growth, development, and maintenance of cells and, ultimately, of the entire organism. Most chronic nutrition-related diseases are influenced by genetic, nutritional, and lifestyle factors. Although some individuals may be genetically predisposed to chronic disease, the actual development of the disease depends on lifestyle and environmental factors. Scientists are currently developing therapies to correct some genetic disorders. Experts recommend that anyone considering genetic testing first undergo genetic counseling.

1.6 Research that creates the foundation for nutrition has developed through the use of the scientific method. To test hypotheses and eliminate coincidental or erroneous hypotheses, scientists perform controlled experiments. The scientific method requires an open, curious mind and a questioning, skeptical attitude. Scientists must not accept hypotheses until they are supported by considerable research evidence. Scientific theories, laws, and discoveries always should be subjected to challenge and change. Experimental approaches used to test research hypotheses in humans include migrant, cohort, case-control, and blinded studies. Once an experiment is complete, scientists summarize the findings and seek to publish the results in a scientific, peer-reviewed journal. The objective of peer review is to ensure that only the most unbiased, objective findings from carefully designed and executed research studies are published.

1.7 Nutrition claims often appear in media stories and in advertisements. It can be difficult to discern whether the claims are true. A cautious approach to nutrition-related claims and products is important. The Dietary Supplement Health and Education Act classified vitamins, minerals, amino acids, and herbal remedies as "foods," effectively restraining the FDA from regulating them as rigorously as food additives and drugs. When selecting nutrition-related products, carefully scrutinize product labels. For those who feel they need to improve their diet and health, a safe approach is to consult a physician or registered dietitian before purchasing dietary supplements.

Study Questions

1. Which nutrient does not provide energy?

    a. carbohydrates
    b. vitamins
    c. protein
    d. lipids

2. Which element is found in protein but is not found in carbohydrates and lipids?

    a. nitrogen
    b. carbon
    c. hydrogen
    d. oxygen

3. How many calories per gram are supplied by fats and oils?

    a. 9
    b. 4
    c. 5
    d. 7

4. A kilocalorie is the amount of heat energy it takes to raise the temperature of 1 gram of water 1 degree Celsius (1°C).

    a. true
    b. false

5. How many calories are in a food that contains 12 g carbohydrate, 3 g alcohol, 0 g fat, and 3 g protein?

    a. 112
    b. 81
    c. 75
    d. 124

6. Animal sources, such as meat, seafood, dairy products, and eggs, supply about two-thirds of the protein intake for most people around the world.

    a. true
    b. false

7. Foods are selected based mainly on _____.

    a. hunger
    b. appetite
    c. custom
    d. cost

8. Anthropometric assessment involves measuring _____.

    a. blood pressure
    b. enzyme activity
    c. skinfold thickness
    d. all of the above

9. Biochemical assessment involves measuring _____.

    a. concentrations of nutrients in the blood
    b. nutrient content in the diet
    c. body circumferences
    d. education and economic levels

10. Genes direct the growth, development, and maintenance of cells.

    a. true
    b. false

11. Which disease has a genetic link?

    a. diabetes
    b. osteoporosis
    c. cancer
    d. all of the above

12. The risk of developing a specific genetic disease is high if you have 2 or more first-degree relatives with the disease, especially if the disease occurred before age 50 to 60 years.

    a. true
    b. false

13. Which type of study examines disease in populations?

    a. epidemiology
    b. double-blind studies
    c. single-blind studies
    d. animal modeling

14. Which type of study follows a healthy population, looking for the development of diseases?

    a. cohort study
    b. case-control study
    c. migrant study
    d. double-blind study

15. Which statement is false about the Dietary Supplement Health and Education Act (DSHEA)?

    a. DSHEA classified vitamins as foods.
    b. DSHEA causes the FDA to regulate herbal supplements as rigorously as it does drugs.
    c. DSHEA effectively restrains the FDA from regulating mineral supplements.
    d. DSHEA requires the FDA to prove a dietary supplement is unsafe before preventing its sale.

16. Compare and contrast the characteristics of each macronutrient and micronutrient.

17. Explain the concept of energy as it relates to foods. What are the physiological fuel (energy) values used for a gram of carbohydrate, fat, protein, and alcohol?

34   **PART 1**   Nutrition Basics

18. According to national nutrition surveys, which nutrients tend to be underconsumed by many adult North Americans? Why is this the case?

19. List 4 health objectives for the U.S. for the year 2020. How would you rate yourself in each area? Why?

20. What nutrition-related disease is common in your family? What step or steps could you take at this point to minimize your risk?

21. Describe the types of studies that are conducted to test hypotheses in nutrition.

22. Describe one nutrition claim you have heard recently that sounds too good to be true. What is the probable motive of the person or company providing the advice?

Answer Key: 1-b; 2-a; 3-a; 4-b; 5-b; 6-b; 7-b; 8-c; 9-a; 10-a; 11-d; 12-a; 13-a; 14-a; 15-b; 16-refer to Section 1.1; 17-refer to Section 1.2; 18-refer to Section 1.3; 19-refer to Section 1.4; 20-refer to Section 1.5; 21-refer to Section 1.6; 22-refer to Section 1.7

Websites

To learn more about the topics covered in this chapter, visit these websites.

Reliable Health and Nutrition Information

www.nutrition.gov

www.eatright.org

healthypeople.gov

www.webmd.com

www.fruitsandveggiesmatter.gov

Nutrition and Health Claims Evaluation

www.acsh.org

www.quackwatch.com

ods.od.nih.gov

www.fda.gov

www.eatright.org

Genetics

genomics.energy.gov

www.hhs.gov/familyhistory

www.geneticalliance.org

www.kumc.edu/gec/support

www.faseb.org/genetics

www.genome.gov

www.dnalc.org

www.ncgr.org

For more websites, see Appendix L.

References

1. U.S. Departments of Health and Human Services and Agriculture. 2011. *Dietary Guidelines for Americans.*

2. Lee S and others. Trends in diet quality for coronary heart disease prevention between 1980–1982 and 2000–2002: The Minnesota Heart Survey. *J Am Diet Assoc.* 2007;107:213.

3. Mokdad AH and others. Actual causes of death in the United States, 2000. *JAMA.* 2004;291:1238.

4. Olshansky SJ and others. A potential decline in life expectancy in the United States in the 21st century. *New Eng J Med* 2005; 352:1138.

5. ADA Reports. Position of the American Dietetic Association. The roles of registered dietitians and dietetic technicians, registered in Health promotion and disease prevention. *J Am Diet Assoc.* 2007;107:1875.

6. USDA National Nutrient Database for Standard Reference 25, 2012; www.ars.usda.gov/main/site_main.htm?modecode= 12-35-45-00.

7. Food and Nutrition Board. *Dietary Reference Intakes for energy, carbohydrate, fiber, fat, fatty acids, cholesterol, protein, and amino acids.* Washington, DC: Food and Nutrition Board; 2002.

8. ADA Reports. Position of the American Dietetic Association. Functional foods. *J Am Diet Assoc.* 2009;109:735.

9. Adams LS and others. Pomegranate ellagitannin–derived compounds exhibit antiproliferative and antiaromatase activity in breast cancer cells in vitro. *Cancer Prev Res.* 2010;3:108.

10. Kim KK and others. Anti-angiogenic activity of cranberry proantho-cyanidins and cytotoxic properties in ovarian cancer cells. *Int J Oncol.* 2012;40:227.

11. Hasler C. Functional foods: Benefits, concerns, and challenges—A position paper from the American Council on Science and Health. *J Nutr.* 2002;132:3772.

12. Institute of Medicine. *Dietary Reference Intakes for energy, carbohydrate, fiber, fat, fatty acids, cholesterol, protein, and amino acids (macronutrients).* Washington, DC: National Academies Press; 2005.

13. Maurer Abbot J, Byrd-Bredbenner C. The state of the American diet. How can we cope? *Topics Clin Nutr.* 2007;3:202.

14. ADA Reports. Position of the American Dietetic Association. Total diet approach to communicating food and nutrition information. *J Am Diet Assoc.* 2007;107:1224.

15. Tholin S and others. Genetic and environmental influences on eating behavior: The Swedish Young Male Twins Study. *Am J Clin Nutr.* 2005;81:564.

16. Devine C and others. Work conditions and the food choice coping strategies of employed parents. *J Nutr Educ Behav.* 2009;41:365.

17. Cordain L and others. Origins and evolution of the Western diet: Health implications for the 21st century. *Am J Clin Nutr.* 2005;81:341.

18. U.S. Department of Health and Human Services. Get to know Healthy People 2020. 2011; HealthyPeople.gov.

19. Roles of registered dietitians and dietetic technicians in health promotion and disease prevention. *J Am Diet Assoc.* 2006;106:1875.

20. Wattendorf DJ, Hadley DW. Family history: The three-generation pedigree. *Am Fam Phys.* 2005;72:441.

21. Genuis SJ. Our genes are not our destiny: Incorporating molecular medicine into clinical practice. *J Eval Clin Pract.* 2008;14:94.

22. Guttmacher AE, Collins FC. Realizing the promise of genomics in biomedical research. *JAMA.* 2005;294:1399.

23. Vitti JJ and others. Human evolutionary genomics: ethical and interpretive issues. *Trends Genet.* 2012;28:137.

24. Making sense of medical news. *Consumer Reports on Health.* 2005; May:8.

25. ADA Reports. Position of the American Dietetic Association. Food and nutrition misinformation. *J Am Diet Assoc.* 2006;106:601.

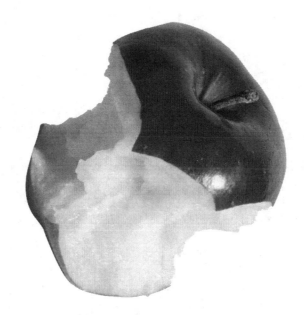

Nutrient composition research helps us plan and select diets that promote optimal health. Learn more at **www.ars.usda.gov.**

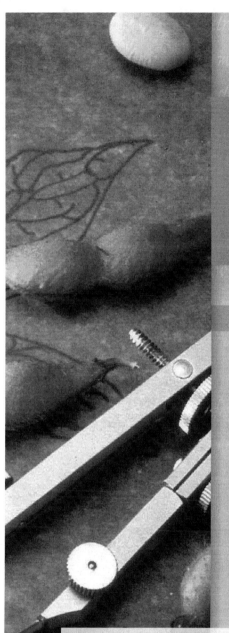

2 Tools of a Healthy Diet

Chapter Outline

2.1 Dietary Reference Intakes (DRIs)

2.2 Daily Values (DVs)

Global Perspective: Front-of-Package Nutrition Labeling

2.3 Nutrient Composition of Foods

Expert Perspective from the Field: Menu Labeling

2.4 Dietary Guidelines for Americans

2.5 MyPlate

Student Learning Outcomes

After studying this chapter, you will be able to

1. Explain the purpose of the Dietary Reference Intake (DRI) and its components (Estimated Average Requirements, Recommended Dietary Allowances, Adequate Intakes, Upper Levels, Estimated Energy Requirements, and Acceptable Macronutrient Distribution Ranges).

2. Compare the Daily Values to the Dietary Reference Intakes and explain how they are used on Nutrition Facts panels.

3. Describe Nutrition Facts panels and the claims permitted on food packages.

4. Describe the uses and limitations of the data in nutrient databases.

5. Discuss the 2010 Dietary Guidelines for Americans and the diseases they are intended to prevent or minimize.

6. Discuss the MyPlate food groupings and plan a diet using this tool.

7. Develop a healthy eating plan based on the concepts of variety, balance, moderation, nutrient density, and energy density.

NUTRITION IS A POPULAR TOPIC in the media. News stories often highlight up-to-the-minute research results. Magazine articles, websites, and books tout the "latest" way to lose weight or improve your diet. Deciding whether to incorporate advice given by the media can be a challenge. Relying on peer-reviewed research and recommendations by experts can help you decide whether to follow any of this nutrition advice. There also are a number of other useful tools based on nutrition research and assessment methods that can assist you in deciding what advice to follow as well as in planning a dietary pattern that helps you live as healthfully as possible now while minimizing the risk of developing nutrition-related diseases later on.

One tool for planning diets that support overall health is the Dietary Reference Intakes—they provide guidance on the quantities of nutrients that are most likely to result in optimal health. Using Daily Values, food labels, nutrient databases, nutrient density, and energy density also can help facilitate efforts to identify foods that contain the array of nutrients needed in the amounts recommended. The Dietary Guidelines outline key steps that support good health and reduce risk of chronic, nutrition-related diseases. Finally, MyPlate is a handy tool you can use to create a dietary pattern that promotes excellent health and lets you eat foods you enjoy.

A key to healthy living is gaining a firm knowledge of these basic diet planning tools. With this understanding, you'll know why scientists believe that optimal nutritional health can be accomplished by doing what you've heard many times before: eat a balanced diet, consume a variety of foods, moderate the amount you eat, and stay physically active.

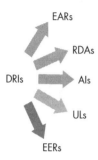

The DRIs are composed of Estimated Average Requirements (EARs), Recommended Dietary Allowances (RDAs), Adequate Intakes (AIs), Tolerable Upper Intake Levels (Upper Levels, or ULs), and Estimated Energy Requirements (EERs).

Dietary Reference Intakes (DRIs)
Term used to encompass nutrient recommendations made by the Food and Nutrition Board of the National Academy of Sciences. These include RDAs, EARs, AIs, EERs, and ULs.

Estimated Average Requirements (EARs)
Nutrient intake amounts estimated to meet the needs of 50% of the individuals in a specific life stage.

Recommended Dietary Allowance (RDA)
Nutrient intake amount sufficient to meet the needs of 97 to 98% of the individuals in a specific life stage.

Adequate Intake (AI) Nutrient intake amount set for any nutrient for which insufficient research is available to establish an RDA. AIs are based on estimates of intakes that appear to maintain a defined nutritional state in a specific life stage.

Tolerable Upper Intake Level (UL)
Maximum chronic daily intake level of a nutrient that is unlikely to cause adverse health effects in almost all people in a specific life stage.

Estimated Energy Requirement (EER)
Estimate of the energy (kcal) intake needed to match the energy use of an average person in a specific life stage.

Acceptable Macronutrient Distribution Range (AMDR) Range of macronutrient intake, as percent of energy, associated with reduced risk of chronic diseases while providing for recommended intake of essential nutrients.

2.1 Dietary Reference Intakes (DRIs)

When many young men were rejected from military service in World War II because of the effects of poor nutrition on their health, scientists realized the need for dietary intake recommendations. As a result, in 1941, a group of scientists formed the Food and Nutrition Board with the purpose of reviewing existing research and establishing the first official dietary standards. These standards were designed to evaluate nutrient intakes of large populations and to plan agricultural production.[1] Since they were first published in 1943, these standards have been periodically reviewed and revised to reflect up-to-date scientific research.

The latest recommendations from the Food and Nutrition Board are called **Dietary Reference Intakes (DRIs).**[2] The DRIs apply to people in both the U.S. and Canada because scientists from both countries worked together to establish them. The DRIs include 5 sets of standards: Estimated Average Requirements (EARs), Recommended Dietary Allowances (RDAs), Adequate Intakes (AIs), Tolerable Upper Intake Levels (Upper Levels, or ULs), and Estimated Energy Requirements (EERs) (see the inside back cover of this textbook).[1] DRIs are set for almost 40 nutrients. Although not a DRI, Acceptable Macronutrient Distribution Ranges (AMDRs) were established for guidance on intake levels of carbohydrates, protein, and fat to help reduce the risk of nutrition-related chronic diseases.[3-5] As you can see from charts on the inside back cover of this book, the DRIs differ by life stage (i.e., age group, by gender after age 9 years, pregnancy, lactation). All of the recommendations should be applied to dietary intake averaged over a number of days, not a single day.

Estimated Average Requirements (EARs)

Estimated Average Requirements (EARs) are daily nutrient intake amounts that are estimated to meet the needs of half of the people in a certain life stage (Fig. 2-1). EARs are set for 17 nutrients. An EAR for a nutrient is set only when the Food and Nutrition Board

DRIs vary by life stage because nutrient needs differ with age and, after age 9 years, by gender. Pregnancy and lactation also affect nutrient needs; thus, there is a set of DRIs specially designed for these women.

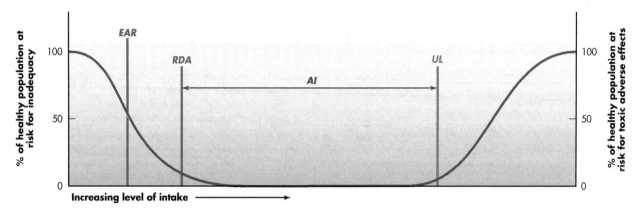

Figure 2-1 This figure shows the relationship of the Dietary Reference Intakes (DRIs) to each other and the percent of the population covered by each.

Estimated Average Requirement (EAR): 50% of healthy North Americans would have an inadequate intake if they consumed the EAR, whereas 50% would have their needs met.

Recommended Dietary Allowance (RDA): 2 to 3% of healthy North Americans would have an inadequate intake if they met the RDA, whereas 97 to 98% would have their needs met.

Upper Level (UL): highest nutrient intake level that is likely to pose no risks of adverse health effects in almost all healthy individuals. At intakes above the UL, the margin of safety to protect against adverse effects is reduced. At intakes between the RDA and UL (Upper Level), the risk of either an inadequate diet or adverse effects from the nutrient is close to 0%.

Adequate Intake (AI): set for some nutrients instead of an RDA; lies somewhere between the RDA and UL. Thus, the AI should cover the needs of more than 97 to 98% of individuals.

agrees that there is an accurate method for measuring whether intake is adequate. These measures, called functional markers, typically evaluate the activity of an enzyme in the body or the ability of a cell or an organ to maintain normal physiological function.[1] If no measurable functional marker is available, an EAR cannot be set. Each EAR is adjusted to account for the amount of the nutrient that passes through the digestive tract unabsorbed. Because EARs meet the needs of only 50% of those in a life stage, they can be used to evaluate only the adequacy of diets of groups, not of individuals.[1] Specific EARs are listed in Appendix J.

To illustrate how EARs are determined, let's take a look at vitamin C. The amount of vitamin C needed daily to prevent scurvy is about 10 mg. However, as you will learn in Chapter 15, vitamin C has other functions as well, including some related to the immune system (see Appendix A for details on the immune system). In fact, the concentration of vitamin C in one component of the immune system—notably, white blood cells (specifically, neutrophils)—can be used as a functional marker for vitamin C. The Food and Nutrition Board concluded that nearly maximal saturation of these white blood cells with vitamin C is the best functional marker for optimal vitamin C status. It takes a daily vitamin C intake of about 75 mg for men and 60 mg for women to nearly saturate these white blood cells. These average amounts became the EARs for young adult men and women.

▶ This online tool displays DRIs based on age and gender: fnic.nal.usda.gov/interactiveDRI.

Recommended Dietary Allowances (RDAs)

Recommended Dietary Allowances (RDAs) are daily nutrient intake amounts sufficient to meet the needs of nearly all individuals (97 to 98%) in a life stage (see inside back cover). RDAs are based on a multiple of the EARs (generally, the RDA = EAR × 1.2). Because of this relationship, an RDA can be set only for nutrients that have an EAR. (Recall that a measurable functional marker is required to set an EAR.) An additional consideration made when setting an RDA is the nutrient's ability to prevent chronic disease rather than just prevent deficiency.[1]

For example, to determine the RDA for vitamin C, its EAR (75 mg for men and 60 mg for women) was multiplied by 1.2. In this case, the RDA was set at 90 mg for men and 75 mg for women. The RDA for other life-stage groups was set similarly. Because smokers break down vitamin C more rapidly, the Food and Nutrition Board recommended that these individuals add 35 mg/day to the RDA set for their life stage.

The RDA is the goal for usual intake. To assess whether vitamin C intake meets the RDA, total the amount of vitamin C consumed in a week and divide by 7 to get an average daily intake. Keep in mind that the RDA is higher than the average human needs, so not everyone needs to have an intake equal to the RDA. Thus, even if average intake is somewhat less than the RDA and the person is healthy, one's need for this vitamin is probably less than the RDA. As a general rule, however, the further intake regularly drops below the RDA—particularly as it drops below the EAR—the greater the risk of developing a nutrient deficiency.[1]

Adequate Intakes (AIs)

Adequate Intakes (AIs) are daily intake amounts set for nutrients for which there are insufficient research data to establish an EAR (see inside back cover). AIs are based on observed or experimentally determined estimates of the average nutrient intake that appears to maintain a defined nutritional state (e.g., bone health) in a specific life-stage group.[1] In determining the AI for a nutrient, it is expected that the amount exceeds the RDA for that nutrient, if an RDA is known. Thus, the AI should cover the needs of more than 97 to 98% of the individuals in a specific life-stage group. The actual degree to which the AI exceeds the RDA likely differs among the various nutrients and life-stage groups. Like the RDA, the AI can be used as the goal for usual intake of that nutrient by an individual. Currently, essential fatty acids, fiber, and certain vitamins and minerals, including some B-vitamins, the vitamin-like compound choline, and fluoride, have AIs.

Although Estimated Energy Requirements (EERs) provide a guide for energy needs, the best estimate of energy need is the amount needed to maintain a healthy weight.

Tolerable Upper Intake Levels (Upper Levels, or ULs)

Tolerable Upper Intake Levels, or Upper Levels **(ULs),** are the maximum daily intake amounts of nutrients that are not likely to cause adverse health effects in almost all individuals (97 to 98%) in a life-stage group (see inside back cover).[1] The amount applies to chronic daily use and is set to protect even those who are very susceptible in the healthy general population. For example, the UL for vitamin C is 2000 mg/day. Intakes greater than this amount can cause diarrhea and inflammation of the stomach lining.

The UL for most nutrients is based on the combined intake of food, water, supplements, and fortified foods. The exceptions are the vitamin niacin and the minerals magnesium, zinc, and nickel—the UL for each refers only to nonfood sources, such as medicines and supplements. This is because niacin, magnesium, zinc, or nickel toxicity from food sources is unlikely.[6]

The UL is not a nutrient intake goal; instead, it is a ceiling below which nutrient intake should remain. Still, for most individuals, there is a margin of safety above the UL before any adverse effects are likely to occur. Too little information is available to set a UL for all nutrients, but this does not mean that toxicity from these nutrients is impossible. Plus, there is no clear-cut evidence that intakes above the RDA or AI confer any additional health benefits for most of us.

Estimated Energy Requirements (EERs)

RDAs and Adequate Intakes for nutrients are set high enough to meet the needs of almost all healthy individuals. In contrast, **Estimated Energy Requirements (EERs)** are set at the average daily energy (calorie) need for each life-stage group. Unlike most vitamins and minerals, energy (carbohydrate, fat, protein, alcohol) consumed in amounts above that needed is not excreted but is stored as body fat. Thus, to promote healthy weight, a more conservative standard is used to set EERs.[5] Overall, EERs are estimates because energy needs depend on energy expenditure and, in some cases, the energy needed to support growth or human milk production. For most adults, the best estimate of energy need is the amount required to achieve and maintain a healthy weight (see Chapter 10 for details).

Acceptable Macronutrient Distribution Ranges (AMDRs)

In addition to EERs, the Food and Nutrition Board established **Acceptable Macronutrient Distribution Ranges (AMDRs)** for intake of carbohydrate, protein, fat, and essential fatty acids (see inside back cover). For each macronutrient, the AMDRs provide a range of intake, as a percent of energy, associated with good health and a reduced risk of chronic diseases while providing for recommended intakes of essential nutrients. The AMDRs complement the DRIs.[1] For example, the AMDR for fat is 20 to 35% of calories. For an average energy intake of 2000 kcal/day, this is equal to 400 to 700 kcal per day from fat. To translate this to grams of fat per day, divide by 9 kcal/g. Thus, a healthy amount of fat for a 2000 kcal diet is 44 to 78 g fat/day.

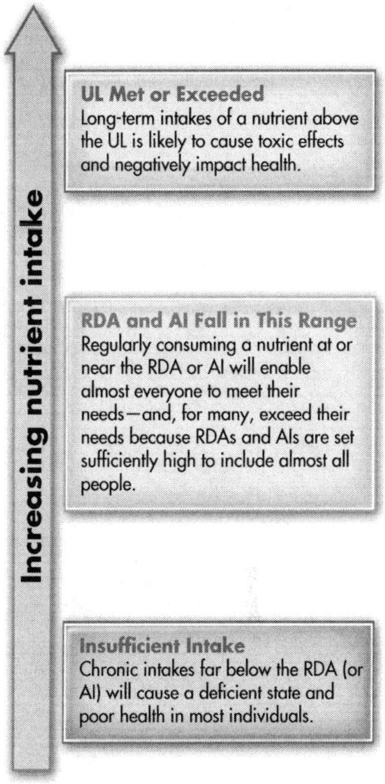

Appropriate Uses of the DRIs

The DRIs are intended mainly for diet planning (Table 2-1). Specifically, a diet plan should aim to meet any RDAs or AIs set. Finally, when planning diets, it is important not to exceed the upper level for a nutrient (Fig. 2-2).[1,6] Keep in mind also that DRIs apply to healthy people—none are necessarily appropriate amounts for undernourished individuals or those with diseases or other health conditions that require higher intakes. This concept will be covered in Chapters 12 through 15.

Increasing nutrient intake

UL Met or Exceeded
Long-term intakes of a nutrient above the UL is likely to cause toxic effects and negatively impact health.

RDA and AI Fall in This Range
Regularly consuming a nutrient at or near the RDA or AI will enable almost everyone to meet their needs—and, for many, exceed their needs because RDAs and AIs are set sufficiently high to include almost all people.

Insufficient Intake
Chronic intakes far below the RDA (or AI) will cause a deficient state and poor health in most individuals.

Figure 2-2 Think of the nutrient standards that are part of DRIs as points along a line ranging from an insufficient intake to a healthy intake level to an excessive intake.

Table 2-1 **Putting the DRIs for Nutrient Needs to Use**
EAR	**Estimated Average Requirement.** Represents average nutrient need. Use only to evaluate adequacy of diets of groups, not individuals.
RDA	**Recommended Dietary Allowance.** Use to evaluate current intake for a specific nutrient. The further intake strays above or below this value, the greater the likelihood a person will develop nutrition-related problems.
AI	**Adequate Intake.** Use to evaluate current intake for a specific nutrient, realizing that an AI implies that further research is required before scientists can establish a more definitive intake amount needed to set an RDA.
UL	**Upper Level.** Use to evaluate the highest amount of daily nutrient intake that is unlikely to cause adverse health effects in the long run. This value applies to chronic use and is set to protect even very susceptible people in the healthy general population. As intake rises higher than the UL, the potential for adverse effects generally increases.
EER	**Estimated Energy Requirement.** Use to estimate energy needs according to height, weight, gender, age, and physical activity pattern.
AMDR	**Acceptable Macronutrient Distribution Range.** Use to determine whether percent of calories from each macronutrient falls within suggested range. The greater the discrepancy with AMDR, the greater the risk for nutrition-related chronic diseases.

42   **PART 1**   Nutrition Basics

Putting the DRIs into Action to Determine the Nutrient Density of Foods

Nutrient density has gained acceptance in recent years as a tool for assessing the nutritional quality of an individual food.[7] To determine the **nutrient density** of a food, divide the amount of a nutrient (protein, vitamin, mineral) in a serving of the food by your daily recommended intake (e.g., RDA, AI). Next, divide the calories in a serving of the food by your daily calorie need (EER). Then, compare these values—a food is said to be nutrient dense if it provides a greater contribution to your nutrient need than your calorie need. The higher a food's nutrient density, the better it is as a source for a particular nutrient. For example, the 70 mg of vitamin C and 65 calories provided by an orange supplies 108% of the RDA for a teenage girl (65 mg vitamin C) and only 4% of her 1800 daily calorie need. It is considered a nutrient-dense food for vitamin C. In contrast, the 52 mg of calcium in an orange provides only 4% of the teenage girl's calcium RDA (1300 mg).

On a nutrient-by-nutrient basis, comparing the nutrient density of different foods is an easy way to identify the more nutritious choice.[8] It's more difficult to obtain an overall picture of nutritional quality. Some experts recommend averaging the nutrient density for key nutrients and comparing the average with the percent of daily calorie need provided. For example, as Figure 2-3 shows, an average of the nutrients in the fat-free milk is about 15% and supplies only 4% of calories, whereas the nutrients in the cola average approximately 0 while supplying 5% of calories. The fat-free milk is much more nutrient dense than a sugared soft drink for many nutrients. Sugared soft drinks and other foods that are not nutrient dense (e.g., chips, cookies, and candy) often are called **empty-calorie foods** because they tend to be high in sugar and/or fat but few other nutrients—that is, the calories are "empty" of nutrients.

Figure 2-3 Comparison of the nutrient density of a sugar-sweetened soft drink with that of fat-free (skim) milk. The milk provides a significantly greater contribution to nutrient intake per calorie than the soft drink. Compare the lengths of the bars indicating vitamin or mineral contribution with the bar that represents energy content. For the soft drink, no nutrient surpasses energy content. Fat-free milk, in contrast, has longer nutrient bars for protein, vitamin A, the vitamins thiamin and riboflavin, and calcium.

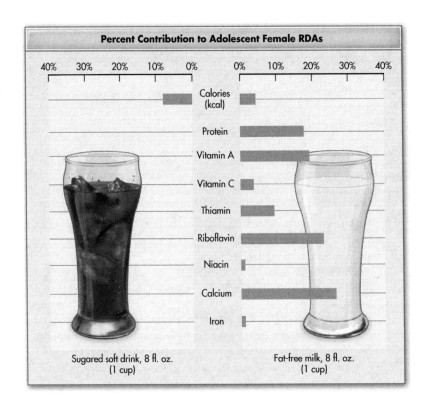

Percent Contribution to Adolescent Female RDAs

Sugared soft drink, 8 fl. oz. (1 cup)

Fat-free milk, 8 fl. oz. (1 cup)

Knowledge Check

1. Which dietary standard is set based on Estimated Average Requirements (EARs)?
2. Which dietary standard is set when an Estimated Average Requirement (EAR) cannot be set?
3. Which of the Dietary Reference Intakes (DRIs) is set at the maximum daily intake amount?

▶ *DV: RDI & DRV*

Daily Value (DV): Generic nutrient standard used on Nutrition Facts labels; it comprises both Reference Daily Intakes (RDIs) and Daily Reference Values (DRVs).

Reference Daily Intakes (RDIs): Part of the DV; generic nutrient standard set for vitamins and minerals (except sodium and potassium).

Daily Reference Values (DRVs): Part of the DV; generic nutrient standard set for energy-producing nutrients (fat, carbohydrate, protein, fiber), cholesterol, sodium, and potassium.

 ## 2.2 Daily Values (DVs)

The Nutrition Facts panel on a food label compares the amount of nutrients in the food with a set of standards called Daily Values (DVs). DVs are generic standards that were developed by the U.S. Food and Drug Administration (FDA) because the DRIs are age- and gender-specific and it isn't practical to have different food labels for men and women or for teens and adults.

DVs have been set for 4 groups: infants, toddlers, pregnant or lactating women, and people over 4 years of age. The DVs that appear on all food labels—except those specially marketed to infants, toddlers, or pregnant or lactating women—are those set for people over age 4 years. This book will focus on the DVs for those over age 4 years.

The DVs are based on 2 sets of dietary standards: Reference Daily Intakes and Daily Reference Values. These terms—*Reference Daily Intakes* and *Daily Reference Values*—do not appear on food labels. Instead, the term *Daily Value* is used to represent the combination of these 2 sets of dietary standards. Table 2-2 displays the DVs. Even though the term *DV* is used on Nutrition Facts panels, it is important for nutrition and health professionals to understand how Reference Daily Intakes and Daily Reference Values differ.

▶ Canada also has a set of Daily Values for use on food labels (see Appendix D).

Fresh fruits, vegetables, and fish are not required to have Nutrition Facts panels. However, many grocers distribute leaflets or display posters or notebooks that include Nutrition Facts panels for these foods. Examples of these posters are available at www.fda.gov/Food/LabelingNutrition. Starting in 2012, nutrition labeling is required on fresh meat and poultry products.

Reference Daily Intakes (RDIs)

Reference Daily Intakes (RDIs) are set for vitamins and most minerals—these nutrients all have established nutrient standards, such as RDAs. RDI values for people over age 4 years tend to be set at the highest value for any life-stage group in the 1968 edition of the RDAs. Consider iron   in 1968, adult women and adolescents had the highest iron RDA (i.e., 18 mg/day). The iron RDI for people over age 4 years was set at this value. The RDI values currently in use are generally slightly higher than current RDAs and related nutrient standards (see Table 2-2). Many nutrition experts believe the RDIs should be revised to reflect the latest nutrient standards.[9]

Daily Reference Values (DRVs)

Daily Reference Values (DRVs) are standards for energy-producing nutrients (fat, saturated fat, carbohydrate, protein, fiber), cholesterol, sodium, and potassium. Many of these nutrients do not have an established RDA or other nutrient standard (e.g., total fat, saturated fat, carbohydrate).

Table 2-2   Comparison of Daily Values with Current RDAs and Other Nutrient Standards

Dietary Constituent	Unit of Measure*	Current Daily Values for People over 4 Years of Age	RDA or Other Dietary Standard	
			Males 19–30 Years Old	Females 19–30 Years Old
Daily Reference Values (DRVs)				
Total fat	g	30% kcal	—	—
Saturated fatty acids	g	10% kcal	—	—
Protein	g	10% kcal	56	46
Cholesterol	mg	<300	—	—
Carbohydrate	g	60% kcal	130	130
Fiber	g	11.5g/1000 kcal	38	25
Sodium†	mg	<2400	1500	1500
Potassium	mg	3500	4700	4700
Reference Daily Intakes (RDIs)				
Vitamin A	µg Retinol Activity Equivalents	1000	900	700
Vitamin D	International units (µg)	400 (10)	600 (15)	600 (15)
Vitamin E	International units (mg)	30 (14–20)	22–33 (15)	22–33 (15)
Vitamin K	µg	80	120	90
Vitamin C	mg	60	90	75
Folate	µg	400	400	400
Thiamin	mg	1.5	1.2	1.1
Riboflavin	mg	1.7	1.3	1.1
Niacin	mg	20	16	14
Vitamin B-6	mg	2	1.3	1.3
Vitamin B-12	µg	6	2.4	2.4
Biotin	mg (µg)	0.3 (300)	0.03 (30)	0.03 (30)
Pantothenic acid	mg	10	5	5
Calcium	mg	1000	1000	1000
Phosphorus	mg	1000	700	700
Iodine	µg	150	150	150
Iron	mg	18	8	18
Magnesium	mg	400	400	310
Copper	mg	2	0.9	0.9
Zinc	mg	15	11	8
Chloride†	mg	3400	2300	2300
Manganese	mg	2	2.3	1.8
Selenium	µg	70	55	55
Chromium	µg	120	35	25
Molybdenum	µg	75	45	45

*Abbreviations: g = gram; mg = milligram; µg = microgram.

†The considerably higher Daily Values for sodium and chloride allow for greater diet flexibility, but the extra amounts are not needed to maintain health.

The DRVs for the energy-producing nutrients are based on daily calorie intake. The FDA selected 2000 calories as the reference for calculating percent DVs for energy-producing nutrients, although larger food packages can display values for both a 2000- and a 2500-calorie diet. Regardless of the calorie level used, the DRVs for energy-producing nutrients are always calculated like this:

- Fat is set at 30% of calories.
- Saturated fat is set at 10% of calories.
- Carbohydrate is set at 60% of calories.
- Protein is set at 10% of calories.
- Fiber is set at 11.5 g of fiber per 1000 calories.

Note that the DRVs for sodium, potassium, and cholesterol, as well as the vitamins and minerals that have RDIs, do not vary with calorie intake.

Putting the Daily Values into Action on Nutrition Facts Panels

With few exceptions, information related to the Daily Values is found on almost every food and beverage sold in the supermarket today. Their labels include the product name, name and address of the manufacturer, amount of product in the package, ingredients listed in descending order by weight, ingredients that are common allergens[10] (milk, eggs, fish, shellfish, peanuts, tree nuts, wheat, and soy; see Chapter 7 for details), and a Nutrition Facts panel. The Nutrition Facts panel lists the amounts of certain food components and reports many of them as % Daily Value. Labels also must indicate the country of origin for certain products (i.e., meat, poultry, fish, fresh and frozen fruits and vegetables, peanuts, pecans, macadamia nuts, and ginseng).[11] This required labeling is monitored in North America by government agencies, such as the FDA in the U.S.

As you can see in Figure 2-4, Nutrition Facts panels present information for a single serving of food. Serving sizes are specified by the FDA so that they are consistent among similar foods. This means that all brands of ice cream, for example, must use the same serving size on their labels. The serving sizes on Nutrition Facts panels are based on typical serving sizes eaten by Americans; as a result, they may differ from the serving sizes recommended by MyPlate (see Section 2.5).

The following components must be listed on most Nutrition Facts panels: total calories (kcal), calories from fat, total fat, saturated fat, *trans* fat, cholesterol, sodium, total carbohydrate, fiber, sugars, protein, vitamin A, vitamin C, calcium, and iron. Labels of foods that contain few nutrients, such as candy and soft drinks, may omit some nutrients. In addition to the components required on Nutrition Facts panels, manufacturers can choose to list other nutrients, such as polyunsaturated fat or potassium. Manufacturers are required to include a nutrient on the Nutrition Facts panel if they make a claim about its health benefits (see Claims on Food Labels later in this chapter) or if the food is fortified with that nutrient.

Notice in Figure 2-4 that the amount of fats, cholesterol, sodium, carbohydrates, and protein in a food is given in grams or milligrams. Most of these nutrients also are given as % Daily Value, as are vitamins and other minerals. Because protein deficiency is not a public health concern in the U.S., listing % Daily Value for protein is not mandatory on foods for people over 4 years of age. If the % Daily Value is given on a label, the FDA requires that the product be analyzed for protein quality (see Chapter 7). This procedure is expensive and time consuming; thus, many companies opt not to list % Daily Value for protein. However, labels on food for infants and children under 4 years of age must include the % Daily Value for protein, as must labels on any food carrying a claim about protein content.

Recall that all of the values shown on Nutrition Facts panels are for a single serving of the food. Thus, to determine the total amount of calories or a nutrient in more than 1 serving, the value on the label must be multiplied by the number of servings consumed.

Use the Nutrition Facts panel to learn more about the nutrient content of the foods you eat. Nutrient content is expressed as a % Daily Value. Canadian food laws and related food labels have a slightly different format (see Appendix D).

Figure 2-4 Food packages must list product name, name and address of the manufacturer, amount of product in the package, and ingredients. The Nutrition Facts panel is required on virtually all packaged food products. The % Daily Value listed on the label is the percent of the amount of a nutrient needed daily that is provided by a single serving of the product.

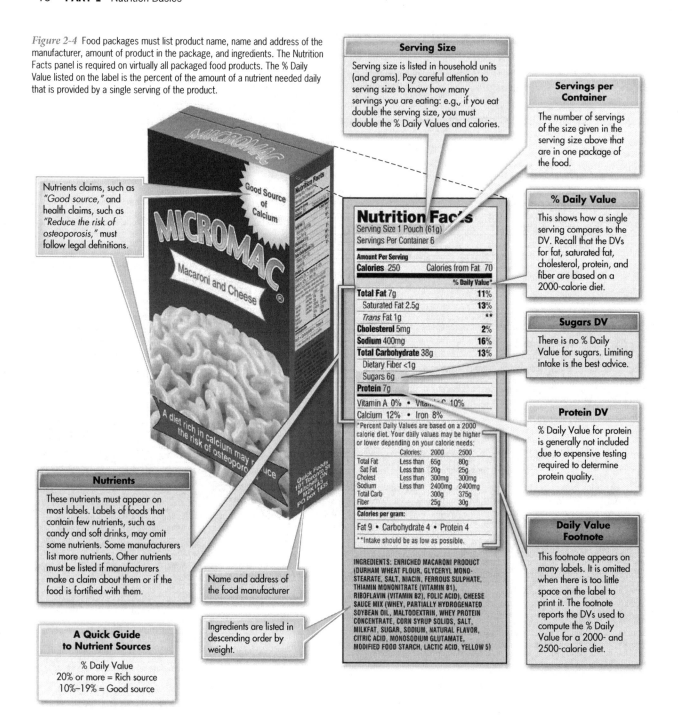

Serving Size

Serving size is listed in household units (and grams). Pay careful attention to serving size to know how many servings you are eating: e.g., if you eat double the serving size, you must double the % Daily Values and calories.

Servings per Container

The number of servings of the size given in the serving size above that are in one package of the food.

% Daily Value

This shows how a single serving compares to the DV. Recall that the DVs for fat, saturated fat, cholesterol, protein, and fiber are based on a 2000-calorie diet.

Sugars DV

There is no % Daily Value for sugars. Limiting intake is the best advice.

Protein DV

% Daily Value for protein is generally not included due to expensive testing required to determine protein quality.

Daily Value Footnote

This footnote appears on many labels. It is omitted when there is too little space on the label to print it. The footnote reports the DVs used to compute the % Daily Value for a 2000- and 2500-calorie diet.

Nutrients claims, such as *"Good source,"* and health claims, such as *"Reduce the risk of osteoporosis,"* must follow legal definitions.

Nutrients

These nutrients must appear on most labels. Labels of foods that contain few nutrients, such as candy and soft drinks, may omit some nutrients. Some manufacturers list more nutrients. Other nutrients must be listed if manufacturers make a claim about them or if the food is fortified with them.

Name and address of the food manufacturer

Ingredients are listed in descending order by weight.

A Quick Guide to Nutrient Sources

% Daily Value
20% or more = Rich source
10%–19% = Good source

For instance, let's say you ate the entire box of MicroMac shown in Figure 2-4—that would be 6 servings. The entire package would provide 1500 calories (250 kcal per serving × 6 servings per container = 1500 calories), 78% of total carbohydrate (13% per serving × 6 servings per container = 78%), 36 grams of sugar, and so on.

You can use the DVs to determine how a particular food fits in an overall diet (Fig. 2-5). If, for example, a single food provides 50% of the DV for fat, then it is a good idea to either select a different food that is lower in fat or be sure other choices that day are low in fat. The DVs also can help you determine how close your overall diet comes to meeting recommendations. For instance, if you consume 2000 calories per day, your total fat intake for the day should be 65 g or less. If you consume 10 g of fat at breakfast, you have 55 grams, or 85%, of your DV for fat left for the rest of the day. If you eat more or less than 2000 calories per day, you can still use the Nutrition Facts panel. For example, if you consume only 1600 calories per day, the total percentage of DV you eat for fat, saturated fat, carbohydrate, protein, and fiber should add up to 80% DV because 1600/2000 = 0.8, or 80%. If you eat 3000 calories daily, the total percentage of DV you eat of fat, saturated fat, carbohydrate, protein, and fiber in all the foods you eat in 1 day can add up to 150% DV because 3000/2000 = 1.5, or 150%. Remember, you need to make adjustments only for the nutrients that are based on calorie intake: carbohydrate, protein, fat, saturated fat, and fiber. For nutrients not based on calorie intake, such as vitamin A and cholesterol, just add percentage of DVs in all the foods you eat to determine how close your diet comes to meeting recommendations.

As you may have noticed, the nutrients listed on Nutrition Facts panels tend to be the ones of greatest health concern in North America. Many people eat too much fat, saturated fat, *trans* fat, cholesterol, sodium, and sugar. Many also are concerned that they don't get enough fiber, calcium, iron, vitamin A, and vitamin C. Thus, for the best health, most people should aim to keep their intake of the following nutrients at or below 100% of the DV: total fat, saturated fat, cholesterol, and sodium. Most people also should plan their diets to achieve 100% of the DV for fiber, vitamin A, vitamin C, iron, and calcium.

Nutrition Facts panels often include a footnote that shows the intake recommendations for dietary components such as fat, saturated fat, cholesterol, sodium, carbohydrate, and fiber. The amounts listed are for a 2000-calorie diet and, when package space allows, a 2500-calorie diet. This footnote helps label readers see how the DVs are calculated for these nutrients.

Claims on Food Labels

As a marketing tool directed toward health-conscious consumers, food manufacturers like to assert that some of their products have certain nutrient levels or health benefits. After reviewing hundreds of comments on the proposed rule allowing nutrient and health claims, the FDA, which has legal oversight for most food products, decided to permit certain specific claims. Although these claims must comply with FDA regulations, you can use Daily Value information on Nutrition Facts panels to verify nutrient content and health claims made on food packages.

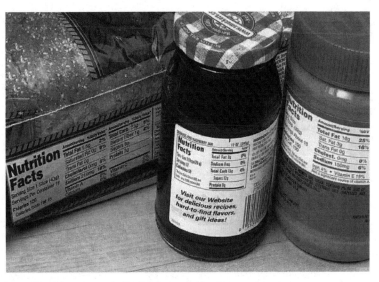

The nutrition information on the Nutrition Facts panels on these products can be combined to determine the nutrient intake for a peanut butter and jelly sandwich. For example, 2 slices of bread, 1 tablespoon of jam, and 2 tablespoons of peanut butter contain 480 calories ([120 × 2] + 50 + 190), which is 24% of the total calories needed on a 2000-calorie diet ((480/2000) × 100).

▶ As you saw in Figure 1-13 (Chapter 1), the labels on nutrient and herbal supplements have a different layout than those on foods. These labels include a "Supplement Facts" heading.

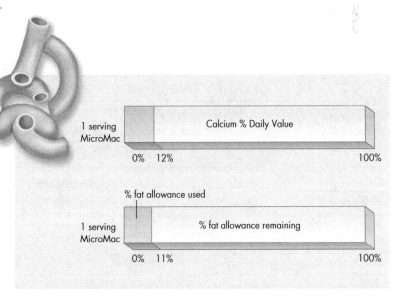

Figure 2-5 Nutrition Facts panels can help you track intake. If you needed 2000 calories and ate a single serving of MicroMac, you would still have 89% Daily Value of your fat allowance left. In addition, you would have met 12% Daily Value for calcium.

▶ Canada has established a set of health claims for nutrition labels (see Appendix D).

▶ Claims on foods fall into these categories:

- Nutrient content claims—closely regulated by the FDA

- Health claims—closely regulated by the FDA

- Qualified health claims—regulated by the FDA, but there is only limited scientific evidence for the claims

- Structure/function claims—not FDA approved; manufacturer is responsible for their accuracy

Nutrient content claims are those that describe the nutrients in a food. Examples are "low in fat," "rich in vitamin A," and "zero calories." All nutrient content claims must comply with regulations set by the FDA. Table 2-3 summarizes the legal definitions of nutrient content claims permitted to appear on food packages. For example, if a product claims to be "low sodium," it must have 140 mg or less of sodium per serving.

Health claims describe a relationship between a disease and a nutrient, food, or food constituent.[12] All permitted health claims have significant scientific agreement that they are true. All health claims must use a *may* or *might* qualifier in the statement. The following are some of the permitted health claims.

- A diet with enough calcium may reduce risk of osteoporosis.
- A diet low in sodium may reduce risk of hypertension.
- A diet low in total fat may reduce risk of some cancers.
- A diet low in fat and rich in fiber-containing grain products, fruits, and vegetables may reduce risk of some cancers.
- A diet low in saturated fat and cholesterol may reduce risk of cardiovascular disease (typically referred to as *heart disease* on the label).
- A diet low in saturated fat and cholesterol and rich in fruits, vegetables, and grains that contain soluble fiber may reduce risk of heart disease.

Table 2-3 Summary of Nutrient Claims on Food Labels

Calories	
Calorie free	Less than 5 kcal per serving
Low calorie	40 kcal or less per serving (if the serving is small,* per 50 g of the food)
Reduced or fewer calories	At least 25% less kcal per serving than reference food
Light or lite	50% less fat if half or more of the food's kcal are from fat; 50% less fat or 33% less kcal if less than half of the food's kcal are from fat
Total Fat	
Fat free	Less than 0.5 g fat per serving
Low fat	3 g or less per serving (if the serving is small, per 50 g of the food)
Reduced or less fat	At least 25% less per serving than reference food
Lean	Seafood, poultry, or meat with less than 10 g total fat, 4.5 g or less saturated fat, and less than 95 mg cholesterol per reference amount
Extra lean	Seafood, poultry, or meat with less than 5 g total fat, less than 2 g saturated fat, and less than 95 mg cholesterol per reference amount
Saturated Fat	
Saturated fat free	Less than 0.5 g saturated fat and less than 0.5 g *trans* fatty acids per serving
Low saturated fat	1 g or less per serving and 15% or less of kcal from saturated fat
Reduced or less saturated fat	At least 25% less per serving than reference food
Cholesterol	
Cholesterol free	Less than 2 mg cholesterol and 2 g or less saturated fat per serving
Low cholesterol	20 mg or less cholesterol and 2 g or less saturated fat per serving (if the serving is small, per 50 g of the food)
Reduced or less cholesterol	At least 25% less cholesterol per serving than reference food and 2 g or less saturated fat
Sugar	
Sugar free	Less than 0.5 g per serving
No added sugar or without added sugar	No sugars or sugar-containing ingredient (e.g., jam, applesauce) added during processing or packing
Reduced sugar	At least 25% less sugar per serving than reference food

*Small serving size or small reference amount = reference amount of 30 g or less or 2 tbsp or less.

- A diet low in saturated fat and cholesterol that also includes 25 g/day of soy protein may reduce risk of heart disease.
- Foods that contain plant stanol or sterol esters may reduce risk of heart disease (see Chapter 6).
- A diet adequate in folate may reduce a woman's risk of having a child with a brain or spinal cord defect (see Chapter 13).
- Sugar alcohols do not promote tooth decay (see Chapter 5).

Only food products that meet the following requirements can bear a health claim. First, the food must be a "good source" (before any fortification) of fiber, protein, vitamin A, vitamin C, calcium, or iron—it must provide at least 10% of the Daily Value for at least 1 of these nutrients. Second, a single serving of the food cannot contain more than 13 g of fat, 4 g of saturated fat, 60 mg of cholesterol, or 480 mg of sodium. If a food exceeds any of these requirements, no health claim can be made for it, despite its other nutritional qualities. For example, even though whole milk is high in calcium, its label can't make a health claim about calcium and a reduced risk of osteoporosis because whole milk contains 5 g of saturated fat per serving. Third, the product must meet criteria specific to the health claim being made. For example, a health claim regarding fat and cancer can be

Nutrition Facts panels can help you locate foods that will provide a nutrient-rich diet.

Table 2-3 Continued

Sodium	
Sodium free or salt free	Less than 5 mg per serving
Very low sodium	35 mg or less per serving (if the serving is small, per 50 g of the food)
Low sodium	140 mg or less per serving (if the serving is small, per 50 g of the food)
Light (for sodium-reduced products)	If food meets definition of low calorie and low fat, and sodium is reduced by at least 50%
Light in sodium	At least 50% less per serving than reference food
Reduced or less sodium	At least 25% less per serving than reference food
Lightly salted	At least 50% less sodium than normally added to reference food; if it doesn't meet definition of low sodium, this must be stated on the label
No salt added, unsalted	If not sodium free, must declare "This Is Not a Sodium-Free Food"
Fiber	
Any claim	If food is not low in total fat, must state total fat in conjunction with fiber claim
Other Claims	
High, rich in, or excellent	20% or more of the DV per reference amount; may be used to describe protein, vitamins, minerals, dietary source
Good source, contains, or provides	10 to 19% of the DV per reference amount; may be used to describe protein, vitamins, minerals, dietary fiber
More, added, extra, or plus	10% or more of the DV per reference amount; may be used for vitamins, minerals, protein, dietary fiber, and potassium
High potency	May be used to describe individual vitamins or minerals present at 100% or more of the DV per reference amount
Fortified or enriched	Vitamins and/or minerals added to the product in amounts at least 10% above levels normally present in food; *enriched* generally refers to replacing nutrients lost in processing, whereas *fortified* refers to adding nutrients not originally present in the specific food
Healthy	Varies with food type; generally is a food that is low fat and low saturated fat, has no more than 480 to 600 mg of sodium or 95 mg of cholesterol per serving, and provides at least 10% of the DV for vitamin A, vitamin C, protein, calcium, iron, or fiber
Light or lite	Used with calories and sodium (see above); also may be used to describe texture and color, as long as the label explains the intent—for example, *light brown sugar* and *light and fluffy*

50   **PART 1**   Nutrition Basics

▶ To learn more about nutrient content claims, visit www.cfsan.fda.gov.

made only if the product contains 3 g or less of fat per serving, which is the standard for low-fat foods.

In December 2002, the FDA began permitting qualified health claims based on incomplete scientific evidence as long as the label qualifies it with a disclaimer, such as "this evidence is not conclusive," and the food meets the definition of being healthy (see Table 2-3).[12] So far, few preliminary health claims have appeared on food packages (nuts, such as walnuts, and fish have been some of the first examples).

Recall from Chapter 1 that another type of claim, structure/function claim, can appear on food labels. **Structure/function claims** describe how a nutrient affects human body structure or function, such as "iron builds strong blood." They do not focus on disease risk reduction, as health claims do. The FDA does not approve or authorize structure/function claims; however, manufacturers are responsible for ensuring that these claims are accurate and not misleading.

Take Action

Applying the Nutrition Facts Label to Your Daily Food Choices

Imagine that you are at the supermarket, looking for a quick meal before a busy evening. In the frozen food section, you find 2 brands of frozen cheese manicotti (see labels *a* and *b*). Which of the 2 brands would you choose? What information on the Nutrition Facts labels contributed to this decision?

(a)

Nutrition Facts

Serving Size 1 Package (260g)
Servings Per Container 1

Amount Per Serving

Calories 390   Calories from Fat 160

	% Daily Value*
Total Fat 18g	**27%**
Saturated Fat 9g	**45%**
Trans Fat 2g	**
Cholesterol 45mg	**14%**
Sodium 880mg	**36%**
Total Carbohydrate 38g	**13%**
Dietary Fiber 4g	**15%**
Sugars 12g	
Protein 17g	

Vitamin A 10%   •   Vitamin C 4%
Calcium 40%   •   Iron 8%

*Percent Daily Values are based on a 2000 calorie diet. Your daily values may be higher or lower depending on your calorie needs:

**Intake of *trans* fat should be as low as possible.

		Calories:	2000	2500
Total Fat	Less than		65g	80g
Sat Fat	Less than		20g	25g
Cholesterol	Less than		300mg	300mg
Sodium	Less than		2400mg	2400mg
Total Carbohydrate			300g	375g
Dietary Fiber			25g	30g

Calories per gram:
Fat 9 • Carbohydrate 4 • Protein 4

(b)

Nutrition Facts

Serving Size 1 Package (260g)
Servings Per Container 1

Amount Per Serving

Calories 230   Calories from Fat 35

	% Daily Value*
Total Fat 4g	**6%**
Saturated Fat 2g	**10%**
Trans Fat 1g	**
Cholesterol 15mg	**4%**
Sodium 590mg	**24%**
Total Carbohydrate 28g	**9%**
Dietary Fiber 3g	**12%**
Sugars 10g	
Protein 19g	

Vitamin A 10%   •   Vitamin C 10%
Calcium 35%   •   Iron 4%

*Percent Daily Values are based on a 2000 calorie diet. Your daily values may be higher or lower depending on your calorie needs:

**Intake of *trans* fat should be as low as possible.

		Calories:	2000	2500
Total Fat	Less than		65g	80g
Sat Fat	Less than		20g	25g
Cholesterol	Less than		300mg	300mg
Sodium	Less than		2400mg	2400mg
Potassium			3500mg	3500mg
Total Carbohydrate			300g	375g
Dietary Fiber			25g	30g

Calories per gram:
Fat 9 • Carbohydrate 4 • Protein 4

GLBAL PERSPECTIVE

Front-of-Package Nutrition Labeling

The Nutrition Facts panel provides U.S. consumers with important, accurate information about a food's nutrient and calorie content. Similar labels appear on foods sold in many other countries. To help busy consumers quickly make healthy food choices, the food industry has tried to condense the nutrition labels into nutrition symbols (e.g., check marks, traffic lights, stars, ratings) that are placed on the front of food packages or supermarket shelves. A variety of nutrition symbols have been used on food packages. For instance, a pink heart might be used to indicate a food is a good source of phytonutrients. A green star on a grocery shelf tag could indicate a food is rich in vitamins and low in calories.

It is important that nutrition symbols accurately reflect nutrient content and not be deceptive because consumers are less likely to check nutrition labels when a symbol appears on the front of food packages.[25] Recently, the FDA expressed concern about the widespread, unregulated use of these symbols.[25] One cause for concern was that the criteria (e.g., calorie and nutrient content) used to determine if a food was eligible for a symbol differed among the programs. This lack of consistency meant that consumers had to learn different eligibility standards and understand that some foods could be eligible for several icons. In addition, many nutrition experts and consumers questioned how the eligibility criteria were established and if the criteria really identified foods that were more nutritious than others.[26] Another concern was that some programs did not reveal the criteria used to calculate ratings, which meant consumers and government regulators could not verify that a food deserved the symbol.[27] These worries also have been voiced by government agencies in many other nations.

As a result of these concerns and to prevent consumer confusion, the FDA invited the food industry to help them develop uniform eligibility criteria for front-of-package food labels. The goal is to create easy-to-understand labels that consumers can trust and use to choose healthier diets.[28] Several other countries already have regulated front-of-package labeling or are working to develop it. For instance, Denmark, Sweden, and Norway use a keyhole symbol to indicate foods meet certain nutritional requirements. Ireland, Australia, and New Zealand are working to standardize and regulate front-of-package labeling. Standardized front-of-package labeling like that shown here may be coming to the U.S. in the future.

Knowledge Check

1. How do Reference Daily Intakes and Daily Reference Values differ?
2. Which nutrients on Nutrition Facts panels should most people aim to keep below 100% Daily Value?
3. What requirements must a food meet before a health claim can be made about it?

 ## 2.3 Nutrient Composition of Foods

Nutrient databases make it possible to estimate quickly the amount of calories and many nutrients in the foods we eat. With this information, it is possible to see how closely intake matches dietary standards, such as the RDA and DV. These databases also can be used to determine the nutrient density and energy density of foods.

The data in nutrient databases are the results of thousands of analytical chemistry studies conducted in laboratories around the world. They are easy to use; however, generating the data requires years of research to develop laboratory methods that produce accurate and reliable data and years more to analyze samples of many different foods and then construct the data tables. Keep in mind that there are many nutrients, and all require a unique laboratory analysis method. To get an idea of the enormity of this task, multiply the number of nutrients by all the different foods (plant and animal species) people eat. As you might guess, countless foods have not been analyzed yet, and some nutrients have been measured in only a limited number of foods.

Nutrient values in the databases are average amounts found in the analyzed samples of the food. Currently, these values cannot account for the many factors that affect nutrient levels in food we eat, factors such as farming conditions (e.g., soil type, fertilizers, weather, season, geographic region, genetic differences in plant varieties and animal breeds, and animal feed), maturity and ripeness of plants when harvested, food processing, shipping conditions, storage

Computerized nutrient data tables provide a quick and easy way to discover just how nutrient and energy dense the foods you eat are. Visit this website: www.nal.usda.gov/fnic/foodcomp/search.

time, and cooking processes. For instance, the vitamin C content of an orange is influenced by where it was grown, the variety of the orange, and how ripe it was when picked. It also is affected by how long it took to get the orange to the store where you bought it, the temperature of the truck that delivered it there, and how long it stayed in your refrigerator before you ate it. Nutrient databases also cannot account for how nutrients are handled in the body—as you'll see in later chapters, the ability to absorb nutrients, especially minerals, can be affected by factors such as medications, compounds in foods, and digestive disorders.

The variations in nutrient content do not mean that nutrient databases are unreliable or that you cannot depend on food to supply nutrients in amounts that support optimal health. But it is wise to view nutrient databases as tools that approximate nutrient intake, rather than precise measurements. Even with these limitations, nutrient databases are important tools for estimating calories and nutrients.

Putting Nutrient Databases into Action to Determine Energy Density and Dietary Intake

Nutrient databases can be used in many ways, including calculating a food's energy density. **Energy density** is determined by comparing a food's calorie content per gram weight of the food. Energy-dense foods are high in calories but weigh very little. Examples include nuts, cookies, most fried foods, and snack foods. For example, there are more than 5.5 kcal in 1 gram of bacon. Foods low in energy density contain large amounts of water, which makes them weigh a lot, but contain few calories (keep in mind that water is calorie free). Low-energy-dense foods include fruits, vegetables, and any other food that incorporates lots of water during cooking, such as stews, casseroles, and oatmeal (Table 2-4). Lettuce, for instance, has about 0.1 calorie in a gram. As you'll see in Chapter 10, foods that are low in energy density help a person feel full, whereas foods with high energy density must be eaten in greater amounts in order to contribute to fullness.[7, 13] Thus, low-energy-dense foods can help keep calorie intake under control.[14, 15] And foods with high energy density can help people with poor appetites, such as some older people, maintain or gain weight.

You also can use nutrient databases to find out the amounts of nutrients and calories you consume. This involves locating a food you ate and noting the quantity of each nutrient. If you ate more or less than the serving size stated, you will need to adjust the values. For instance, if you ate 4 ounces of cheese and the database values are for 2 ounces, you'll need to double the values in the table. Because not every food has been analyzed, you may need to select a food that is similar to the one you actually ate. If you ate Roquefort cheese or Bob's Pizza, for example, you may need to use the values for blue cheese or Tom's Pizza. Many combination foods (e.g., tuna salad, bean burritos) may not be included in the tables; for these foods, you will need to identify the ingredients used, estimate the amounts in the recipe (e.g., 2 oz tuna, 2 tbsp mayonnaise), and look up the nutrient values for each ingredient. Becoming aware of the amounts of nutrients and calories in the foods you eat can help you improve the healthfulness of your diet.

Table 2-4 Energy Density of Common Foods (Listed in Relative Order)

Very Low Energy Density (Less Than 0.6 kcal/g)	Low Energy Density (0.6 to 1.5 kcal/g)	Medium Energy Density (1.5 to 4 kcal/g)	High Energy Density (Greater Than 4 kcal/g)
Lettuce	Whole milk	Eggs	Graham crackers
Tomatoes	Oatmeal	Ham	Fat-free sandwich cookies
Strawberries	Cottage cheese	Pumpkin pie	Chocolate
Broccoli	Beans	Whole-wheat bread	Chocolate chip cookies
Salsa	Bananas	Bagels	Tortilla chips
Grapefruit	Broiled fish	White bread	Bacon
Fat-free milk	Non-fat yogurt	Raisins	Potato chips
Carrots	Ready-to-eat breakfast cereals with 1% low-fat milk	Cream cheese	Peanuts
Vegetable soup	Plain baked potato	Cake with frosting	Peanut butter
	Cooked rice	Pretzels	Mayonnaise
	Spaghetti noodles	Rice cakes	Butter or margarine
			Vegetable oils

Data adapted from Rolls B, Barnett RA. *Volumetrics*. New York: HarperCollins; 2000.

Expert Perspective from the Field

Menu Labeling: How Many Calories Are in That?

When eating out, have you ever wondered how many calories are in the food you are ordering? Or, if it is high in fat or sodium? Keeping track of calorie and nutrient intake when eating out is challenging because few restaurants, delis, and cafeterias provide nutrition information about menu items. In addition, many consumers and nutrition experts greatly underestimate the calories in restaurant meals. You might be surprised to learn that a small milkshake has more calories than a large fries or that the calorie count of a fast-food fish sandwich surpasses that of a cheeseburger.

Legislators mandated labels on packaged foods because they believed that consumers have the right to know the nutrition content of these foods. However, the regulations governing packaged foods do not include foods sold in restaurants. Although many chain restaurants have posters or websites that provide nutrition information for menu items,[29] Dr. Margo Wootan* pointed out that "these usually are not easily accessible when placing food orders, so consumers do not have the option of making informed menu selections at most restaurants." Having access to nutrition information is important because restaurant food represents a significant portion of the food we eat. In fact, about half of the money Americans spend on food is used to buy foods prepared outside the home. Eating out can have an important effect on health. For instance, those who frequently eat at fast-food restaurants have an increased risk of obesity—probably because restaurant foods tend to be calorie rich and their large portion sizes promote overeating.[30]

Many consumers and nutrition experts support menu labeling, and growing evidence indicates that stating calorie content on menus can lead to dietary improvements. One study found that fast-food customers who reported seeing calorie information at the point of purchase ordered meals with fewer calories.[31] Another study reported that, when calorie information was included on menus, customers ordered lower-calorie dinners for themselves and their children.[32-34] And, when menus listed both calorie content and recommended daily calorie intake for adults, customers ordered dinners with even fewer calories.[34] "A number of states and municipalities require menu labeling at the point of purchase—but, that's only a start. A comprehensive law that covers restaurants throughout the nation is needed to give all Americans the chance to make informed decisions that can help protect their health," says Dr. Wootan. To learn more about menu labeling, visit www.menulabeling.org.

Margo G. Wootan, DSc, is Director of Nutrition Policy at the Center for Science in the Public Interest (CSPI), a consumer advocacy organization focusing on food, nutrition, and health. She cofounded the National Alliance for Nutrition and Activity and serves on the National Fruit and Vegetable Alliance steering committee. Dr. Wootan has testified before Congress and state legislatures about nutrition and health issues. She has received awards from the American Public Health Association, Association of State and Territorial Public Health Nutrition Directors, and Society for Nutrition Education.

Knowledge Check

1. What are some factors that affect nutrient levels in food?
2. What is energy density?
3. What are some examples of high-energy-density and low-energy-density foods?

2.4 Dietary Guidelines for Americans

The diets of many people in the U.S. and Canada are too high in calories, fat, saturated fat, *trans* fat, cholesterol, sugar, salt, and alcohol.[16] Many consume insufficient amounts of whole grains, fruits, and vegetables. These dietary patterns put many of us at risk of

54   **PART 1**   Nutrition Basics

major chronic "killer" diseases, such as cardiovascular disease and cancer. In response to concerns about the prevalence of these killer disease patterns, every 5 years since 1980, the U.S. Department of Agriculture (USDA) and U.S. Department of Health and Human Services (DHHS) publish the Dietary Guidelines for Americans (Dietary Guidelines, for short).

The Dietary Guidelines are the foundation of the U.S. government's nutrition policy and education. They reflect what scientific experts believe is the most accurate and up-to-date scientific knowledge about nutritious diets, physical activity, and related healthy lifestyle choices. The Dietary Guidelines are designed to meet nutrient needs while reducing the risk of obesity, hypertension, cardiovascular disease, type 2 diabetes, osteoporosis, alcoholism, and foodborne illness. The Dietary Guidelines also guide government nutrition programs, research, food labeling, and nutrition education and promotion. For example, the Dietary Guidelines provide the scientific basis for the design of federal nutrition assistance programs, such as the USDA's school breakfast and lunch programs, the Food Stamp

Figure 2-6 Key recommendations within each general topic from the latest Dietary Guidelines for Americans.

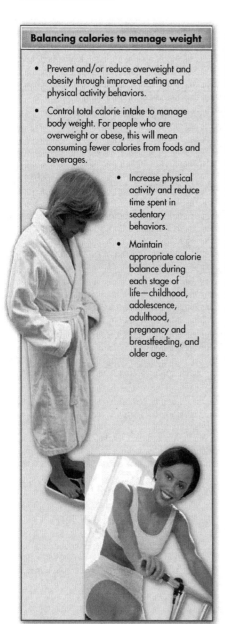

Balancing calories to manage weight

- Prevent and/or reduce overweight and obesity through improved eating and physical activity behaviors.

- Control total calorie intake to manage body weight. For people who are overweight or obese, this will mean consuming fewer calories from foods and beverages.

   - Increase physical activity and reduce time spent in sedentary behaviors.

   - Maintain appropriate calorie balance during each stage of life—childhood, adolescence, adulthood, pregnancy and breastfeeding, and older age.

Foods and food components to reduce

- Reduce daily sodium intake to less than 2300 milligrams (mg) and further reduce intake to 1500 mg among persons who are 51 and older and those of any age who are African-American or have hypertension, diabetes, or chronic kidney disease. The 1500 mg recommendation applies to about half of the U.S. population, including children, and the majority of adults.

- Consume less than 10% of calories from saturated fatty acids by replacing them with monounsaturated and polyunsaturated fatty acids.

- Consume less than 300 mg per day of dietary cholesterol.

- Keep *trans* fatty acid consumption as low as possible by limiting foods that contain synthetic sources of *trans* fats, such as partially hydrogenated oils, and by limiting other solid fats.

- Reduce the intake of calories from solid fats and added sugars.

- Limit the consumption of foods that contain refined grains, especially refined grain foods that contain solid fats, added sugars, and sodium.

- If alcohol is consumed, it should be consumed in moderation—up to 1 drink per day for women and 2 drinks per day for men—and only by adults of legal drinking age. There are many circumstances in which people should not drink alcohol:

   - Individuals who cannot restrict their drinking to moderate levels.

   - Anyone younger than the legal drinking age. Besides being illegal, alcohol consumption increases the risk of drowning, car accidents, and traumatic injury, which are common causes of death in children and adolescents.

   - Women who are pregnant or who may be pregnant. Drinking during pregnancy, especially in the first few months of pregnancy, may result in negative behavioral or neurological consequences in the offspring. No safe level of alcohol consumption during pregnancy has been established.

   - Individuals taking prescription or over-the-counter medications that can interact with alcohol.

   - Individuals with certain specific medical conditions (e.g., liver disease, hypertriglyceridemia, pancreatitis).

   - Individuals who plan to drive, operate machinery, or take part in other activities that require attention, skill, or coordination or in situations where impaired judgment could cause injury or death (e.g., swimming).

Program, and the WIC Program (Special Supplemental Nutrition Program for Women, Infants, and Children). In addition, MyPlate is based on the recommendations of the Dietary Guidelines (see the next section in this chapter).

A basic premise of the Dietary Guidelines is that nutrient needs should be met primarily by consuming foods.[17] Foods provide an array of nutrients and other compounds that may have beneficial effects on health. In certain cases, fortified foods and dietary supplements may be useful sources of one or more nutrients that otherwise might be consumed in less than recommended amounts. These practices are especially important for people whose typical food choices lead to a diet that cannot meet nutrient recommendations, such as for calcium. However, dietary supplements are not a substitute for a healthful diet.

The latest Dietary Guidelines for Americans have 29 key recommendations for people aged 2 years and older; of these, 6 are for special population groups, such as pregnant women and older adults. The Dietary Guidelines recommendations are grouped into the 4 general topics shown in Figure 2-6.

Foods and food components to increase

Individuals should meet the following recommendations as part of a healthy eating pattern while staying within their calorie needs.

- Increase vegetable and fruit intake.
- Eat a variety of vegetables, especially dark-green and red and orange vegetables and beans and peas.
- Consume at least half of all grains as whole grains. Increase whole-grain intake by replacing refined grains with whole grains.
- Increase intake of fat-free or low-fat milk and milk products, such as milk, yogurt, cheese, or fortified soy beverages.
- Choose a variety of protein foods, which include seafood, lean meat and poultry, eggs, beans and peas, soy products, and unsalted nuts and seeds.
- Increase the amount and variety of seafood consumed by choosing seafood in place of some meat and poultry.
- Replace protein foods that are higher in solid fats with choices that are lower in solid fats and calories and/or are sources of oils.
- Use oils to replace solid fats where possible.
- Choose foods that provide more potassium, dietary fiber, calcium, and vitamin D, which are nutrients of concern in American diets. These foods include vegetables, fruit, whole grains, and milk products.

Recommendations for specific population groups

Women capable of becoming pregnant
- Choose foods that supply heme iron, which is more readily absorbed by the body, additional iron sources, and enhancers of iron absorption such as vitamin C-rich foods.
- Consume 400 micrograms (μg) per day of synthetic folic acid (from fortified foods and/or supplements) in addition to food forms of folate from a varied diet.

Women who are pregnant or breastfeeding
- Consume 8 to 12 ounces of seafood per week from a variety of seafood types.
- Due to their high methyl mercury content, limit white (albacore) tuna to 6 ounces per week and do not eat the following 4 types of fish: tilefish, shark, swordfish, and king mackerel.
- If pregnant, take an iron supplement, as recommended by an obstetrician or other health-care provider.

Individuals ages 50 years and older
- Consume foods fortified with vitamin B-12, such as fortified cereals, or dietary supplements.

Building healthy eating patterns

- Select an eating pattern that meets nutrient needs over time at an appropriate calorie level.
- Account for all foods and beverages consumed and assess how they fit within a total healthy eating pattern.
- Follow food safety recommendations when preparing and eating foods to reduce the risk of foodborne illnesses.

56   **PART 1**   Nutrition Basics

For helpful publications related to the Dietary Guidelines for Americans, visit www.dietaryguidelines.gov.

► The Academy of Nutrition and Dietetics suggests 5 basic principles with regard to diet and health:

- Be realistic; make small changes over time.

- Be adventurous; try new foods regularly.

- Be flexible; balance some sweet and fatty foods with physical activity.

- Be sensible; include favorite foods in smaller portions.

- Be active; include physical activity in daily life.

Table 2-5 Recommended Diet Changes Based on the Dietary Guidelines

If You Usually Eat This,	Try This Instead.	Benefit
White bread	Whole-wheat bread	• Higher nutrient density • More fiber
Sugary breakfast cereal	Low-sugar, high-fiber cereal with fresh fruit	• Higher nutrient density • More fiber • More phytochemicals
Cheeseburger with french fries	Hamburger and baked beans	• Less saturated fat and *trans* fat • Less cholesterol • More fiber • More phytochemicals
Potato salad	Three-bean salad	• More fiber • More phytochemicals
Doughnuts	Bran muffin or bagel with light cream cheese	• More fiber • Less fat
Regular soft drinks	Diet soft drinks	• Fewer kcal • Less sugar
Fruit canned in syrup	Fresh or frozen fruit Fruit canned in water or juice	• Less sugar • Fewer kcal
Boiled vegetables	Steamed or sauteed vegetables	• Higher nutrient density due to reduced loss of water-soluble vitamins
Canned vegetables	Fresh or frozen vegetables Low-sodium canned vegetables	• Lower in sodium
Fried meats	Broiled meats	• Less saturated fat
Fatty meats, such as ribs or bacon	Lean meats, such as ground round, chicken, or fish	• Less saturated fat
Whole milk	Low-fat or fat-free milk	• Less saturated fat • Fewer kcal
Ice cream	Frozen yogurt	• Less saturated fat • Fewer kcal
Mayonnaise or sour cream salad dressing	Oil and vinegar dressings or light creamy dressings	• Less saturated fat • Less cholesterol • Fewer kcal
Cookies	Air-popped popcorn with minimal margarine or butter	• Less *trans* fat • Fewer kcal
Heavily salted foods	Foods flavored primarily with herbs, spices, lemon juice	• Less sodium
Chips	Pretzels	• Less fat

Other scientific groups, such as the American Heart Association, American Cancer Society, Canadian Ministries of Health, and World Health Organization, also have issued dietary recommendations. All are consistent with the spirit of the Dietary Guidelines for Americans. These scientific groups, like the Dietary Guidelines, encourage people to modify their eating behavior in ways that are both healthful and pleasurable.

For practical reasons, nutrition recommendations, such as the Dietary Reference Intakes, Daily Values, Dietary Guidelines, and MyPlate, are made on a population-wide basis. The key to making these recommendations work for you is considering your personal health status and then applying the recommendations to your diet and lifestyle.

Putting the Dietary Guidelines into Action

The Dietary Guidelines can be easily incorporated into our diets.[18, 19] Table 2-5 provides a variety of easy-to-implement suggestions that can improve any diet. Despite popular misconceptions, the healthy diet recommended by the Dietary Guidelines is not especially expensive. Fruits, vegetables, and low-fat and fat-free milk often are similar in price to the chips, cookies, and sugared soft drinks they should replace. Plus, there are many lower-cost options, including canned and frozen fruits and vegetables and non-fat dry milk.

When applying the Dietary Guidelines to yourself, start by taking into account your current health status and family history for specific diseases. Then, identify specific changes you need to make and develop a plan for incorporating the changes into your lifestyle. MyPlate can help you design a nutritious diet that meets your needs. When your plan is ready, make a couple of changes. As changes become part of your usual routine, add another change.[20] Continue making changes until your diet is healthful and reflects the Dietary Guidelines.

When making changes, it is a good idea to see whether they are effective. Keep in mind that results of dietary changes sometimes take a while to occur. Also, note that sometimes changes don't result in the outcome you anticipated. Some people, for instance, who eat a diet low in saturated fat may not see a decrease in blood cholesterol because of genetic background.[21] If the changes are not leading to the health improvements you anticipated, it is a good idea to see a registered dietitian or physician.

Knowledge Check

1. Which government agencies published the Dietary Guidelines for Americans?
2. What are the Dietary Guidelines?
3. How are the Dietary Guidelines used?

CASE STUDY

Andy is like many other college students. He grew up on a quick bowl of cereal and milk for breakfast and a hamburger, fries, and cola for lunch, either in the school cafeteria or at a local fast-food restaurant. At dinner, he generally avoided eating any salad or vegetables, and by 9 P.M. he was deep into bags of chips and cookies. Andy has taken these habits to college. He prefers coffee for breakfast and possibly a chocolate bar. Lunch is still mainly a hamburger, fries, and cola, but pizza and tacos now alternate more frequently than when he was in high school. What dietary advice do you think Andy needs? Start with his positive habits and then provide some constructive criticism based on what you now know.

CRITICAL THINKING

Shannon has grown up eating the typical American diet. Having recently read and heard many media reports about the relationship between nutrition and health, she is beginning to look critically at her diet and is considering making changes. However, she doesn't know where to begin. What advice would you give her?

58   **PART 1** Nutrition Basics

Take Action

Are You Putting the Dietary Guidelines into Practice?

The advice provided by the Dietary Guidelines for Americans can help you determine the healthfulness of your diet and identify changes to make. This checklist includes the major points to consider. How closely are you following the basic intent of the Dietary Guidelines?

Yes	No	
		Do you consume a variety of nutrient-dense foods and beverages within and among the basic food groups of MyPlate?
		Do you choose foods that limit the intake of
		Saturated fat?
		Trans fats?
		Cholesterol?
		Added sugars?
		Salt?
		Alcohol (if used)?
		Do you emphasize in your food choices
		Vegetables?
		Fruits?
		Legumes (beans)?
		Whole-grain breads and cereals?
		Fat-free or low-fat milk or equivalent milk products?
		Do you keep your body weight in a healthy range by balancing energy intake from foods and beverages with energy expended?
		Do you engage in at least 30 minutes of moderate-intensity physical activity (above usual activity) at work or home on most days of the week?
		Do you wash your hands, food contact surfaces, and fruits and vegetables before preparation?
		Do you cook foods to a safe temperature to kill harmful microorganisms?

2.5 MyPlate

Since the early 20th century, researchers have worked to translate the science of nutrition into practical terms, so that consumers could estimate whether their nutritional needs were being met. A plan with 7 food groups, based on foods traditionally eaten by North Americans, was one of the first formats designed by the USDA. Daily food choices were to include items from each group. This plan was simplified in the mid-1950s to a 4-food-group plan: milk, meat, fruit and vegetable, and bread and cereal groups. In 1992, this plan was depicted using a pyramid shape. It was updated in 2005 to reflect new scientific knowledge and was called MyPyramid, Steps to a Healthier You. In 2011, the plan was simplied to make it easier for consumers to make healthy food choices. The most current healthy eating plan is called MyPlate (Fig. 2-7).[22]

1992

2005

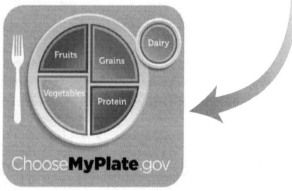

2011

Figure 2-7 Evolution of USDA Food Guides over the past 2 decades.

MyPlate depicts the key elements of a healthy diet. It emphasizes the fruit, vegetable, grain, protein, and dairy food groups. The goal of MyPlate is to remind consumers to think about building a healthy plate at meal times and to visit the www.choosemyplate.gov website to learn more about healthy eating. MyPlate recommendations are consistent with the 2010 Dietary Guidelines for Americans and focuses on these key behaviors:

Balancing Calories

- Enjoy your food, but eat less.
- Avoid oversized portions.

Foods to Increase

- Make half your plate fruits and vegetables.
- Make at least half your grains whole grains.
- Switch to fat-free or low-fat (1%) milk.

Foods to Reduce

- Compare sodium in foods like soup, bread, and frozen meals and choose the foods with lower numbers.
- Drink water instead of sugary drinks.

▶ Nations around the world have created graphics to symbolize the components of a healthy diet. In the U.S., we have a plate. In Japan, they have a spinning top. Canadians use a rainbow (see Appendix D). Visit these websites to learn more.

- Argentina: ftp.fao.org/es/esn/nutrition /dietary_guidelines/arg_fg.pdf
  ftp.fao.org/es/esn/nutrition/dietary _guidelines/arg_fg.pdf
- Great Britain: food.gov.uk/multimedia/pdfs /bghbooklet.pdf
- Japan: www.maff.go.jp/j/balance_guide /b_use/pdf/eng_reinasi.pdf
- Mexico: www.nutreymuevetuvida.uady.mx /articulos/plato.php
- Namibia: ftp.fao.org/es/esn/nutrition/dietary _guidelines/nam.pdf
- Philippines: ftp.fao.org/es/esn/nutrition /dietary_guidelines/pac_2.pdf
- Spain: www.nutricion.org/img/Rueda _Alimentos_SEDCA.jpg

▶ Special versions of MyPlate are planned for preschool children, elementary school–age children, pregnant and lactating women, and older adults.[22]

	Calorie Range (kcal)		
Children	Sedentary	⟶	Active
2–3 years	1000	⟶	1400
Females			
4–8 years	1200	⟶	1800
9–13	1600	⟶	2200
14–18	1800	⟶	2400
19–30	2000	⟶	2400
31–50	1800	⟶	2200
51+	1600	⟶	2200
Males			
4–8 years	1400	⟶	2000
9–13	1800	⟶	2600
14–18	2200	⟶	3200
19–30	2400	⟶	3000
31–50	2200	⟶	3000
51+	2000	⟶	2800

Figure 2-8 Estimates of calorie needs by age and activity levels. *Sedentary* means a lifestyle that includes only the light physical activity associated with typical day-to-day life. *Active* means a lifestyle that includes physical activity equivalent to walking more than 3 miles per day at 3 to 4 miles per hour in addition to the light physical activity associated with typical day-to-day life.

The www.choosemyplate.gov website has many resources to help consumers use MyPlate and personalize it to their life stage. One program at this website, *Daily Food Plan,* provides a quick estimate of what and how much food a person should eat from the different food groups based on age, gender, and activity level. *The Tracker* program provides detailed information on diet quality and physical activity status by comparing all foods a person eats and all the exercise completed in 1 day to the recommendations. Nutrition and physical activity advice messages are based on the need to maintain current weight or lose weight. Another program, *My Foodpedia,* provides in-depth information for every food group, including recommended daily intake amounts expressed in commonly used measures, such as cups and ounces, with examples and everyday tips. The section also includes recommendations for choosing healthy oils and physical activity. The *Food Planner* program provides tips and resources on nutrient-dense food choices, portion sizes, and physical activity and helps consumers plan food choices to meet MyPlate goals.

Putting MyPlate into Action

To put MyPlate into action, begin by estimating your energy needs (see Fig. 2-8 or visit www.choosemyplate.gov). Next, use Table 2-6 to discover how your energy needs correspond to the recommended number of servings from each food group. The servings are based on the sizes listed in Table 2-7.

When planning menus using MyPlate, keep these points in mind:

1. No one food is required for good nutrition. Every food supplies some nutrients but provides insufficient amounts of at least 1 essential nutrient.
2. No one food group provides all essential nutrients in adequate amounts (Table 2-8). Each food group makes an important, distinctive contribution to nutritional intake.
3. The foods within a group may vary widely with respect to nutrients and energy content. For example, the energy content of 3 ounces of baked potato is 98 calories, whereas that of 3 ounces of potato chips is 470 calories.

Table 2-6 MyPlate Recommendations for Daily Amounts of Foods to Consume from the Food Groups Based on Energy Needs												
Energy Intake	**1000**	**1200**	**1400**	**1600**	**1800**	**2000**	**2200**	**2400**	**2600**	**2800**	**3000**	**3200**
Grains[a]	3 oz-eq	4 oz-eq	5 oz-eq	5 oz-eq	6 oz-eq	6 oz-eq	7 oz-eq	8 oz-eq	9 oz-eq	10 oz-eq	10 oz-eq	10 oz-eq
Vegetables[b,c]	1 c	1.5 c	1.5 c	2 c	2.5 c	2.5 c	3 c	3 c	3.5 c	3.5 c	4 c	4 c
Fruits	1 c	1 c	1.5 c	1.5 c	1.5 c	2 c	2 c	2 c	2 c	2.5 c	2.5 c	2.5 c
Dairy[d]	2 c	2–2.5 c	2–2.5 c	2.5–3 c	2.5–3 c	2.5–3 c	3 c	3 c	3 c	3 c	3 c	3 c
Protein Foods[e]	2 oz-eq	3 oz-eq	4 oz-eq	5 oz-eq	5 oz-eq	5.5 oz-eq	6 oz-eq	6.5 oz-eq	6.5 oz-eq	7 oz-eq	7 oz-eq	7 oz-eq
Oils[e]	3 tsp	4 tsp	4 tsp	5 tsp	5 tsp	6 tsp	6 tsp	7 tsp	8 tsp	8 tsp	10 tsp	11 tsp
Empty calorie maximum[f]	140	120	120	120	160	260	270	330	360	400	460	600

Abbreviations: c = cup or cups; oz-eq = ounces or equivalent; tsp = teaspoon.
[a]At least half of these servings should be whole-grain varieties.
[b]Vegetables are divided into 5 subgroups [dark-green vegetables, orange vegetables, beans and peas (legumes), starchy vegetables, and other vegetables]. Over a week's time a variety of vegetables should be eaten.
[c]Beans and peas (legumes) can be counted *either* as vegetables (beans and peas subgroup) *or* in the protein foods group.
[d]Most dairy servings should be fat free or low fat.
[e]Oils are not a food group, but they provide essential nutrients. Fish, nuts, and vegetable oils (e.g., olive, sunflower, and Canola oils) are healthiest. Limit solid fats, such as butter, stick margarine, shortening, and meat fat, as well as foods that contain these.
[f]*Empty calories* refers to food choices with added sugars, solid fat, or alcohol.

Structurel function

Table 2-7 MyPlate Food Serving Sizes

Grains Group

1-ounce equivalent =	1 slice of bread
	1 cup of ready-to-eat breakfast cereal
	½ cup of cooked cereal, rice, pasta, or bulgur
	1 mini bagel or small tortilla
	½ muffin
	3 cups popcorn

Vegetable Group

1 cup =	1 cup of raw or cooked vegetables
	1 cup of vegetable juice
	2 cups of raw leafy greens

Fruits Group

1 cup =	1 cup of fruit
	1 cup of 100% fruit juice
	½ cup of dried fruit

Dairy Group

1 cup =	1 cup of milk, yogurt, or calcium-fortified soymilk
	1 cup frozen yogurt or pudding made with milk
	1½ cups ice cream
	1½ ounces of natural cheese
	2 ounces of processed cheese

Protein Group

1-ounce equivalent =	1 ounce of meat, poultry, fish, or cooked tempeh
	1 egg
	1 tablespoon of peanut butter or hummus
	¼ cup of cooked beans
	½ ounce of nuts or seeds

Oils

| 1 teaspoon | 1 teaspoon of vegetable, fish oil, oil-rich foods (e.g., mayonnaise, soft margarine) |

Table 2-8 Major Nutrient Contributions of Groups in the MyPlate Food Guide Plan

Grains	Vegetables	Fruits	Dairy	Protein	Oils
Carbohydrate	Carbohydrate	Carbohydrate	Calcium	Protein	Fat
Thiamin[‡]	Vitamin A	Vitamin A	Phosphorus	Thiamin	Essential fatty acids
Riboflavin[‡]	Vitamin C	Vitamin C	Carbohydrate	Riboflavin	Vitamin E
Niacin[‡]	Folate	Folate	Protein	Niacin	
Folate[‡]	Magnesium	Magnesium	Riboflavin	Vitamin B-6	
Magnesium[§]	Potassium	Potassium	Vitamin A	Folate[*]	
Iron[‡]	Fiber	Fiber	Vitamin D	Vitamin B-12[†]	
Zinc[§]			Magnesium	Phosphorus	
Fiber[§]			Zinc	Magnesium[*]	
				Iron	
				Zinc	

[*]Primarily in plant protein sources.   [†]Only in animal foods.   [‡]Both enriched or whole grain.   [§]Whole grains.

Portion sizes

| 2 tbsp salad dressing, peanut butter, margarine, etc. | = 2 tbsp |

| Baked potato Small/medium fruit Ground or chopped food Bagel English muffin | = ½ to ⅔ cup |

| 3 oz meat, poultry, or fish | = ½ to ¾ cup |

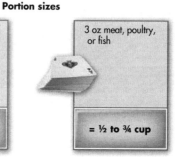

| Large apple or orange 1 cup ready-to-eat breakfast cereal | = 1 cup |

Figure 2-9 A golf ball, tennis ball, deck of cards, and baseball are standard-size objects that make convenient guides for judging MyPlate serving sizes. Your hand provides an additional guide (for the greatest accuracy, compare your fist with a baseball and adjust the following guides accordingly).

Fist = 1 cup   Thumb = 1 oz of cheese   Thumb tip to first joint = 1 tsp   Palm of hand = 3 oz   Handful = 1 or 2 oz of a snack food

Table 2-9 Putting MyPlate into Practice: How Many MyPlate Servings from Each Food Group Does This Menu Provide?

Breakfast

1 orange	Fruits
¾ cup low-fat granola	Grains
topped with 2 tbsp dried cranberries	Fruits
1 cup fat-free milk	Dairy
Optional: coffee or tea	

Lunch

8-inch pizza	Grains
topped with ⅓ cup chopped vegetables and 2 oz low-fat cheese	Vegetables
	Dairy
2 cups green salad	Vegetables
topped with ¾ oz nuts	Protein
5 tsp salad dressing	Oils
Optional: diet soft drink or iced tea	

Study Break Snack

| 1 cup non-fat yogurt | Dairy |
| *topped with* ½ cup fresh fruit | Fruit |

Dinner

3.5 oz salmon	Protein
½ cup asparagus	Vegetables
1¼ cups salsa	
(½ cup fresh fruit and	Fruits
¾ cup vegetables)	Vegetables
Sparkling water	

Late-Night Snack

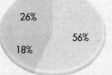

3 small chocolate chip cookies as empty calories

Nutrient Breakdown

Calories: 1800
Carbohydrate: 56% of kcal
Protein: 18% of kcal
Fat: 26% of kcal

26%   56%   18%

4. To keep calories under control, pay close attention to the serving size of each choice when following MyPlate. Figure 2-9 provides a convenient guide to estimating portion sizes. Note that serving sizes listed for 1 serving in a MyPlate group are often less than individuals typically serve themselves or the sizes of portions served in many restaurants.[23, 24]

5. Variety is the key to getting the array of nutrients offered by each food group. Variety starts with including foods from every food group and then continues by consuming a variety of foods within each group. The nutritional adequacy of diets planned using MyPlate depends greatly on the selection of a variety of foods (Table 2-9).

Here are some points that will help you choose the most nutritious diet.

- *Grains group:* Make at least half of your grain choices those that are whole grain. Whole-grain varieties of breads, cereals, rice, and pasta have the greatest array of nutrients and more fiber than other foods in this group. A daily serving of a whole-grain, ready-to-eat breakfast cereal is an excellent choice because the vitamins and minerals typically added to it, along with fiber it naturally contains, help fill in potential nutrient gaps. Although cakes, pies, cookies, and pastries are made from grains, these foods are higher in calories, fat, and sugar and lower in fiber, vitamins, and minerals than other foods in this group. The most nutritious diets limit the number of grain products with added fat or sugar.

- *Vegetables group:* Variety within the vegetables group (Table 2-10) is especially important because different types of vegetables are rich in different nutrients and phytochemicals (see

▶ Some research suggests that increasing variety in a diet can lead to overeating. Thus, as you include a wide variety of foods in your diet, pay attention to total energy intake as well.

▶ There are no "good" or "bad" foods—to make all foods fit into a nutritious dietary pattern and reduce the risk of many chronic diseases, balance calories eaten with needs, eat a variety of foods, and limit empty calorie foods.

CRITICAL THINKING

Margit would benefit from more variety in her diet. What are some practical tips she can use to increase her fruit and vegetable intake?

Table 2-10 Vegetable Subgroup Recommendations per Week*

Life-Span Group	Dark-Green Vegetables 	Orange Vegetables 	Beans and Peas 	Starchy Vegetables 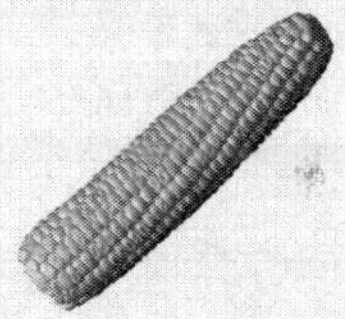	Other Vegetables 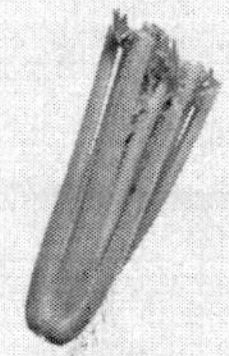
Children					
2–3 years old	½ cup	2½ cups	½ cup	2 cups	1½ cups
4–8 years old	1 cup	3 cups	½ cup	3½ cups	2½ cups
Girls					
9–13 years old	1½ cups	4 cups	1 cup	4 cups	3½ cups
14–18 years old	1½ cups	5½ cups	1½ cups	5 cups	4 cups
Boys					
9–13 years old	1½ cups	5½ cups	1½ cups	5 cups	4 cups
14–18 years old	2 cups	6 cups	2 cups	6 cups	5 cups
Women					
19–30 years old	1½ cups	5½ cups	1½ cups	5 cups	4 cups
31–50 years old	1½ cups	5½ cups	1½ cups	5 cups	4 cups
51+ years old	1½ cups	4 cups	1½ cups	4 cups	3½ cups
Men					
19–30 years old	2 cups	6 cups	2 cups	6 cups	5 cups
31–50 years old	2 cups	6 cups	2 cups	6 cups	5 cups
51+ years old	1½ cups	5½ cups	1½ cups	5 cups	4 cups

*It is not necessary to eat vegetables from each subgroup daily; however, over a week they should be varied, as shown in this table.

64 **PART 1** Nutrition Basics

Typical restaurant portions contain numerous servings from the individual groups in MyPlate.

▶ The Exchange System is another menu-planning tool. It organizes foods based on energy, protein, carbohydrate, and fat content. The result is a framework for designing diets, especially for the treatment of diabetes. For more information on the Exchange System, see Appendix E.

▶ For more suggestions on how to increase fruit, vegetable, and phytochemical intake, visit

www.fruitsandveggiesmorematters.org

www.fruitsandveggiesmatter.gov

Fruits are a rich source of nutrients and phytochemicals.

Table 1-2 in Chapter 1). For instance, dark-green vegetables (e.g., kale, bok choy) tend to be good sources of iron, calcium, folate, and vitamins A and C. Vegetables with orange flesh (e.g., carrots, acorn squash) are rich in beta-carotene, the precursor to vitamin A. Starchy vegetables (e.g., corn) provide B-vitamins and carbohydrates. Legumes (beans and peas) are also in the protein group because they are rich in protein. Other vegetables, including celery, onions, and radishes, provide a wide array of phytochemicals, vitamins, and minerals. It is important to eat a variety of vegetables each week from all 5 vegetable subgroups. A goal of MyPlate is for the vegetables group and fruits group to make up half your plate.

- *Fruits group:* Like vegetables, fruits also vary in the nutrients and phytochemicals they contain. To be sure you get the fiber that fruits have to offer, keep the amount of fruit juice to less than half of total fruit intake. Select 100% fruit juice—punches, ades, fruit-flavored soft drinks, and most fruit drinks contain little or no juice but do have substantial amounts of added sugar and do not count toward fruit servings.

- *Dairy group:* Choose primarily low-fat (1%) and fat-free items from the dairy group, such as part skim cheese, fat-free milk, and low-fat yogurt. These foods contain all the nutrients in other milk products, except they are lower in fat, saturated fat, and cholesterol. In addition, go easy on dairy desserts (e.g., pudding, ice cream) and chocolate milk because of the added sugar. By reducing energy intake in this way, you free up calories that can be used to select more items from other food groups.

- *Protein group:* Keep meat serving sizes under control—many people eat far more meat than is considered healthful. Except for beans and seafood, most foods in this group are high in fat. Meat, poultry, seafood, and eggs also supply cholesterol. When selecting foods from the protein group, focus on seafood, lean meat, poultry without skin, and beans—these foods are lower in fat than others in this group. To further reduce fat, avoid fried foods and trim away any fat you see on meat. Include protein-rich plant foods, such as beans and nuts, at least several times a week because many are rich in vitamins (e.g., vitamin E), minerals (e.g., magnesium), and fiber and contain less saturated fat than meat.

- *Oils:* Although not a food group, small amounts of oils are needed to supply you with health-promoting fats, called essential fatty acids (see Chapter 6). Oils are the fats from fish and plants that are liquid at room temperature. Include some plant oils on a daily basis, such as those in salad dressing and olive oil, and eat fish at least twice a week.

- *Empty Calorie Foods:* These are foods from the grains, vegetables, fruits, dairy, and protein groups that are high in solid fats and/or added sugars. The calories from solid fats and added sugars in a food are called empty calories because they add calories to the food but few or no nutrients (these calories are "empty" of nutrients). Most people eat far more empty calories than is considered healthy. Empty calories should be kept at the level that matches your calorie needs (see Table 2-6). These provide the most empty calories for Americans:

  - cakes, cookies, pastries, donuts, and ice cream (contain both solid fat and added sugars)
  - beverages (soft, energy, sports, and fruit drinks contain added sugars)
  - cheese, pizza, sausages, hot dogs, bacon, and ribs (contain solid fat)

Remember, eating a healthy diet includes foods from the grains, vegetables, fruits, dairy, and protein food groups in the recommended amounts. Variety means eating many different foods from each of these food groups. Variety makes meals more interesting and helps ensure that a diet contains sufficient nutrients. For example, carrots—a rich source of a pigment that forms vitamin A in our bodies—may be your favorite vegetable; however, if you choose carrots every day as your only vegetable source, you may miss out on other important vitamins supplied by other types of vegetables. This concept is true for all groups of foods.

It also is important to keep portion sizes under control so that you can eat a balanced and varied diet without consuming more calories, fat, cholesterol, sugar, and sodium than you need. Portion control requires only some simple planning and doesn't have to mean deprivation and misery. For example, if you eat a food that is relatively high in fat, salt, and energy, such as a bacon cheeseburger, it is a good idea to choose foods the rest of the day that are less concentrated sources of these nutrients, such as fruits and salad greens. If you prefer reduced-fat milk to fat-free milk, decrease the fat in other foods you eat. You could use low-fat salad dressings, choose a baked potato instead of french fries, or opt for jam instead of butter on toast. You also could choose smaller servings of high-fat or high-sugar foods you enjoy, such as regular soft drinks or chocolate. Overall, it's best to strive for smaller serving sizes of some foods (rather than eliminate these foods altogether) and include mostly nutrient-dense foods.

Rating Your Current Diet

Regularly comparing your daily food intake with MyPlate recommendations for your age, gender, and physical activity level is a relatively simple way to evaluate your overall diet. The diets of many adults don't match the recommendations—many eat too few servings of whole grains, vegetables, fruits, and dairy products and go overboard on meat, oil, and empty calorie intake. Knowing how your diet stacks up can help you determine which nutrients likely are lacking and how you can take steps to improve. For example, if you do not consume enough servings from the dairy group, your calcium intake is most likely too low, so you'll need to find calcium-rich foods you enjoy, such as calcium-fortified orange juice or non-fat yogurt.

Customizing MyPlate to accommodate your own food habits may seem a daunting task now, but it is not difficult once you start using it. The *Food Tracker* program at the www.choosemyplate.gov website is easy to use and can help you follow your progress. Implementing even small diet changes can have positive results. Better health will likely follow as you strive to meet your nutrient needs and balance calorie intake with your needs. In addition, the guidance from the Dietary Guidelines for Americans regarding alcohol and sodium intake and safe food preparation can help you incorporate other important changes to safeguard your health.

▶ A meal consisting of a bean burrito, a lettuce and tomato salad with oil and vinegar dressing, a glass of milk, and an apple covers all groups.

Choosing a variety of foods every day helps meet all of your nutrient needs.

Knowledge Check

1. What are examples of foods in each MyPlate food group?
2. What are empty calories?
3. What types of vegetables should be selected over a week's time?

CRITICAL THINKING

Andy, described in this chapter's Case Study, would benefit from more variety in his diet. What are some practical tips he can use to increase his fruit and vegetable intake?

66   **PART 1**   Nutrition Basics

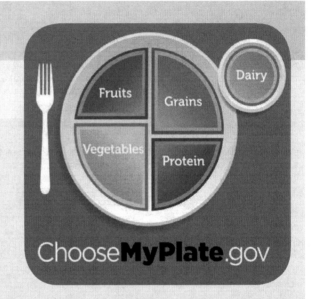

Take Action

Does Your Diet Meet MyPlate Recommendations?

In the accompanying chart, list all the foods you ate in the past 24 hours. For each food, indicate how many servings it contributes to each group based on the amount you ate (see Table 2-7 for serving sizes). Note that many of your food choices may contribute to more than 1 group. For example, toast with soft margarine contributes to the grains group and oils. After entering all the values, add the number of servings consumed in each group. Finally, compare your total in each food group with the recommended number of servings shown in Table 2-6 or at the www.choosemyplate.gov website. Enter a minus sign (−) if your total falls below the recommendation, a zero (0) if it matches the recommendation, or a plus sign (+) if it exceeds the recommendation.

Food or Beverage	Amount Eaten	Grains	Vegetables	Fruits	Dairy	Protein	Oils	Empty Calories
Group Totals								
Recommended Servings								
Shortages in Numbers of Servings								

CASE STUDY FOLLOW-UP

The most positive aspect of Andy's diet is that it contains adequate protein, zinc, and iron because it is rich in animal protein. On the downside, his diet is low in calcium, some B-vitamins (such as folate), and vitamin C. This is because it is low in dairy products, fruits, and vegetables. It is also low in many of the phytochemical substances discussed in Chapter 1. In addition, his fiber intake is low because fast-food restaurants primarily use refined-grain products rather than whole-grain products. His diet is likely excessive in fat and sugar, too.

He could alternate between tacos and bean burritos to gain the benefits of plant proteins in his diet. He could choose a low-fat granola bar instead of the candy bar for breakfast, or he could take the time to eat a bowl of whole-grain breakfast cereal with low-fat or fat-free milk to increase fiber and calcium intake. He also could order milk at least half the time at his restaurant visits and substitute diet soft drinks for the regular variety. This would help moderate his sugar intake. Overall, Andy could improve his intake of fruits, vegetables, and dairy products if he focused more on variety in food choice and balance among the food groups.

Summary

2.1 The Dietary Reference Intakes (DRIs) differ by life stage and include Estimated Average Requirements (EARs), Recommended Dietary Allowances (RDAs), Adequate Intakes (AIs), Tolerable Upper Intake Levels (Upper Levels, or ULs), and Estimated Energy Requirements (EERs). EARs are daily nutrient intake amounts estimated to meet the needs of half of the people in a life stage. EARs are set only if a method exists for accurately measuring whether intake is adequate. RDAs are daily nutrient intake amounts sufficient to meet the needs of nearly all individuals (97 to 98%) in a life stage. RDAs are based on a multiple of the EAR. AIs are daily intake amounts set for nutrients for which there are insufficient data to establish an EAR. AIs should cover the needs of virtually all individuals in a specific life stage. ULs are the maximum daily intake amount of a nutrient that is not likely to cause adverse health effects in almost everyone. EERs are average daily energy needs. For each macronutrient, the Acceptable Macronutrient Distribution Ranges (AMDRs) provide a range of recommended intake, as a percent of energy. DRIs are intended mainly for diet planning. Nutrient density is a tool for assessing the nutritional quality of individual foods.

2.2 Daily Values (DVs) are generic standards developed by the FDA for Nutrition Facts panels. DVs are based on Reference Daily Intakes and Daily Reference Values. Nutrition Facts panels present information for a single serving of food using serving sizes specified by the FDA. These components must be listed on most Nutrition Facts panels: total calories (kcal), calories from fat, total fat, saturated fat, *trans* fat, cholesterol, sodium, total carbohydrate, fiber, sugars, protein, vitamin A, vitamin C, calcium, and iron. Food labels may include nutrient content claims, health claims, preliminary health claims, and structure/function claims.

2.3 Nutrient databases make it possible to estimate quickly the amount of calories and many nutrients in the foods we eat. The data in nutrient databases are the results of thousands of analytical chemistry studies. Nutrient values in the nutrient databases are average amounts found in the analyzed samples of the food. It is wise to view nutrient composition databases as tools that approximate nutrient intake, rather than precise measurements. Energy density is determined by comparing a food's calorie content with the weight of food.

2.4 The Dietary Guidelines are the foundation of the U.S. government's nutrition policy and education. They reflect what experts believe is the most accurate and up-to-date scientific knowledge about nutritious diets and related lifestyle choices. Dietary Guideline recommendations are grouped into 4 topics: balancing calories to manage weight, foods and food components to reduce, foods and nutrients to increase, and building healthy eating patterns.

2.5 MyPlate depicts the key elements of a healthy diet. It emphasizes the fruit, vegetable, grain, protein, and dairy food groups. The goal of MyPlate is to remind consumers to think about building a healthy plate at meal times and to visit www.choosemyplate.gov to learn more about healthy eating. MyPlate recommendations are consistent with the 2010 Dietary Guidelines for Americans. The nutritional adequacy of diets planned using MyPlate depends on selecting a variety of foods, including grains, vegetables, fruits, dairy, protein, and oils in the recommended amounts and keeping portion sizes under control.

68   **PART 1** Nutrition Basics

Study Questions

1. Which dietary standard is set at a level that meets the needs of practically all healthy people?

   a. RDA   **c.** UL
   b. DRI   **d.** EER

2. Which dietary standard is set at a level that meets the needs of about half of all healthy people?

   a. RDA   **d.** EER
   b. AI   **e.** both c and d
   c. EAR

3. Daily Reference Values are standards established for Nutrition Facts panels for energy-producing nutrients.

   a. true   **b.** false

4. Most people should aim to keep intake of which nutrient at or below 100% Daily Value?

   a. total fat   **c.** vitamin A
   b. fiber   **d.** calcium

5. Foods that are a "good source" of a nutrient must contain at least _____% Daily Value of that nutrient.

   a. 5   **c.** 25
   b. 10   **d.** 50

6. Which factor affects nutrient levels in food?

   a. food processing   **c.** ripeness when harvested
   b. plant variety   **d.** all of the above

7. A food's energy density is determined by comparing its calorie content with the weight of the food.

   a. true   **b.** false

8. The FDA publishes the Dietary Guidelines for Americans.

   a. true   **b.** false

9. Which is true about the Dietary Guidelines for Americans?

   a. They are the foundation of the U.S. government's nutrition policy.
   b. They are designed to reduce the risk of obesity and hypertension.
   c. They guide government programs, such as the USDA's school lunch program.
   d. All of the above are true.

10. Which food group is missing from this meal: cheese sandwich, macaroni salad, and orange juice?

    a. dairy group   **d.** protein group
    b. vegetables group   **e.** b and d
    c. fruits group
    f. a, b, and c

11. MyPlate recommends that at least 75% of the foods from the grain group should be whole grains.

    a. true   **b.** false

12. MyPlate recommends making at least half your plate fruits and vegetables.

    a. true   **b.** false

13. Which type of vegetables tend to be good sources of iron, calcium, folate, and vitamins A and C?

    a. starch vegetables
    b. legumes
    c. vegetables with orange flesh
    d. dark-green vegetables
    e. all of the above

14. Describe the relationship between Estimated Average Requirements (EARs) and Recommended Dietary Allowances (RDAs).

15. How do RDAs and Adequate Intakes differ from Daily Values in their intention and application?

16. Why should values in nutrient composition tables be considered as approximate, not precise, values?

17. Based on the Dietary Guidelines, what are 2 changes the typical adult in the U.S. should consider making?

18. What changes would you need to make to meet the MyPlate guidelines on a regular basis?

19. What are empty calories? Which empty calorie foods do you eat most often?

Answer Key: 1-a; 2-c; 3-a; 4-a; 5-b; 6-d; 7-a; 8-b; 9-d; 10-e; 11-b; 12-a; 13-d; 14-refer to Section 2.1; 15-refer to Section 2.2; 16-refer to Section 2.3; 17-refer to Section 2-4; 18-refer to Section 2-5; 19-refer to Section 2-5

Websites

To learn more about the topics covered in this chapter, visit these websites.

fnic.nal.usda.gov

www.fda.gov/Food/LabelingNutrition

www.nal.usda.gov/fnic/foodcomp/search

www.dietaryguidelines.gov

www.choosemyplate.gov

www.fruitsandveggiesmorematters.org

www.fruitsandveggiesmatter.gov

www.cnpp.usda.gov

www.ams.usda.gov/AMSv1.0/cool

References

1. Murphy S and Barr SI. Using the Dietary Reference Intakes. *J Am Diet Assoc.* 2011;111:762.

2. Chung M and others. Systematic review to support the development of nutrient reference intake values: challenges and solutions. *Am J Clin Nutr.* 2010;92:273.

3. Barr S. Introduction to Dietary Reference Intakes. *Appl Physio Nutr Metab.* 2006;31:61.

4. Food and Nutrition Board. *Dietary Reference Intakes: Guiding principles for nutrition labeling and fortification.* Washington, DC: National Academies Press; 2003.

5. Institute of Medicine. *Dietary Reference Intakes for energy, carbohydrate, fiber, fat, fatty acids, cholesterol, protein, and amino acids (macronutrients).* Washington, DC: National Academies Press; 2005.

6. Barr S and others. Planning diets for individuals using the Dietary Reference Intakes. *Nutr Rev.* 2003;61:352.

7. Pennington J and others. Practice paper of the American Dietetic Association. Nutrient density: Meeting nutrient goals within calorie needs. *J Am Diet Assoc.* 2007;107:860.

8. Kolodinsky J and others. Knowledge of current dietary guidelines and food choice by college students: Better eaters have higher knowledge of dietary guidance. *J Am Diet Assoc.* 2007;107:1409.

9. Yates A. Which Dietary Reference Intake is best suited to serve as the basis for nutrition labeling for daily values? *J Nutr.* 2006;136:2457.

10. Food Allergen Labeling and Consumer Protection Act of 2004, Public Law 108-282;2004.

11. USDA, Agricultural Marketing Service. Country of origin labeling. 2012; www.ams.usda.gov/AMSv1.0/cool.

12. Food and Drug Administration. Labeling & nutrition: Food labeling and nutrition overview. 2011; www.fda.gov/Food /LabelingNutrition.

13. Ledikwe J and others. Dietary energy density is associated with energy intake and weight status in US adults. *Am J Clin Nutr.* 2006;83:1362.

14. Duffey KJ, Popkin BM. Energy Density, Portion Size, and Eating Occasions: Contributions to Increased Energy Intake in the United States, 1977 -2006. *PLoS Med.* 2011:8(6): e1001050.

15. Ledikwe J and others. Low-energy-density diets are associated with high diet quality in adults in the United States. *J Am Diet Assoc.* 2006;106:1172.

16. Maurer Abbot J, Byrd-Bredbenner C. The state of the American diet. How can we cope? *Top Clin Nutr.* 2007;3:202.

17. USDHHS/USDA. Dietary Guidelines for Americans, 2010; www.dietaryguidelines.gov.

18. ADA Reports. Position of the American Dietetic Association. Total diet approach to communicating food and nutrition information. *J Am Diet Assoc.* 2007;107:1224.

19. Smitasiri S and others. Beyond recommendations: Implementing food-based dietary guidelines for healthier populations. *Food Nutr Bull.* 2007;28:S141.

20. Bickley P. Start by picking low hanging fruit. *BMJ.* 2012;344:e869.

21. Go V and others. Nutrient-gene interaction: Metabolic genotype-phenotype relationship. *J Nutr.* 2005;135:3016S.

22. USDA. MyPlate. 2011; www.choosemyplate.gov.

23. Young L, Nestle M. Expanding portion sizes in the US marketplace: implications for nutrition counseling. *J Am Diet Assoc.* 2003;103:231.

24. Schwartz J, Byrd-Bredbenner C. Portion distortion: Typical portion sizes selected by young adults. *J Am Diet Assoc.* 2006;106:1412.

25. Food and Drug Administration. Guidance for industry: Letter regarding point of purchase food labeling. 2009; www.fda.gov /Food/GuidanceComplianceRegulatoryInformation /GuidanceDocuments/FoodLabelingNutrition/ucm187208.htm.

26. Consumer Reports. Better cereal choices for kids? 2008; www .consumerreports.org/cro/food/food-shopping/breads-grain /cereals/breakfast-cereals/overview/breakfast-cereals-ov.htm.

27. Sharma L and others. The food industry and self-regulation: Standards to promote success and to avoid public health failures. *Am J Public Health.* 2010;100:240.

28. Food and Drug Administration. Guidance for industry: Dear manufacturer letter regarding front-of-package symbols. 2008; www.fda. gov/Food/GuidanceComplianceRegulatoryInformation /GuidanceDocuments/FoodLabelingNutrition/ucm120274.htm.

29. Wootan M, Osborn M. Availability of nutrition information from chain restaurants in the United States. *Am J Prev Med.* 2006;30:266.

30. Pereira M and others. Fast food habits, weight gain, and insulin resistance (the CARDIA study) 15-year prospective analysis. *Lancet.* 2005;365(9453):36.

31. Bassett MT and others. Purchasing behavior and calorie information at fast-food chains in New York City, 2007. *Am J Public Health.* 2008;98:1457.

32. Roberto CA and others. Evaluating the impact of menu labeling on food choices and intake. *Am J Public Health.* 2010;100:312.

33. Pulos E, Leng K. Evaluation of a voluntary menu-labeling program in full-service restaurants. *Am J Public Health.* 2010;100:1035.

34. Tandon PS and others. Nutrition menu labeling may lead to lower-calorie restaurant meal choices for children. *Pediatr.* 2010;125:244.

Both synthetic and natural color additives are used to make foods more appealing. *Dactylopius coccus* is an insect (white, fuzzy areas) that lives on certain types of cactus and is the source of the natural red dye cochineal, used since at least Aztec times. Cochineal dye adds color to sausages, dried shrimp, candies, jams, yogurt, beverages, and maraschino cherries. Learn more at **www.food-info.net/uk/colour/cochineal.htm.**

3   The Food Supply

Student Learning Outcomes

After studying this chapter, you will be able to

1. Compare food security and food insecurity and identify the factors that contribute to each.

2. Discuss the effects of hunger and malnutrition and their impact on children.

3. Describe U.S. government programs designed to increase food security.

4. Describe organic food production, its regulation, and its potential benefits.

5. Discuss the current and potential uses of genetically modified foods, along with concerns related to safety.

6. Explain how food-preservation and -processing methods affect food availability.

7. Describe the role of food additives in the food supply, along with how they are regulated.

8. List the major causes of foodborne and waterborne illnesses in the U.S. and describe how consumers can reduce the risk of these illnesses.

9. Describe common environmental contaminants (heavy metals, industrial chemicals, pesticides, and antibiotics), their potential harmful effects, and how to reduce exposure to them.

A BOUNTIFUL, VARIED, NUTRITIOUS, and safe food supply is available to many individuals, especially those in developed countries. For example, most Americans have ready access to generous food supplies—more than 35,000 supermarkets in the U.S. stock, on average, nearly 47,000 items. In addition to purchases from food stores, Americans are buying more ready-to-eat food than ever from restaurants, cafeterias, vending machines, and the like. Despite ample food supplies and the efforts of private and government programs to help at-risk individuals obtain enough healthy foods, malnutrition and poor health from poor diets still plague people throughout the world.

Food-preservation and -processing methods (e.g., refrigeration, canning, and irradiation) and food additives, along with food-production practices (e.g., conventional and organic farming and biotechnology), continue to expand the variety and availability of food. These processing and production methods offer many benefits; however, there are still concerns about the safety of food and water. For example, common foods, such as fresh produce and ground beef, sometimes are contaminated with harmful bacteria that cause foodborne illness. The safety of and need for pesticides, antibiotic use in food animals (animals intended for consumption), biotechnology processes that genetically modify plants and animals, and food additives we see listed on food labels continue to be debated. This chapter addresses the complex issues of food access, food constituents, and food safety, as well as steps you can take to keep food safe in your home.

Poverty aggravates the problem of hunger in the developing world. One in 6 do not have enough food to eat.

▶ A comparison between soft drinks and milk demonstrates the cost disparity between low- and high-nutrient-dense foods. Recently advertised prices for generic supermarket brand soda and milk were 99 cents for a dozen 12-ounce cans (total: 144 oz) of the soft drink and $3.69 for a gallon (128 oz) of fat-free milk. The soft drink is just 6 cents for 8 ounces, but the milk is 23 cents for the same amount. The milk costs 383% more than the soda.

Fresh produce may be too expensive for some low-income families.

3.1 Food Availability and Access

Good nutritional status and health for each of us requires access to a safe and healthy food supply. Worldwide, agriculture produces enough food to provide each person with 2720 kcal/day—more than enough to meet the energy requirements of each of the nearly 7 billion persons on earth. Even with this abundance, 1 in 6 (1.02 billion) people do not have enough food to lead healthy and active lives; that is, they are food insecure.[1] Another 2 billion people suffer from micronutrient (vitamin and mineral) deficiencies, sometimes called "hidden hunger." The serious problems of food insecurity, hunger, and malnutrition exist in virtually every nation but are most common in the developing world, especially Asia and the Pacific, sub-Saharan Africa, Latin America, and the Caribbean. Nearly all people suffering from hunger or malnutrition are poor.

According to the Food and Agriculture Organization (FAO) of the United Nations, the problems of malnutrition (including too much food) and hunger account for over half of the world's disease burden.[1] Overnutrition that results in overweight and obesity is the primary problem in industrialized countries, such as the U.S., Canada, and the countries of Western Europe. However, overnutrition also is becoming a problem in developing countries—for example, more than half of the adults in Mexico are now overweight or obese.[2] As developing countries become Westernized, their diets contain more meat, dairy, sugar, fat, and processed foods but fewer whole grains and vegetables. This phenomenon, known as the *nutrition transition,* is especially common in urban areas and poses new challenges for nutritionists and other health-care providers in developing countries; however, undernutrition from lack of food and nutrient-poor diets remains the most pressing nutritional problem in these countries.

Health Consequences of Food Insecurity

When individuals don't get enough to eat or have access to only a few foods, problems related to hunger and malnutrition arise. The United Nations estimates that adults require a minimum of 2100 kcal per day to support a normal, healthy life (children require less). When energy intake falls below needs, a variety of problems arise—physical and mental activity declines; growth slows or ceases altogether; muscle and fat wasting occurs; the immune system weakens, increasing susceptibility to disease; and death rates rise (Fig. 3-1). The consequences of micronutrient deficiencies can be equally devastating. For example, vitamin A deficiency, found in approximately one-third of the children under age 5 in developing countries, damages the eye, sometimes causes blindness, and increases vulnerability to common diseases, such as measles and respiratory infections. Iodine deficiency is the world's leading cause of preventable mental retardation and brain damage. Vitamin A, iodine, iron, zinc, and folate are the micronutrients most likely to be in short supply in developing countries.[4] (See Chapters 12 through 15 for more details on micronutrient deficiencies.)

Food insecurity in Westernized countries, although not as widespread and profound as that in developing countries, contributes to serious health and nutritional problems for millions of people.[5, 6] For instance, in the U.S., those who are **food insecure** often eat fewer servings of nutrient-dense foods, such as vegetables, milk, and meat, and consume poorer-quality diets in general. These nutrient-poor diets can impair physical and mental health status. Food-insecure children are more likely to have poorer general health and report more asthma, stomachaches, headaches, and colds, and they may not grow normally.[6-8] Behavioral problems in school, lower educational achievement, higher rates of depression and suicidal symptoms, and increased levels of psychological distress also have been linked to food insecurity.[6-9] Parents may compromise their own diets to allow children to have

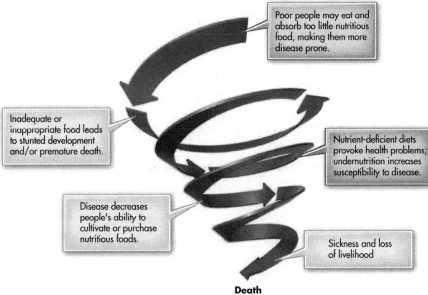

Poor people may eat and absorb too little nutritious food, making them more disease prone.

Inadequate or inappropriate food leads to stunted development and/or premature death.

Nutrient-deficient diets provoke health problems; undernutrition increases susceptibility to disease.

Disease decreases people's ability to cultivate or purchase nutritious foods.

Sickness and loss of livelihood

Death

Figure 3-1 The downward spiral of poverty and illness can ultimately end in death (based on World Food Program graphic).

better diets. Food-insecure adults have a higher risk of chronic diseases, such as diabetes, and poorer management of these diseases.[10]

In the U.S., food insecurity and poverty also are linked with obesity, particularly in women, perhaps because food insecurity predisposes individuals to overeating when food is more plentiful or because they purchase mostly inexpensive, high-energy-density foods.[11, 12] In fact, many low-nutrient-density foods cost less than foods that are more nutrient dense, which means that food-insecure individuals often get enough (or too many) calories without meeting some vitamin and mineral needs.[6]

Food Insecurity and Malnutrition in the U.S.

The U.S. Department of Agriculture (USDA) has monitored the food security of U.S. households since 1995. There are 4 levels of household food security: high, marginal, low, and very low (Table 3-1). In food-secure households, food needs are met at all times, whereas food-insecure households may run out of food or manage food supplies by skipping meals, reducing meal size, or not eating when hungry. In 2008 and 2009, more U.S. households experienced food insecurity

▶ In the 1940s, a group of researchers, led by Dr. Ancel Keys, examined the effects of undernutrition on 32 healthy male volunteers. They ate about 1800 calories daily for 6 months, losing an average of 24% of their body weight. The men experienced profound physiological and psychological symptoms, including fatigue, muscle soreness, cold intolerance, decreased heart rate and muscle tone, fluid retention, poor concentration abilities, moodiness, apathy, and depression. When the men were permitted to eat normally again, feelings of fatigue, recurrent hunger, and food cravings persisted, even after 12 weeks of rehabilitation. Full recovery required about 18 months. This study tells us much about the general state of undernourished adults worldwide.[3]

Unemployment can move a household into food insecurity. A safety net of programs exists, but it is porous.

Table 3-1	USDA Descriptions for Food Security and Food Insecurity	
Food Security	**High-Food-Security Household**	No indications of food-access problems or limitations.
	Marginal-Food-Security Household	1 or 2 indications of food-access problems—typically, anxiety over food sufficiency or shortage of food in the house. Little or no change in diets or food intake.
Food Insecurity	**Low-Food-Security Household**	Reduced quality, variety, or desirability of diet. Little or no reduced food intake.
	Very-Low-Food-Security Household	Multiple indications of disrupted eating patterns and reduced food intake.

74 **PART 1** Nutrition Basics

Figure 3-2 Food insecurity in the U.S., average 2007–2009.

Source: USDA, Economic Research Service.

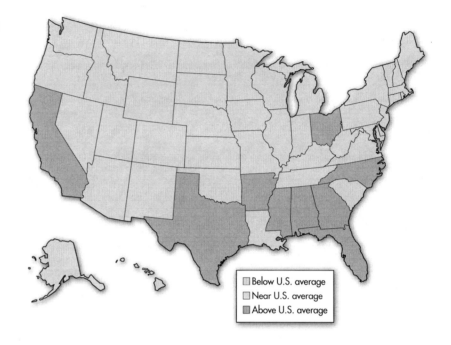

☐ Below U.S. average
☐ Near U.S. average
■ Above U.S. average

than ever before—nearly 15% (17.4 million households), with one-third of these households reporting very low food security.[13] Figure 3-2 shows how food security varies by state in the U.S.

Food insecurity is closely linked to poverty. In the U.S., about 39 million people (13.2% of the population)—more than a third of whom are children—live at or below the **poverty guidelines,** currently estimated at $22,050 for a family of 4.[14] Poverty rates are even greater for children living in single-parent households and for certain racial and ethnic groups. One-quarter of African-Americans and Native Americans and 21% of Hispanics live in poverty, compared with approximately 10.5% of Asians and Caucasians. Low-paying jobs and unemployment, coupled with a lack of health-care benefits, high housing costs, family break-ups, and catastrophic illness, contribute to economic hardship and poverty.

▶ One goal of *Healthy People 2020* is to increase food security among U.S. households and, in doing so, reduce hunger. Unfortunately, with the economic recession that began in 2008, food security has moved in the wrong direction.

▶ The federal minimum wage is $7.25 per hour. A full-time worker earning this wage makes $15,080 per year. If this person is the sole wage earner in a family of 2, they will live just above the poverty guideline of $14,570. If that family's rent is $700 per month, $8400 of the $15,080 goes to housing, leaving just $6680 for all other expenses, including food, in the year.

poverty guidelines Preferred term for the federal poverty level; income level calculated each year by the U.S. Census Bureau. Guidelines are used to determine eligibility for many federal food and nutrition assistance programs.

Programs to Increase Food Security in the U.S.

Since the 1930s, the U.S. government has provided food assistance to individuals and families in need. Today, the 15 food and nutrition assistance programs administered by the USDA account for more than two-thirds of the USDA budget, and about 25% of Americans participate in at least 1 of the programs.[15] Food and nutrition assistance programs increase access to food and help reduce food insecurity. However, not everyone in need of assistance receives it—individuals may not know about the programs, may find the application process too difficult, may not have transportation to the program site, or may feel uncomfortable about participating. The following are the largest government assistance programs; the websites of these programs are listed at the end of the chapter.

- *Supplemental Nutrition Assistance Program* (*SNAP*). SNAP (known in some states as the Food Stamp Program) is regarded as the cornerstone of the food assistance programs. It provides monthly benefits in the form of an Electronic Benefit Transfer card, which works as a debit card. The average benefit per person is $124 per month. About 34 million persons per month, or 11% of Americans, participate in the program.[15] Benefits can be used to purchase food, as well as seeds to grow food; they cannot be used to buy tobacco, alcoholic beverages, and nonedible products. SNAP Nutrition Education, intended to help SNAP participants make healthier food choices, is available in almost all states.

- *Special Supplemental Nutrition Program for Women, Infants, and Children (WIC).* This program provides low-income pregnant, breastfeeding, and postpartum women, infants, and children up to age 5 who are at nutritional risk with vouchers to purchase specific nutrient-dense foods. These individuals also receive nutrition education and referrals to health care and social services. Currently, about 75% of WIC participants are infants and children.

- *National School Lunch Program.* This program helps schools provide nutritious lunches to children, thereby helping them concentrate and learn. About 60% of children at participating schools take part in the program. The program subsidizes lunches by providing schools with cash and food. All children can participate, but children from families with qualifying incomes receive either free or reduced-price lunches, which must meet federal nutrition guidelines. Summer food service programs operate in some locations across the country to meet the need for food assistance during the summer break.

- *School Breakfast Program.* This program began in response to concerns about children attending school hungry. It operates similarly to the National School Lunch Program. Breakfasts must meet federal nutrition guidelines.

- *Child and Adult Care Food Program.* Reimbursement is provided to eligible child-care and nonresidential adult day-care centers that provide meals and snacks. Like the School Lunch and School Breakfast Programs, the meals must meet certain nutrition criteria.

- *Programs for seniors.* The Older Americans Act provides funding for nutrition programs targeted at older adults. Many communities offer congregate meal programs (often, lunch served daily at a variety of sites in a community) and home-delivered meals—popularly known as Meals on Wheels. Meals must meet nutrition guidelines and are available at little or no cost. Senior Farmers' Market Nutrition Programs also are available in many states.

- *Food distribution programs.* Commodity foods are agricultural products purchased by the government. They typically include canned foods (fruits, vegetables, juices, meat, tuna), dry food (ready-to-eat cereal, non-fat dry milk, beans, dehydrated potatoes, pasta, rice, infant cereal), and limited amounts of fresh foods, such as cheese, fruits, and vegetables. These programs distribute commodity foods and provide nutrition assistance to low-income households, emergency feeding programs, disaster relief programs, Indian reservations, and older adults. Many food banks and pantries distribute commodity foods to their clients.

In addition to the government programs, many private programs provide food assistance to individuals at food banks and pantries, soup kitchens, and homeless shelters. Each year, about 37 million people in the U.S. obtain food from these programs.[16] The programs rely on support from individuals, faith-based organizations, businesses, foundations, and grants. Many of these programs greatly depend on volunteer workers.

The largest contributor of food to these emergency food programs is Feeding America (formerly called America's Second Harvest). This organization distributes food it receives from private and corporate donations and government commodities to large regional food banks, which then distribute to individual food pantries, soup kitchens, and shelters. In 2009, Feeding America provided 2.5 billion pounds of food to 33,500 food pantries, 4500 soup kitchens, and 3600 emergency shelters.[16] Table 3-2 lists some ways individuals can help fight hunger.

The National School Breakfast Program serves 11 million students per day.

▶ One of the many challenges faced by food banks and pantries is the lack of culturally appropriate foods. For example, providing dehydrated mashed potatoes or non-fat dry milk to a Chinese family unaccustomed to these foods may do little to help them meet their nutritional needs.

Food pantries and soup kitchens are important sources of nutrients for a growing number of people in the U.S. Consider volunteering some of your time at a local program.

Food security is fostered by communities raising and distributing locally grown food.

Table 3-2 **Ways Individuals Can Help Fight Hunger in Their Communities**
• Donate food—high-protein foods (e.g., tuna and peanut butter), baby food, and culturally appropriate foods are often in high demand.
• Start or participate in a campus or community program that targets hunger. Community gardens are an example.
• Organize or work at a food drive.
• Donate money to organizations that fight hunger and food insecurity.
• Volunteer at a local food bank or pantry.
• Advocate for hunger programs by writing letters to newspapers, contacting state and national legislators, or joining an organization that advocates politically for hungry people.
• Attend events targeted at food security.
• Stay informed about hunger- and food-security-related issues.
• Pay special attention to World Food Day, October 16 each year.

Food Insecurity and Malnutrition in the Developing World

Undernutrition disproportionately affects young children and women. Every year, more than 3.5 million children under the age of 5 in the developing world die of causes related to undernutrition; these deaths account for 35% of all deaths among infants and preschool children.[17] About a quarter of the world's children are underweight, and almost a third have stunted growth.[18] Such children are more likely to suffer from infectious diseases and to have problems learning. Many women have access to less food than men in the household because some social customs dictate that women eat last. When a woman is poorly nourished, her developing fetus or breastfed infant also may suffer malnutrition.

Many hungry people in developing countries live in rural areas where they are unemployed or work as **subsistence farmers**—those who can grow food only for their families, with not enough extra to sell for an income. Farming is difficult in many regions because of poor-quality farmland; lack of fertilizer, seeds, and farming equipment; and droughts or flooding. The poor health caused by food insecurity and malnutrition limits farmers' physical capabilities and ability to work. Natural disasters, war, and political unrest worsen conditions and can trigger food shortages and famine. Famine disrupts every aspect of life: rates of disease and death increase, jobs disappear, poverty worsens, crime increases, civil wars may erupt or intensify, and government corruption may plague relief efforts. Many people who migrate to cities in hopes of finding work live in crowded, extremely poor-quality, unsafe housing and lack access to clean water, sufficient food, and medical care.

By the year 2050, the earth's population will have increased to 9 billion. Reducing malnutrition and improving food security as the population grows will present ever increasing challenges. Most experts agree that economic development to reduce poverty and improve agricultural development are key. Agricultural development is especially important because most poor people live in rural areas and because current crop yields are too low to support the expected population growth.[19, 20] With agricultural improvements, households can grow more crops, eat healthier diets, and earn an income from the extra food and crops they grow. Increasing agricultural productivity is costly and complex, though, and requires infrastructure (e.g., roads, irrigation, electricity, and banks), agricultural research, education, and a healthy population. Improvements in health, especially by eliminating micronutrient deficiencies, providing clean food and water, and offering family-planning methods, are critical because economic growth requires healthy people who are able to work, learn, and make improvements.

Insufficient calories, protein, zinc, and other nutrients limit the growth of children worldwide. About 30% of children in developing countries show evidence of poor growth rates.

At the September 2000 United Nations Millennium Summit, the world's leaders agreed upon a goal to reduce extreme poverty and hunger by half by 2015. Although some progress has been made toward this goal, gains have slowed or even reversed because of a steep rise in food prices in 2008 and the global economic recession. Hunger hotspots include sub-Saharan Africa and southern Asia, where 29% and 21%, respectively, of people have too little food.[21]

Knowledge Check

1. What are the causes of food insecurity?
2. What are the effects of food insecurity and malnutrition?
3. How does food insecurity and hunger in developing countries differ from what is seen in the U.S.?
4. What are some of the federal food and nutrition programs? Which of these programs serve children?

3.2 Food Production

Agriculture, the production of food and livestock, has supplied humans with food for millennia. At one time, nearly everyone was involved in food production. Only about 1 in 3 people around the globe, and far fewer in the U.S. (less than 1%), are now involved in farming. Today, numerous advances in agricultural sciences are affecting our food supply; of particular note are organic food production and biotechnology.

> **biological pest management** Control of agricultural pests by using natural predators, parasites, or pathogens. For example, ladybugs can be used to control an aphid infestation.

Organic Foods

Organic foods are increasingly available in supermarkets, specialty stores, farmers' markets, and restaurants. Consumers can select organic fruits, vegetables, grains, dairy products, meats, eggs, and many processed foods, including sauces and condiments, breakfast cereals, cookies, and snack chips. Interest in personal and environmental health has contributed to the increasing availability and sales of organic foods. Almost 12% of the fruit and vegetables sold are organic; overall, organic foods account for less than 4% of foods sold.[22] Organic foods, because they often cost more to grow and produce, are typically more expensive than comparable conventional foods.

The term *organic* refers to the way agricultural products are produced. Organic production relies on farming practices such as **biological pest management,** composting, manure applications, and crop rotation to maintain healthy soil, water, crops, and animals. Synthetic pesticides, fertilizers, and hormones; antibiotics; sewage sludge (used as fertilizer); genetic engineering; and irradiation are not permitted in the production of organic foods (pesticides, antibiotics, and genetic engineering are discussed later in the chapter). Additionally, organic meat, poultry, eggs, and dairy products must come from animals allowed to graze outdoors and fed only organic feed.[23]

Foods labeled and marketed as organic must have at least 95% of their ingredients (by weight) meet USDA organic standards. The term "made with organic" can be used if at least 70% of the ingredients are organic. Small organic producers and farmers with sales less than $5000 per year

The USDA organic seal identifies organic foods grown on USDA-certified organic farms.

Farmers' markets are a good place to shop for organic foods.

78   **PART 1**   Nutrition Basics

Take Action

A Closer Look at Organic Foods

Visit one or more supermarkets to see what organic foods are available. Note your findings below.

	Available	Not Available
Meat		
Poultry		
Milk		
Eggs		
Cheese		
Lettuce		
Apples		
Bananas		
Broccoli		
Other produce		
Breakfast cereal		
Snack chips		
Crackers		
Bread		
Pasta		
Beer		

Do you currently purchase organic foods? Why or why not?

sustainable agriculture Agricultural system that provides a secure living for farm families; maintains the natural environment and resources; supports the rural community; and offers respect and fair treatment to all involved, from farmworkers to consumers to the animals raised for food.

are exempt from the certification regulation. Some farmers use organic production methods but choose not to be USDA certified. Their foods cannot be labeled as organic, but many of these farmers market and sell to those seeking organic foods.

Organic Foods and Health

Consumers may choose to eat organic foods to reduce their pesticide intake, to protect the environment, and to improve the nutritional quality of their diets. Those who consume organic produce do ingest lesser amounts of pesticides (only 1 in 4 organically grown fruits and vegetables contains pesticides and in lower amounts than conventional produce), but it's still not known whether or how this affects the health of most consumers. However, organic foods may be a wise choice for young children because pesticide residues may pose a greater risk to them. Consumers also may opt for organic foods to encourage environmentally friendly **sustainable agriculture** practices.

Most studies do not show that organic foods have higher amounts of vitamins and minerals.[24, 25] However, researchers have found that, in some cases, organic fruits and vegetables contain more vitamin C and antioxidants[26] that help protect cells against damage, but more research investigating the nutrition-related health benefits of organic foods is needed. At this point, it's not possible to recommend organic foods over conventional foods based on nutrient content—both can meet nutritional needs. A healthy dose of common sense also is important—an "organic" label does not change a less healthy food into a more healthy food. Organic potato chips have the same calorie and fat content as conventional potato chips. Another consideration for food selection is the possibility of contamination by microbial pathogens—like conventional foods, organic foods may be contaminated with pathogens. Consumers always should use safe food-handling practices to prevent foodborne illness.

Biotechnology—Genetically Modified Foods

Traditional biotechnology is almost as old as agriculture. The first farmer to improve his stock by selectively breeding the best bull with the best cows was implementing biotechnology in a simple sense. By the 1930s, biotechnology had made possible the selective breeding of better plant hybrids. As a result, corn production in the U.S. quickly doubled. Through similar methods, agricultural wheat was crossed with wild grasses to confer more desirable properties, such as greater yield, increased resistance to mildew and bacterial diseases, and tolerance to salt and adverse climatic conditions.

Development of the biotechnology processes now known as genetic engineering or modification, allowed scientists to directly alter the genetic makeup of an organism. Using **recombinant DNA technology,** scientists can transfer a gene that confers a specific trait, such as disease resistance, from almost any plant, animal, or microorganism into another (Fig. 3-3).[27] The resulting organism is commonly referred to as a genetically modified food (GM food), a genetically engineered food (GE food), or a transgenic plant or animal. (The term *genetically modified organism,* or *GMO,* is no longer recommended.) A GM food differs from the original food by only 1 or 2 genes (plants contain thousands of genes). Compared with traditional breeding, this process allows access to a wider gene pool and faster, more accurate transfer of genes. Note, however, that developing a transgenic plant often takes years of careful research because it can be very difficult to identify the specific genes associated with desired traits.

GM Foods

Genetic engineering is widely used in agriculture. The U.S. grows about half of such crops, with Argentina, Brazil, India, Canada, and China accounting for most of the rest.[28, 29] GM soybeans, corn, and cotton are planted on almost half of U.S. cropland; other GM crops include papayas, canola, squash, sugar beets, and alfalfa. Currently, biotechnology is used primarily to improve the control of pests, weeds, and plant diseases. Farmers growing crops genetically modified to be tolerant to herbicides (weed killers) can apply herbicides without harming the crop itself. This helps increase crop yield, decrease use of the most toxic herbicides (but with a higher use of lower-toxicity herbicides), and reduce tilling to decrease weeds; less tilling can reduce soil erosion and save fuel. To aid pest control, the gene for a protein made by the soil bacterium *Bacillus thuringiensis*, Bt, was introduced into corn. The Bt protein is a naturally occurring pesticide that kills caterpillars, a major threat to corn. Before Bt corn was introduced, farmers often applied toxic pesticides to protect corn. Today, nearly all U.S. soybean and corn crops are genetically modified.[29] GM potatoes can produce a beetle-killing toxin in their leaves, and genetic engineering created resistance (much like a vaccine) against a devastating virus common in papayas; over half of all papayas are genetically engineered.

There are currently no genetically engineered animals on the market, but scientists have developed many such animals. Potential applications of GE animals include pharmaceutical production and the provision of more healthful or efficiently produced food.[30] As an example, GE salmon, developed several years ago as an efficient food source for people, can grow to

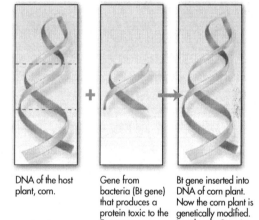

DNA of the host plant, corn.

Gene from bacteria (Bt gene) that produces a protein toxic to the European corn borer.

Bt gene inserted into DNA of corn plant. Now the corn plant is genetically modified. It makes the Bt toxin and, so, is resistant to the European corn borer.

Figure 3-3 In this diagram, a gene from the bacterium *Bacillus thuringiensis* (Bt) is spliced into the DNA of a host corn plant. The corn plant, now referred to as a GM plant, is resistant to the European corn borer.

recombinant DNA technology Test tube technology that rearranges DNA sequences in an organism by cutting the DNA, adding or deleting a DNA sequence, and rejoining DNA molecules using a series of enzymes.

80   **PART 1**   Nutrition Basics

▶ One very successful application of genetic engineering is the production of insulin, a drug used to treat diabetes. Genetically engineered insulin, known as humulin, was approved by the FDA in 1982. It is produced by introducing the human gene for insulin into *E. coli* bacteria and letting the bacteria grow in the laboratory and produce insulin. Today, almost all insulin produced in the U.S. is made this way.

7 times their normal size. In one study, wild salmon grown with the transgenic salmon in an experimental setting did not survive when food supplies were low.[31] This study raised concern about the release of transgenic fish into the ocean and about the compatibility of wild species with transgenic species.

Another agricultural application of biotechnology is the use of recombinant bovine growth hormone (rBGH) (also called recombinant bovine somatotropin, rBST), approved by the Food and Drug Administration (FDA) in 1993, to increase milk production in dairy cows. Bovine growth hormone is a protein, normally produced in the pituitary gland of cows, that triggers the production of another protein, insulin-like growth factor, which in turn stimulates milk production. Using rBGH typically increases milk production 10 to 15%. Concerns about the use of rBGH relate to animal health, especially mastitis (inflammation of cow udders), which may require extra use of antibiotics. Although there is evidence that elevated insulin-like growth factor is associated with certain cancers in humans,[32] there is no evidence that drinking milk is associated with these cancers. The FDA allows farmers who do not use rBGH in their dairy herds to indicate this on milk labels. U.S. organic food regulations do not permit the use of rBGH in organic milk, nor is it approved for use in Canada and Europe.

Chymosin, also known as rennin, is the enzyme used to make cheese from milk. Traditionally, chymosin was harvested from the stomachs of calves, an expensive process. Now almost all chymosin is produced by genetically engineered bacteria or yeast. Chymosin produced in this manner has the advantage of being much purer than that extracted from calves.

GM foods of the future   A variety of new GM foods are under study.[19, 30] Some of these, like those currently grown in the U.S., are designed to help farmers grow foods more easily and to increase yields. Others are being developed to withstand harsh growing conditions, such as drought, extreme heat, and salty soil. Still others are designed to provide more direct benefits to consumers. These include fresh produce with extended shelf lives and more nutrient-dense foods. For example, rice with increased levels of beta-carotene, a yellow-orange compound that can be converted to vitamin A in the body, is in development.[33] This "golden rice" may help improve nutritional status in regions where low vitamin A intakes are a problem. Vegetable oils with a more "heart-healthy" profile are being developed, along with peanuts, soybeans, wheat, eggs, and milk that no longer cause allergic reactions in susceptible individuals.

Many scientists believe that the improvements biotechnology can bring have great potential to help reduce hunger and malnutrition.[19, 28] However, there are some obstacles to its use. One frequently cited barrier concerns the ability of poor farmers to access this technology.[19] Biotechnology research often is conducted by large corporations that patent their products and sell them to farmers at higher prices than conventional seed. Poor farmers who cannot afford the seeds may suffer economic losses. One positive development is that researchers at public universities are developing a variety of GM crops—the problem has been that these researchers haven't been able to readily get them tested and into use. Another closely related concern is that most of the crops developed by corporations (corn, cotton, soybeans) tend to have industrial uses, whereas far less research has focused on foods that are the dietary staples of millions of people, such as rice, wheat, yams, chickpeas, and peanuts.

Regulation of GM foods   In the U.S., GM foods are regulated by the FDA, USDA, and Environmental Protection Agency (EPA). The FDA's role is to ensure that the food is safe for humans and animals to eat (e.g., no toxins or allergens are present). It is the responsibility of the USDA to make sure GM crops are safe to grow. The EPA ensures that pesticides introduced into foods (e.g., Bt corn) are safe for consumption and for the environment. Companies with a new GM plant to release to the marketplace enter into a consultation process with the FDA to ensure its safety. Although the process is not mandatory, the FDA has evaluated all GM

Both traditional plant breeding and biotechnology have produced high-yielding and disease-resistant plant varieties, as with corn.

foods on the market and has found them safe to eat. Critics contend that this process should be required instead of voluntary and should be more stringent.

Labeling for GM foods or those with GM ingredients is not required in the U.S.; however, some countries, including New Zealand, Australia, Japan, South Korea, and many European countries, do require this information on food labels. The FDA contends that such labeling is not required because GM foods are not tangibly different from foods that are not genetically modified. Many critics of GM food disagree, arguing that consumers have a right to information about the food they consume. Because corn (to make sweeteners and oil) and soybeans (to make vegetable oil) are so widely used in the U.S. food supply and are fed to cattle, most people have consumed GM foods.

Safety of GM foods Consumers often question if the benefits of GM foods outweigh their risks. Concerns about food and environmental safety include the following:

- The addition of allergens, such as those in peanuts, eggs, milk, wheat, and shellfish, to GM foods that previously did not contain them. Evidence of allergen contamination was seen in one instance in soybeans but, in more than 15 years of the use of GM crops, there has been no evidence of any harmful reactions or effects in humans. The FDA examines all GM products and will enforce labeling requirements regarding potential allergens that may be present in food altered by biotechnology.
- The possibility of "gene flow" from GM crops to plants not intended for modification. One result of this hybridization might be the development of "superweeds" resistant to herbicides and insecticides.
- The development of Bt-resistant insects. This is of particular concern to organic farmers who, although they do not grow GM crops, apply the *Bacillus thuringiensis* bacteria to crops as a biological pest-management method. Bt resistance also may lead to increased pesticide use by nonorganic farmers.
- The loss of genetic diversity. If GM crops are widely adopted, the use of local indigenous conventional seeds may decline and these plants may disappear.
- Insufficient regulation and oversight of GM plants and animals. Some argue that more rigorous regulation, testing, and oversight are needed to assure safety and benefits for consumers.

Still other concerns relate to ways the technology might be used in the future: the transfer of animal (even human) genes into plants, the genetic engineering of animals to create new species, and the bioengineering of plants to produce medications (known as biopharming). Biopharming is not yet approved as a way to manufacture medications in the U.S.; one concern is that biopharmed crops might mix with crops intended for food, thus exposing many people to a potentially harmful medication. Other fears relate to unknowns, such as how widespread use of GM crops might affect both the agricultural system and the overall ecosystem. Some fear that scientists know too little about how genes function to ensure benefits and safety. Many consumers, especially in countries where food is abundant, question the need for GM crops and believe that they benefit mainly large-scale farmers and the corporations that have developed the technology.

Meat and Milk from Cloned Animals

In 1997, the famous sheep Dolly introduced the world to animal cloning—the process of making genetically identical animals by nonsexual reproduction. Because the DNA is not altered, cloned animals are not genetically modified. Cloning is done by extracting the genetic material from a donor adult cell and transferring it to an egg that has had its own genetic material removed. The cloned embryo that results is transferred to the uterus of a female, where it continues to grow and develop until birth.[34] The biological process of cloning is not new—plants have been cloned for centuries and some animals, such as worms and frogs, can clone on their own.

Some ranchers and farmers are interested in cloning as a way to reproduce their best growing, best milk-producing, or best egg-laying animal for economic gain. After several

Nanotechnology is the study of controlling matter at the atomic or molecular level. A nanometer is one-billionth of a meter. Nanoparticle properties differ significantly from larger particles. For instance, gold nanoparticles created the ruby red color in stained glass windows during the Middle Ages. This color depended on both the element (gold) and its particle size—gold atoms allow red light to pass through and block blue and yellow. Today, nanoparticles are used to detoxify hazardous waste, clean polluted water, brighten food and cosmetic colors, and preserve foods and drugs. Nanoparticles are so small they can penetrate cells and the blood-brain barrier, making it possible to target delivery of drugs and create clearer images of tumors; however, nanoparticles have been linked to lung damage. Considerable research is underway to determine how to capture the benefits and minimize the risks of nanotechnology.

CRITICAL THINKING

The FDA requires a GM food to be labeled as such only if there is a substantial difference in nutrient content, the food contains an allergen that would not normally be present, or the food contains a toxicant beyond a certain limit. Do you think consumers should know if their food contains GM ingredients? What are some of the advantages and disadvantages of labeling foods as either containing GM ingredients or as "GM free"? How would you use this information?

Food-Preservation Methods

Methods That Decrease Water Content to Deter Microbial Growth

Drying (raisins)

Salting (salted fish)

Sugaring (candied fruit)

Smoking (smoked fish)

Methods That Increase Acidity or Alcohol to Deter Microbial Growth

Fermentation and pickling (e.g., sauerkraut, kimchi, pickles, cheese, yogurt, wine)

Methods That Use Heat to Eradicate or Reduce Number of Microbes

Pasteurization (milk)

Sterilization (aseptic cartons of milk, soup)

Canning (beef stew)

Methods That Slow Rate of Microbial Growth

Refrigeration (eggs)

Freezing (meat)

Methods That Inhibit Microbial Growth

Food additives: chemical preservatives (sodium nitrate in cured meat)

Irradiation (raspberries)

radiation Energy that is emitted from a center in all directions. Various forms of radiation energy include X rays, microwaves, and ultraviolet rays from the sun.

years of study, the FDA announced in 2008 that it had determined that both meat and milk from cloned cattle, swine, and goats are safe to eat.[34] However, these foods cannot enter the marketplace until the USDA gives its approval. Although meat and milk from cloned animals appear safe for human consumption, many consumers are uncomfortable with cloning for religious and ethical reasons, and others question the need to add food produced from cloned animals to the food supply.

Knowledge Check

1. What substances and practices are not allowed in organic food production?
2. What are the potential advantages and disadvantages of eating organic foods?
3. What is the main use of GM crops today?
4. What is golden rice? How might it help improve nutritional status in the future?
5. How are GM foods regulated in the U.S.?
6. What are at least 3 objections related to using GM foods?

 ## 3.3 Food Preservation and Processing

The vast majority of foods we purchase have been preserved or processed—frozen, refrigerated, canned, dehydrated, or milled, to name a few methods. Food-preservation methods extend a food's shelf life by slowing the rate at which microorganisms (e.g., bacteria, mold, yeast) and enzymes in food cause spoilage. Food preservation permits a wide variety of good-quality, nutritious, and safe foods to be available year round. The oldest food-preservation methods, some in use for thousands of years, are drying, salting, sugaring, smoking, and fermenting. Over the last 200 years, scientific discoveries and technological innovations have added pasteurization, sterilization, canning, aseptic processing, refrigeration, freezing, nitrogen packing, food irradiation, and preservative food additives to the list of food-preservation techniques.

Food Irradiation

Food irradiation, sometimes known as cold or electronic pasteurization, is one of the newest food-preservation methods. It uses radiant energy, or **radiation**, from gamma rays, X rays, or electron beams to extend the shelf life of food and to control the growth of insects and pathogens (bacteria, fungi, parasites) in foods.[35, 36] Foods are exposed to controlled doses of radiant energy, which essentially passes through the food. Just as an airport scanner or dental X rays do not make your luggage or teeth radioactive, irradiated food is not radioactive. The history of food irradiation goes back nearly a century and includes scientific research, evaluation, and testing.[37] Irradiated foods are safe in the opinion of the FDA and many other health authorities, including the American Academy of Pediatrics.

This Radura symbol indicates that a food has been irradiated.

Foods approved for irradiation in the U.S. include fresh meat and poultry, wheat and wheat powder, white potatoes, spices and dry vegetable seasonings, fresh shell eggs, and fresh produce.[36] Irradiated food, except for dried seasonings, must be labeled with the international food irradiation symbol, the Radura, and a statement that the product has been treated by irradiation. Although the demand for irradiated foods is still low in the U.S., other countries, including Canada, Japan, Italy, and Mexico, use food irradiation technology widely. Barriers to its use in the U.S. include consumers' lack of familiarity with the technology, the potentially higher cost of irradiated foods, and concerns about the taste and safety of irradiated foods.[38]

Food Additives

Food additives, especially those that help preserve and flavor foods (e.g., salt, vinegar, and alcohol), have been used for thousands of years. However, until the 20th century, food production and safety were not regulated, and harmful substances were sometimes added to foods. In the 1800s, toxic minerals (arsenic, lead, mercury) were used to color foods such as candies, pickles, meat, and even milk. Flour was diluted with chalk or limestone and preserved with borax, a substance commonly used to kill ants. Concern about such dangerous practices led Harvey Wiley, the chief chemist at the USDA, to test the safety of food additives. He enlisted the help of the "poison squad," a group of human volunteers who ate foods with high amounts of additives (fortunately, none of the volunteers suffered lasting ill effects). Wiley's work led to the first federal law regulating food, The Pure Food and Drugs Act of 1906.

Today, the FDA regulates over 3000 food additives. **Food additives** are substances added to foods to produce a desired effect, such as a longer shelf life (preservative), greater nutritional value, or a more appealing color. As the demand for convenient, time-saving prepared foods has increased, so have the need for and use of food additives. Many foods are prepared at large, central processing plants, transported long distances, and then held in warehouses for some time before purchase. Food additives can help keep foods appetizing, fresh, nutritious, and safe. Consider a typical lunch menu of a hamburger, cucumber salad with dressing, and lemonade. The hamburger bun is enriched with nutrient additives and contains a preservative to keep it fresh. The cucumber skin may be waxed to extend its shelf life and may contain an infinitesimal amount of pesticide residue, which technically is an additive. The dressing contains an emulsifier additive to keep it from separating and a preservative to keep it from spoiling. The convenient lemonade mix consists of additives (sweeteners, flavors, and colors) dissolved in water.

Intentional vs. Incidental Food Additives

All food additives are classified as either intentional or incidental. Intentional food additives are purposely added to achieve a goal, such as keeping a food fresh or enhancing its flavor. These additives are listed on food ingredient labels. Incidental additives, also called indirect additives, are not intentionally added but become part of a food through some aspect of food production, processing, packaging, transport, or storage. They have no function in finished products. One example is benzene, a carcinogen found in very small amounts in some beverages. It forms when benzoate salts (preservatives) and vitamin C react. The small amount in beverages is not thought to be a risk for consumers.[39] Another example is bisphenol A (BPA), used in the lining of some food and beverage containers to prevent corrosion and improve heat resistance. Long-term exposure to BPA from leaching into foods is widespread. A number of adverse health effects, including damage to liver and pancreatic cells, thyroid dysfunction, and higher risk of cardiovascular disease and diabetes, have been linked to BPA.[40] The FDA is currently evaluating whether the use of BPA in food containers should be decreased.

Synthetic vs. Natural Additives

Although most food additives are synthetic compounds, this does not make them inherently less safe than natural compounds. The toxicity of a substance is determined by its effects in the body, not whether it is synthesized in a laboratory or a plant. The dose of the substance also is critical. Even a common substance, such as table salt, can cause illness or even death when ingested in large amounts. Further, many plants contain natural toxins that are even more potent and prevalent than the additives intentionally added to foods. Some cancer researchers suggest that we ingest at least 10,000 times more (by weight) natural toxins produced by plants than synthetic additives or pesticides.[41]

To help keep processed food, such as potato chips and bagged salad greens, fresh longer, they are packed in airtight bags, which are then filled with nitrogen gas.

▶ Many additives are ingredients you know, such as sodium chloride (salt), sucrose (table sugar), and sodium bicarbonate (baking soda). The complete list of food additives is in the FDA database "Everything Added to Foods in the US." Visit www.fda.gov/food /foodingredientspackaging.

Many soft drinks contain several intentional food additives, including colors, flavors, and sweeteners.

84 **PART 1** Nutrition Basics

Color additives make some foods more desirable.

▶ These 2 brands of tortilla chips differ greatly in their use of food additives:

Brand 1

Whole corn, vegetable oil, salt, cheddar cheese, maltodextrin, wheat flour, whey, monosodium glutamate, buttermilk solids, Romano cheese from cow's milk, whey protein concentrate, onion powder, partially hydrogenated soybean and cottonseed oils, corn flour, disodium phosphate, lactose, natural and artificial flavor, tomato powder, spices, lactic acid, artificial color (including Yellow 6, Yellow 5, and Red 40), citric acid, sugar, garlic powder, red and green bell pepper powder, sodium caseinate, disodium inosinate, disodium guanylate, non-fat milk solids, whey protein isolate, corn syrup solids.

Brand 2

Organic stone-ground blue corn with a trace of lime, organic vegetable oil, sea salt.

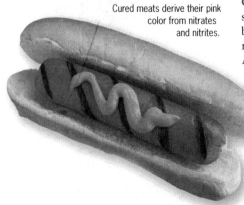

Cured meats derive their pink color from nitrates and nitrites.

Uses of Food Additives

Intentional food additives are used to (1) improve freshness and safety, (2) enhance or maintain nutritional value, (3) enhance or maintain color and flavor, and (4) contribute to functional characteristics, such as the texture and acidity of a food. Examples of additives in each of these categories appear in Table 3-3. In the U.S., regulations do not permit food additives to be used to hide defective food ingredients or poor product quality (as they were earlier in history), to deceive customers, or to replace good manufacturing practices.

Flavors and flavor enhancers are the largest and most commonly used groups of additives—nearly 2000 are approved. In most food products, flavors and flavor enhancers are used in small amounts. (Some flavors are so potent that a single drop could flavor the entire contents of an Olympic-size swimming pool.) Additives such as salt, sugar, corn syrup, citric acid, baking soda, vegetable colors, and spices are among the most commonly used.

Regulation and Safety of Food Additives

The responsibility for the safety of food additives lies with the FDA, as set out by the 1958 Food Additives Amendment of the Food, Drug, and Cosmetics Act. Another amendment, enacted in 1960, specifies regulations for color additives. These laws require food manufacturers to test and prove the safety of an additive and obtain FDA approval before it can be used in food. However, some additives are exempt from this approval and testing process. These include additives designated as prior-sanctioned substances and those on the Generally Recognized as Safe (GRAS) list. Prior-sanctioned substances are additives approved by the FDA and USDA as being safe to use prior to 1958; examples include sodium nitrate and sodium nitrite, used to preserve processed meats. GRAS additives have an extensive history of safe use in foods and include salt, spices, vinegar, vitamins, and monosodium glutamate. There are several hundred GRAS additives. Since 1958, some substances on the GRAS list have been reviewed and some have been deleted from the list and the food supply. One example is safrole, a natural flavoring once used in root beer. Many certified color additives have been removed because they were found to cause cancer or organ damage. Most chemicals on the GRAS list have not been reviewed (e.g., vanilla, salt, vinegar), primarily because of expense, their long histories of use, and lack of evidence for toxicity.

New food additive approval Food additive approval and use are strictly regulated in the U.S. Manufacturers must offer proof from rigorous laboratory tests that the additive will accomplish its intended purpose in a food, that it is safe, and that it is to be used in amounts no greater than needed to achieve its purpose. Safety testing must be conducted in at least 2 species, usually mice and rats. Manufacturers also must give the FDA information about how the additive is manufactured and how it can be detected in foods. Two recently approved food additives are the non-nutritive sweeteners sucralose (Splenda®) and stevia (Truvia™ and PureVia™).

Concerns about food additives Many people continue to wonder about the long-term safety of some food additives. Of course, many food additives on the GRAS list have not been adequately tested. It also is possible that new, more sensitive research methods will reveal that currently permitted additives are not as safe as they are currently believed to be. Alternately, newer scientific techniques may indicate that some nonpermitted substances are safer than currently thought. Recall that the scientific method requires us to challenge current knowledge and reassess our thinking when credible new findings are presented.

Food additives that may be of concern to some include aspartame, sodium nitrite, sodium nitrate, and artificial colors. For example, one study indicated that rats exposed throughout their life spans to the non-nutritive sweetener aspartame had a higher risk of cancer.[42] Some consumers report dizziness and headaches after consuming it, but scientific studies do not support that it causes cancer or these effects.[43]

Table 3-3 Functions and Examples of Common Food Additives

Type of Food Additive	Examples of Additives	Examples of Uses
Improve Freshness and Safety		
Antimicrobial agents	Sodium benzoate Sorbic acid Calcium propionate	Inhibit growth of molds, fungi, and bacteria in beverages, baked goods, jams, jellies, salad dressings, processed meats
Antioxidants	Butylated hydroxyanisole (BHA) Butylated hydroxytoulene (BHT) Ascorbic acid Erythorbic acid Alpha-tocopherol Sulfites	Control adverse effects of oxygen and/or prevent fats from spoiling; used in breakfast cereals, chewing gums, nuts, processed meats Prevent light-colored foods (sliced potatoes, white wine, fruit) from discoloring
Curing agents	Sodium nitrate Sodium nitrite	Prevent growth of *Clostridium botulinum* in bacon, ham, salami, hot dogs, other cured meats Contribute to pink color of cured meats
Acidic agents	Acetic acid, ascorbic acid, phosphoric acid, lactic acid	Add tartness and inhibit growth of microorganisms in foods such as beverages, salad dressings, candies, frozen desserts, salsas, pickles, processed meats
Alter Nutritional Value		
Vitamins, minerals, protein	Thiamin, vitamin A, protein	Fortification (add nutrients): iodine in salt Enrichment (replace nutrients lost in processing): thiamin, riboflavin, niacin, folic acid, iron in cereal and grain products
Alternative sweeteners	Aspartame, saccharin	Saccharin in soft drinks
Fat replacers	Olestra, salatrim	Fried snack foods
Enhance Flavor or Color		
Flavors and spices	Salts, sugars, herbs, spices, flavors	Grape flavor in popsicles
Flavor enhancers	Monosodium glutamate (MSG) Guanosine monophosphate (GMP)	Enhance existing flavor or contribute savory flavor to foods, such as soups, rice, noodle mixes
Color additives	Beta-carotene, annatto, beet coloring, cochineal, caramel coloring	Natural colors or humanmade counterparts of natural color derivatives used in many foods; exempt from FDA certification
Certifiable color additives	FD&C Blue #1, FD&C Blue #2, FD&C Green #3, FD&C Red #3, FD&C Red #40, FD&C Yellow #5, FD&C Yellow #6, Citrus Red #2	The only humanmade dyes currently certified by the FDA for use in foods; found in a variety of foods
Enhance Functional Characteristics		
Emulsifiers	Egg yolks, soy lecithin, mono- and diglycerides	Salad dressings, peanut butter, frozen desserts, baking mixes, margarine
Anticaking agents	Calcium silicate, ammonium citrate, magnesium stearate	Keep foods, especially powdered mixes, free flowing
Humectants	Glycerol, sorbitol	Retain moisture, flavor, and texture in foods, such as marshmallows, soft candies, energy bars
Stabilizers, thickeners	Pectin, gums (guar, carrageenan, xanthan), gelatin	Add creaminess and thickness to foods, such as frozen desserts, yogurt, dairy products, salad dressings, pudding, gelatin mixes
Enzymes	Lactase, rennet, chymosin, pectinase	Act on proteins, fats, or carbohydrates in foods. Lactase makes milk more digestible; rennet and chymosin are required for cheese making; pectinase improves the clarity of some jellies and fruit juices
Leavening agents	Yeast, baking soda, baking powder	Contribute leavening gases (mainly CO_2) to improve texture of baked products, such as breads, cookies, cakes, baking mixes

86 **PART 1** Nutrition Basics

Take Action

A Closer Look at Food Additives

Evaluate the food label of a food item, either one in the supermarket or one you have available.

1. Write out the list of ingredients.

2. Identify the ingredients you think are food additives.

3. Based on the information available in this chapter, what are the functions and relative safety of these food additives?

(a)

(b)

Depending on food choices, a diet can be either (a) essentially devoid of food additives or (b) high in food additives.

Sodium nitrate and sodium nitrite, added to cured meats to prevent growth of the deadly bacterium *Clostridium botulinum,* can be converted to carcinogenic nitrosamines in the stomach. Adding ascorbic acid or erythorbic acid to cured meats limits nitrosamine production. Many deem the benefit of minimizing deadly botulism infections greater than the small risk of nitrosamine formation. Some artificial colors have been reported to cause allergic-type reactions in children and to increase hyperactive behavior;[44] others have been linked to cancer in animals. If credible future research confirms these effects, the amount permitted in food might be reduced or banned altogether. On the other hand, a banned additive might once again be permitted. For instance, cyclamate was banned in the U.S. and other countries when some research indicated it was a carcinogen. However, when a number of subsequent studies found no cancer risk, dozens of countries, including Canada, once again permitted it as a food additive. It is possible that the FDA will reapprove cyclamate in the future.

A few food additives cause adverse symptoms in sensitive individuals. Sulfites, a group of sulfur-based chemicals, are used as antioxidants and preservatives in foods. About 1 in 100 persons, particularly those with asthma, experiences shortness of breath or gastrointestinal symptoms after ingesting sulfites. Because of this, the use of sulfites is prohibited on salad bars and other raw vegetables. However, sulfites are found in a variety of foods, such as frozen or dehydrated potatoes, wine, and beer. Food labels indicate their presence. Monosodium glutamate, a flavor enhancer, also can cause problems; some individuals report flushing, chest pain, dizziness, rapid heartbeat, high blood pressure, headache, and/or nausea after consuming monosodium glutamate.

Many food producers are making foods with fewer additives to meet consumer preferences for **natural foods**—those free of added colors and synthetic substances. Reading ingredient lists will help you identify foods with fewer additives. Also, keep in mind that the more processed a food is, the more additives it is likely to contain. Many prepackaged, precooked, frozen, canned, and instant foods, mixes, and snack foods contain additives. To lower your intake of additives, read food labels and eat fewer highly processed foods. Although no evidence shows that limiting additives will make you healthier, replacing highly processed foods with fruits, vegetables, whole grains, meats, and dairy products is a healthy practice.

Knowledge Check

1. How do food-preservation methods preserve foods and decrease spoilage?
2. How can irradiated foods be identified?
3. How do intentional food additives differ from incidental food additives?
4. What are GRAS food additives?
5. What are the broad functions of intentional food additives?

3.4 Food and Water Safety

In addition to having access to abundant, varied, and nutritious foods, we must have safe food and water supplies to support good health. Scientific knowledge of the pathogens in food and of safe food-handling practices, technological developments (e.g., refrigeration, water purification, and milk pasteurization), and laws and regulations have greatly improved the safety of the food and water supplies and have contributed to a steep decline in foodborne and waterborne illness.

Scientists and health authorities agree that North Americans enjoy relatively safe water and food supplies. Nonetheless, pathogens and certain chemicals in foods and water still pose a health risk. Thus, the nutritional and health benefits of food and water must be balanced against related hazards. The next 3 sections of the chapter examine these hazards and how you can minimize your exposure.

Foodborne Illness

Foodborne illness caused by microbial pathogens remains a significant public health problem in the 21st century. According to the U.S. Centers for Disease Control and Prevention, foodborne pathogens cause about 47.8 million illnesses each year. These illnesses result in an estimated 127,839 hospitalizations and 3037 deaths.[45, 46] In 80% of these illnesses, the specific microbial pathogen is unknown. The World Health Organization (WHO) estimates that, in developed nations, a third of the population has a foodborne illness event yearly, accounting for about 20 million deaths.[47] Foodborne illnesses are expensive—annual costs in the U.S. may be as high as $152 billion when medical costs, loss of productivity, quality-of-life losses, and lost life expectancy are considered.[48]

The importance of foodborne illness is underscored by the increasing numbers of at-risk individuals—in the U.S., one-quarter of the population is at increased risk of foodborne illness. At-risk individuals include those with weakened immune systems due to disease, pharmaceutical, or radiological treatments (e.g., HIV/AIDS, transplant and cancer patients); pregnant women and their fetuses; lactating mothers; infants and young children; and elderly persons. Others who may be at disproportionately greater risk are those living in institutional settings and homeless persons.

Most cases of foodborne illness go undiagnosed because the symptoms are mild enough that the ill persons do not seek medical care. These symptoms typically include gastrointestinal effects, such as nausea, vomiting, diarrhea, and intestinal cramping. However, some bouts of foodborne illness, especially when coupled with ongoing health problems, are lengthy and lead to food allergies, seizures, blood poisoning (from microorganisms or their toxins in the bloodstream), organ failure, chronic complications (e.g., arthritis), and even death (see the Medical Perspective in this chapter).

Our food system affects the spread of foodborne illness. Most of the food we eat is grown on large farms far from our homes (even in other countries) and is transported either to supermarkets, where we buy it fresh, or to food-processing plants, where it is cleaned, prepared, and packaged before shipment to warehouses and then on to grocery stores. Large-scale production means that, if contamination occurs at any point, many people can be affected. This was evident in an outbreak associated with contaminated hot peppers that were used to make salsa and other foods and eventually sickened over 1400 people in 43 states, causing at least 286 hospitalizations and possibly contributing to 2 deaths.[49] Similar multi-state outbreaks have occurred with spinach, peanuts, ground meat, and chocolate chip cookie dough. Food mishandling in food service establishments, such as cafeterias and restaurants, can cause illness in many people, too. Although mishandling by food processors and food service establishments can lead to widespread problems, it is important to remember that food mishandling in home kitchens also is a cause of foodborne illness.

HISTORICAL PERSPECTIVE

A Safe Food Supply

Finding ways to preserve food to keep it safe and delicious has been a challenge for millennia. Starting in the early 1900s, Lloyd Augustus Hall found many new ways to preserve food. For example, he discovered that a mixture of sodium nitrate and nitrite helped prevent botulism in cured meats, like bologna. He also developed ways to treat spices and cereals to make them safer to eat. Many of the food preservative compounds used today were the direct result of Dr. Hall's research. Learn more at:

webfiles.uci.edu/
mcbrown/display/
hall.html

natural food Food that has undergone minimal processing and does not contain food additives.

foodborne illness Sickness caused by the ingestion of food containing pathogenic microorganisms or toxins made by these pathogens.

Food contaminated in a central plant can go on to produce illness in people in surrounding states or even across the nation. In the case of juices, shown here, it is important that they are pasteurized to reduce the risk of foodborne illness.

Microbial Pathogens

The greatest health risk from food and water today is contamination by viruses and bacteria and, to a lesser extent, by various forms of fungi and parasites. Foodborne illness occurs when microorganisms either directly infect the cells of the gastrointestinal tract, and sometimes other organs in the body, or secrete a toxin into food, which harms us when we eat it (called food intoxication). Unlike foodborne infections, live pathogens need not be present in food for a foodborne intoxication to occur. Toxin-producing bacteria need only to have, at some point, infused the food with their toxin.

Most of the pathogenic bacteria and viruses that cause foodborne illness originate in an infected human or animal and reach food by these fairly well defined routes:

Spinach, lettuce, unpasteurized milk and juice, and undercooked ground beef have been implicated in outbreaks of *E. coli* 0157:H7.

▶ To find information about the microbial pathogens in food and water, visit www.cdc.gov/DiseasesConditions.

- *Contamination by feces.* Many foodborne illness-causing bacteria and viruses are excreted profusely in the feces of infected humans and animals. In countries with inadequate sanitation, the water used for drinking, cooking, washing dishes and produce, irrigating crops, and fishing is frequently contaminated with raw sewage and is a major source of illness. Even in the U.S., fecal contamination of soil and irrigation water from farm and wild animals contributes to the spread of pathogens. Fecal contamination also occurs when food is handled by a person who has come in contact with feces or sewage (as in using the bathroom or changing diapers) and has not thoroughly washed his or her hands. Insects, such as houseflies, also may carry bacteria from sewage to food. Foodborne illnesses that are acquired from fecal matter in one of these ways are said to be transmitted by the fecal-oral route.
- *Contamination by an infected individual.* Some pathogenic bacteria and viruses can be transferred to food directly by an infected individual. For example, a food handler who has an open wound or who coughs or sneezes onto food may contaminate the food. Pets also may be a source of foodborne pathogens that can contaminate food via the unwashed hands of food preparers.
- *Cross-contamination.* Cross-contamination occurs when an uncontaminated food touches a pathogen-contaminated food or any object, such as a plate, knife, or cutting board, that has come in contact with contaminated food. For instance, let's say a person cuts up a raw chicken contaminated with pathogenic bacteria and then chops lettuce for a salad. When the person is cutting the chicken, the cutting board, the knife, and the food preparer's hands become contaminated with bacteria. If these items are not thoroughly washed before the person chops the lettuce, it will be cross-contaminated with bacteria. Although the bacteria on the chicken will be killed with cooking, the lettuce is not cooked and can cause foodborne illness.

Most types of *E. coli* are not dangerous, but *E. coli* 0157:H7 is the leading cause of bloody diarrhea in the U.S. In children and the elderly, it can cause kidney failure and death.

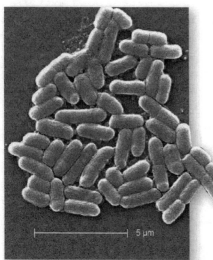

5 μm

Bacteria

Bacteria are single-cell organisms found in the food we eat, the water we drink, and the air we breathe. They live in our intestines, on our skin, in our refrigerators, and on kitchen countertops. Luckily, most are harmless, but some are pathogenic and can cause illness. Any food can transmit pathogenic bacteria; however, the most common sources are meats, poultry, eggs, fish, shellfish, dairy products, and fresh produce.

Table 3-4 lists many of the bacteria that cause foodborne illness and describes typical food sources and the symptoms of the illnesses they cause. *Salmonella* spp., *Clostridium perfringens,* and *Campylobacter* spp. cause most bacterial foodborne illness in the U.S.[45] Others, such as *Clostridium botulinum, Listeria monocytogenes,* and *Vibrio vulnifcus,* cause fewer cases but are more likely to result in serious illness and death. In developing countries, pathogens such as *Vibrio cholerae* are more important.

Table 3-4 Bacterial Causes of Foodborne Illness

Bacteria	Typical Food Sources	Symptoms	Additional Information
Salmonella species	Raw and undercooked meats, poultry, eggs, and fish; produce, especially raw sprouts; peanut butter; unpasteurized milk	Onset: 12–72 hours; nausea, fever, headache, abdominal cramps, diarrhea, and vomiting; can be fatal in infants, the elderly, and those with impaired immune systems; lasts 4–7 days	Estimated 1.028 million infections/year; bacteria live in the intestines of animals and humans; food is contaminated by infected water and feces; about 2000 strains of *Salmonella* bacteria can cause disease, but 3 strains account for almost 50% of cases; *Salmonella enteritidis* infects the ovaries of healthy hens and contaminates eggs; almost 20% of cases are from eating undercooked eggs or egg-containing dishes; reptiles, such as turtles, also spread the disease
Campylobacter jejuni	Raw and undercooked meat and poultry (more than half of raw poultry in the U.S. is contaminated), unpasteurized milk, contaminated water	Onset: 2–5 days; muscle pain, abdominal cramping, diarrhea (sometimes bloody), fever; lasts 2–7 days	Estimated 845,024 infections/year; produces a toxin that destroys intestinal mucosal surfaces; can cause Guillain-Barré syndrome, a rare neurological disorder that causes paralysis
Escherichia coli (0157:H7 and other strains)	Undercooked ground beef; produce—lettuce, spinach, sprouts; unpasteurized juice and milk	Onset: 1–8 days; bloody diarrhea, abdominal cramps; in children under age 5 and the elderly, hemolytic uremic syndrome (HUS) is a serious complication; red blood cells are destroyed and kidneys fail; can be fatal; lasts 5–10 days	Leading cause of bloody diarrhea in the U.S.; estimated 173,800 cases/year; lives in the intestine of healthy cattle; cattle and cattle manure are chief sources; illness caused by a powerful toxin made by the bacteria; petting zoos, lakes, and swimming pools can contain pathogenic *E. coli*
Shigella species	Fecal/oral transmission; water supplies, produce, and other foods contaminated by infected food handlers with poor hygiene	Onset: 1–3 days; abdominal cramps, fever, diarrhea (often bloody); lasts 5–7 days	Estimated 131,254 cases/year; humans and primates are the only sources; common in day-care centers and custodial institutions from poor hygiene; traveler's diarrhea often caused by *Shigella dysenteriae*
Staphylococcus aureus	Ham, poultry, egg salads, cream-filled pastries, custards, whipped cream	Onset: 1–6 hours; diarrhea, vomiting, nausea, abdominal cramps; lasts 1–3 days	Bacteria on skin and nasal passages of up to 25% of people; can be passed to foods; multiplies rapidly when contaminated foods are held for extended time at room temperature; illness caused by a heat-resistant toxin that cannot be destroyed by cooking; estimated 241,128 cases/year

continued

Table 3-4   Continued

Bacteria	Typical Food Sources	Symptoms	Additional Information
Clostridium perfringens	Beef, poultry, gravy, Mexican food	Onset: 8–24 hours; abdominal pain and diarrhea, usually mild; can be more serious in elderly or ill persons; lasts 1 day or less	Estimated 965,958 cases/year; anaerobic bacteria widespread in soil and water; multiplies rapidly in prepared foods, such as meats, casseroles, and gravies, held for extended time at room temperature
Listeria monocytogenes	Unpasteurized milk and soft cheeses, raw meats, uncooked vegetables, ready-to-eat deli meats and hot dogs, refrigerated smoked fish	Onset: 9–48 hours for early symptoms, 14–42 days for severe symptoms; fever, muscle aches, headache, vomiting; can spread to nervous system, resulting in stiff neck, confusion, loss of balance, or convulsion; can cause premature birth and stillbirth	Estimated 1591 cases with 255 fatalities/year; widespread in soil and water and can be carried in healthy animals; grows at refrigeration temperatures; about one-third of cases occur during pregnancy; high-risk persons should avoid uncooked deli meats, soft cheeses (e.g., feta, Brie, and Camembert), blue-veined cheeses, Mexican-style cheeses (e.g., queso blanco made from unpasteurized milk), refrigerated meat spreads or pâtés, uncooked refrigerated smoked fish
Clostridium botulinum	Incorrectly home-canned vegetables, meats, and fish; incorrectly canned commercial foods; herb-infused oils; bottled garlic; potatoes baked in foil and held at room temperature; honey	Onset: 18–36 hours but can be 6 hours to 10 days; neurological symptoms—double and blurred vision, drooping eyelids, slurred speech, difficulty swallowing, muscle weakness, and paralysis of face, arms, respiratory muscles, trunk, and legs; can be fatal; lasts days to weeks	Estimated 55 cases/year; caused by a neurotoxin; *C. botulinum* grows only in the absence of air in nonacidic foods; incorrect home canning causes most botulism, but in 2007 commercially canned chili sauce caused an outbreak; honey can contain botulism spores and should not be given to infants younger than 1 year of age
Vibrio	*V. parahemolyticus*: raw and undercooked shellfish, especially oysters	Onset: 24 hours; watery diarrhea, nausea, vomiting, fever, chills; lasts 3 days	Found in coastal waters; more infections in summer; number of infections hard to determine because it is difficult to isolate in the lab
	V. vulnificus: raw and undercooked shellfish, especially oysters	Onset: 1–2 days; vomiting, diarrhea, abdominal pain; in more severe cases, bloodstream infection with fever, chills, decreased blood pressure, blistering skin lesions; lasts 3 or more days	Estimated 95 cases/year; found in coastal waters; more infections in summer; those with impaired immune systems and liver disease at higher risk of infection; fatality rate of 35% with bloodstream infection
	V. cholerae: contaminated water and food, human carriers	Onset: 2–3 days; severe, dehydrating diarrhea, vomiting; dehydration, cardiovascular collapse, and death can occur	Occurs mainly in countries without adequate water purification and sewage treatment
Yersinia enterocolitica	Raw or undercooked pork, particularly pork intestines (chitterlings); tofu; water; unpasteurized milk	Onset: 4–7 days; fever, abdominal pain, diarrhea (often bloody); lasts 1–3 weeks or longer	Yersinosis most common in children under age 5 years; relatively rare; bacteria live mainly in pigs but can be found in other animals

To proliferate, bacteria require nutrients, water, and warmth. Most grow best in **danger zone** temperatures of 41° to 135°F (5° to 57°C) (Fig. 3-4). Pathogenic bacteria typically do not multiply when food is held at temperatures above 135°F (57°C) or stored at safe refrigeration temperatures, 32° to 40°F (0° to 4.4°C). One important exception is *Listeria* bacteria, which can multiply at refrigeration temperatures. Also note that high temperatures can kill toxin-producing bacteria, but any toxin produced in the food will not be inactivated by high temperatures. Most pathogenic bacteria also require oxygen for growth, but *Clostridium botulinum* and *Clostridium perfringens* grow only in anaerobic (oxygen-free) environments, such as those found in tightly sealed cans and jars. Food acidity can affect bacterial growth, too. Although most bacteria do not grow well in acidic environments, some, such as disease-causing *E. coli,* can grow in acidic foods, such as fruit juice.

As you can see, different types of pathogenic bacteria can thrive in a variety of environmental conditions. Some can even survive in harsh environmental conditions (e.g., dry conditions or very hot or cold temperatures) through spore formation. In the spore state, bacteria can remain viable for months or years—then, when environmental conditions improve, they begin proliferating. For example, uncooked rice contains little water, which prevents bacterial growth. When you add water and cook it, especially if you leave it sitting on the kitchen counter (danger zone temperatures) instead of refrigerating it, you provide a hospitable environment (moisture, nutrients, warmth) for disease-causing bacteria and their spores to multiply rapidly. Measures to prevent bacterial and other foodborne illness are described later in this chapter.

Viruses

Viruses, like bacteria, are widely dispersed in nature. Unlike bacteria, however, viruses can reproduce only after invading body cells, such as those that line the intestines. Thus, the key to preventing foodborne viral illnesses is to use sanitary food-preparation practices to keep viruses from contaminating food and to cook food thoroughly to kill any that have found their way into food via contamination from infected food handlers, other foods, and feces.

Table 3-5 describes the 2 most common viral causes of foodborne illness and describes typical food sources and symptoms of the illnesses they cause. Noroviruses are thought to account for an estimated 5.46 million foodborne illnesses per year—if you have had the "stomach flu," you may well have experienced a norovirus infection. There are many reports of norovirus outbreaks on cruise ships, in hotels and restaurants, and even in hospitals. Rotaviruses, a type of norovirus, are an important cause of diarrhea in children (see Chapter 4). Hepatitis A virus causes liver disease and is spread by contaminated food or water.

Avian bird flu, a serious influenza caused by a virus found in wild birds, can spread to domestic poultry flocks. However, it is important to know that the Centers for Disease Control and Prevention (CDC) states that avian bird flu is not a foodborne illness. It is of great concern because it can cross the species barrier and be transmitted to humans who handle the infected birds. Outbreaks in poultry and humans have occurred in Asia, the Near East, Europe, and North America. Eradicating infected flocks is the chief way of controlling an outbreak. There is no scientific evidence that the influenza is contracted through consuming poultry or eggs. Further, the safe handling and cooking of poultry and eggs eliminates the virus.[50]

Parasites

Parasites live in or on another organism, known as the host, from which they absorb nutrients. Humans can serve as a host to parasites. These tiny ravagers rob millions of people around the globe of their health and, in some cases, their lives. Those hardest hit live in tropical countries

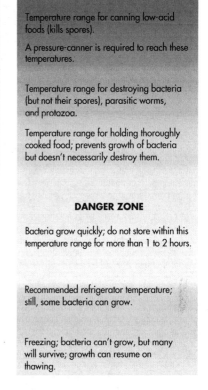

Figure 3-4 Effects of temperature on microbes that cause foodborne illness.

▶ The temperature range for the danger zone is listed by some sources as 41° to 140°F (5° to 60°C). The FDA has lowered the upper end of the range to 135°F (57°C) because the risk posed by holding food between 135° and 140°F (57° and 60°C) is minimal.

▶ Food recalls occur when food products are found to be contaminated. Examples include

- Sliced apples, avocado pulp, and sliced turkey for *Listeria*

- Bagged spinach and ground beef for *E. coli*

- Spices, pot pies, peanut butter, and hazelnuts for *Salmonella*

Table 3-5 **Viral Causes of Foodborne Illness**

Viruses	Typical Food Sources	Symptoms	Additional Information
Norovirus (Norwalk and Norwalk-like viruses), human rotavirus	Foods prepared by infected food handlers; shellfish from contaminated waters; vegetables and fruits contaminated during growing, harvesting, and processing	Onset: 1–2 days; "stomach flu"—severe diarrhea, nausea, vomiting, stomach cramping, low-grade fever, chills, muscle aches; lasts 1–2 days or longer	Viruses found in stool and vomit of infected persons; food handlers can contaminate foods or work surfaces; noroviruses are very infectious—as few as 10–100 particles can lead to infection; workers with norovirus symptoms should not work until 2 or 3 days after they feel better
Hepatitis A virus	Foods prepared by infected food handlers, especially uncooked foods or those handled after cooking, such as sandwiches, pastries, and salads; shellfish from contaminated waters; vegetables and fruits contaminated during growing, harvesting, and processing	Onset: 15–50 days; anorexia, diarrhea, fever, jaundice, dark urine, fatigue; may cause liver damage and death; lasts several weeks up to 6 months	Infected food handlers contaminate food and transmit the disease to dozens of persons; children and young adults are more susceptible; a vaccine is available, decreasing the number of infections dramatically; immunoglobulin given within 1 week to those exposed to hepatitis A virus can also decrease infection

Raw shellfish, especially bivalves (e.g., oysters and clams), present a particular risk related to foodborne viral disease. These animals filter feed, a process that concentrates viruses, bacteria, and toxins present in the water as it is filtered for food. Adequate cooking of shellfish will kill viruses and bacteria, but toxins may not be affected. It's important to buy shellfish from reliable sources who have harvested these foods from safe areas.

where poor sanitation fosters the growth of parasites. However, epidemiologists report that parasitic infections seem to be on the increase in the U.S. and other industrialized countries.[51] For example, in 1993 a *Cryptosporidium* outbreak involving more than 400,000 people occurred in Milwaukee due to contamination of the water supply. *Cyclospora* outbreaks have occurred from the ingestion of raspberries.

The more than 80 foodborne parasites known to affect humans include mainly **protozoa** (one-celled animals), such as *Cryptosporidium* and *Cyclospora,* and **helminths,** such as tapeworms and the roundworm *Trichinella spiralis*. Table 3-6 describes common parasites and typical food sources and the symptoms of the illnesses they cause. Parasitic infections spread via person-to-person contact and contaminated food, water, and soil.

Prions

A very rare, but fatal, brain disease in humans has been linked to a similar fatal disease in cattle widely known as mad cow disease. More formally known as bovine spongiform encephalopathy (BSE), it is caused by an infectious protein particle called a **prion,** found mainly in the brain and spinal cord. An epidemic of BSE in the mid-1980s in the United Kingdom (UK), followed by the discovery of a similar fatal brain disease in humans, now known as variant Creutzfeldt-Jakob disease (vCJD), focused attention on the relationship between the diseases. Both BSE and vCJD are chronic, degenerative brain and nerve disorders for which there is no known cure.[52, 53]

Table 3-6 Parasitic Causes of Foodborne Illness

Parasite	Typical Food Sources	Symptoms	Additional Information
Trichinella spiralis	Pork, wild game	Onset: weeks to months; GI symptoms followed by muscle weakness, fluid retention in the face, fever, flulike symptoms	The number of trichinosis infections has decreased greatly because pigs are now less likely to harbor this parasite; cooking pork to 145°F (63°C) plus 3 minutes of rest time before carving will kill *trichinella,* as will freezing it for 3 days at −4°F (−20°C).
Anisakis	Raw or undercooked fish	Onset: 12 hours or less; violent stomach pain, nausea, vomiting	It is caused by eating the larvae of roundworms; the infection is more common where raw fish is routinely consumed.
Tapeworms	Raw beef, pork, and fish	Abdominal discomfort, diarrhea	It is caused by eating tapeworm cysts in undercooked or raw meat. In the human intestine, the cyst develops into a mature tapeworm, usually 6 to 23 feet in length. Infected persons often pass segments of the tapeworm in the stool. Rarely, the tapeworm infects muscle and central nervous tissues.
Toxoplasma gondii	Raw or undercooked meat, unwashed fruits and vegetables	Onset: 5–20 days; most people are asymptomatic; those with symptoms have fever, headache, sore muscles, diarrhea; can be fatal to the fetus of pregnant women	The parasite is spread to humans from animals, including cats, the main reservoir of the disease; humans acquire the disease from ingesting contaminated meat or from fecal contamination from handling cat litter; there are an estimated 86,700 cases/year.
Cyclospora cayetanensis	Water, contaminated food	Onset: 1 week; watery diarrhea, vomiting, muscle aches, fatigue, anorexia, weight loss; lasts 10–12 weeks	It is most common in tropical and subtropical areas, but approximately 11,400 illnesses occur each year in the U.S.
Cryptosporidium	Water, contaminated food	Onset: 2–10 days; watery diarrhea, abdominal pain, fever, nausea, vomiting, weight loss; those with impaired immune systems become more ill; lasts 1–2 weeks in otherwise healthy persons	Outbreaks occur worldwide; the largest U.S. outbreak was in 1993 in Milwaukee, with more than 443,000 persons affected; it also can be spread in water parks and community swimming pools.

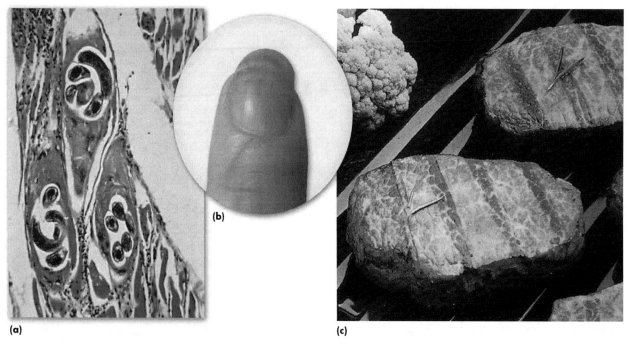

(a) Muscle tissue with *Trinchinella spiralis* roundworm cysts. Eating meat that contains *Trichinella* cysts causes the disease trichinosis. (b) Splinter hemorrhages under fingernails are common in those with trichinosis. (c) Grill pork to an internal temperature of 145°F (63°C) plus 3 minutes of rest time before carving. This eliminates the risk of trichinosis and produces a desirable product. Trichinosis cases from pork are rare today because of more sanitary hog-feeding practices.

Scientists determined that BSE was spread through cattle feed, which at that time contained by-products (e.g., brain, spinal cord, intestines) from sheep infected with scrapie, a disease like BSE. Scientists now believe that vCJD is similarly transmitted to humans by the consumption of beef from BSE-afflicted cattle. The risk of developing vCJD is very low—it is estimated that 1 case develops for every 10 billion servings of beef in a BSE-affected country (about 97% of all reported BSE cases are from the UK; only 21 cases have been discovered in the U.S. and Canada).[53] Only 217 cases of vCJD have been reported worldwide, most from the UK and only 4 from the U.S. and Canada.[52]

Even when heated to high temperatures, prions remain infective. Thus, many countries, including the UK, the U.S., and Canada, have programs to prevent BSE-infected meat from entering the food supply. In the U.S., this program includes banning imports from countries where BSE is reported, prohibiting the use of animal by-products in cattle feed, monitoring and testing cattle for BSE, and banning the use of cattle parts that might contain prion particles (eyes, brain, spinal cord, intestines) in human foods.[53] Cattle suspected of having BSE are destroyed. Milk and other dairy products do not pose any risk of transmitting vCJD. At this point, it's safe to conclude that the risk of acquiring vCJD from eating beef is negligible in the U.S. Even for travelers to countries where BSE rates are higher, the CDC believes that the risk is extremely low—almost zero.[52] Of course, travelers who wish to reduce their risk even more can choose to avoid beef.

Toxins

A number of toxins produced by molds, algae, and plants can cause serious illness (Table 3-7). **Molds** are a type of fungus that can be scattered by the wind or carried by animals. Molds grow best in moist, dark places where air circulates. When conditions are right, the mold grows by sending rootlike "threads" deep into the food it lives on and forming endospores on the outside of the food. These endospores give mold its fuzzy, colorful look and are the form in which the mold travels to new locations. The foods most likely to mold in U.S. homes are cheese, breads, and fresh produce.

CRITICAL THINKING

Recognizing that José is taking a nutrition class, his roommate asks him, "What is more risky: the bacteria that can be present in food or the additives listed on the label of my favorite cookie?" How should José respond? On what information should he base his conclusions?

Table 3-7　Toxins in Food

Toxin	Typical Food Sources	Symptoms	Additional Information
Mycotoxins			
Aflatoxin (from *Apergillus flavus* and *Aspergillus parasiticus*)	Corn, peanuts, rice, wheat, spices, nuts, especially when these foods are stressed due to drought or disease	Acute toxicity: liver damage or failure, malnutrition, malaise, impaired immune function; can be fatal Chronic toxicity: vomiting, abdominal pain, liver failure, liver cancer; can be fatal	Aflatoxin B-1 is the most common fungal toxin to contaminate grains and nuts. It causes significant crop losses around the world and disease when consumed by humans.
Ergot (from *Claviceps purpurea*)	Inappropriately stored grains, especially rye	Hallucinations, spontaneous abortion, severely constricted blood flow to limbs (which can lead to gangrene), tingling and burning sensations, involuntary muscle twitching and contractions	Ergot poisoning is thought to be the cause of the odd physical behaviors attributed to women tried at the Salem witch trials.
Algae Toxins			
Ciguatera toxin	Tropical and subtropical fish (e.g., amberjack, barracuda, grouper, hogfish, moray eels, snapper, scorpion fish, surgeonfish, triggerfish) that have ingested toxin-producing algae	Onset: 6 hours; nausea, vomiting, neurological symptoms (weakness, temperature reversal—hot feels cold and vice versa); symptoms can last days, months, or years	The number of cases is not known.
Shellfish poisoning (paralytic, diarrheic, neurotoxic, and amnesic)	Mussels, cockles, clams, scallops, oysters, crabs, lobster	*Paralytic* onset: 15 minutes to 10 hours; numb and tingling skin, respiratory paralysis, death *Diarrheic* onset: few minutes to a few hours; nausea, vomiting, diarrhea, abdominal pain, chills, headache, fever *Neurotoxic* onset: 30 minutes to 3 hours; tingling and numbness of mouth and throat, muscle aches, dizziness, reversal of sensations of hot and cold, diarrhea, vomiting *Amnesic* onset: 24 to 48 hours. Vomiting, diarrhea, abdominal pain, confusion, memory loss, disorientation, seizure, coma	It is associated with red tide algal blooms. The toxin accumulates in the shellfish. It is common in both the Pacific and Atlantic Oceans.
Scombroid poisoning	Scombridae family (tunas and mackerels) and related fish (bluefish, mahi-mahi, amberjacks)	Onset: 2 to several hours; rash, diarrhea, flushing, sweating, headache, vomiting, difficulty breathing; symptoms resolve quickly	Bacterial decomposition of fish results in histamine production, which causes symptoms.
Tetrodotoxin	Pufferfish (fugu) liver	Onset: 20 minutes to 3 hours; mouth numbness, headache, nausea, diarrhea, vomiting, paralysis	Fugu is a traditional delicacy in Japan, where chefs must be licensed to prepare and serve this fish.

continued

Table 3-7 Continued

Toxin	Typical Food Sources	Symptoms	Additional Information
Plant Toxins			
Safrole	Sassafras, mace, nutmeg	Cancer when consumed in high doses	It was previously used as a food additive but is now banned.
Solanine	Potato sprouts, green spots on potato skins	Onset: 8–12 hours; nausea, diarrhea, vomiting, hallucinations, loss of sensation, paralysis	It can be prevented by storing potatoes in a dark area and discarding the sprouts, the peel, bruised or cut areas, and any green-tinged spots.
Mushroom toxins	Some mushroom species, such as amanita	Stomach upset, dizziness, hallucinations, and other neurological symptoms; more lethal varieties can cause liver and kidney failure, coma, and death	Illness is almost always caused by wild mushrooms picked by nonexperts.
Herbal teas	Teas containing senna or comfrey	Onset: depends on dose; diarrhea and liver damage	Teas are used in folk medicines and are not considered safe for internal use.
Lectins	Raw or undercooked legumes, usually kidney beans	Onset: 1–3 hours; nausea, vomiting, abdominal pain, diarrhea	As few as 4 or 5 raw beans can cause symptoms. Outbreaks have occurred when beans were insufficiently cooked in crockpots and casseroles.

Thousands of types of mold grow on foods. Most just alter the color, texture, taste, and/or odor of foods, making them unpalatable and inedible. Some destroy crops and shorten the length of time a food will remain fresh and safe to eat. Others cause allergies or respiratory problems. A few fungi produce toxins known as **mycotoxins** (*myco* means "mold"), which cause blood diseases, nervous system disorders, and kidney and liver damage. The most important mycotoxins are aflatoxin, ergot, and those produced by the *Fusaria* fungi. Liver cancer–causing **aflatoxin** is produced by a mold that attacks peanuts, tree nuts (e.g., walnuts and pecans), corn, and oilseeds (e.g., cottonseed). Ergot is produced by a dark purple mold that grows on inappropriately stored grains, especially rye. Several types of *Fusaria* fungi can grow on grains stored for long periods and produce deadly mycotoxins.

Mycotoxins are rarely a problem in most industrialized nations because food production practices are designed to minimize mold growth. In addition, food producers and government inspectors closely monitor foods to detect molds and destroy any foods found to contain them. Unfortunately, mycotoxin poisonings are frequent in other parts of the world. For example, in Kenya in 2004 an aflatoxin poisoning caused liver damage in many people and many deaths.

Toxin-containing algae ingested by some fish and shellfish also can cause foodborne disease. One example is the **ciguatera toxin** found in some large tropical and subtropical fish. Another example is **shellfish poisoning** caused by shellfish harvested from waters experiencing an algae population explosion called a red tide (sometimes the algae are so thick they color the water red). The fish and shellfish are not harmed by the toxins, and the toxins are not destroyed by cooking or freezing. To avoid ciguatera, do not eat large fish that may contain a higher amount of this toxin; instead, choose the smaller specimens and don't eat fish heads or organs where toxins concentrate. The only protection against shellfish poisoning is to avoid shellfish from affected waters until nature thins the algae population. Both the U.S. and Canada quarantine waters experiencing an algae surge and prohibit shellfish harvesting until the shellfish are safe to eat. However, some countries are not as rigid in their regulations regarding shellfish and red tides.

Scombroid poisoning is caused by eating certain fish left at room temperature for several hours after being caught. The toxin is not destroyed by freezing or cooking but can be prevented by refrigerating or freezing the fish immediately after they're caught.

Foods contain a variety of **natural toxins** that can cause illness (see Table 3-6) but, in actuality, rarely do.[54] For instance, licorice contains a natural toxicant that can elevate blood pressure and cause heart failure. There is cyanide in lima beans and almonds. Nutmeg, bananas, and some herbal teas contain substances that can cause hallucinations. Plants produce and concentrate toxins to compete with their neighbors and protect themselves from plant-eating molds, bacteria, insects, and other predators, including people. When stressed by environmental conditions or damaged, plants tend to produce even greater quantities of toxins. An example is the production of **solanine,** a powerful, narcotic-like toxin, produced by potatoes. The amount produced is normally small, but it increases when potatoes sprout and when they are stored in a brightly lit place.

Humans have coped with natural toxins for thousands of years by learning to avoid some of them and to limit intake of others. Farmers know potatoes must be stored in the dark, so that solanine won't be synthesized. Cooking limits the potency of certain natural toxins. Spices are used in such small amounts that health risks from any toxins are unlikely to result. Another important way to cope with these toxins is to eat a wide variety of foods to minimize the chance that any single toxin is eaten in amounts that exceed the body's ability to detoxify it. Natural toxins are so widespread in foods that it would be unrealistic to try to avoid them totally— and doing so would likely limit food choices so severely that nutrient deficiency diseases would occur. Nevertheless, it's important to remember that some potentially harmful chemicals in foods occur naturally.

Hunting wild mushrooms should be left to experts. Many varieties contain deadly toxins.

CASE STUDY

Aaron and his wife attended an international potluck on a warm July afternoon. Their contribution was Argentine beef, a stewlike dish. They followed the recipe and the cooking time carefully, removed the dish from the oven at 1 P.M., and kept it warm by wrapping the pan in a towel. They drove to the party and set the dish out on the buffet table at 3 P.M. Dinner was to be served at 4 P.M., but the guests were enjoying themselves so much that no one began to eat until 6 P.M. Aaron made sure he sampled the Argentine beef they had prepared, but his wife did not. He also had some salads, garlic bread, and a sweet coconut dessert. The couple returned home at 11 P.M. and went to bed. At 2 A.M., Aaron knew something was wrong. He had severe abdominal pain and had to make a mad dash to the toilet. He spent most of the next 3 hours in the bathroom with diarrhea. By dawn, the diarrhea had subsided and he was feeling better. He ate a light breakfast and felt fine by noon. It's very likely that Aaron contracted foodborne illness from the Argentine beef. What precautions for avoiding foodborne illness were ignored by Aaron and the rest of the people at the party? How might this case study be rewritten to substantially reduce the risk of foodborne illness?

98   **PART 1**   Nutrition Basics

▶ To find information about the purity of the water provided by municipal water departments, visit www.EPA.gov/water.

Bottled water is a convenient but relatively expensive source of water. In most cases, tap water is just as healthy a choice to meet water needs.

▶ A website providing information on efforts to promote U.S. food safety is www.foodsafety.gov. For tips on food safety in the home, go to www.homefoodsafety.org.

▶ Hazard Analysis and Critical Control Point, or HACCP (pronounced HAS-sip), was developed more than 30 years ago as a food-safety system for astronauts. Today, it is widely used by food processors to ensure food safety. Some food-service establishments, such as restaurants and cafeterias, have adopted it, too. The goal of the HACCP system is to identify potential problems *before* they happen and thereby prevent food-safety problems. To learn more, visit www.FoodSafety.gov.

Water Safety

Clean water is vital for good health. The disinfection of water is widely regarded as one of the major advances in public health in the last century, responsible for substantially reducing infectious diseases, especially the deadly typhoid fever. Today, public water supplies are regulated by the EPA, but the actual delivery and safety of water are under the jurisdiction of local municipal water departments in the U.S. Under the Safe Drinking Water Act, all public drinking water suppliers are required to rigorously test for contaminants, such as bacteria, various chemicals, and toxic metals (e.g., lead and arsenic) and submit test results to the EPA.[55] Water treatments vary, depending on the water source, but all water is disinfected, usually with a chlorine-based chemical. Private water supplies, such as wells, are not regulated by the EPA but still should be tested for chemical and microbial contaminants. Local health departments usually can give advice on testing and keeping well water safe.

Bottled water is another popular source of water. Many consumers are attracted to its convenience, perceived health value, or taste. All bottled waters must list the source of the water on the label. This source can include wells, spas, springs, geysers, and quite often the public water supply. The FDA has defined the terms used on labels, such as *artesian water, distilled water, purified water, spring water,* and *mineral water.* For example, spring water must come from an underground spring. Some bottled water contains minerals, such as calcium, magnesium, and potassium, that either occur naturally or are added by the bottling company to improve the water's taste. The water is carbonated when carbon dioxide gas naturally occurs in the water source (called *naturally sparkling water*) or is added. Additives such as flavors and vitamins also are common. Bottled waters are regulated by the FDA, which sets high standards for their purity. It periodically collects and analyzes samples, but not to the extent that municipal water supplies are monitored. Water that is bottled in a sanitary manner and kept sealed will not spoil, though off-flavors may develop over time.

Threats to Safe Water

The U.S. enjoys one of the cleanest water supplies in the world, but there are numerous threats to the safety of our water—agricultural runoff (animal waste, pesticides, fertilizer), inappropriate disposal of chemicals, municipal solid waste (containing bacteria, viruses, nitrates, synthetic detergents, household chemicals) leaking into waterways, inadequate treatment of human wastes, and pollution from boats and ships (contains solvents, gas, detergents, raw sewage), to name just a few. This makes regular testing of the water supply critical.

The EPA requires that the public be notified if water contamination is a danger to public health. For instance, nitrate contamination from fertilizer runoff is particularly dangerous to infants because it prevents oxygen from circulating in the body. As related earlier, *Cryptosporidium* can contaminate water supplies (it is not affected by normal chlorination procedures). Boiling tap water for a minimum of 1 minute is the best way to kill *Cryptosporidium.* Alternatively, individuals can purchase a water filter that screens out this parasite.

Even though the U.S. has one of the cleanest water supplies in the world, illnesses from contaminated drinking water do occur. The CDC monitors water-related outbreaks, which average about 30 per year.[56] Water safety experts note that these data likely underestimate the true number of illnesses caused by contaminated water.

> *Knowledge Check*
>
> 1. What groups of people are particularly susceptible to foodborne illness?
> 2. Which bacterial and viral pathogens cause most foodborne illnesses?
> 3. How are viruses and bacteria spread by the fecal-oral route?
> 4. Why do natural toxins in plant food rarely affect people?
> 5. Which government agencies regulate drinking water?
> 6. What are 3 threats to public water supply systems?

MEDICAL PERSPECTIVE

Foodborne Illness Can Be Deadly

Foodborne illness often means a few hours or even a few days of discomfort and then the illness resolves on its own. In some cases, though, foodborne illness causes more serious medical problems that can have lifelong effects. High-risk populations—infants and young children, the elderly, pregnant women and their fetuses, and those with impaired immune systems—have the greatest risk of serious complications like these:

- Hemolytic uremic syndrome (HUS). Most cases of HUS are caused by the toxin produced by *E. coli* O157:H7. The toxin attacks red blood cells, causing them to break apart (called hemolysis), and the kidneys, causing waste products to build up (called uremia). Early symptoms of HUS include bloody diarrhea, vomiting, sleepiness, and low urine output. In the worst cases, the toxin damages multiple organs, causing seizures, permanent kidney failure, stroke, heart damage, liver failure, and even death. Fortunately, most individuals recover completely, although usually after weeks of intensive medical care. HUS afflicts children more often than adults, but adults experience the most severe infections.

- Listeriosis. *Listeria monocytogenes* bacteria cause listeriosis, a rare, but serious, disease. Listeriosis begins with muscle aches, fever, and nausea. It can spread to the nervous system, causing severe headache, stiff neck, loss of balance, and confusion. Pregnant women and their fetuses are particularly vulnerable—listeriosis can cause miscarriage, premature delivery, infection in the fetus, and fetal death. During pregnancy, women are 20 times more likely to develop the disease. The elderly also are susceptible. A 2008 outbreak in Canada from contaminated deli meats resulted in 29 deaths; almost all of them were elderly individuals. About 1 in 5 persons with listeriosis will die from the infection.

- Guillain-Barré syndrome (GBS). *Campylobacter jejuni* is one cause of this rare nervous system disorder. In GBS, peripheral nerves (those that connect the spinal cord and brain to the rest of the body) are damaged by the body's own immune system. Early symptoms of GBS include tingling and pain in the legs, followed by severe muscular weakness. Paralysis can occur, and some individuals need help breathing with a ventilator. Recovery can take weeks to months and about 30% of those with GBS do not fully recover, experiencing lifelong pain, weakness, and/or paralysis.

- Reactive arthritis. Foodborne illness caused by *Salmonella, Shigella, Campylobacter*, and others can cause reactive arthritis. This condition usually develops 2 to 6 weeks after the initial infection and causes inflammation throughout the body, but especially in the joints and eyes. Pain and swelling of the knees, ankles, and feet are common. Inflammation of the urinary tract and blistering of the palms of the hands and soles of the feet also are common. Genetic factors play an important role in determining who develops the disease. Most people with reactive arthritis require medical treatment and will recover after 2 to 6 months, but about 20% experience mild arthritis for a much longer time.

These diseases highlight the need for a safe food supply and safe food handling all along the food chain.

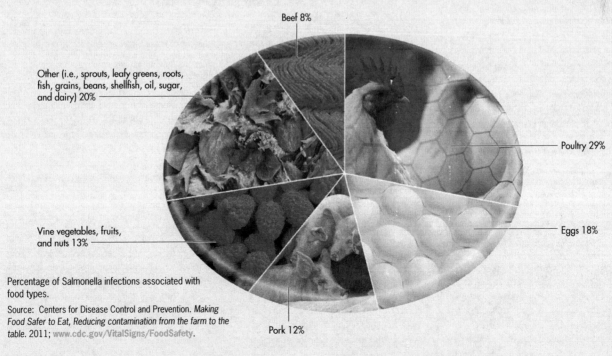

Beef 8%

Other (i.e., sprouts, leafy greens, roots, fish, grains, beans, shellfish, oil, sugar, and dairy) 20%

Poultry 29%

Vine vegetables, fruits, and nuts 13%

Eggs 18%

Pork 12%

Percentage of Salmonella infections associated with food types.

Source: Centers for Disease Control and Prevention. *Making Food Safer to Eat, Reducing contamination from the farm to the table.* 2011; www.cdc.gov/VitalSigns/FoodSafety.

100 **PART 1** Nutrition Basics

▶As the old adage says, when in doubt, throw the food out!

Inspect cans for bulges and foul-smelling liquid as signs of the presence of the botulism toxin.

▶Raw milk has not undergone pasteurization, the heat-treatment process that kills pathogenic bacteria and makes milk safe to drink. Pasteurization does not alter milk's nutrient content, or make milk less healthy or allergenic. According to the FDA "raw milk is an inherently dangerous product and it should not be consumed by anyone at any time for any purpose."[57] Many states prohibit the sale of raw milk to consumers and interstate commerce is prohibited. In the first 6 months of 2010, there were at least 8 separate disease outbreaks in the U.S. caused by raw milk or dairy products.[58]

CRITICAL THINKING

Ahmed wants to buy a cutting board for his new kitchen. He's been looking at all the possibilities: glass, plastic, and wood. How would you advise him, so that he can minimize the risk of foodborne illness?

🍑 3.5 Preventing Foodborne and Waterborne Illnesses

Safe food and water supplies require a "farm-to-fork" approach. All those who grow our food, along with processors, distributors, and consumers, are responsible for food and water safety. Several government agencies regulate and coordinate these efforts, monitor food and water, conduct research, enforce wholesomeness and quality standards and laws, and educate consumers (Table 3-8).

To do their part, consumers need to know how to handle food safely at home. In general, foodborne illness prevention focuses on using good personal and kitchen hygiene; handling food safely by using appropriate thawing, cooking, chilling, and storage procedures; and knowing which foods pose extra risk to those more susceptible to foodborne illness.

Select and Purchase Foods Carefully

- Don't use food from damaged cans or jars that leak, bulge, or are severely dented or cracked. Don't taste food that smells or looks odd. Discard canned foods that spurt liquid when the can is opened; the deadly botulism toxin may be present.
- When food shopping, place perishable foods, such as milk, eggs, and raw meat, poultry, and seafood, in your cart last and keep them separate from other foods in the cart, so that they don't contaminate them. Placing them in separate plastic bags prevents cross-contamination.
- Take groceries home promptly and refrigerate or freeze perishable foods right away. Leaving them in a warm car allows pathogens to grow.
- Use the sell-by, use-by, and expiration dates found on many food products. *Sell-by* is the last date a retailer can sell the product so that it still maintains its quality with normal use in the home. *Use-by* (also called the freshness date) indicates when quality may start to decline, although the product will still be safe to eat. Expiration dates, found on foods such as infant formulas, are the last dates foods should be eaten.

Avoid Unsafe Food and Water

- Avoid eating foods likely to be contaminated with pathogens, including raw or undercooked meat, fish, shellfish, poultry, and eggs.
- Drink only milk and juice that have been pasteurized.
- If at increased risk of foodborne illness, avoid soft cheeses, cold deli salads, and cold smoked fish, and heat hot dogs and deli meats to 165°F (75°C) before consumption.
- Use only purified water for drinking, cooking, and washing food and food-preparation equipment. If you have a well, test it for pathogens.

Practice Good Personal Hygiene

- Thoroughly wash hands for 20 seconds with warm, soapy water after using the bathroom, changing diapers, playing with pets, coughing, sneezing, or smoking. Also wash them before and after handling food, especially if you have touched unwashed produce or raw meat, fish, poultry, and eggs. Plain soap works as well as antibacterial soaps—just be sure to wash frequently and thoroughly.
- Cover any cuts, burns, sores, or infected areas when preparing foods. This helps keep bacteria (often *Staphylococcus*) from wounds out of food.
- Avoid preparing food when sick with diarrhea.

Keep a Clean Kitchen

- Prevent cross-contamination by cleaning counters, cutting boards, dishes, and other equipment thoroughly before and after use. Wash them with hot, soapy water or in the dishwasher. They also can be sanitized with a dilute solution of bleach. Regularly cleaning surfaces and equipment with a dilute bleach solution (1 part bleach to 10 parts water) helps reduce the risk of cross-contamination.
- Replace sponges and wash kitchen towels frequently. (Microwaving wet sponges for 2 minutes helps kill bacteria.)

Table 3-8 U.S. Agencies Responsible for Monitoring the Food Supply

Agency Name	Responsibilities	Methods	How to Contact
Food and Drug Administration (FDA)	• Ensures safety and wholesomeness of foods in interstate commerce (except meat, poultry, and processed egg products) • Regulates seafood • Controls product labels	• Conducts inspections • Conducts food sample studies • Sets standards for specific foods	www.fda.gov or call 1-800-FDA-4010
U.S. Department of Agriculture (USDA)	• Enforces wholesomeness and quality standards for grains and produce (while in the field), meat, poultry, milk, eggs, and egg products	• Conducts inspections • Monitors imported meat and poultry • Administers "Safe Handling Label"	www.usda.gov/fsis or www.cdc.gov /outbreaknet or call 1-800-535-4555
Centers for Disease Control and Prevention (CDC)	• Promotes food safety	• Responds to emergencies concerning foodborne illness • Surveys and studies environmental health problems • Conducts research on foodborne illness • Directs/enforces quarantines • Conducts national programs for prevention and control of foodborne and other diseases	www.cdc.gov
Environmental Protection Agency (EPA)	• Regulates pesticides • Establishes water quality standards	• Approves all U.S. pesticides • Sets pesticide residue limits in food	www.epa.gov
National Marine Fisheries Service or NOAA Fisheries	• Monitors domestic and international conservation and management of living marine resources	• Conducts voluntary seafood inspection program • Can use mark to show federal inspection	www.nmfs.noaa .gov
Bureau of Alcohol, Tobacco, and Firearms and Explosives (ATF)	• Enforces laws on alcoholic beverages	• Conducts inspections	www.atf.gov /alcohol-tobacco
State and local governments	• Promote milk safety • Monitor food industry within their borders	• Conduct inspections of food-related establishments	Government pages of telephone book, Internet

The Fight BAC! Program (check out www. fightbac.org) has 4 simple rules for preventing foodborne illness.

1. Clean. Wash hands and surfaces often.
2. Separate. Don't cross-contaminate.
3. Cook. Cook to proper temperatures.
4. Chill. Refrigerate promptly.

Wash fresh fruits and vegetables under running water to remove bacteria and soil. Antibacterial washing products are not necessary.

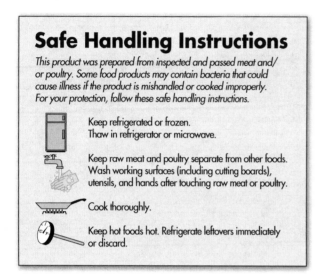

Safe Handling Instructions

This product was prepared from inspected and passed meat and/or poultry. Some food products may contain bacteria that could cause illness if the product is mishandled or cooked improperly. For your protection, follow these safe handling instructions.

Keep refrigerated or frozen.
Thaw in refrigerator or microwave.

Keep raw meat and poultry separate from other foods. Wash working surfaces (including cutting boards), utensils, and hands after touching raw meat or poultry.

Cook thoroughly.

Keep hot foods hot. Refrigerate leftovers immediately or discard.

▶ The USDA answers questions about the safe use of animal products (1-888-674-6854, 10 A.M. to 4 P.M. weekdays, Eastern time; or go to www.fsis.usda.gov/Food_Safety_Education /USDA_Meat_&_Poultry_Hotline).

▶ **Safe Refrigeration Storage**

Food	Use Within
Raw meat	
• Ground beef, poultry, fish	1–2 days
• Steaks, chops, roasts	3–5 days
• Bacon	1 week
• Hot dogs	2 weeks
Cooked meat, poultry, casseroles, soups	3–5 days
Tuna, egg, ham, chicken, or macaroni salads	3–5 days
Fresh eggs in shell	3–5 weeks
Hard-cooked eggs	1 week

Find more information at fightbac.org.

- Cutting boards should be made of nonporous, smooth material, such as hard plastic, marble, glass, or hardwood (oak, maple). Bacteria are hard to remove from porous or deeply scratched cutting boards.

Handle Food Safely

- Wash fresh fruits and vegetables under running water just before eating them to remove bacteria, soil, and pesticides.
- Scrub firm produce, such as melons and cucumbers, under running water with a brush before slicing them. (Bacteria on the skin can contaminate the inside of produce when it is cut.)
- Discard soft or liquid foods (e.g., jam, syrups) that are moldy. If a firm-textured food has molded, trim off a large area around the mold and at least 1 inch below the mold. Prevent mold growth by storing food at cold temperatures and using food promptly.
- Be aware of how long foods have been in your refrigerator. Freezing keeps foods safe indefinitely, but quality deteriorates if they are kept too long.
- Store raw meats and poultry below other foods in the refrigerator to prevent cross-contamination by drippings from leaky packages.
- Be careful not to recontaminate cooked food with raw meat or juices on hands, cutting boards, or dirty equipment. For example, when grilling burgers, don't put cooked burgers on the same plate that was used to carry the raw patties out to the grill.
- For outdoor cooking, cook food completely at the picnic site, with no partial cooking in advance.

Keep Foods Out of the Danger Zone and Cook Foods Appropriately

- Never thaw foods on the counter. Thaw foods in the refrigerator, under cold running water, or in a microwave oven. Cook foods immediately after thawing in the microwave because cooking may have begun, putting the food temperature in the danger zone (41° to 135°F [5° to 57°C]).
- Use a refrigerator thermometer to assure your refrigerator operates at a safe temperature range (32° to 40°F [0° to 4.4°C]).
- Marinate food in the refrigerator.
- Cook food to a safe internal temperature. Don't rely on how the food looks—use a food thermometer. Cook to at least the minimum temperatures shown in Figure 3-5.

CASE STUDY FOLLOW-UP

Although the dish was cooked thoroughly, it was held at an unsafe temperature from the time it was removed from the oven at 1:00 P.M. until it was served at 6:00 P.M. This 5-hour time span greatly exceeded the maximum time of 2 hours at room temperature for a cooked food. This allowed the growth of a foodborne illness–causing pathogen. Ideally, this product should have been transported on ice in a cooler to the party, refrigerated at the party, and then reheated to 165°F (74°C) before serving at 6:00 P.M. Overall, it is risky to leave perishable items, such as meat, fish, poultry, eggs, and dairy products, at room temperature for more than 2 hours.

GL BAL PERSPECTIVE

Traveler's Diarrhea

Traveler's diarrhea afflicts 30 to 50% of those who travel to areas that tend to be hot and lack advanced water treatment systems and refrigeration, such as most of Central and South America, Africa, Asia, and the Middle East. Traveler's diarrhea usually occurs abruptly and lasts for 3 to 4 days, or longer.[59] According to the Centers for Disease Control and Prevention, most traveler's diarrhea is caused by bacterial infections, especially *Enterotoxigenic Escherichia coli,* spread through contaminated food and water. The following guidelines can help reduce the risk of traveler's diarrhea.

- Eat foods that are freshly cooked and served piping hot.
- Avoid food from street vendors and buffets.
- Avoid salads and raw fruits and vegetables.
- Avoid raw or undercooked meat and seafood.
- Avoid tap water and beverages reconstituted with tap water (including ice and possibly fruit juice and milk).
- Bottled and sealed beverages, including soft drinks, water, beer, and wine, are generally safe.
- Beverages made with boiled water, such as coffee and tea, are generally safe.
- Travelers also can treat tap water by boiling, chemical disinfection, or filtering. To learn how, visit www.nc.cdc.gov/travel.

Even when following these guidelines, traveler's diarrhea can be hard to avoid. Pepto-Bismol®, an over-the-counter drug used to treat indigestion, can reduce traveler's diarrhea substantially when it is taken throughout the stay. However, before traveling to a high-risk area, it is wise to consult with a physician about using any medication, getting needed vaccinations, and taking other health precautions.

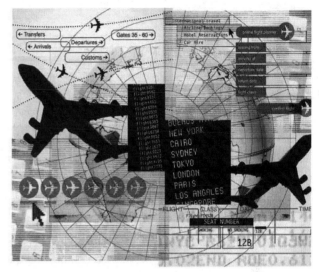

▶ A phrase familiar to those traveling to developing countries is "boil it, peel it, or don't eat it." Of course, this advice is simplistic—many foods that may be safe to eat can't be boiled or peeled.

▶ For more health advice, visit the CDC website for travelers: wwwnc.cdc.gov/travel.

- Cook eggs until yolks and whites are firm, not runny. *Salmonella* bacteria may survive in sunny-side up or over-easy eggs. Avoid homemade ice cream, eggnog, mayonnaise, and other foods made with unpasteurized raw eggs.
- Avoid eating raw animal products. Raw fish dishes, such as sushi, can be eaten safely by most people who are not at increased risk of foodborne illness if the dish is made with very fresh fish that has been commercially frozen (freezing helps eliminate parasites) and purchased from a reputable establishment.
- Cook stuffing separately from poultry or stuff immediately before cooking and cook to 165°F (74°C). Immediately after cooking, transfer the stuffing to a clean bowl.
- Once a food is cooked, consume it right away, or refrigerate or freeze it within 2 hours. In hot weather (90°F [32°C] and above), refrigerate it within 1 hour.
- Cool foods in shallow pans (not deep containers) to provide a large surface area for rapid cooling.
- Reheat leftovers thoroughly to 165°F (74°C).

Figure 3-5 Minimum internal temperatures for cooking or reheating foods.

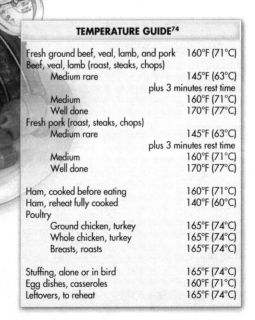

TEMPERATURE GUIDE[74]	
Fresh ground beef, veal, lamb, and pork	160°F (71°C)
Beef, veal, lamb (roast, steaks, chops)	
Medium rare	145°F (63°C)
	plus 3 minutes rest time
Medium	160°F (71°C)
Well done	170°F (77°C)
Fresh pork (roast, steaks, chops)	
Medium rare	145°F (63°C)
	plus 3 minutes rest time
Medium	160°F (71°C)
Well done	170°F (77°C)
Ham, cooked before eating	160°F (71°C)
Ham, reheat fully cooked	140°F (60°C)
Poultry	
Ground chicken, turkey	165°F (74°C)
Whole chicken, turkey	165°F (74°C)
Breasts, roasts	165°F (74°C)
Stuffing, alone or in bird	165°F (74°C)
Egg dishes, casseroles	160°F (71°C)
Leftovers, to reheat	165°F (74°C)

3.6 Environmental Contaminants in Foods

In addition to pathogens and natural toxins, a number of environmental toxins can contaminate food and cause health problems. Common environmental contaminants include heavy metals (lead, mercury), industrial chemicals (dioxins, polychlorinated biphenyls), and agricultural chemicals (pesticides, antibiotics).

Lead

Lead can damage every organ system in the body—especially the nervous system and kidneys—and it impairs the synthesis of hemoglobin, the oxygen-carrying protein in the blood. Lead is particularly toxic to the developing nervous system of children; even low amounts in the body can lower IQ, cause behavior disorders, and impair coordination. It also can impair growth and hearing and predispose children to high blood pressure and kidney disease later in life. About 2% of children ages 1 to 5 years in the U.S. have dangerously high blood lead levels.[60] In developing countries, many more children are affected.

Sources of lead include home plumbing and lead-based paints; both are more likely in be found in buildings constructed prior to 1986. In homes with lead pipes or solder, running cold water for a minute or so before using it allows lead leached from pipes to go down the drain. Hot tap water should not be used for food preparation or consumption because more lead leaches into hot than cold tap water. Filters that remove lead also are available. Dust and chips from lead-based paint can be inadvertently ingested, especially by children. Keeping the home and hands clean can help reduce exposure. Also, never serve or store foods or beverages in lead-containing containers, such as leaded crystal, some pottery, and older or imported dishes.

Other documented lead sources include certain candies from Mexico, vegetables grown in contaminated soils, mineral supplements, herbal remedies, and toys painted with lead-containing paints. (Children often place toys in their mouths, making them particularly dangerous.) In one study, 20% of the herbal remedies tested contained dangerous levels of lead, mercury, and/or arsenic.[61] Lead is no longer used in food cans in the U.S., but food cans from other countries may contain lead.

Preventing lead poisoning is best done by removing lead from the environment. Good nutrition plays a role, too. Children with iron deficiency absorb more iron and lead, so preventing iron deficiency (see Chapter 14) may help limit lead absorption.[62]

▶ Contamination of the food supply by nuclear power plant accidents poses a real, yet poorly understood, threat. Radioactive cesium and iodine released into the air after the 1986 Chernobyl (Ukraine) and 2011 Fukushima Daiichi (Japan) nuclear disasters settled on plants, soil, and water. Radioactive particles (radionuclides) entered our food supply from the milk and meat of animals grazing in contaminated areas. After nuclear accidents, radioactivity of the food supply is monitored carefully because consuming radionuclides may increase the risk for thyroid and other cancers. However, there is much to be learned about what constitutes an unsafe exposure to radionuclide-contaminated foods. Those exposed to radioactive iodine often are prescribed potassium iodine pills to prevent the thyroid gland from absorbing radioactive iodine.

▶ For more information about lead, visit www.epa.gov/lead or call the National Lead Information Center and Clearinghouse at 1-800-424-LEAD.

Eating a healthy diet with plenty of iron may help prevent lead poisoning in children.

Dioxins

Dioxins (chlorine and benzene-containing chemicals) are by-products of certain industrial processes and the incineration of waste; they increase the risk of cancer. They also cause liver and nerve damage and may have adverse effects on reproduction and increase the risk of type 2 diabetes mellitus. Exposure is primarily from dioxin-contaminated food and inhalation of contaminated air. Food sources are animal fats, where dioxins tend to accumulate, and fish from dioxin-contaminated waterways. The EPA recommends absolutely no consumption of some fish species and fish from certain waterways because they are so contaminated. Eating commercially caught fish is usually safe because these fish come from a variety of sources, and most of these rivers, streams, and lakes are not contaminated. Eating a variety of fish, not just one species, also is a good idea.

Mercury

Mercury is abundant in the environment; in aquatic environments, bacteria convert mercury to the neurotoxin methylmercury. The FDA first limited the amount of mercury in foods in 1969, after 120 people in Japan became ill from eating mercury-contaminated fish. Birth defects in the offspring of some of these people also were traced to mercury exposure. Methylmercury can cause nerve damage, fatigue, and poor learning abilities. As with dioxins, fish are the primary source of the toxic chemical. Most at risk are children and pregnant and breastfeeding women—the FDA and EPA suggest that these individuals limit their exposure to mercury by following these guidelines:

Swordfish is a common source of mercury in our diets. Children and pregnant and lactating women should avoid swordfish and other fish that contain high levels of mercury.

- Do not eat shark, swordfish, king mackerel, or tilefish because they contain high levels of mercury. (Large fish concentrate mercury in their tissues.)

- Limit albacore (white) tuna to 6 ounces or 1 meal per week because it is higher in mercury.

- Limit the intake of fish containing less mercury (e.g., shrimp, canned light tuna, pollock, salmon, and catfish) to 12 ounces per week or no more than 2 meals per week. Children should have smaller portions.

- Check the EPA advisories for the mercury content of fish from local waterways. If no advice is available, eat 1 fish meal per week from these sources, but don't eat any other fish that week.

These guidelines are controversial, however. Fish is an important source of fatty acids that promote brain and nervous system development in fetuses and infants. Ongoing research suggests that the benefits from these fatty acids outweigh the risk of mercury from fish.[63] As scientists learn more about the risks and benefits of eating fish, these guidelines may be relaxed to encourage fish intake.

Polychlorinated Biphenyls (PCBs)

Polychlorinated biphenyls (PCBs) were widely used for years in a variety of industrial processes. They were linked to liver tumors and reproductive problems in animals and are no longer produced. However, they do not degrade quickly and can still be detected in the environment. The FDA has established limits for PCBs in susceptible foods and in paper used for food-packaging material. The most significant food source of PCB residues is fish, primarily freshwater fish from contaminated waterways. Again, a key guideline for fish consumption is variety and moderation when local sources have the potential for contamination.

▶ For information on fish contamination with dioxins, mercury, and PCBs, visit www.epa.gov /waterscience/fish.

106   **PART 1**   Nutrition Basics

Pesticide use poses a risk-versus-benefit question. Each side has points that deserve to be considered. Rural communities, where exposure is more direct, experience the greatest short-term risk.

Pesticides

Pesticides, products used to eliminate pests, include insecticides, herbicides (weed killers), fungicides, and rodenticides. Farmers have used them since the 1940s to limit crop-damaging pests and thereby increase agricultural production. Pesticides also can help improve the appearance of fruits and vegetables. For example, a fungicide helps prevent apple scab fungus, which makes apples look unappealing (and less likely to sell), but the fruit is still tasty and nutritious. Fungicides also help prevent carcinogenic aflatoxin from forming on some crops.

The EPA permits the use of about 10,000 pesticides, containing over 1000 active ingredients. This amounts to about 1.2 billion pounds of pesticides (about half are herbicides) being used each year in the U.S., with much of this being applied to agricultural crops. However, pesticide use is not limited to agriculture—many pesticides are used in homes, businesses, schools, and health-care facilities for insect and rodent control. Pesticides also are widely applied to lawns, golf courses, and home gardens.

The 2 major classes of pesticides are synthetic pesticides and biopesticides. Many of the earliest synthetic pesticides were persistent chemicals—they did not break down easily and remained in water, soil, and plants for decades, thus posing a risk to the humans and animals that ingested contaminated water and plants. Many of these early pesticides have been banned. The synthetic compounds in use today break down much more quickly (they are less persistent), but they also are more powerful chemicals. Organophosphates, carbamates, organochlorine insecticides, and pyrethroid pesticides are the main classes of synthetic pesticides.[64]

Three types of biopesticides were developed to provide safer pesticide alternatives. The first type consists of microbial pesticides, such as the soil bacterium *Bacillus thuringiensis* (Bt), which produces proteins that are toxic to various insects. The second type is plants that are genetically modified to produce their own pesticides, such as the Bt protein. The third type is biochemical pesticides that don't directly kill an organism but limit its reproduction or growth.

A number of problems are associated with pesticide use. One is that the organisms intended for elimination can become resistant to the pesticide action. This means that either more of the pesticide must be applied or a new pesticide must be used. Another problem is pesticide drift; once a pesticide is applied to a field, it can be carried by wind currents to nontarget sites. Pesticides that remain in the soil may be taken up by nontarget organisms or enter groundwater and aquatic habitats. Each of these paths is a route to the food chain. Still another problem is the unintended effects; pesticides can harm nontarget species, such as frogs, fish, and beneficial insects (e.g., bees); decrease biological diversity by acting on the lower levels of the food chain; have harmful effects on water quality; disrupt natural wildlife habitats; damage soil and the nutrients in it; and contribute to erosion.

Regulating Pesticides

The EPA, FDA, and USDA share responsibility for regulating pesticides. The EPA is responsible for determining that a pesticide is beneficial and will not pose unreasonable health or environmental risks. The EPA sets limits on how much of a pesticide may be used on food during growth and processing and how much may remain on the food you buy—this is known as pesticide tolerance. Because children are thought to be more vulnerable to any adverse effects of pesticides,[65] the Food Quality Protection Act of 1996 requires the EPA to consider children's pesticide exposure from foods they normally eat, such as apples and apple juice, potatoes, sugar, eggs, chicken, and beef.

The FDA and USDA are jointly responsible for testing foods for pesticides and enforcing the EPA pesticide tolerances. The USDA reports indicate that about 75% of fresh fruits and vegetables have detectable pesticide residues, but only 0.5% exceed pesticide tolerances.[66] The low level of residues that exceeded tolerance confirms that farmers are using pesticides according to EPA regulations.

Common Types of Pesticides

Organophosphates: compounds toxic to the nervous system of insects and animals; some were used in World War II as nerve agents; they usually are not persistent in the environment

Carbamates: compounds that act similarly to the organophosphates but are less toxic

Organochlorine insecticides: commonly used in the past, but many (e.g., DDT and chlordane) have been removed from the market due to their health and environmental effects and their persistence

Pyrethroid pesticides: compounds that mimic naturally occurring pesticides found in chrysanthemums, some of which are toxic to the nervous system

Minimizing Exposure to Pesticides

There is no doubt that pesticides are toxic. Their purpose, after all, is to eliminate pests. Accidental pesticide poisonings occur each year, often related to careless use or storage of these chemicals. Studies also link people who work with pesticides, such as farmers and those who apply pesticides for a living, with higher rates of asthma, Parkinson disease (a neurological disorder), prostate cancer, leukemia, and other cancers.[67, 68] However, there is much less certainty about the effects of long-term exposure to much lower doses, such as occurs when we eat our usual diets. In this regard, infants (including before birth) and children deserve special attention.[64, 68, 69] Young animals exposed to chemicals such as pesticides can experience damage to their developing reproductive, nervous, and immune systems. Risk may increase in young children because they often consume relatively higher doses of pesticides, when their lower body weight is considered. Infants and young children also may not metabolize the pesticides as readily as adults because the liver, the main organ that breaks down drugs and toxins for excretion, is still immature.

Even though government agencies work to keep pesticide residues in food to a minimum, consumers should take steps to minimize their exposure. The EPA recommends washing and peeling fruits and vegetables and trimming away fat in meat (where pesticides may accumulate), along with selecting a variety of foods. Although these measures cannot eliminate all pesticide residues, the fear of pesticides should not deter consumers from eating fruits and vegetables. These foods provide an abundance of important vitamins, minerals, and phytochemicals; eating a *variety* of them is key to meeting nutrient needs and will reduce the likelihood of exposure to a single pesticide.

Certified organic foods are grown without synthetic pesticides and can further minimize exposure to pesticides. However, these foods may contain very small amounts of pesticide residues because of background contamination (pesticides persisting in soil and water) and pesticide drift from nearby conventional farms. One study of 23 school-aged children showed that eating an organic diet can decrease exposure to pesticides.[70] After the children consumed an organic diet for 5 days, organophospate pesticides disappeared from their urine.

Antibiotics

Farmers can give low-dose antibiotics to food animals to promote animal growth and to prevent and treat disease. One estimate is that 60 to 80% of all antibiotics produced in the U.S. are used for this purpose.[71] Many of these antibiotics are the same medications used to treat human infections. Scientists are concerned that this practice fosters the growth and spread of antibiotic-resistant bacteria strains in the animals (and, thus, foodborne illness in humans), as well as in the water, soil, and air around large-scale feeding areas. The development of antibiotic-resistant bacteria is a major public health concern. Infections from antibiotic-resistant bacteria are very difficult to treat and, further, the arsenal of antibiotics available to health-care providers is limited. This issue is currently receiving considerable attention from health-care professionals and scientists.[72] Note that the use of antibiotics is prohibited in organically produced animals.

▶ The environmental damage caused by the pesticide DDT (dichlorodiphenyltrichloroethane) was chronicled by Rachel Carson in her book *Silent Spring*, published in 1962. DDT was widely used around the world because it increased crop yields and was inexpensive. But scientists soon learned that DDT and its metabolites are toxic to humans and animals, especially young fish and birds, and that it persists for years in the environment. DDT can no longer be used in the U.S. and many other countries, but it is still used in some developing countries to kill malaria-carrying mosquitoes.

Parkinson's or Parkinson Disease?

Many health conditions are named for the person who discovered them or the location where they were first observed. The name can be possessive (Parkinson's) or not (Parkinson)—both are correct. However, in a move to improve simplicity and consistency, international biomedical organizations have been endorsing the use of the nonpossessive form for the past decade. Throughout this text, we use the nonpossessive form.[75]

Antibiotics are added to animal feed and water to promote growth and prevent disease. This practice is increasingly questioned by scientists because it may lead to the development of antibiotic-resistant bacteria.

Knowledge Check

1. What are the sources of lead in the diet?
2. Which environmental contaminants are likely to be found in fish? Where can you find out if fish caught from lakes, rivers, and streams in your area are safe to eat?
3. What is a pesticide tolerance?
4. What methods can you use to reduce the amount of pesticides you ingest?

Expert Perspective from the Field

Organic Foods and Local Food Systems

Nutrition, agriculture, access to food and water, food processing and preparation, public policy, personal health, and environmental quality are all interrelated. When these relationships are out of balance and practices are not sustainable, the quality, quantity, and future of our food and water supplies may be negatively affected. Concern about these interrelationships, as well as environmental quality and personal health, may affect food choices. For example, consumers are increasingly choosing organic foods because of personal and environmental health concerns.

According to Angie Tagtow,* a registered dietitian and sustainable food systems advocate, the most important reason for eating organic fruits and vegetables is to decrease exposure to pesticide residues. By consuming organic meat, dairy, and eggs, she notes, consumers avoid the antibiotics and synthetic hormones commonly used in conventional farming. Another benefit is that certified organic animals often are treated humanely and have access to pasture. Tagtow's own concerns about health and the environment have led her to seek locally grown organic food. The benefits of local food systems, where local farmers and producers grow and sell foods to local consumers, may include increased biodiversity of farm products, increased access to fresh food, decreased impact on the environment, and greater community economic development.[73]

Tagtow states that her vision of an ideal food system is one that provides food that is

- *Healthy*—food that has optimal nutritional value, is free of preservatives and additives, and does not promote the development of diet-related chronic diseases
- *Green*—food production that has no or low environmental impact, keeps ecosystems in balance, uses minimal nonrenewable energy (e.g., oil and coal), and recycles wastes
- *Fair*—food production that does not exploit anyone or anything, enables farmers to earn enough income to be economically self-sufficient, keeps local food systems economically sound, and contributes to the overall economic development of communities
- *Affordable and accessible*—food that is safe and nutritious, is produced in a sustainable manner, and is equally and regularly available to everyone

When asked for advice on how those with a limited budget can incorporate organically grown foods in their diets, Tagtow recommended identifying local organic farmers and buying fruits, vegetables, dairy, eggs, or meat directly from them. Visiting farmers' markets, food co-ops, Community Supported Agriculture (CSA) farms, or Cooperative Extension System websites can help consumers learn which foods are produced locally. Many CSA farms rely on volunteers during the growing season—this may provide those with limited budgets an opportunity to access high-quality, fresh food. To save money, she also recommends buying fresh food when it is in season.

Consumers who find it too costly to buy all organic foods may want to focus on specific foods. For instance, Tagtow pointed out that the foods with the highest pesticide residues are celery, peaches, strawberries, apples, blueberries, nectarines, bell peppers, spinach, cherries, kale, potatoes, and imported grapes—consumers concerned about pesticide residues may want to choose organic versions of these foods whenever they can. To learn more about local food systems and organic foods, visit the Leopold Center at www.leopold.iastate.edu; The Organic Center at www.organic-center.org; Local Harvest at www.localharvest.org; and the Organic Farming Research Foundation at ofrf.org.

*Angie Tagtow, MS, RD, LD, is a 2008–2009 Food and Society Policy Fellow, owner of Environmental Nutrition Solutions, managing editor of the Journal of Hunger & Environmental Nutrition, a member of the Academy of Nutrition and Dietetics' Sustainable Food System Task Force, past chair of the Hunger and Environmental Nutrition Dietetic Practice Group of the Academy of Nutrition and Dietetics, and a member of the Leopold Center for Sustainable Agriculture Regional Food System Working Group.

Summary

3.1 Food insecurity and hunger occur in virtually every country. About 1 billion people (1 in 6) worldwide do not get enough food to meet their requirements and another 2 billion suffer micronutrient deficiencies, especially of vitamin A, folate, zinc, iron, and iodine. Food insecurity is linked to poverty. Food-insecure people tend to have poorer diets and suffer more health problems. Children without enough food do not grow normally and are more likely to suffer diseases and death. In the U.S., the USDA monitors food insecurity. About 15% of U.S. households are food insecure, with a third of these having very low food security. The Supplemental Nutrition Assistance Program is the most important food-assistance program offered by the U.S. government. Other programs include WIC and the National School Lunch and Breakfast Programs. Emergency food programs also play an important role.

3.2 Organic foods are grown in ways that promote healthy soils, waterways, crops, and animals. Many substances and processes cannot be applied to organic foods. The USDA certifies foods as organic. Organic foods contain fewer pesticides but their nutritional value may not differ from conventionally grown food. Genetically modified (GM) foods have new or modified genes to produce a plant, an animal, or another organism with a new trait. The most common GM foods in the U.S. are soybeans, corn, and cotton altered either to be herbicide resistant or to produce their own pesticides. Other GM applications are used to increase milk production and to produce chymosin for cheese making. GM foods are regulated by the FDA, USDA, and EPA. Labeling of GM foods is not required. Many concerns have been voiced about GM foods, including the safety of these foods for people and the environment.

3.3 Food spoilage results from microorganism and enzyme action. Food-preservation methods stop or slow the rate of spoilage. Food irradiation is approved for some foods. Irradiated foods are not radioactive. Food additives are regulated by the FDA. Some food additives are considered GRAS and have not had formal testing. New food additives must be carefully tested by the manufacturer and evaluated by the FDA. Over 3000 food additives are approved for use in the U.S. Intentional food additives are used for a specific purpose, whereas incidental food additives become a part of food because of some aspect of production. Some people are concerned about the safety of food additives; however, no evidence shows that limiting additives will make you healthier. To lower your intake of additives, read food labels and eat fewer highly processed foods.

3.4 Foodborne pathogens are a significant cause of illness and death in the U.S. People more at risk are infants, children, the elderly, people with certain diseases, pregnant women, and those who have weakened immune systems. Foodborne illness usually causes gastrointestinal effects but can have more serious

lasting effects. Over 250 pathogens, including viruses, bacteria, parasites, and toxins, can cause foodborne illness, but most are caused by bacteria (*Salmonella, Campylobacter, Shigella,* and *E. coli*) and viruses. Meats, poultry, eggs, shellfish, dairy products, and fresh produce are often implicated in outbreaks of foodborne illness. Clean water is vital to good health. Public water supplies are regulated by the EPA and municipal water systems. Bottled water is regulated by the FDA. There are numerous threats to safe water, including chemical and microbial contamination.

3.5 Several government agencies, including the USDA, FDA, and CDC, are responsible for coordinating food safety efforts, but everyone has a responsibility for keeping food safe to eat. The risk of foodborne illness can be reduced by using good personal and kitchen hygiene, handling food safely, and avoiding foods that present extra risk. Washing hands, preventing cross-contamination, washing produce, keeping foods out of danger zone temperatures, and cooking meat, poultry, eggs, fish, and casseroles to safe temperatures are especially important. Cooked foods should be either consumed right away or refrigerated within 2 hours. Traveler's diarrhea is common in visitors to developing countries. Following guidelines about water and produce consumption can help reduce the likelihood of contracting traveler's diarrhea.

3.6 Environmental contaminants in food include lead, mercury, industrial contaminants (e.g., dioxins and polychlorinated biphenyls [PCBs]), pesticides, and antibiotics. Lead can damage the developing nervous system; children are most at risk. Iron-deficient children may be at more risk of lead toxicity. Dioxins can contaminate food, especially fish. They are carcinogens and cause liver and nerve damage. Mercury is found in fish, especially large fish such as shark, swordfish, king mackerel, and tilefish. The FDA and EPA recommend that children and pregnant and breastfeeding women limit their exposure to high-mercury fish. PCBs can be found in fish, too. Farmers use pesticides to increase agricultural productivity. Pesticides are regulated by the EPA, USDA, and FDA. Pesticides in foods are a special concern for young children. The widespread use of antibiotics in animal feed is a concern because they foster the growth of antibiotic-resistant bacteria.

110 **PART 1** Nutrition Basics

Study Questions

1. Which of the following is a sign of malnutrition caused by insufficient food and nutrient intake?

   a. stunted growth
   b. wasting (loss of fat and muscle tissue)
   c. vitamin and mineral deficiencies, especially vitamin A, iron, and iodine
   d. all of the above

2. About _____ of U.S. households are food insecure.

   a. 20%   c. 4%
   b. 15%   d. 1%

3. The Supplemental Nutrition Assistance Program benefits _____.

   a. only low-income women, infants, and children
   b. poor households that meet eligibility guidelines
   c. food banks and pantries in communities across the country
   d. seniors in adult day-care settings

4. Populations disproportionately affected by hunger and malnutrition include _____.

   a. preschool children and women
   b. working adults
   c. teenagers
   d. all of the above

5. Which of the following statements about organic foods is *not* true?

   a. They are more nutritious than conventionally raised foods.
   b. Synthetic fertilizers, pesticides, antibiotics, synthetic hormones, and sewage sludge are prohibited in their production.
   c. A food labeled organic must have 95% of its ingredients by weight meet organic standards.
   d. The USDA is responsible for organic certification of farms and foods.

6. The main use of genetically modified foods in the U.S. food supply is to _____.

   a. improve nutritional quality by the production of additional amounts of beta-carotene
   b. eliminate potential allergens by altering the proteins synthesized in the plant or animal
   c. produce pharmaceutical products in an inexpensive way
   d. improve pest control and weed management and protect crops against diseases

7. In the U.S., food labels must indicate the presence of genetically modified ingredients.

   a. true   b. false

8. Which of the following statements about food irradiation is true?

   a. Irradiated food is radioactive.
   b. Irradiation can be used to destroy pathogens in food, such as *Salmonella* bacteria.
   c. All foods in the U.S. legally can be irradiated.
   d. Irradiation is used in only 2 countries around the world.

9. Food additive use and safety are regulated mainly by the _____.

   a. FDA   c. CDC
   b. USDA   d. EPA

10. Which of the following pathogens cause the most foodborne illness in the U.S.?

    a. Hepatitis A, *Clostridium botulinum, Listeria monocytogenes,* and *Staphylococcus aureus*
    b. *Campylobacter jejuni, Cryptosporidium, Aspergillus,* and *Clostridium botulinum*
    c. *Cryptosporidium,* hepatitis A, *Clostridium perfringens,* and *Salmonella*
    d. *Salmonella, Campylobacter jejuni, Shigella,* and noroviruses

11. Aflatoxin is produced by a mold that grows most often on _____.

    a. cheese
    b. bread products
    c. peanuts and corn
    d. fruit and other produce

12. The temperature danger zone is _____.

    a. 41° to 135°F (5° to 57°C)
    b. 32° to 40°F (0° to 4°C)
    c. 120° to 160°F (48° to 71°C)
    d. 0° to 212°F (0° to 100°C)

13. Thawing foods, such as chicken, on the counter overnight is a safe food-handling practice.

    a. true
    b. false

14. Which of the following statements about pesticides is *not* true?

    a. Organic foods sometimes contain very low amounts of pesticides.
    b. Some pesticides can persist in the environment for many years.
    c. Washing produce removes all pesticide residues.
    d. The EPA regulates the type and amount of pesticides that may be applied to food.

15. The food most likely to contain mercury, dioxins, or PCBs is _____.

    a. water from plumbing in older homes
    b. vegetables and fruits grown with pesticides
    c. fish from rivers, streams, and lakes
    d. milk from transgenic dairy cattle

16. Describe how the U.S. food security "safety net" protects people against food insecurity.

17. List the potential advantages and disadvantages of genetically modified foods.

18. Describe intentional, incidental, and GRAS food additives.

19. Describe the types of microbial pathogens that cause foodborne illness.

20. Create a checklist you could use at home for keeping foods safe.

21. Explain how you can minimize exposure to foods contaminated with environmental toxins.

Answer Key: 1-d; 2-b; 3-b; 4-a; 5-a; 6-d; 7-b; 8-b; 9-a; 10-d; 11-c; 12-a; 13-b; 14-c; 15-c; 16-refer to Section 3.1; 17-refer to Section 3.2; 18-refer to Section 3.3; 19-refer to Section 3.4; 20-refer to Section 3.5; 21-refer to Section 3.6

Websites

To learn more about the topics covered in this chapter, visit these websites.

Major USDA Food Assistance Programs

Supplemental Nutrition Assistance Program

www.fns.usda.gov/snap

Special Supplemental Nutrition Program for Women, Infants, and Children (WIC)

www.fns.usda.gov/wic

National School Lunch Program

www.fns.usda.gov/cnd/lunch

National School Breakfast Program

www.fns.usda.gov/cnd/breakfast

Child- and Adult-Care Food Programs

www.fns.usda.gov/cnd/Care

Food Insecurity and Hunger

www.bread.org

www.feedingamerica.org

www.foodsecurity.org

www.frac.org

www.ers.usda.gov/briefing/foodsecurity

www.whyhunger.org

Food Additives

www.fda.gov/Food/FoodIngredientsPackaging

www.food-info.net/uk/colour/cochineal.htm

Water Safety

www.EPA.gov/water

Food Safety

www.foodsafety.gov

www.homefoodsafety.org

www.fightbac.org

wwwnc.cdc.gov/travel

www.epa.gov/waterscience/fish

Government Agencies

www.cdc.gov

www.fsis.usda.gov

www.nal.usda.gov

www.atf.gov/alcohol-tobacco

www.epa.gov

www.fda.gov

www.nmfs.noaa.gov

References

1. Food and Agriculture Organization, United Nations. The state of food insecurity in the world 2011. 2012; www.fao.org.

2. Popkin BM and others. Global nutrition transition and the pandemic of obesity in developing countries. *Nutr Rev.* 2012; 70:3.

3. Keys A. *The biology of human starvation.* Minneapolis: University of Minnesota Press; 1950.

4. Investing in the future. A united call to action on vitamin and mineral deficiencies. Global report summary 2009. www.unitedcalltoaction.org.

5. Hampton T. Food insecurity harms health, well-being of millions in the United States. *JAMA.* 2007;298:1851.

6. Holben DH. Position of the American Dietetic Association: Food insecurity in the United States. *J Am Diet Assoc.* 2010;110:1368.

7. Cook J and others. Child food insecurity increases risks posed by household food insecurity to young children's health. *J Nutr.* 2006;136:1073.

8. Kirpatrick S and others. Child hunger and long-term adverse consequences for health. *Arch Pediatr Adolesc Med.* 2010;164:754.

9. Alaimo K and others. Food insufficiency and American school-aged children's cognitive, academic and psychosocial development. *Pediatrics.* 2001;108:44.

10. Seligman HK and others. Food insecurity is associated with chronic disease among low income NHANES participants. *J Nutr.* 2010;140:304.

11. Miech R and others. Trends in the association of poverty with overweight among US adolescents, 1971–2004. *JAMA.* 2006;295:2385.

12. Franklin B and others. Exploring mediators of food insecurity and obesity: a review of recent literature. *J Community Health* 2012;37:253.

13. Nord M and others. Household food security in the United States, 2009. ERR-108, U.S. Department of Agriculture, Economic Research Service: 2010.

14. U.S. Department of Health and Human Services. The 2009 HHS poverty guidelines. 2009; aspe.hhs.gov/poverty/09poverty.shtml.

15. Economic Research Service, U.S. Department of Agriculture. The food assistance landscape annual report. 2009; www.ers.usda.gov/media/142369/eib6-7_1.pdf.

16. Feeding America. Hunger report 2010. www.feedingamerica.org.

17. Black RE and others. Maternal and child undernutrition: Global and regional exposures and health consequences. *Lancet.* 2008;371:243.

18. United Nations Children's Fund (UNICEF). The state of the world's children, 2008. Women and children: Child survival. 2008; www.unicef.org/sowc08.

19. Godfray HCJ and others. Food security: The challenge of feeding 9 billion people. *Science.* 2010;327:812.

20. Pinstrup-Andersen P, Cheng F. Still hungry. *Scientific Am.* 2007;297(3):96.

21. United Nations. UN millennium development goals. 2009; www.un.org/millenniumgoals.

22. Organic Trade Association. U.S. organic product sales reach 26.6 billion in 2009. 2010; www.organicnewsroom.com.

23. Agriculture Market Service, U.S. Department of Agriculture. National Organic Program. 2008; www.ams.usda.gov/NOP/indexIE.htm.

24. Williamson CS. Is organic food better for our health? *Nutr Bulletin.* 2007;32:104.

25. Dangour AD and others. Nutrition-related health effects of organic foods: A systematic review. *Am J Clin Nutr.* 2010;92:203.

26. Mitchell AE and others. Ten-year comparison of the influence of organic and conventional crop management practices on the content of flavonoids in tomatoes. *J Agric Food Chem.* 2007;55:6154.

27. Raney T, Prabhu P. Sowing a gene revolution. *Scientific Am.* 2007;297(3):104.

28. James C. *Brief 41: Global status of commercialized biotech/GM crops: 2009.* Ithaca, NY: International Service for the Acquisition of Agri-biotech Applications; 2009.

29. Economic Research Service, U.S. Department of Agriculture. Agricultural biotechnology. 2010; www.ers.usda.gov/Briefing/Biotechnology.

30. U.S. Food and Drug Administration. Genetically engineered animals. 2010; www.fda.gov/AnimalVeterinary/DevelopmentApprovalProcess/GeneticEngineering/GeneticallyEngineeredAnimals/default.htm.

31. Devlin RH and others. Population effects of growth hormone transgenic coho salmon depend on food availability and genotype by environment interactions. *Proc National Acad Sci.* 2004;101:9303.

32. Rowlands MA and others. Circulating insulin-like growth factor peptides and prostate cancer risk: A systematic review and meta-analysis. *Int J Cancer.* 2009;124:2416.

33. Tang G and others. Golden rice is an effective source of vitamin A. *Am J Clin Nutr.* 2009;89:1776.

34. U.S. Food and Drug Administration, Center for Veterinary Medicine. CVM and animal cloning. 2008; www.fda.gov/cvm/cloning.htm.

35. Osterholm M, Norgan A. The role of food irradiation in food safety. *New Eng J Med.* 2004;350:1898.

36. U.S. Department of Agriculture Food Safety and Inspection Service. Irradiation and food safety. Answers to frequently asked questions. 2005; www.fsis.usda.gov/Fact_Sheets/Irradiation_and_Food_Safety/index.asp.

37. O'Bryan CA and others. Impact of irradiation on the safety and quality of poultry and meat products: A review. *Crit Rev Food Sci Nutr.* 2008;48:442.

38. Palmer S. Irradiation: What it is, what it does, and how it affects the food supply. *Today's Dietitian.* 2009;11(1):32.

39. U.S. Food and Drug Administration Office for Food Safety and Applied Nutrition. Data on benzene in soft drinks and other beverages. 2007; www.fda.gov/Food/FoodborneillnessContaminants/ChemicalContaminants/ucm055815.htm.

40. Lang IA and others. Association of urinary bisphenol: A concentration with medical disorders and laboratory abnormalities in adults. *JAMA.* 2008;300:1303.

41. Ames B and others. Ranking possible carcinogenic hazards. *Science.* 1987;236:271.

42. Soffriti M and others. Life-span exposure to low doses of aspartame beginning during prenatal life increases cancer effects in human. *Environ Health Perspect.* 2007;115:1293.

43. Magnuson BA and others. Aspartame: A safety evaluation based on current use levels, regulations, and toxicological and epidemiological studies. *Crit Rev Toxic*. 2007;37:629.

44. McCann D and others. Food additives and hyperactive behaviour in 3-year-old and 8/9 year-old children in the community: A randomised, double-blinded, placebo controlled trial. *Lancet*. 2007;350:1560.

45. Scallan E and others. Foodborne illness acquired in the United States—Major pathogens. *Emerg Infect Dis*. 2011;17:7.

46. Scallan E and others. Foodborne illness acquired in the United States—Unspecified agents. *Emerg Infect Dis*. 2011;17:16.

47. World Health Organization. Food safety and foodborne illness, fact sheet no 237. 2007; www.who.int/mediacentre/factsheets/fs237/en.

48. Scharff RL. Health-related costs for foodborne illness in the United States. 2010; www.producesafetyproject.org/reports?id=0008.

49. Jungk J and others. Outbreak of Salmonella Saintpaul infections associated with multiple raw produce items—United States, 2008. *MMWR*. 2008;57:929.

50. Centers for Disease Control and Prevention. Avian influenza (bird flu). 2008; www.cdc.gov/flu/avian.

51. Karanis P and others. Waterborne transmission of protozoan parasites: A worldwide review of outbreaks and lessons learnt. *J Water Health*. 2007;5(1):1.

52. Centers for Disease Control and Prevention. vCJD (variant Creutzfeldt-Jakob disease). 2010; www.cdc.gov/ncidod/dvrd/vcjd/factsheet_nvcjd.htm.

53. Centers for Disease Control and Prevention. BSE (bovine spongiform encephalopathy, or mad cow disease). 2010; www.cdc.gov/ncidod/dvrd/bse/index.htm.

54. Taylor SL. Food additives, contaminants and natural toxicants. In: Shils M and others, eds. *Modern nutrition in health and disease*. 10th ed. Baltimore: Lippincott Williams & Wilkins; 2006.

55. Environmental Protection Agency. Drinking water. 2009; www.epa.gov/ebtpages/watedrinkingwater.html.

56. Yoder J and others. Surveillance for waterborne disease and outbreaks associated with drinking water and water not intended for drinking: United States, 2005–2006. *MMWR*. 2009;57(SS09):39.

57. U.S. Food and Drug Administration. Questions and answers: Raw milk. 2010; www.fda.gov/Food/FoodSafety/ProductSpecificInformation/MilkSafety.

58. Marler B. Outbreaks, illnesses, and recalls, linked to raw (unpasteurized) dairy products, United States, 2010 (through July 23, 2010). 2010; www.marlerblog.com.

59. Tuteja AK and others. Development of functional diarrhea, constipation, irritable bowel syndrome, and dyspepsia during and after traveling outside the USA. *Digest Dis Sci*. 2008;53:271.

60. Meyer PA and others. Surveillance for elevated blood lead levels among children: United States, 1997–2001. *MMWR*. 2003;52(SS10):1.

61. Saper RB and others. Heavy metal content of Ayurvedic herbal medicine products. *JAMA*. 2004;292:2868.

62. Zimmermann MB and others. Iron fortification reduces blood lead levels in children in Bangalore, India. *Pediatrics*. 2006;117:2014.

63. Mozaffarian D, Rimm EB. Fish intake, contaminants and human health. *JAMA*. 2006;296:1885.

64. Environmental Protection Agency. Pesticides. 2010; www.epa.gov/pesticides.

65. National Research Council. *Pesticides in the diets of infants and children*. Washington, DC: National Academy Press; 1993.

66. U.S. Department of Agriculture. Pesticide Data Program—Progress report. 2009; www.ams.usda.gov/science/pdp.

67. Agricultural Health Study. Publications. 2010; aghealth.nci.nih.gov/publications.html.

68. Sanbourn M and others. *Pesticides literature review: Systematic review of pesticides human health effects*. Ontario, Canada: Ontario College of Physicians; 2004.

69. Grandjean P and others. The Faroes statement: Human health effects of developmental exposure to chemicals in our environment. *Basic Clin Pharmacol Tox*. 2007;102:73.

70. Lu C and others. Organic diets significantly lower children's exposure to organophosphorus pesticides. *Environ Health Perspect*. 2006;114:260.

71. Mellon M and others. Hogging it: Estimates of antimicrobial abuse in livestock. 2001; www.ucsusa.org/food_and_environment/antibiotics_and_food/hogging-it-estimates-of-antimicrobial-abuse-in-livestock.html.

72. Food and Drug Administration. Center for Veterinary Medicine. The judicious use of medically important antibiotics in food-producing animals. 2010; www.fda.gov/AnimalVeterinary/default.htm.

73. Swenson D. The economic impact of fruit and vegetable production in Iowa. 2006; www.leopold.iastate.edu/pubs-and-papers/2006-05-fruit-and-vegetable-production-phase-two.

74. U.S. Department of Agriculture. Cooking meat? Check the new recommended temperatures. 2011; www.foodsafety.gov/blog/meat_temperatures.html.

75. Jana N and others. Current use of medical eponyms—a need for global uniformity in scientific publications. *BMC Med Res Method*. 2009;9:18.

The stomach has millions of tiny gastric pits like this. The pits produce mucus to protect the stomach and glands at the bottom of the pits secrete digestive juices (see Fig. 4-12). After a person eats, the muscles in the stomach contract and cause the pits to squirt their contents into the stomach and begin digesting food. Learn more at **digestive.niddk.nih.gov**.

4   *Human Digestion and Absorption*

Student Learning Outcomes

After studying this chapter, you will be able to

1. Outline the roles played by the gastrointestinal tract and the related accessory organs (liver, gallbladder, and pancreas) in digestion and absorption.

2. Describe how foods are moved along the digestive tract.

3. Explain the 4 main types of absorption.

4. Identify the key enzymes and hormones involved in digestion and absorption, as well as their functions.

5. Identify major nutrition-related gastrointestinal diseases and disorders and typical approaches to prevention and treatment.

6. Explain why diarrhea represents a serious health challenge to infants and young children around the world.

EARLY KNOWLEDGE OF DIGESTIVE PHYSIOLOGY came from a surprising source—"the man with a hole in his stomach." In 1822, a fur trapper, Alexis St. Martin, was accidentally hit by a shotgun blast. The blast wound to his stomach never closed completely, allowing an opportunity for William Beaumont, a U.S. Army physician, to study for several years how foods are digested. For example, he lowered food tied to string through the hole in St. Martin's stomach and then periodically removed it to observe changes. Beaumont learned that the stomach releases its secretions in response to food in the stomach, rather than building up secretions between meals, as was commonly believed. He also discovered that the stomach secretions contain not only acid but also a substance that allows meat to be digested. We now know this substance as the digestive enzyme pepsin. Beaumont also observed that, when his subject was distressed or angry, digestion was impaired. Throughout his life, St. Martin remained in poor health, but he lived almost 60 years after the shooting accident.

Since the time of Beaumont and St. Martin, scientists have continued to study how the digestive system functions and the many digestive system disorders and diseases. This chapter will explore the processes of digestion and absorption and the related aspects of human physiology that support nutritional health. You will become acquainted with the basic anatomy (structure) and physiology (function) of the digestive system. You also will learn the causes of some common digestive system disorders, along with ways to prevent and manage them.

116 **PART 1** Nutrition Basics

4.1 Organization of the Human Body

The cell is the smallest functional unit of the human body. (Appendix A reviews the parts of a cell.) The body's 10 trillion cells have the ability to grow; take in (absorb) substances, including nutrients; use energy; synthesize and secrete new compounds; and excrete waste. Cellular processes and chemical reactions, which occur constantly in every living cell, require a continuous supply of energy in the form of dietary carbohydrate, protein, and fat. Almost all cells need oxygen to transform the energy in nutrients into the form the body can use—**adenosine triphosphate (ATP)** (see Chapter 9 for more on ATP). Cells also need water, building materials (e.g., amino acids and minerals), and chemical regulators (e.g., vitamins). Of course, adequately supplying all nutrients to the body's cells begins with a healthful diet.

Cells of the same type join together to form tissue (Fig. 4-1). **Tissue** is made of groups of similar cells working together to perform a specific task. Humans are composed of 4 primary types of tissue: epithelial, connective, muscle, and nervous.

- **Epithelial tissue** is composed of cells that cover surfaces outside and inside the body. The skin and linings of the gastrointestinal (GI) tract are examples. Epithelial cells absorb nutrients, secrete important substances, excrete waste, and protect underlying tissues.
- **Connective tissue** supports and protects the body by holding structures (e.g., cells and cell parts) together, stores fat, and produces blood cells. Tendons, cartilage, and parts of bone, arteries, and veins are made of connective tissue.
- **Muscle tissue** can contract and relax and permits movement.
- **Nervous tissue,** found in the brain and spinal cord, transmits nerve impulses from one part of the body to another.

adenosine triphosphate (ATP) Chemical that supplies energy for many cellular processes and reactions.

tissue Collection of cells adapted to perform a specific function.

organ A structure (e.g., heart, kidney, or eye) consisting of cells and tissues that perform a specific function in an organism.

organ system Group of organs classified as a unit because they work together to perform a function or set of functions.

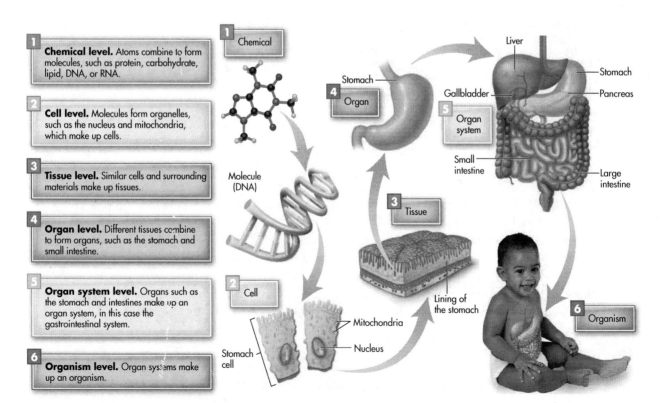

1 **Chemical level.** Atoms combine to form molecules, such as protein, carbohydrate, lipid, DNA, or RNA.

2 **Cell level.** Molecules form organelles, such as the nucleus and mitochondria, which make up cells.

3 **Tissue level.** Similar cells and surrounding materials make up tissues.

4 **Organ level.** Different tissues combine to form organs, such as the stomach and small intestine.

5 **Organ system level.** Organs such as the stomach and intestines make up an organ system, in this case the gastrointestinal system.

6 **Organism level.** Organ systems make up an organism.

Figure 4-1 The levels of organization of the human body are chemical, cell, tissue, organ, organ system, and organism. Each level is more complex than the previous level. The organ system shown is the digestive system.

Tissues combine in a specific way to form structures, known as **organs,** which perform specific functions. All organs play a role in nutritional health, and nutrient intake affects how well each organ functions. An **organ system** is formed when several organs work together to perform a specific function. For example, the digestive system includes the GI tract (mouth, esophagus, stomach, small intestine, and large intestine, which terminates with the rectum and anus), liver, pancreas, and gallbladder (Fig. 4-2). The coordinated work of all organ systems allows the entire body to function normally. Table 4-1 summarizes the components and functions of the body's organ systems.

The primary theme of human nutrition is to understand how nutrients affect different cells, tissues, organs, organ systems, and finally overall health. This chapter focuses on the digestive system. Learning how the digestive system makes nutrients in foods available to body organs, tissues, and cells is critical to understanding human nutrition.

Knowledge Check

1. What is the form of energy that can be used by almost all cells?
2. Which tissue type covers the surfaces that are both outside and inside the body?
3. What are the main organ systems of the body?

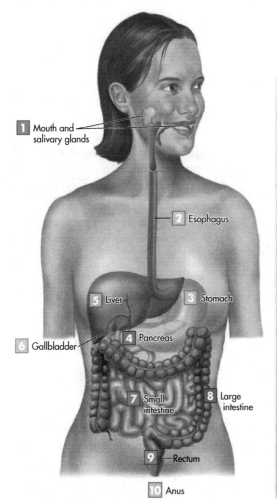

1. Mouth and salivary glands
2. Esophagus
5. Liver
3. Stomach
6. Gallbladder
4. Pancreas
7. Small intestine
8. Large intestine
9. Rectum
10. Anus

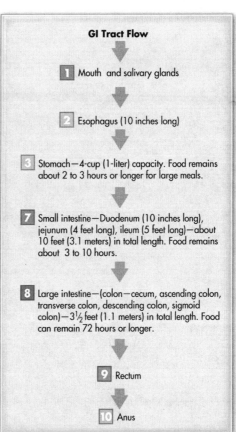

GI Tract Flow

1. Mouth and salivary glands

2. Esophagus (10 inches long)

3. Stomach—4-cup (1-liter) capacity. Food remains about 2 to 3 hours or longer for large meals.

7. Small intestine—Duodenum (10 inches long), jejunum (4 feet long), ileum (5 feet long)—about 10 feet (3.1 meters) in total length. Food remains about 3 to 10 hours.

8. Large intestine—(colon—cecum, ascending colon, transverse colon, descending colon, sigmoid colon)—3½ feet (1.1 meters) in total length. Food can remain 72 hours or longer.

9. Rectum

10. Anus

Figure 4-2 Major organs of the gastrointestinal (GI) tract (1, 2, 3, 7, 8, and 9) and accessory organs (4, 5, and 6) used in digestion and the absorption of nutrients.

Table 4-1 Organ Systems of the Body

Digestive System

Major components: mouth, esophagus, stomach, intestines, and accessory organs (liver, gallbladder, and pancreas)

Functions: performs the mechanical and chemical processes of digestion of food, absorption of nutrients, and elimination of wastes

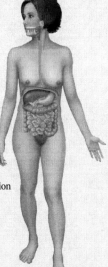

Nervous System

Major components: brain, spinal cord, nerves, and sensory receptors

Functions: detects and interprets sensation; controls movements and physiological and intellectual functions

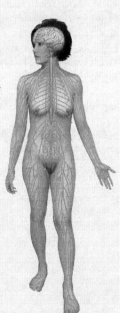

Cardiovascular System

Major cardiovascular components: heart, blood vessels, and blood

Functions: carries blood and regulates blood supply; transports nutrients, waste products, hormones, and gases (oxygen and carbon dioxide) throughout the body; and regulates blood pressure

Endocrine System

Major components: endocrine glands, such as the pituitary, thyroid, and adrenal glands; hypothalamus; and pancreas

Functions: regulates metabolism, growth, reproduction, and many other functions by producing and releasing hormones

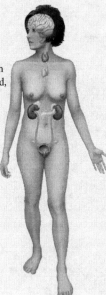

Lymphatic and Immune Systems

Major lymphatic components: lymph, lymphocytes, lymphatic vessels, and lymph nodes

Major immune components: mechanical (e.g., skin), chemical (e.g., lysozyme), and cellular (e.g., white blood cells)

Lymphatic functions: aids in fluid balance, fat absorption and transport, and immune functions

Immune functions: protects against microorganisms and other foreign substances

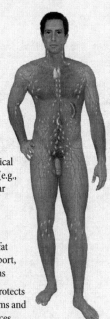

Urinary System

Major components: kidneys, urinary bladder, and the ducts that carry urine

Functions: removes waste products from the blood and forms urine; regulates blood acid-base (pH) balance, overall chemical balance, and water balance

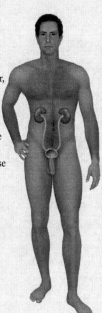

Table 4-1 Continued

Integumentary System

Major components: skin, hair, nails, and sweat glands

Functions: protects the body, regulates body temperature, prevents water loss, and produces vitamin D

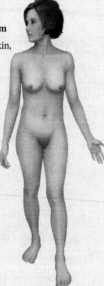

Skeletal System

Major components: bones, cartilage, ligaments, and joints

Functions: protects organs, supports body weight, allows body movement, produces blood cells, and stores minerals

Muscular System

Major components: smooth, cardiac, and skeletal muscle

Functions: produces body movement, heartbeat, and body heat; propels food in the digestive tract; and maintains posture

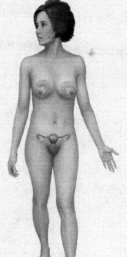

Respiratory System

Major components: lungs and respiratory passages

Functions: exchanges gases (oxygen and carbon dioxide) between the blood and the air; regulates blood acid-base (pH) balance

Reproductive System

Major components: gonads (ovaries and testes) and genitals

Functions: performs the processes of sexual maturation and reproduction; influences sexual functions and behaviors

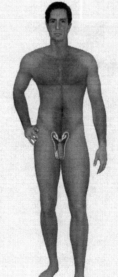

The cardiovascular and lymphatic organ systems together make up the circulatory system and so contribute to circulatory functions in the body. The lymphatic system is part of the immune system. The endocrine and nervous organ systems contribute to the regulatory functions. The digestive, urinary, integumentary, and respiratory organ systems contribute to the excretory functions, whereas the muscular and skeletal organ systems contribute to storage abilities in the body.

120 **PART 1** Nutrition Basics

4.2 Digestive System Overview

Digestion, the process of breaking down foods into a form the body can use, and absorption, the uptake of nutrients from the GI tract into either the blood or the lymph, are accomplished by the digestive system. Figure 4-3 provides an overview of the functions of the organs of the digestive system. All of the nutrients found in foods—proteins, fats, carbohydrates, vitamins, minerals, and water—are made ready for use in the body's cells by the digestive system. About 29 cups (7 liters) of fluid containing water, mucus, acid, digestive enzymes, bile, and hormones are secreted into the GI tract each day to assist with the processes of digestion and absorption. Finally, at the end of the GI tract, the excretion of

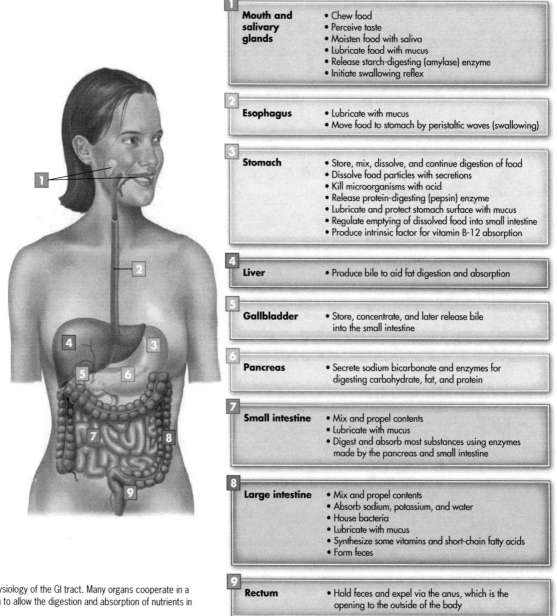

Organ	Digestive Functions
1 Mouth and salivary glands	• Chew food • Perceive taste • Moisten food with saliva • Lubricate food with mucus • Release starch-digesting (amylase) enzyme • Initiate swallowing reflex
2 Esophagus	• Lubricate with mucus • Move food to stomach by peristaltic waves (swallowing)
3 Stomach	• Store, mix, dissolve, and continue digestion of food • Dissolve food particles with secretions • Kill microorganisms with acid • Release protein-digesting (pepsin) enzyme • Lubricate and protect stomach surface with mucus • Regulate emptying of dissolved food into small intestine • Produce intrinsic factor for vitamin B-12 absorption
4 Liver	• Produce bile to aid fat digestion and absorption
5 Gallbladder	• Store, concentrate, and later release bile into the small intestine
6 Pancreas	• Secrete sodium bicarbonate and enzymes for digesting carbohydrate, fat, and protein
7 Small intestine	• Mix and propel contents • Lubricate with mucus • Digest and absorb most substances using enzymes made by the pancreas and small intestine
8 Large intestine	• Mix and propel contents • Absorb sodium, potassium, and water • House bacteria • Lubricate with mucus • Synthesize some vitamins and short-chain fatty acids • Form feces
9 Rectum	• Hold feces and expel via the anus, which is the opening to the outside of the body

Figure 4-3 Physiology of the GI tract. Many organs cooperate in a regulated fashion to allow the digestion and absorption of nutrients in foods.

waste matter occurs in a convenient, voluntary process. Like many other processes, such as breathing and the beating of the heart, digestion and absorption are carefully controlled by hormones and the nervous system.

    In addition to its main functions of digestion and absorption, the GI tract also has an important role in the body's immune system. Bacteria, viruses, and other microorganisms are continually introduced into the body with the food we eat. The GI tract is a physical barrier to the entry of these microorganisms into the body, and it produces a host of immune components, such as antibodies, lymphocytes, and macrophages, that destroy microorganisms in the gut. Further, healthy bacteria in the large intestine help keep pathogenic (disease-causing) bacteria under control. They also synthesize nutrients, such as folate, vitamin K, and biotin, along with short-chain fatty acids, which can serve as an energy source for the large intestine.

> **alimentary canal** Tubular portion of the digestive tract that extends from the mouth to the anus. The word *alimentary* means "relating to nourishment or nutrition."
>
> **sphincter** Muscular valve that controls the flow of foodstuffs in the alimentary canal.

Anatomy of the GI Tract

The GI tract, also known as the **alimentary canal,** is a long, hollow, muscular tube that extends almost 15 feet from mouth to anus. Nutrients must pass through the wall of this tube to be absorbed into the body. The wall consists of 4 layers (Fig. 4-4):

Figure 4-4 The wall of the intestinal tract consists of 4 layers: mucosa, submucosa, muscle, and serosa.

- Mucosa, the innermost layer, is lined with epithelial cells and glands. The mucosa is not smooth and in some areas has tiny, fingerlike structures that project into the hollow interior of the tube known as the **lumen.** These projections increase the surface area of the mucosa.
- Submucosa, the second layer, consists of loose connective tissue, glands, blood vessels, and nerves. The blood vessels carry substances, including nutrients, both to and from the GI tract.
- Muscle, the next layer, occurs as double layers in most parts of the GI tract: an inner layer of circular smooth muscle that encircles the tube and an outer layer of longitudinal muscle fibers that runs up and down the tube. These muscles move food forward through the GI tract. The stomach has a third layer of muscle fiber running diagonally around it.
- Serosa, the outermost layer, protects the GI tract. The serosa secretes fluid that cushions the GI tract and reduces friction as it and other organs move.

    Along the GI tract are **sphincters,** ringlike muscles that open and close like valves to control the flow of the contents (Fig. 4-5). The sphincters prevent food from moving through

Figure 4-5 Sphincters of the GI tract. These circular muscles control the flow of contents through the GI tract. They open and close in response to stimuli from nerves, hormones, hormonelike compounds, and pressure that builds up around the sphincters.

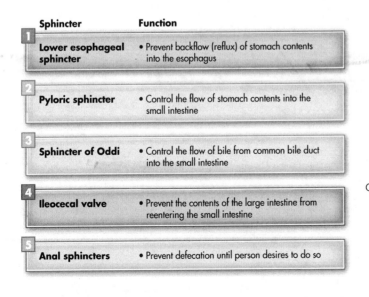

Sphincter	Function
1 Lower esophageal sphincter	• Prevent backflow (reflux) of stomach contents into the esophagus
2 Pyloric sphincter	• Control the flow of stomach contents into the small intestine
3 Sphincter of Oddi	• Control the flow of bile from common bile duct into the small intestine
4 Ileocecal valve	• Prevent the contents of the large intestine from reentering the small intestine
5 Anal sphincters	• Prevent defecation until person desires to do so

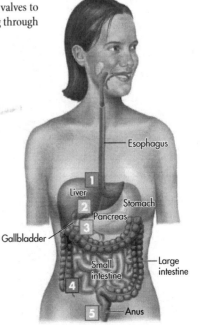

122   **PART 1**   Nutrition Basics

Figure 4-6 Peristalsis and segmentation. (a) Peristalsis is a coordinated wave of contraction and relaxation that moves the bolus (chewed food) ahead of the wave through the GI tract toward the anus. (b) Segmentation is a back-and-forth action in the small intestine that breaks apart the bolus into increasingly smaller pieces and mixes them with digestive juices.

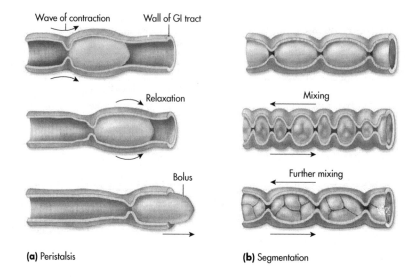

Wave of contraction   Wall of GI tract

Relaxation

Mixing

Bolus

Further mixing

(a) Peristalsis   **(b)** Segmentation

the GI tract too quickly. This allows food in the GI tract to be mixed thoroughly with digestive system secretions. The sphincters also help propel food through the GI tract.

GI Motility: Mixing and Propulsion

Food is mixed with digestive secretions and propelled down the GI tract by a process called peristalsis. A snake swallowing its prey graphically illustrates the process. Recall that most of the GI tract has 2 layers of muscles—circular and longitudinal. Peristalsis consists of a coordinated wave of contraction (squeezing and shortening) and relaxation of these muscles (Fig. 4-6). This process begins in the esophagus as 2 waves of muscle action closely following each other. The thickest and strongest muscles of the GI tract are in the stomach, where the contraction of 3 opposing muscle layers promotes complete mixing and churning of food and gastric juices. This contraction occurs as often as 3 times per minute after a meal.

The most frequent peristalsis takes place in the small intestine, where contractions occur about every 4 to 5 seconds. The small intestine also experiences segmental contractions (segmentation), which move the intestinal contents back and forth, causing the contents to break apart and mix with digestive juices. The large intestine has comparatively sluggish peristaltic waves. These lead to occasional mass movements, which are peristaltic waves that simultaneously coordinate contractions over a widespread area of the large intestine. Mass movements propel fecal matter from one part of the large intestine to the next and finally into the rectum for elimination.

Vomiting reverses the normal digestive tract flow. Vomiting, controlled by the vomiting center in the brain, is triggered by toxins in the gastrointestinal tract, rapid changes in body position, and stomach distension.

Digestive System Secretions

Throughout the GI tract, many secretions that aid in digestion are released. Digestive tract secretions include saliva, mucus, hydrochloric acid, **digestive enzymes,** hormones, bicarbonate, and bile (Table 4-2).

Saliva, from salivary glands in the mouth, moistens food and begins the process of digestion. Mucus and digestive enzymes are secreted in the mouth, stomach, and small intestine and by the pancreas. Mucus is a thick fluid that protects body cells and lubricates digesting food to help it move smoothly along the GI tract. Digestive enzymes are

▶ Hunger pangs are strong, somewhat uncomfortable peristaltic contractions that usually occur several hours after the last meal.

▶ The naming system for many enzymes is quite simple. The first part of the enzyme name usually indicates the target and is followed by the suffix *-ase.* For instance, sucrase is the enzyme that digests the sugar sucrose; similarly, lactase digests lactose.

▶ In cystic fibrosis, the most common lethal inherited genetic disease in white populations, thick, sticky mucus builds up in organs, especially the lungs and pancreas. This buildup prevents pancreatic enzymes from reaching the small intestine. If the condition is not treated, malabsorption of nutrients, weight loss, and malnutrition occur. Most individuals with cystic fibrosis are prescribed pancreatic enzyme replacements, which are taken right before eating. An enteric coating protects the enzymes from destruction by stomach acid. Maintaining good nutritional status helps prevent the respiratory infections common in those with cystic fibrosis.

digestive enzymes Compounds that aid in the breakdown of carbohydrates, fats, and proteins.

protein molecules that speed up digestion by catalyzing chemical reactions. Catalysis brings certain molecules close together and then creates a favorable environment for the chemical reaction. (Appendix B provides details on enzyme action.) Digestive enzymes catalyze chemical reactions known as **hydrolysis reactions.** In these reactions, water (*hydro-*) breaks apart (*-lysis*) molecules that are too large to pass through the GI tract wall. Hydrolysis reactions eventually yield simple molecules that are small enough to be absorbed through the intestinal wall. For example, sucrose (table sugar) is unabsorbable because it is too large to pass through the GI tract wall. In Figure 4-7, you can see how a molecule of the sugar sucrose is hydrolyzed to form the smaller glucose and fructose molecules, both of which can be absorbed through the intestinal wall.

Table 4-2 **Important Secretions of the Digestive System**

Secretion	Sites of Production	Functions
Saliva	Mouth	Contributes to starch digestion, lubrication, swallowing
Mucus	Mouth, stomach, small and large intestines	Protects GI tract cells, lubricates digesting food
Enzymes (amylases, lipases, proteases)	Mouth, stomach, small intestine, pancreas	Breaks down carbohydrates, fats, and protein into forms small enough for absorption
Acid (HCl)	Stomach	Promotes digestion of protein, destroys microorganisms, increases solubility of minerals
Bile	Liver (stored in gallbladder)	Aids in fat digestion (emulsifies fat)
Bicarbonate	Pancreas, small intestine	Neutralizes stomach acid when it reaches small intestine
Hormones	Stomach, small intestine, pancreas	Regulates digestion and absorption

Digestive enzymes aid mostly in the breakdown of carbohydrates, proteins, and fats. Each enzyme usually acts on a specific substance; for example, an enzyme that recognizes sucrose ignores lactose (milk sugar). Notice in Figure 4-7 that the sucrase enzyme hydrolyzes sucrose.

The mouth and the stomach make a few digestive enzymes. Most, however, are synthesized by the pancreas and small intestine (Chapters 5, 6, and 7 review these enzymes in detail). The pancreas adjusts its enzyme production to match the macronutrient content of the diet. Increased protein intake results in an increase in protein-digesting enzymes.

hydrolysis reaction Chemical reaction that breaks down a compound by adding water. One product receives a hydrogen ion (H⁺); the other product receives a hydroxyl ion (OH⁻). Hydrolytic enzymes break down compounds using water in this manner.

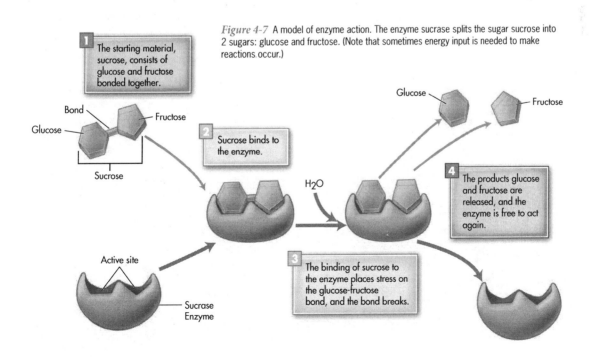

Figure 4-7 A model of enzyme action. The enzyme sucrase splits the sugar sucrose into 2 sugars: glucose and fructose. (Note that sometimes energy input is needed to make reactions occur.)

1. The starting material, sucrose, consists of glucose and fructose bonded together.

2. Sucrose binds to the enzyme.

3. The binding of sucrose to the enzyme places stress on the glucose-fructose bond, and the bond breaks.

4. The products glucose and fructose are released, and the enzyme is free to act again.

Bond
Glucose
Fructose
Sucrose
Active site
Sucrase Enzyme
H_2O
Glucose
Fructose

> **hormone** Chemical substance produced in the body that controls or regulates the activity of certain cells or organs.
>
> **bolus** Mass of food that is swallowed.
>
> **lysozymes** Enzymes produced by a variety of cells that can destroy bacteria by rupturing cell membranes.
>
> **amylase** Starch-digesting enzyme from the salivary glands or pancreas.

A low-fat diet will result in a decrease of the lipase enzymes that aid fat digestion. Inadequate amounts of digestive enzymes may be produced when the small intestine or the pancreas is diseased or when an individual is malnourished. This scarcity can result in incomplete digestion and limited absorption. If food is not completely digested, bacteria in the large intestine convert some of it into gases and acids. The gases often distend (bloat) the abdomen. In addition, the feces look foamy and greasy because of trapped gases and the presence of undigested fat.

Some digestive enzymes not only digest food but also can digest the GI tract itself! For this reason, these enzymes are synthesized and stored in an inactive form. Their release and activation are tightly controlled by nerves and hormones. Four **hormones** that play key roles in digestion are gastrin, secretin, cholecystokinin (CCK), and gastric inhibitory peptide. The functions of these hormones, as well as those of hydrochloric acid, bicarbonate, and bile, are described later in this chapter in Sections 4.4 and 4.5.

Knowledge Check

1. What is the difference between digestion and absorption?
2. What are the 4 layers of the GI tract?
3. How are the contents of the GI tract propelled along its length?
4. How do enzymes aid digestion?
5. Where are most digestive enzymes synthesized?

4.3 Moving through the GI Tract: Mouth and Esophagus

Before we eat a bite of most foods, the work of digestion has already started. Food preparation, such as cooking, marinating, pounding, and dicing, often begins the process. Starch granules in food swell as they soak up water during cooking, making them much easier to digest. Cooking also softens tough connective tissues in meats and fibrous tissue of plants, such as that in broccoli stalks. As a result, the food is easier to chew, swallow, and break down during digestion.

In the body, digestion begins in the mouth, or oral cavity (Fig. 4-8). The teeth tear and grind solid food into smaller pieces, which increases the surface area exposed to saliva. During chewing, the tongue presses morsels of food against the hard palate and helps mix the food with saliva. The food is now referred to as a **bolus.**

The salivary glands produce about 4 cups (1 liter) of saliva each day. Saliva is a dilute, watery fluid that contains several substances, including mucus to lubricate the bolus and hold it together; **lysozyme** to kill bacteria; and **amylase** to break down starch into simple sugars. However, food remains in the mouth such a short time that only about 5% of the starch gets broken down by salivary amylase. Lingual lipase, also released from salivary glands, is a fat-digesting enzyme that is produced mainly during infancy. Saliva also helps prevent tooth decay because it contains antibacterial agents, minerals to repair teeth, and substances that neutralize acid.

Figure 4-8 (a) The oral cavity (mouth) is the beginning of the GI tract. Incisor and canine (pointed) teeth are useful in tearing food, such as from a chicken leg. Molars (flat teeth) are used to grind food into smaller pieces. (b) The salivary glands near the oral cavity produce saliva to aid in swallowing and digesting food.

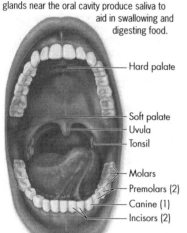

- Hard palate
- Soft palate
- Uvula
- Tonsil
- Molars
- Premolars (2)
- Canine (1)
- Incisors (2)

(a) Oral cavity

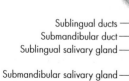

- Parotid salivary gland
- Parotid duct
- Sublingual ducts
- Submandibular duct
- Sublingual salivary gland
- Submandibular salivary gland

(b) Salivary glands

Taste and Smell

Saliva enhances our perception of the flavor of foods by dissolving the taste-forming compounds in foods. Taste buds, found on the papillae of the tongue and soft palate, contain specialized taste-receptor cells that can detect taste compounds in foods. The ability to detect the following 5 basic tastes is present in all areas of the tongue.

- Salty, from a variety of salts, such as NaCl (table salt) or KCl (potassium chloride)
- Sour, from acids, such as citric acid (think about how sour—and acidic—a lemon is)
- Sweet, from organic compounds, such as sugars; humans have an innate preference for sweetness
- Bitter, from a diverse group of compounds, including caffeine and quinine, and numerous other compounds in vegetables and fruits; many bitter compounds are toxic, but others are beneficial phytochemicals and have antioxidant and cancer-protecting activity[1]
- Umami, a savory, brothy, or meaty taste, from amino acids (primarily glutamate); foods such as mushrooms, cooked tomatoes, Parmesan cheese, and seaweed cause the umami taste sensation, and the seasoning monosodium glutamate (MSG) often is added to processed and restaurant foods to enhance the umami sensation

There also is evidence that we have taste receptors for calcium, magnesium, and other minerals.[2] The sense of taste is enhanced by input from approximately 6 million **olfactory** cells in the nose, which are stimulated when we chew. Thus, it makes perfect sense that, with nasal congestion, even strong-tasting foods may have little flavor. A variety of diseases and drugs, as well as the effects of aging, can alter taste and smell sensations. Taste perception also is affected by human genetic variation in both taste and olfactory sensations. For example, the ability to taste sweet and bitter compounds varies widely among people in different racial and ethnic groups.[1,3] It is not yet known how this influences food choices and health.

Swallowing

Swallowing moves food from the mouth into the esophagus, the 10-inch-long muscular tube that extends to the stomach (Fig. 4-9). At its entrance is the **epiglottis**, a flaplike structure that prevents food from entering the **trachea** (windpipe). When food is swallowed, the epiglottis closes over the **larynx** (the opening of the trachea). The food bolus drops onto the epiglottis

> ▶ When we talk about liking the taste of a food, we mean we like its flavor. That's because aromatic and taste compounds, combined with the physical effect caused by food textures and certain chemicals in foods (e.g., the hot and irritating capsaicin in chili peppers), create flavor sensations.

olfactory Related to the sense of smell.

epiglottis Flap that folds down over the trachea during swallowing.

trachea Airway leading from the larynx to the lungs.

larynx Structure located between the pharynx and trachea; contains the vocal cords.

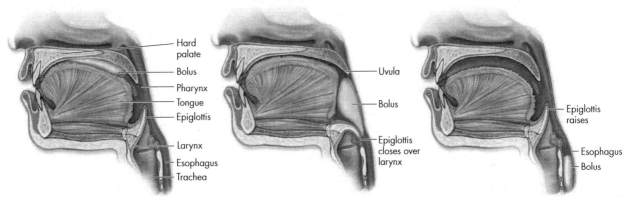

(a) Bolus of food is pushed by tongue against hard palate and then moves toward pharynx.

(b) As bolus moves into pharynx, epiglottis closes over larynx.

(c) Esophageal muscle contractions push bolus toward stomach. Epiglottis then returns to its normal position.

Figure 4-9 The process of swallowing. Swallowing occurs as the food bolus is forced (a) into the pharynx (throat) from the oral cavity, (b) through the pharynx, and (c) into the esophagus on the way to the stomach. Choking occurs when the bolus becomes lodged in the trachea (windpipe), blocking air to the lungs, instead of passing into the esophagus.

126 **PART 1** Nutrition Basics

and the esophagus relaxes and opens. These involuntary responses ensure that swallowed bolus, aided by peristalsis of the esophagus and gravity, travels down the esophagus, not into the trachea. Small pieces of food that enter the trachea may end up in the lungs and cause a serious infection. Larger pieces of food entering the trachea may cause choking (the victim is not able to speak or breathe). A series of steps to treat such a person is called the Heimlich maneuver.

parietal cell Gastric gland cell that secretes hydrochloric acid and intrinsic factor.

pepsinogen Inactive precursor to the protein-digesting enzyme pepsin; produced in the stomach.

chief cells Gastric gland cells that secrete pepsinogen.

gastrin Hormone that stimulates HCl and pepsinogen secretion by the stomach.

prostaglandins Potent compounds that are synthesized from polyunsaturated fatty acids and produce diverse effects in the body.

nonsteroidal anti-inflammatory drugs (NSAIDS) Class of medications that reduce inflammation, fever, and pain but are not steroids. Aspirin, ibuprofen (Advil®), and naproxen (Aleve®) are some examples.

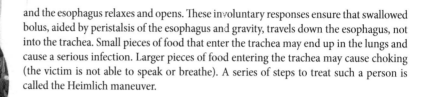

Knowledge Check

1. What substances are found in saliva?
2. For each of the 5 basic taste sensations, name at least 1 chemical compound that elicits the sensation.
3. How does the swallowing process prevent food from entering the trachea?

4.4 Moving through the GI Tract: Stomach

The entry of food into the stomach is through the lower esophageal sphincter (sometimes called the cardiac sphincter due to its proximity to the heart), located between the esophagus and the stomach (Fig. 4-10). It prevents backflow (reflux) of the highly acidic stomach contents into the esophagus. If the sphincter malfunctions, causing reflux, the pain commonly known as **heartburn** occurs.

The stomach is essentially a holding and mixing tank. The average adult stomach holds about 2 ounces (50 ml) when empty and expands to 4 to 6 cups (1–1.5 liters) after a typical meal, but it can hold up to 16 cups (4 liters) when extremely full. Little digestion occurs in the stomach, and only water, a few forms of fats, and about 20% of any alcohol consumed can be absorbed there.

Each day, the stomach secretes about 8 cups (2 liters) of "gastric juice" that aids in the digestive process. Gastric juices are released when we see, smell, taste, or even think about food. These secretions include a very strong acid, called hydrochloric acid (HCl) (Figs. 4-11 and 4-12), from the **parietal cells; pepsinogen,** an inactive protein-digesting enzyme; and gastric lipase from the **chief cells. Gastrin,** a hormone made in the stomach, controls the release of HCl and pepsinogen. Gastrin secretion is highest at the beginning of a meal and declines as the meal progresses. The decline in gastrin secretion causes the release of HCl and pepsinogen to taper off.

The HCl produced by the stomach is very important. It inactivates the biological activity of ingested proteins, such as certain plant and animal hormones. This prevents them from affecting human functions. HCl also destroys most harmful bacteria and viruses (pathogens) in foods; dissolves dietary minerals (e.g., calcium), so that they can be more easily absorbed; and converts pepsinogen into the active protein-digesting enzyme pepsin.

The stomach also secretes mucus from mucous cells found on the gastric mucosa. Mucus lubricates and protects the stomach from being digested by HCl and pepsin. Mucus production relies on the presence of hormonelike compounds called **prostaglandins.** Heavy use of aspirin and other **nonsteroidal anti-inflammatory drugs (NSAIDs)** (e.g., ibuprofen, naproxen) can damage the stomach wall because they inhibit prostaglandin production. The reduced mucous barrier in the stomach means stomach acid may damage the stomach wall.

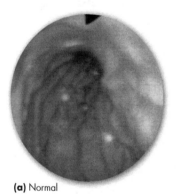

(a) Normal

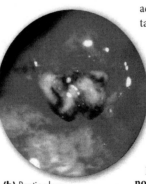

(b) Peptic ulcer

Figure 4-10 The esophagus can be seen opening into the stomach. (a) A healthy gastric mucosa; the small, white spots are reflections of light. (b) A bleeding peptic ulcer. An ulcer is a small erosion of the top layer of cells. A peptic ulcer typically has an oval shape and yellow-white color. Here the yellowish floor of the ulcer is partially obscured by black blood clots, and fresh blood is visible around the margin of the ulcer.

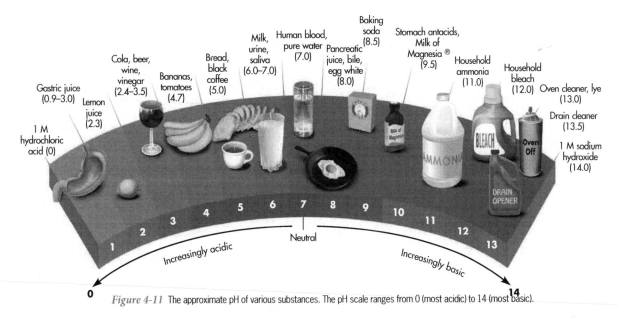

Figure 4-11 The approximate pH of various substances. The pH scale ranges from 0 (most acidic) to 14 (most basic).

Contraction of the 3 muscle layers in the stomach thoroughly mixes food with gastric secretions. Mixing transforms solid food into **chyme** (pronounced kime), a soupy, acidic mixture. The pyloric sphincter, located between the stomach and the duodenum (the first part of the small intestine), controls the flow of chyme into the small intestine. Only 1 teaspoon of chyme is released at a time into the small intestine. **Gastric inhibitory peptide,** a hormone, helps slow the release of chyme into the small intestine, giving the small intestine time to neutralize the acid and digest the nutrients. The pyloric sphincter also prevents the backflow of bile into the stomach (bile, discussed later in the chapter, can damage the stomach

chyme Liquid mixture of stomach secretions and partially digested food.

gastric inhibitory peptide Hormone that slows gastric motility and stimulates insulin release from the pancreas.

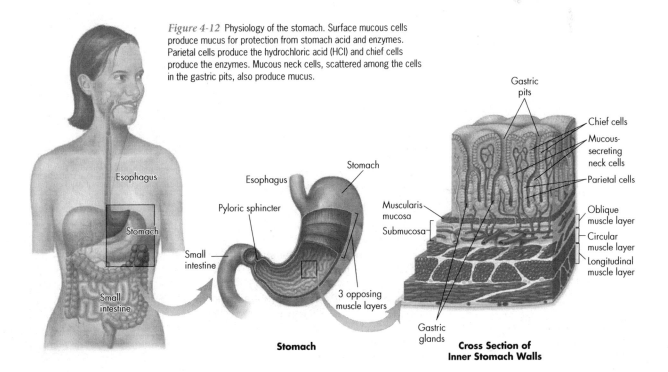

Figure 4-12 Physiology of the stomach. Surface mucous cells produce mucus for protection from stomach acid and enzymes. Parietal cells produce the hydrochloric acid (HCl) and chief cells produce the enzymes. Mucous neck cells, scattered among the cells in the gastric pits, also produce mucus.

128 **PART 1** Nutrition Basics

The heavy use of aspirin, an NSAID, may result in ulcer formation.

lining). It typically takes 1 to 4 hours for meals to move out of the stomach into the small intestine; less time is needed when meals are mostly liquid, more time when meals are large and high in fat.

Another important function of the stomach is the production of a substance called intrinsic factor (IF). This substance is required for the absorption of vitamin B-12 in the small intestine (discussed further in Chapter 13).

Knowledge Check

1. What are the components of gastric juice?
2. How do HCl and the enzyme pepsin aid in digestion?
3. Describe the location and function of the pyloric sphincter.

CASE STUDY

Elise is a 20-year-old college sophomore. Over the last few months, she has been experiencing regular bouts of esophageal burning, pain, and a sour taste in the back of her mouth. This usually happens after a large lunch or dinner. Elise often takes an over-the-counter antacid to relieve these unpleasant symptoms. However, the symptoms have worsened and Elise has decided to visit the university health center.

The nurse practitioner at the center tells Elise it is good she came in for a checkup because she suspects Elise is experiencing heartburn and acid indigestion, but she might also be experiencing gastroesophageal reflux disease (GERD). What types of lifestyle and dietary changes may help reduce or prevent heartburn and GERD? What types of medications are especially helpful in treating this problem?

pH1 2 3 4 5 6 7

pH8 9 10 11 12 13 14

In a laboratory setting, pH test paper strips can be used to measure acidity and alkalinity.

4.5 Moving through the GI Tract: Small Intestine and Accessory Organs

The small intestine is the major site of digestion and absorption of food. It is coiled below the stomach in the abdomen (Fig. 4-13). The small intestine is divided into 3 sections: the first part, the **duodenum,** is about 10 inches (25 cm) long; the middle segment, the **jejunum,** is about 4 feet (122 cm) long; and the last section, the **ileum,** is about 5 feet (152 cm) long. The small intestine is considered small because of its narrow, 1-inch (2.5 cm) diameter, not its length.

The interior of the small intestine has circular folds and fingerlike projections (**villi** and **microvilli**) that increase its surface area 600 times over that of a smooth tube. This large surface area contributes to the thoroughness and efficiency of digestion and absorption. The **circular folds** make the chyme flow slowly, following a spiral path as it travels through the small intestine. Slow spiraling completely mixes the chyme with digestive juices and brings it in contact with the villi that extend into the lumen (Fig. 4-14). Villi are lined with goblet cells that make mucus, endocrine cells that produce hormones and hormonelike substances, and cells that produce digestive enzymes and absorb nutrients (**enterocytes**).

enterocytes Specialized absorptive cells in the villi of the small intestine.

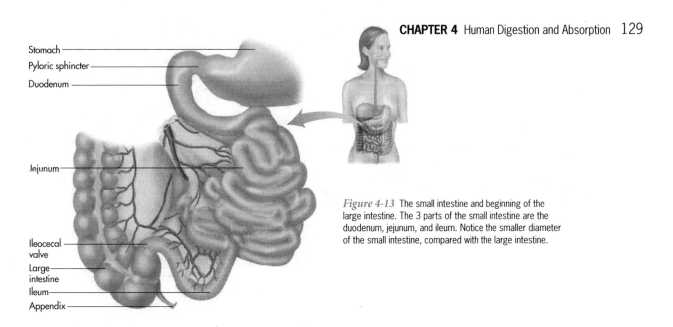

Stomach

Pyloric sphincter

Duodenum

Jejunum

Ileocecal valve

Large intestine

Ileum

Appendix

Figure 4-13 The small intestine and beginning of the large intestine. The 3 parts of the small intestine are the duodenum, jejunum, and ileum. Notice the smaller diameter of the small intestine, compared with the large intestine.

Figure 4-14 Organization of the small intestine. The small intestine has several structural levels. Because of the circular folds in the intestinal wall, the villi "fingers" that project into the intestine, and the microvilli (brush border) on each absorptive cell that makes up the villi, the surface area for absorption is up to 600 times that of a smooth tube.

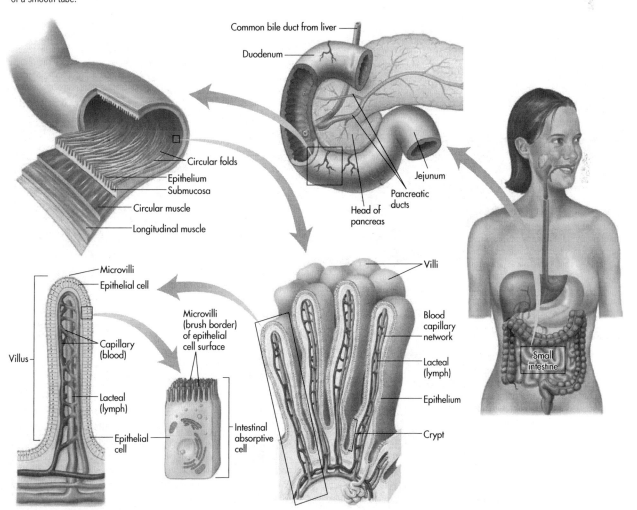

Common bile duct from liver

Duodenum

Circular folds

Epithelium

Submucosa

Circular muscle

Longitudinal muscle

Jejunum

Pancreatic ducts

Head of pancreas

Microvilli

Epithelial cell

Microvilli (brush border) of epithelial cell surface

Villus

Capillary (blood)

Lacteal (lymph)

Epithelial cell

Intestinal absorptive cell

Villi

Blood capillary network

Lacteal (lymph)

Epithelium

Crypt

Small intestine

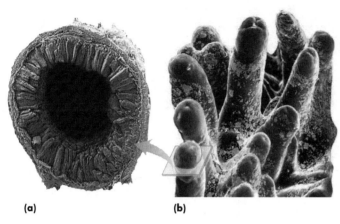

(a)   **(b)**

Figure 4-15 (a) Cross section of the small intestine shows the villi that project into the lumen. (b) The millions of villi in the small intestine increase the surface area for absorption of nutrients. Each villus is about 1 mm high.

Each enterocyte has a brush border made up of microvilli that are covered with the digestive enzyme–containing **glycocalyx.** The villi and microvilli make the small intestine interior look fuzzy, like terrycloth or velvet (Fig. 4-15).

Most digestion in the small intestine occurs in the duodenum and upper part of the jejunum and requires many secretions from the small intestine itself, as well as the pancreas, liver, and gallbladder. Table 4-2 reviews these secretions and their functions. Each day, the small intestine secretes about 6 cups (1.5 liters) of mucus, enzyme, and hormone-containing fluid. Enzymes produced in the small intestine, also known as brush border enzymes, are responsible for the chemical digestion of the macronutrients. They typically complete the last steps of digestion, resulting in compounds that are small enough to be absorbed.

---

glycocalyx Projections of proteins on microvilli. They contain enzymes to digest protein and carbohydrate.

enterohepatic circulation Continual recycling of compounds between the small intestine and the liver. Bile is one example of a recycled compound.

Liver, Gallbladder, and Pancreas

The liver, gallbladder, and pancreas, known as the accessory organs of the digestive system, work with the small intestine but are not a physical part of it. Secretions from these organs are delivered through the common bile duct and the pancreatic duct. These ducts come together at the sphincter of Oddi (also called the hepatopancreatic sphincter) and empty into the duodenum (Fig. 4-16).

The liver produces bile, a cholesterol-containing, yellow-green fluid that aids in fat digestion and absorption. Bile emulsifies fat—it breaks the large fat globules into micelles, tiny fat droplets that are suspended in the watery chyme. The liver secretes about 2 to 4 cups (500 to 1000 ml) of bile per day. Bile released into the duodenum is reabsorbed in the ileum and returned to the liver. During a meal, bile is recirculated 2 or more times. This system of bile recycling is called the **enterohepatic circulation.** A small amount of bile is not reabsorbed and is excreted in feces—this is the body's only way to excrete cholesterol, one of the components of bile. Bile is stored in the gallbladder until needed.

The pancreas produces about 5 to 6 cups (1.5 liters) of pancreatic juice per day. This juice is an alkaline (basic) mixture of sodium bicarbonate ($NaHCO_3$) and enzymes. The sodium bicarbonate neutralizes the acidic chyme arriving from the stomach, thereby protecting the small intestine from damage by acid. Digestive enzymes from the pancreas include pancreatic amylase (to digest starch), pancreatic lipase (to digest fat), and several proteases (to digest protein). Pancreatic enzymes break large macronutrient molecules into smaller subunits.

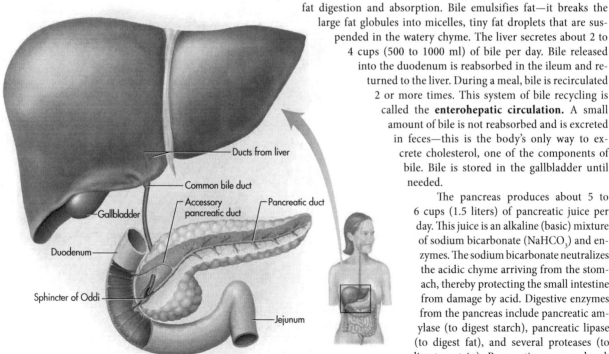

Ducts from liver

Common bile duct

Accessory pancreatic duct

Pancreatic duct

Gallbladder

Duodenum

Sphincter of Oddi

Jejunum

Figure 4-16 The common bile duct from the liver and gallbladder and the pancreatic duct join together at the sphincter of Oddi to deliver bile, pancreatic enzymes, and bicarbonate to the duodenum.

Gastrointestinal Hormones— A Key to Orchestrating Digestion

The remarkable work of the digestive system requires the careful regulation and coordination of several processes, including the production and release of hormones throughout the length of the GI tract. Four hormones, part of the endocrine system, play key roles in this regulation: gastrin, secretin, cholecystokinin (CCK), and gastric inhibitory peptide (Table 4-3). To illustrate their functions, let's follow a turkey sandwich through the digestive system.

1. As you eat a turkey sandwich (or even just think about it), gastrin is produced by cells in the stomach. Gastrin signals other stomach cells to release HCl and pepsinogen (for protein digestion). After thorough mixing, the turkey sandwich, now chyme, is released in small amounts into the small intestine.
2. As chyme is released from the stomach into the small intestine, gastrin production slows and the small intestine secretes secretin and CCK. Both hormones trigger the release of enzyme- and bicarbonate-containing pancreatic juices that digest carbohydrate, fat, and protein and reduce the acidity of the intestinal contents. Fat in the small intestine (from the mayonnaise and the turkey) further stimulates the secretion of CCK by the small intestine. CCK promotes contraction of the gallbladder, which releases the stored bile that aids fat digestion. Relaxation of the sphincter of Oddi allows bile and pancreatic juices to flow into the small intestine. CCK also slows GI motility to give digestive enzymes from the small intestine and pancreas enough time to do their work.
3. The sandwich becomes progressively digested and absorbed. The small intestine now releases gastric inhibitory peptide. This hormone, as its name suggests, signals the stomach to slow motility and decrease the release of gastric juice.

Many other hormones, synthesized throughout the GI tract and in the brain and pancreas, contribute to the regulation of digestion and absorption. Some of these hormones are listed in Table 4-3.

Table 4-3 Major Regulatory Hormones of the GI Tract

Hormone	Released By	Functions
Gastrin	Stomach and duodenum in response to food reaching the stomach	Triggers the stomach to release HCl and pepsinogen; stimulates gastric and intestinal motility
Cholecystokinin (CCK)	Small intestine in response to dietary fat in chyme	Stimulates release of pancreatic enzymes and bile from the gallbladder
Secretin	Small intestine in response to acidic chyme Small intestine as digestion progresses	Stimulates release of pancreatic bicarbonate
Motilin	Small intestine in response to gastric distension and dietary fat	Regulates motility of the gastrointestinal tract
Gastric inhibitory peptide	Ileum and large intestine in response to fat in the large intestine	Signals the stomach to limit the release of gastric juices and slows gastric motility
Peptide YY	Ileum and large intestine in response to fat in the large intestine	Inhibits gastric and pancreatic secretions
Somatostatin	Stomach, small intestine, and pancreas	Inhibits release of GI hormones; slows gastric emptying, GI motility, and blood flow to the intestine

Absorption in the Small Intestine

The absorptive cells of the small intestine originate in crypts (open-ended pits) located at the base of the villi. The absorptive cells migrate from the crypts to the villi. As they migrate, absorptive cells mature and their absorptive capabilities increase. By the time they reach the tips of the villi, they have been partially destroyed by digestive enzymes and have shed into the lumen. The body's entire supply of absorptive cells is replaced every 2 to 5 days.

The digestive capabilities and health of the small intestine rapidly deteriorate during a nutrient deficiency or in semistarvation. This is because cells that turn over rapidly, such as absorptive cells, depend on a constant supply of nutrients. These nutrients are provided by the diet, as well as from broken-down cell parts that are recycled.

CRITICAL THINKING

Cancer treatments often involve the use of chemotherapy medications to prevent rapid cell production and growth. Cancer cells are the intended target. Diarrhea is a common side effect of chemotherapy. Why does chemotherapy often cause diarrhea?

132   **PART 1**   Nutrition Basics

The GI tract digests the foods eaten. Despite what you may have heard, the order in which foods are eaten has no effect on digestive processes.

CRITICAL THINKING

The medical history of a young girl who is greatly underweight shows that she had three-quarters of her small intestine removed after she was injured in a car accident. Explain how this accounts for her underweight condition, even though her medical chart shows that she eats well.

Most nutrient absorption occurs in the small intestine (Fig. 4-17). The small intestine absorbs about 95% of the food energy in protein, carbohydrate, fat, and alcohol. Nutrients move from the lumen of the small intestine into the absorptive cells in the ways illustrated in Figure 4-18.

- **Passive diffusion:** When the concentration of a nutrient is higher in the lumen of the small intestine than in the absorptive cells, the difference in concentration, known as the concentration gradient, forces the nutrient into the absorptive cells. Fats, water, and some minerals are absorbed by passive diffusion.
- **Facilitated diffusion:** A higher concentration of a nutrient in the lumen than in the absorptive cells is not enough to move some nutrients into the absorptive cells. They need carrier proteins to shuttle them from the lumen into absorptive cells. For instance, the sugar fructose is absorbed by facilitated diffusion.
- **Active absorption:** In addition to the need for a carrier protein, some nutrients also require energy (ATP) for absorption. Active absorption, also known as active transport, allows the cell to concentrate nutrients on either side of the cell membrane. Amino acids and some sugars, such as glucose, are actively absorbed.
- **Endocytosis (phagocytosis and pinocytosis):** In this type of active absorption, absorptive cells engulf compounds (phagocytosis) or liquids (pinocytosis). In both these processes, an absorptive cell forms an invagination in its cell membrane that engulfs the particles or fluid to form a vesicle. The vesicle is finally pinched off from the cell membrane and taken into the cell. This process allows immune substances (large protein particles) in human breast milk to be absorbed by infants.

Knowledge Check

1. What are the 3 sections of the small intestine?
2. Where is bile synthesized and what is its function?
3. What is the role of the pancreas in digestion?
4. Which type of absorption requires energy?

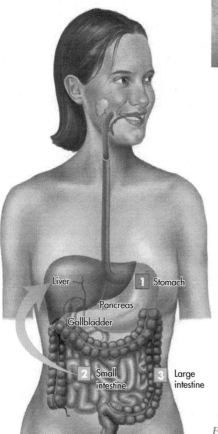

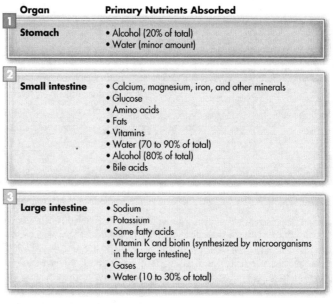

Organ	Primary Nutrients Absorbed
1 Stomach	• Alcohol (20% of total) • Water (minor amount)
2 Small intestine	• Calcium, magnesium, iron, and other minerals • Glucose • Amino acids • Fats • Vitamins • Water (70 to 90% of total) • Alcohol (80% of total) • Bile acids
3 Large intestine	• Sodium • Potassium • Some fatty acids • Vitamin K and biotin (synthesized by microorganisms in the large intestine) • Gases • Water (10 to 30% of total)

Figure 4-17 Major sites of absorption along the GI tract. Note that some synthesis and absorption of vitamin K and biotin takes place in the large intestine.

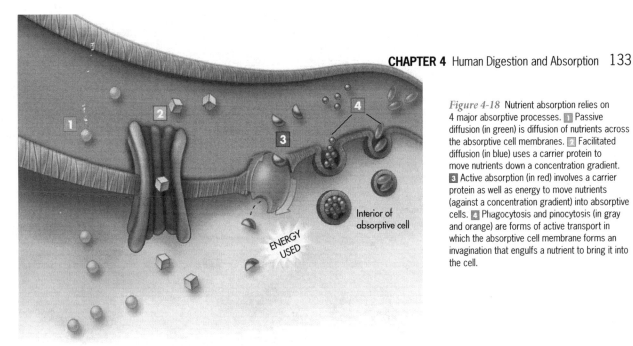

CHAPTER 4 Human Digestion and Absorption 133

Figure 4-18 Nutrient absorption relies on 4 major absorptive processes. **1** Passive diffusion (in green) is diffusion of nutrients across the absorptive cell membranes. **2** Facilitated diffusion (in blue) uses a carrier protein to move nutrients down a concentration gradient. **3** Active absorption (in red) involves a carrier protein as well as energy to move nutrients (against a concentration gradient) into absorptive cells. **4** Phagocytosis and pinocytosis (in gray and orange) are forms of active transport in which the absorptive cell membrane forms an invagination that engulfs a nutrient to bring it into the cell.

GL◯BAL PERSPECTIVE

Diarrhea in Infants and Children

Diarrhea is rarely considered a serious threat to young children in countries such as the U.S. and Canada. However, in developing countries, diarrhea is a leading killer of children—it is responsible for 1 of every 7 deaths in children less than age 5 years. In fact, more children die from diarrhea each year in developing countries than from malaria, measles, and HIV/AIDS combined.[4] Diarrhea in young children is typically caused by pathogenic microorganisms—viruses, bacteria, and parasites—found in water, food, and human and animal waste. One of the most common causes of severe diarrhea in young children around the world is rotavirus.[5] Scientists believe that rotavirus infects virtually all children between the ages of 3 months and 5 years. Rotavirus, like many other microbial pathogens, replicates rapidly in the epithelial cells of the intestinal mucosa. Toxins produced by the virus cause the epithelial cells to slough off faster than they can be replaced. Fluid and **electrolytes,** which normally would have been absorbed in the intestine, are excreted rapidly. Infants and young children can become dangerously dehydrated very quickly. Death occurs if fluids are not replaced. Of the 1.5 million deaths diarrhea causes each year in young children, one-third are attributed to rotavirus.

Being well nourished helps lower the risk of developing diarrhea. Breastfeeding also can prevent diarrhea in young children. Unfortunately, malnutrition afflicts many children in developing countries. In parts of Asia and Africa, more than 40% of preschool children are malnourished.[6] Malnutrition increases susceptibility to diarrhea in several ways. When a child is malnourished, the mucosa of the intestine can become thin, damaged, and leaky—this allows pathogens to invade more easily. Additionally, immune function declines in malnourished children. Moreover, repeated bouts of diarrhea can make malnutrition even worse due to decreased food intake and poor absorption during illness.

To prevent severe illness and death, it is vital that children with diarrhea be treated with oral rehydration therapy. This treatment consists of providing the ill child with oral rehydration salts (small amounts of the electrolytes sodium, chloride, and potassium) and the sugar glucose dissolved in water.[7] This simple recipe has helped decrease the number of diarrhea-related deaths from 4.5 million in 1979 to 1.5 million today. Supplemental zinc (an essential mineral) may be useful, too.[7] Children treated with supplemental zinc are less likely to suffer from diarrhea and, if they do have diarrhea, it is less severe. Another promising advance in the prevention of diarrhea is the rotavirus vaccine. This vaccine substantially reduces rotaviral disease.[8-10]

Life-threatening diarrhea can be successfully treated in many cases. Equally important is the prevention of diarrhea. In many developing countries, the keys to prevention are improved sanitation that keeps food and water pathogen free and the ready availability of affordable, nutritious foods that promote good health. Unfortunately, access to these basic needs is limited for many.

electrolytes Compounds that separate into ions in water and, in turn, are able to conduct an electrical current. These include sodium, chloride, and potassium.

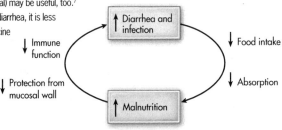

134 **PART 1** Nutrition Basics

4.6 Moving Nutrients around the Body: Circulatory Systems

Nutrients absorbed in the small intestine are delivered to one of the body's 2 circulatory systems: the cardiovascular (blood) system and the **lymphatic system** (Fig. 4-19). The choice of system used to transport nutrients is based primarily on whether the nutrients are water or fat soluble.

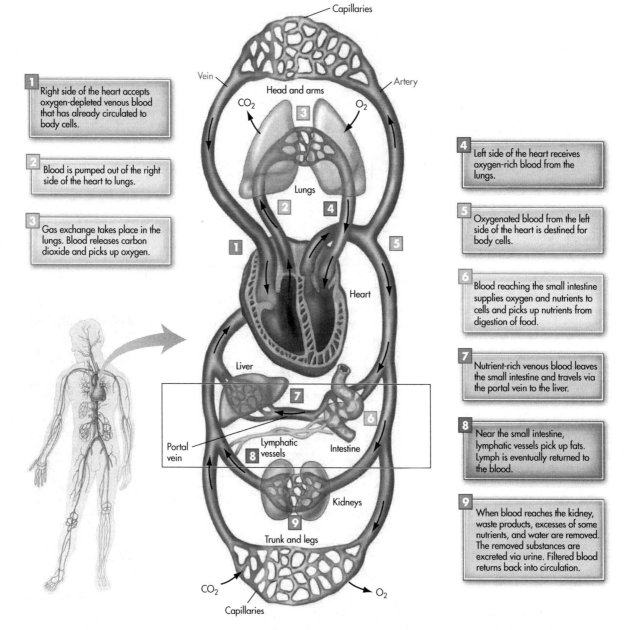

1 Right side of the heart accepts oxygen-depleted venous blood that has already circulated to body cells.

2 Blood is pumped out of the right side of the heart to lungs.

3 Gas exchange takes place in the lungs. Blood releases carbon dioxide and picks up oxygen.

4 Left side of the heart receives oxygen-rich blood from the lungs.

5 Oxygenated blood from the left side of the heart is destined for body cells.

6 Blood reaching the small intestine supplies oxygen and nutrients to cells and picks up nutrients from digestion of food.

7 Nutrient-rich venous blood leaves the small intestine and travels via the portal vein to the liver.

8 Near the small intestine, lymphatic vessels pick up fats. Lymph is eventually returned to the blood.

9 When blood reaches the kidney, waste products, excesses of some nutrients, and water are removed. The removed substances are excreted via urine. Filtered blood returns back into circulation.

Figure 4-19 Blood circulation through the body. This figure shows the paths that blood takes from the heart to the lungs (1–3), back to the heart (4), and through the rest of the body (5–9). The reddish-orange color indicates blood that is richer in oxygen; blue is for blood carrying more carbon dioxide. Keep in mind that arteries and veins go to all parts of the body. Pay particular attention to sites 7 and 8. These sites are key parts of the process of nutrient absorption.

Cardiovascular System

The cardiovascular system includes the heart, blood vessels (arteries, capillaries, veins), and blood. Water-soluble nutrients (proteins, carbohydrates, B-vitamins, and vitamin C) and **short-** and **medium-chain fatty acids** are transported by the cardiovascular system. These nutrients are absorbed directly into the bloodstream in the **capillary** beds inside the villi (see Fig. 4 14). Blood flows from the capillary beds into the **hepatic portal vein system** and collects in the large hepatic portal vein, which leads directly to the liver. The liver metabolizes or stores a portion of the absorbed nutrients, especially protein, lipids, glucose, and several vitamins and minerals. Nutrients not utilized or stored in the liver enter the general circulation. This nutrient-rich blood circulates throughout the body, delivering nutrients to all cells, where they are used for energy, growth, development, maintenance of tissues, and regulation of body processes. The carbon dioxide and other waste products produced by these processes are released into the blood and excreted by the lungs and kidneys.

Lymphatic System

The lymphatic system contains lymph, which flows throughout the body in lymphatic vessels, which are similar to veins. Unlike blood, lymph is not pumped through the vessels. Instead, it slowly flows as muscles contract and squeeze the lymphatic vessels.

The lymphatic system provides an alternative route into the bloodstream for large molecules that cannot be absorbed by the capillary beds. Fat-soluble nutrients (most fats and the fat-soluble vitamins A, D, E, and K) and other substances, such as some proteins, are transported in lymph. Usually a clear fluid, lymph looks milky when it leaves the small intestine because of its fat content. Special lymphatic vessels (**lacteals**) in the villi transport nutrients to larger lymphatic vessels that connect to the thoracic duct. The thoracic duct extends from the abdomen to the neck, where it connects to the bloodstream at a large vein called the left subclavian vein. Once in the blood, nutrients originally absorbed by the lymphatic system are transported to body tissues in the cardiovascular system.

short-chain fatty acid Fatty acid that contains fewer than 6 carbon atoms.

medium-chain fatty acid Fatty acid that contains 6 to 10 carbon atoms.

capillary Smallest blood vessel; the major site for the exchange of substances between the blood and the tissues.

hepatic portal vein system Veins leaving from the stomach, intestines, spleen, and pancreas that drain into the hepatic portal vein, which flows into the liver.

lacteals Tiny vessels in the small intestine villus that absorb dietary fat.

Knowledge Check

1. What are 3 nutrients that are transported by the cardiovascular system?
2. What are 3 nutrients that are transported first in the lymphatic system?
3. Which organ first receives nutrients from the cardiovascular system?
4. Why is diarrhea life threatening for many young children in developing countries?

 ## 4.7 Moving through the GI Tract: Large Intestine

The small intestine empties into the large intestine through the ileocecal valve, the sphincter between the ileum and the colon. After digestion and absorption in the small intestine, normally only water, some minerals, and undigested food fibers and starches are left. About 5% of carbohydrate, protein, and fat escapes absorption in the small intestine.

The large intestine, so called because its 2½-inch (6 cm) lumen diameter is larger than that of the small intestine, is about 5 feet (1.5 meters) long. It has 3 main parts: the colon,

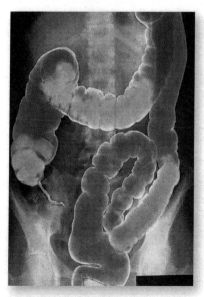

A radiograph of the large intestine.

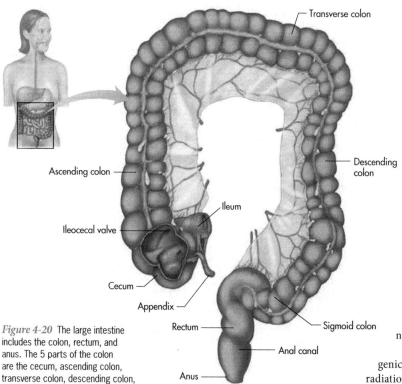

Figure 4-20 The large intestine includes the colon, rectum, and anus. The 5 parts of the colon are the cecum, ascending colon, transverse colon, descending colon, and sigmoid colon.

rectum, and anus. The colon, the largest portion of the large intestine, has 5 sections: cecum, ascending colon, transverse colon, descending colon, and sigmoid colon (Fig. 4-20).

The large intestine performs 3 main functions. It houses bacterial flora that keep the GI tract healthy; it absorbs water and electrolytes, such as sodium and potassium; and it forms and expels feces.

Bacterial Flora

The large intestine is home to over 400 species of bacteria, collectively numbering more than 100 trillion microbial cells, or more than 10 times the number of cells in the human body! Some of the bacteria are beneficial but others are pathogenic. The ileocecal valve prevents these bacteria from migrating into the small intestine (where they could disrupt normal function and compete with the body for nutrients).

Beneficial bacteria keep the growth of pathogenic bacteria under control. Antibiotic treatment, radiation therapy, surgery, and some diseases often reduce the number of beneficial bacteria cells, which can allow pathogenic bacteria to multiply quickly. Disrupting the normal balance between beneficial and pathogenic bacteria can cause conditions such as vomiting, diarrhea, and dehydration.

Beneficial bacteria also synthesize vitamins, most notably vitamin K and the B-vitamin biotin, both of which can be absorbed in the colon. The bacteria also aid lactose digestion, and they ferment (digest) some of the fibers and starches not digested in the small intestine. **Fermentation** creates short-chain fatty acids that can be absorbed and used as an energy source in the colon.[11] Nutrition scientists are studying how fiber, beneficial intestinal bacteria, and short-chain fatty acids may prevent diseases such as irritable bowel syndrome, colon cancer, and inflammatory bowel disease. Intestinal bacteria also produce gas, or flatus, discussed later in this chapter.

Probiotics and Prebiotics

One proposed strategy for achieving a healthy balance of intestinal bacteria is the consumption of probiotics and prebiotics. **Probiotics** are live microorganisms that, when consumed in sufficient amounts, colonize the large intestine and provide health benefits.[12] Probiotics are found in fermented foods, such as yogurt, kefir (a type of fermented milk), and miso (fermented soybean paste), and they are sold in capsules and powders. Common probiotic preparations include various strains of *Lactobacilli* and *Bifidobacteria* bacteria and *Saccharomyces* yeast; others may contain strains of *Enterococcus, Bacillus,* and *Escherichia* bacteria.[12]

Probiotic bacteria are thought to provide certain health benefits, such as preventing diarrhea and food allergies and treating diarrhea, irritable bowel syndrome, and inflammatory bowel disease. However research supporting many of these claims is lacking.[12] Probiotics are difficult to study because of the many types and doses of microorganisms available to test. Most studies have had relatively few participants and short treatment durations.

fermentation Breakdown of large organic compounds into smaller compounds, especially organic acids. The breakdown is often by anaerobic bacteria.

probiotic Live microorganism that when ingested in adequate amounts confers a health benefit on the host.

prebiotic Substance that stimulates bacterial growth in the large intestine.

Currently, the best evidence is that probiotics can help prevent and treat diarrhea caused by microbial pathogens (known as infectious diarrhea), antibiotic-associated diarrhea, and traveler's diarrhea that afflicts many individuals visiting less developed nations.[13, 14] There also is evidence that probiotics can help prevent the bowel damage common in premature infants.[15]

Prebiotics are food ingredients that promote the growth of beneficial bacteria in the large intestine.[12] One example is **inulin,** a carbohydrate known as a fructan because it is made of several units of the sugar fructose. Inulin is found in many foods, including chicory, wheat, onions, garlic, asparagus, and bananas. Inulin also is added to some processed foods to add texture, bulk, and potential health benefits. **Resistant starch,** found in unprocessed whole grains, seeds, legumes, unripe fruit (e.g., bananas), and cooked and chilled pasta, potatoes, and rice, also functions as a prebiotic.[12] Resistant starch is not digested in the small intestine; thus, bacteria in the large intestine can ferment it. Prebiotics fermented in the large intestine produce short-chain fatty acids and other organic acids. In studies of prebiotics, participants typically ingest 10 to 20 grams per day; such large amounts can cause flatulence, bloating, and other GI distress. As with probiotics, the research that prebiotics improve health is not yet conclusive.

Yogurt is a convenient source of probiotic bacteria, which contribute to GI tract health.

Absorption of Water and Electrolytes

The GI tract receives a total of 10 liters of water (3 liters from the diet and 7 liters from intestinal secretions) per day. The small intestine absorbs about 90% of the water and the large intestine completes the job. Just 1% (less than ½ cup, or 120 ml) of the water in the GI tract remains in excreted feces. The large intestine also is the main site where electrolytes, especially sodium and potassium, are absorbed (see Fig. 4-17). Electrolyte absorption occurs mostly in the first half of the large intestine.

Defecation of Feces

It takes 12 to 24 hours for the residue of a meal to travel through the large intestine. By the time the contents have passed through the first two-thirds of its length, a semisolid mass has been formed. This mass remains in the large intestine until peristaltic waves and mass movements, usually greatest following the consumption of a meal, push it into the rectum. Feces in the rectum are a powerful stimulation for defecation, the expulsion of feces. This process involves muscular reflexes in the sigmoid colon and rectum, as well as relaxation of the internal and external anal sphincters. Only the external sphincter is under voluntary control. Once toilet-trained, a person can determine when to relax the sphincter for defecation, as well as when to keep it constricted.

When excreted, feces are normally about 75% water and 25% solids. The solids are primarily indigestible plant fibers, tough connective tissue from animal foods, and bacteria from the large intestine. During episodes of diarrhea, the percentage of water in feces rises.

Inulin, a prebiotic, is found in asparagus.

Knowledge Check

1. What are the 3 main functions of the large intestine?
2. What are some of the beneficial actions of bacteria in the large intestine?
3. What is the difference between a prebiotic and a probiotic? Where can they be found in the diet?

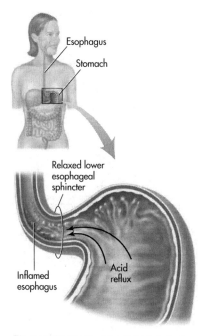

Figure 4-21 Heartburn results from stomach acid refluxing into the esophagus.

▶Individuals with heartburn often take a class of drugs that suppress HCl production in the stomach. Long-term use of these medications may increase the risk of bone fractures because, with less HCl in the stomach, calcium is not dissolved normally and less is absorbed.[40]

anemia Decreased oxygen-carrying capacity of the blood. It occurs for many reasons, including blood loss.

hiatal hernia Protrusion of part of the stomach upward through the diaphragm into the chest cavity.

peptic ulcer Hole in the lining of the stomach or duodenum.

 # 4.8 When Digestive Processes Go Awry

The fine-tuned organ system we call the digestive system can develop problems. Knowing about common problems can help you avoid or lessen them.

Heartburn and Gastroesophageal Reflux Disease

About half of U.S. adults occasionally experience heartburn (acid indigestion), making this the most commonly diagnosed GI disorder in U.S. adults. Heartburn has nothing to do with the heart; it occurs when stomach acid backs up into the esophagus (Fig. 4-21), causing a burning sensation or sour taste in the back of the mouth. Experiencing heartburn 2 or more times per week may signal the more serious gastroesophageal reflux disease (GERD).[16] GERD occurs when the lower esophageal sphincter relaxes and lets stomach contents backflow into the esophagus. (Normally, this sphincter relaxes only with swallowing.) Not everyone with GERD has heartburn—other symptoms include hoarseness, trouble swallowing, coughing, gagging, and nausea. In addition to the uncomfortable physical symptoms of GERD, more serious complications can occur. These include weight loss, ulceration, bleeding in the esophagus, **anemia,** and a higher risk of adenocarcinoma of the esophagus, a cancer that has a poor prognosis. Reflux and GERD can occur in infants and children, too, usually due to an immature digestive system. It can cause frequent spitting up, or vomiting, and coughing. Most children outgrow this by 1 year of age.[16]

The cause of GERD is not known, but factors that may contribute to it include **hiatal hernia,** alcohol use, overweight, smoking, and even pregnancy. Studies have shown that obesity slows stomach emptying and relaxes the lower esophageal sphincter.[16-18] Large meals and foods such as citrus fruits, chocolate, caffeinated drinks (e.g., coffee), fatty and fried foods, garlic, onion, spicy foods, and tomato-based foods (e.g., spaghetti sauce and pizza) may increase reflux.

Heartburn and GERD are treated with both lifestyle modification and medications.[16, 19] Lifestyle change recommendations include eating small meals instead of large ones, avoiding foods that cause reflux, waiting several hours before lying down after eating (remaining upright limits reflux), losing weight, stopping smoking, and limiting alcohol intake. The following medications are used to treat GERD:

- Antacids (Tums*, Maalox*) are over-the-counter medications that neutralize stomach acid. Excessive intake of those that contain magnesium can cause diarrhea, and those that contain aluminum or calcium may cause constipation.
- H$_2$ blockers (cimetidine [Tagamet*] and famotidine [Pepcid AC*]) block the increase of stomach acid production caused by histamine. Histamine, a breakdown product of the amino acid histidine, stimulates acid secretion by the stomach and has many other effects on the body. H$_2$ blockers are available in both prescription and less potent, nonprescription forms.
- Proton pump inhibitors (esomeprazole [Nexium*] and lansoprazole [Prevacid*]) are the most potent acid-suppressing medications. They inhibit the ability of gastric cells to secrete hydrogen ions and make acid. Low doses of this class of medication also are available without prescription, such as omeprazole (Prilosec-OTC*).
- Prokinetic drugs (metoclopromide [Reglan*]) strengthen the lower esophageal sphincter and promote more rapid peristalsis in the small intestine.
- Surgery to strengthen the lower esophageal sphincter may be needed when lifestyle modifications and medications do not work.

Ulcers

An **ulcer** is a very small (usually no larger than a pencil eraser) erosion of the top layer of cells in the stomach or duodenum (Fig. 4-22). The general term for this condition is **peptic ulcer.** About 20 million North Americans develop ulcers during their lifetimes.[20]

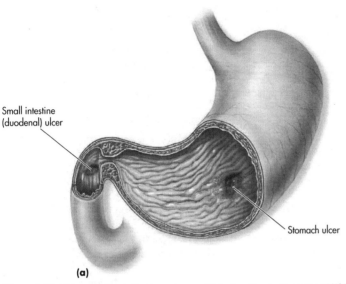

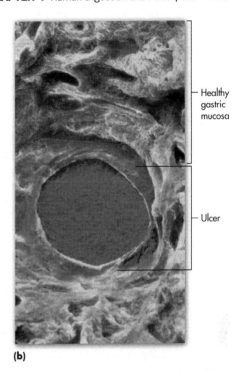

Figure 4-22 (*a*) A peptic ulcer in the stomach or small intestine. *H. pylori* bacteria and NSAIDs (e.g., aspirin) cause ulcers by impairing mucosal defense, especially in the stomach. In the same way, smoking, genetics, and stress can impair mucosal defense, as well as cause an increase in the release of pepsin and stomach acid. All of these factors can contribute to ulcers. (*b*) Close-up of a stomach ulcer. This needs to be treated or eventual perforation of the stomach is possible.

Ulcers in younger people tend to develop in the small intestine, whereas in older people they occur in the stomach.

There are 2 main causes of peptic ulcers, infection with the bacteria *Helicobacter pylori* (*H. pylori*) and heavy use of NSAID medications, such as aspirin and ibuprofen.[21] Alcohol use, smoking, and emotional stress were previously thought to cause ulcers, but evidence to support this is lacking. Eating spicy foods also does not cause ulcers.

Being infected with *H. pylori* does not necessarily lead to an ulcer. In fact, over half of people over the age of 60 are infected with *H. pylori* and most do not have an ulcer.[20] *H. pylori* causes an ulcer by weakening the mucous coating that protects the stomach and duodenum. This allows HCl and digestive juices to attack and erode stomach and duodenal cells. *H. pylori* itself also irritates these cells. Recall that aspirin and other NSAID medications can cause ulcers by suppressing the synthesis of prostaglandins, compounds that promote the formation of the protective mucus.

The most common symptom of an ulcer is a gnawing or burning pain in the stomach region between meals or during the night. This pain often can be relieved by eating or taking antacids. Other, less common symptoms are nausea, vomiting, loss of appetite, and weight loss. The primary complications of ulcers are bleeding and perforation. Slow bleeding eventually can cause anemia and fatigue. Rapid bleeding makes the feces tarry and black from the digested blood, or the person may vomit what looks like coffee grounds. Perforated ulcers (those that eat through the stomach or intestinal wall) allow chyme to escape and enter the abdomen, where it may cause a major, even deadly, infection. It is important to pay attention to the early warning signs of an ulcer.

Today, a combination of approaches is used for ulcer therapy (Table 4-4).[20,21] Those infected with *H. pylori* are treated with antibiotics and either proton pump inhibitors or an H_2 blocker to suppress acid production. Bismuth subsalicylate (a component of Pepto-Bismol®) is taken to protect the stomach lining from acid. Most people (80 to 95%) treated with these drugs heal their ulcers. Smoking can slow ulcer healing. A dietary recommendation is to avoid foods that increase ulcer symptoms, but a bland diet is not necessary.

Table 4-4 Recommendations to Prevent Ulcers and Heartburn from Occurring or Recurring

Ulcers

1. Stop smoking if you smoke.

2. Avoid large doses of aspirin, ibuprofen, and other NSAID compounds unless a physician advises otherwise. For people who must use these medications, the FDA has approved taking an NSAID along with a medication that reduces gastric damage.

3. Limit intake of coffee, tea, and alcohol (especially wine), if this helps.

4. Limit consumption of pepper, chili powder, and other strong spices, if this helps.

5. Eat nutritious meals on a regular schedule; include enough fiber (see Chapter 5 for sources of fiber).

6. Chew foods well.

7. Lose weight if you are currently overweight.

Heartburn

1. Follow ulcer prevention recommendations.

2. Wait about 2 hours after a meal before lying down.

3. Don't overeat. Eat smaller meals that are low in fat.

4. Elevate the head of the bed at least 6 inches.

Figure 4-23 Gallbladder and gallstones after surgical removal from the body. Size and composition of the stones vary from one case to another.

Table 4-5 **Factors Associated with Gallstone Formation**
• High-calorie, low-fiber diet
• Prolonged fasting
• Obesity—especially excess abdominal fat
• Rapid weight loss (more than 3 lb per week)
• Type 2 diabetes
• High blood lipids
• Sedentary lifestyle
• Some medications, especially estrogen replacement therapy and birth control pills
• Female gender
• Pregnancy
• Increasing age
• Family history of gallstones
• Ethnicity—especially Native American and Mexican-American

Gallstones

Gallstones, a frequent cause of illness and surgery, affect 10 to 20% of U.S. adults. The stones develop in the gallbladder when substances in the bile—mainly cholesterol (80% of gallstones) and bile pigments (20%)—form crystal-like particles. Gallstones can be as small as a grain of sand or as large as a golf ball (Fig. 4-23). Gallstone formation is related to slow gallbladder motility and bile composition. Too little bile and phospholipids and too much cholesterol allow cholesterol to crystallize into stones.[22] Factors that increase the risk of gallstone formation are listed in Table 4-5.[22–26]

Preventing gallstones includes maintaining a healthy weight, especially for women. Avoiding rapid weight loss, choosing plant instead of animal protein, eating a high-fiber diet and magnesium-rich foods,[23] and using unsaturated fats, such as olive oil, may help prevent stone formation, too. Regular physical activity also is important.

Most individuals with gallstones do not have symptoms; stones are usually detected during an examination for another illness. Symptoms can include intermittent pain in the right upper abdomen, pain between the shoulder blades or near the right shoulder, nausea, vomiting, gas, and bloating. Gallstone "attacks" occur when stones block the bile ducts and stop the free flow of bile. Attacks may last from 20 minutes to several hours.

Surgical removal of the gallbladder is the most common treatment for gallstones (500,000 surgeries per year in the U.S.).[26] Fortunately, removal of the gallbladder does not have serious consequences. Instead of being stored in the gallbladder, bile flows directly from the liver through the common bile duct to the small intestine.

Food Intolerances

Food intolerances are caused by an individual's inability to digest certain food components, usually due to low amounts of specific enzymes. Note that food allergies and food intolerances are not the same. Food allergies cause an immune response as a result of exposure to certain food proteins (allergens) (see Chapter 7). Food intolerances afflict many individuals. Symptoms vary widely, depending on the cause of the food intolerance. Common causes include:

- Deficiencies in digestive enzymes, such as lactase (see Chapter 5)
- Sensitivities to food components, such as gluten (see Expert Perspective from the Field)
- Certain synthetic compounds added to foods, such as food-coloring agents, sulfites, and monosodium glutamate (MSG). The food coloring tartrazine, for instance, causes airway spasms, itching, and reddening skin in some people. Sulfites, which often are added to protect the color of wine, dried foods (fruit, potatoes, soup mixes), and salad greens, may cause flushing, airway spasms, and a drop in blood pressure in susceptible people. MSG, a flavor enhancer frequently added to restaurant and processed foods, may increase blood pressure and cause numbness, sweating, vomiting, and headache in certain people.
- Residues of medications (e.g., antibiotics) and other chemicals used in the production of livestock and crops, as well as insect parts not removed during processing (see Chapter 3)
- Toxic contaminants, such as mold or bacteria (see Chapter 3)

Intestinal Gas

Everyone has gas. In fact, we produce about 1 to 4 pints of gas each day and pass gas about 14 times a day, although there is considerable variability from one person to the next.[27] Gas is eliminated by burping and passing it through the rectum. Intestinal gas (also known as flatulence) is a mixture of carbon dioxide, oxygen, nitrogen, hydrogen, methane, and small amounts of sulfur-containing gas. The sulfur is responsible for the unpleasant odor associated with flatulence. Large quantities of intestinal gas can cause bloating and abdominal pain.

Gas comes from swallowed air and the breakdown of undigested carbohydrates by bacteria in the large intestine. The bacteria produce gas as they metabolize carbohydrate. Some people are particularly sensitive to certain carbohydrates (Table 4-6), whereas others can eat them with little problem. Enzyme preparations, such as Beano˚, and lactase may help prevent gas by limiting the amount of undigested carbohydrate available to the bacteria in the large intestine. The enzyme in Beano˚ breaks down raffinose and other similar carbohydrates, whereas the lactase enzyme digests the lactose in milk. Eating fewer gas-forming foods also can help reduce intestinal gas. A "trial and error" approach is usually required.

Constipation

Constipation is defined as difficult or infrequent (fewer than 3 times per week) bowel movements. Slow movement of fecal material through the large intestine causes constipation. As fluid is increasingly absorbed during the extended time the feces stay in the large intestine, they become dry and hard. Constipation is commonly reported by older adults because the colon becomes more sluggish as we age.

Constipation is caused by many factors. It can occur when people regularly ignore normal urges to defecate for long periods. Constipation also can result from conditions such as diabetes mellitus, irritable bowel syndrome, and depression.[28] Pregnant women frequently experience constipation because hormones released in pregnancy slow GI motility. Antacids, antidepressants, and calcium and iron supplements are examples of medications that can cause constipation. Low-fiber diets also contribute to constipation.

Eating foods with plenty of fiber, such as whole-grain breads and cereals, beans, fruits, and vegetables, and drinking more fluid help treat typical cases of mild constipation.[29] The recommended fiber intake for most adults is 25 to 38 grams per day. Fiber stimulates peristalsis by drawing water into the large intestine and helping form bulky, soft feces. The bulky fecal material stretches the peristaltic muscles; the muscles respond by constricting, causing the feces to be propelled forward.

People with constipation may need to develop more regular bowel habits—setting the same time each day for a bowel movement (usually on awakening or shortly after a meal) can help train the large intestine to respond routinely. Additionally, relaxation and daily exercise promote regular bowel movements.

Laxatives, medications that stimulate emptying of the intestines, can lessen more serious cases of constipation.[28] There are several types of laxatives:

- Bulk-forming laxatives (Metamucil˚ and Citrucel˚) contain different types of fiber (e.g., psyllium fiber, methylcellulose). Like fiber in food, bulk-forming laxatives draw water into the intestine and increase fecal volume.
- Osmotic laxatives (Milk of Magnesia˚) keep fluid in the intestine, which helps keep the fecal matter soft and bulky.
- Stimulant laxatives (Dulcolax˚ and ExLax˚) agitate intestinal nerves to stimulate the peristaltic muscles.
- Stool softeners (Colace˚) allow water to enter the bowel more readily.
- Lubricant laxatives (mineral oil) are not recommended because they may block absorption of fat-soluble vitamins.

For most people, bulk-forming laxatives are the safest to use. However, the regular use of laxatives, especially stimulant laxatives, may lead to dependence and damage the intestine. Consult a physician before using laxatives longer than a week.

Physicians infrequently treat more severe cases of constipation with an enema. An enema is the insertion of fluid into the rectum and colon via the anus. The fluid stimulates the

Table 4-6 Carbohydrates That May Contribute to Intestinal Gas Formation

Carbohydrate(s)	Description and Food Sources
Raffinose and stachyose	Complex sugars found in beans and vegetables, such as cabbage, Brussels sprouts, and broccoli, that are poorly absorbed
Lactose	Sugar found in milk and milk products (lactose intolerance is discussed in Chapter 5)
Fructose	Sugar found in fruit, onions, artichokes, and wheat
Sorbitol	Sugar alcohol that is poorly absorbed, found in many fruits (apples, pears, prunes) and used to sweeten some sugar-free products
Starches	Some of the starch found in potatoes, corn, noodles, and wheat that is not fully digested
Fiber	Soluble fiber found in beans, oat bran, and fruits

CRITICAL THINKING

Joci is considering going on a new diet that emphasizes eating only fruits before noon, meat at lunchtime, and starch and vegetables at dinner. In addition, the diet recommends "cleansing" the intestines with laxatives and enemas every other week. What reasons would you give Joci to steer clear of this regimen? What are some possible harmful effects?

bowel, and the liquid and feces are expelled. Some alternative health practitioners advocate the use of enemas to remove toxins from the colon and the body, but there is little evidence that this practice is beneficial.

Diarrhea

Diarrhea—loose, watery stools occurring more than 3 times per day—is a common GI tract problem. It usually lasts only a few days and goes away on its own. Most cases of diarrhea result from bacterial or viral infection, often from contaminated food or water (see Chapter 3).

Expert Perspective from the Field

Celiac Disease

A recent National Institutes of Health panel has drawn attention to celiac disease, an immune-mediated disorder that affects primarily the gastrointestinal tract. Celiac disease, sometimes known as gluten intolerance, is caused by a physiological response to a protein called *gluten*, found in wheat and related grains, such as rye, barley, spelt, and triticale. In persons with celiac disease, these proteins damage the villi of the small intestine, causing the villi to flatten. In many persons with celiac disease, damage to the villi results in the malabsorption of nutrients. Currently, health experts believe that celiac disease results from both genetic and immunological factors.

Celiac disease is increasingly common—approximately 0.8% of the U.S. population (1 in 133 people) is thought to have celiac disease, compared with 0.2% 50 years ago.[30] Most of these individuals are not yet diagnosed. Further, according to Cynthia Kupper,* executive director of the Gluten Intolerance Group of North America and a celiac disease sufferer, 2 to 3 times more people do not meet the diagnostic criteria for celiac disease but are sensitive to gluten and experience health improvements when gluten is eliminated from their diets.

Celiac disease can affect a number of body systems. Classic symptoms of celiac disease include intestinal gas, bloating, diarrhea, constipation, abdominal pain, and weight loss or gain. Nongastrointestinal symptoms include anemia, early bone disease, autoimmune diseases (e.g., type 1 diabetes and thyroid disease), fatigue, slower than normal growth in children, ataxia (impaired coordination) and other neurological conditions, a skin condition called dermatitis herpetiformis, and infertility.[31]

People with gluten intolerance should avoid foods, such as bread, that are made with wheat.

Although there is research underway to develop drug therapies, currently the only treatment is a lifetime of eating a gluten-free diet.[31, 32] A healthy diet that includes all food groups is important. However, the only foods consumed from the grain group should be those that are gluten free, such as corn, rice, quinoa, and buckwheat. A registered dietitian can help a person plan a healthy gluten-free diet. Kupper has pointed out that food labels can help consumers avoid foods with ingredients that contain gluten because any food that contains wheat must state this clearly on the label. To further assist those following a gluten-free diet, the FDA is considering regulations for voluntary labeling by food manufacturers of gluten-free products.

Those with a gluten intolerance disorder who consume gluten risk experiencing the symptoms of this health condition in the short term. In the long term, untreated celiac disease may lead to weight loss, diarrhea, anemia, headaches, and muscle pain. In addition, without treatment, there is an increased risk of aggressive GI tract cancers and associated health conditions related to malabsorption and malnutrition.

Kupper recommends that those who have symptoms of gluten intolerance should not try to treat the symptoms themselves because they might be caused by another condition, such as inflammatory bowel disease, discussed later in this chapter. Also, following a gluten-free diet is challenging and can be expensive. Kupper notes that it's best to get a diagnosis from a physician. Blood tests for celiac disease are accurate, and a small intestinal biopsy can confirm the condition. To learn more about celiac disease, visit the websites listed at the end of the chapter.

The Gluten Intolerance Group of North America reviews scientific research and translates it into practical information to help individuals with gluten intolerance disorders manage their diseases. Ms. Kupper often provides expert input to the food industry and government agencies, such as the National Institutes of Health (NIH) and the FDA.

Take Action

Investigate Over-the-Counter Medications for Treating Common GI Tract Problems

Visit your local pharmacy and check out the medications for treating indigestion, heartburn, constipation, diarrhea, and hemorrhoids. Select a category and compare 4 brands for the following characteristics.

Characteristic	Brand 1	Brand 2	Brand 3	Brand 4
1. Price				
2. Usual daily dose				
3. Active ingredients				
4. Warning to users				
5. Advice as to when to see a physician				

Write a critique of your discoveries about these products, and summarize what you would say about their safety and effectiveness.

These infections cause the intestinal tract to secrete fluid instead of absorbing it. Diarrhea also can be caused by parasites, food intolerances, medications (e.g., magnesium-containing antacids and certain antibiotics), megadoses of vitamin C supplements, intestinal diseases, and irritable bowel syndrome. Consuming substances that are not readily absorbed, such as the sugar alcohol sorbitol found in sugarless gum and candy, can cause diarrhea as well (see Chapter 5). When ingested in large amounts, unabsorbed substances draw excess water into the intestine, causing diarrhea.

The treatment of diarrhea generally requires consuming plenty of fluid (beverages, soups, broths) to replace lost fluid and electrolytes. Prompt treatment is vital for infants and older people because they are more susceptible to the effects of dehydration associated with diarrhea. Most infants and children with diarrhea can be treated at home. Special fluids, such as Pedialyte®, can be given for fluid and electrolyte replacement. Most children can continue to eat a normal diet. A health-care provider should evaluate children with diarrhea who are less than 6 months of age or who have blood in the stool, frequent vomiting, high fever, and signs of dehydration (fewer than 6 wet diapers per day, weight loss, extreme thirst, or dry, sticky mouth).[33] Diarrhea in adults that lasts more than 3 days, especially if accompanied by fever, blood in the stool, or severe abdominal pain, also warrants investigation by a health-care provider. When recovering from diarrhea, it is best to avoid greasy, high-fiber, and very sweet foods because they can aggravate diarrhea.

▶ You may have heard that taking laxatives after overeating prevents the body from storing the excess calories as body fat. This erroneous and dangerous idea has gained popularity among some fad dieters. Laxatives may cause you to feel less full temporarily because they speed up the emptying of the large intestine and increase fluid loss. Most laxatives, however, do not speed the passage of food through the small intestine, where most digestion and most nutrient absorption take place. As a result, laxatives won't prevent fat gain from excess energy intake.

Irritable Bowel Syndrome

About 10 to 15% of the U.S. population suffers from irritable bowel syndrome (IBS).[34, 35] This disorder is more common in women than in men. IBS symptoms include irregular bowel function (diarrhea, constipation, or alternating episodes of both), abdominal pain, and abdominal distension. Symptoms often worsen after eating. The irregular bowel function is thought to be caused by abnormal intestinal motility; the abdominal pain is caused by a decreased pain threshold for abdominal distension. Even a minor amount of abdominal bloating, which most people would not sense, may cause pain in those with IBS. The abdominal pain is often relieved by a bowel movement. IBS symptoms may be mild or very severe, but the disorder does not increase the risk of other serious digestive problems or cancer. Diagnosis of IBS should be made by a physician.

The cause of IBS is not known; factors that may play a role include stress and diet. Although many studies relating diet to IBS symptoms have been published, most had

Elise's GERD can be treated, but it may be a lifelong condition. To reduce the risk of GERD, Elise should eat small, frequent meals that are low in fat, not overeat at mealtime, wait about 2 hours after meals before lying down, and elevate the head of her bed about 6 inches (see Table 4-4). Additionally, she should limit her intake of chili powder, onions, garlic, peppermint, caffeine, alcohol, and chocolate; lose excess weight; and not smoke. If this advice does not control Elise's symptoms, her physician may turn to medications. The primary medications used to control GERD inhibit acid production in the stomach. If this and other medical therapy fail to control the problem, surgery to strengthen the lower esophageal sphincter is possible but generally does not cure the problem. Lifetime diet and lifestyle management, and most likely medications, will still be needed to manage the problem. Such management is important because long-standing GERD increases the risk of esophageal cancer.

colitis Inflammation of the colon that can lead to ulcers (ulcerative colitis).

Crohn's disease Inflammatory disease of the GI tract that often reduces the absorptive capacity of the small intestine. Family history is a major risk factor.

inadequate research methods or inconsistent results. Dietary factors that appear to aggravate IBS symptoms include poorly absorbed carbohydrates, such as fructose (in honey, fruit, and high-fructose corn syrup added to many processed foods) and sugar alcohols (see Chapter 5); gas-forming foods (e.g., cabbage, beans, broccoli); wheat; and large, high-fat meals.[36] Food allergy reactions and intolerances may trigger symptoms in some people with IBS.[36] Increasing dietary fiber (either via diet or supplements) has long been touted as a way to manage IBS, but research does not support this practice.[35] Studies of different types of fiber show no benefit, although one exception may be improvement in those with constipation. Peppermint oil, which relaxes the smooth muscle of the gastrointestinal tract, and low-fat, frequent, small meals may improve IBS symptoms. Eliminating dairy products (which contain lactose), wheat, bananas, corn, potatoes, milk, eggs, peas, and coffee provides relief to some with IBS.[36] A registered dietitian can help those with IBS identify problem foods and plan a nutritionally adequate diet.

Inflammatory Bowel Disease

Inflammatory bowel disease (IBD) is a group of serious, chronic intestinal diseases that afflict about 1 in every 500 people in the U.S. IBD is not related to IBS. The most common forms are **ulcerative colitis** and **Crohn's disease.**[37] With ulcerative colitis, recurring inflammation and ulceration occur in the innermost layer of the large intestine. However, with Crohn's disease, the inflammation and ulceration can extend through all layers of the GI tract. Crohn's disease can occur in any part of the GI tract but is most common in the ileum and the ascending colon. The inflammation causes swelling and scar tissue, which can narrow the GI tract, creating a stricture. The ulcers can form fistulae, or deep tunnels, that extend from one area of the intestine to another or even to another organ outside the GI tract. IBD is most commonly diagnosed at around age 20; symptoms include rectal bleeding, diarrhea, abdominal pain, weight loss, and fever. Complications of IBD are caused by nutritional deficiencies and inflammation in other parts of the body. Nutritional problems include anemia due to blood loss; osteoporosis from lack of bone-forming nutrients; and protein-calorie malnutrition from low food intake, malabsorption, and high nutrient requirements for healing the damaged gastrointestinal tract.[38] Poor growth and delayed puberty may occur in those who develop IBD in childhood. Individuals with IBD are also at a higher risk of colon cancer.

The cause of IBD is not yet known, but an overactive inflammatory response to antigens (foreign substances such as bacteria or toxins) in the GI tract is suspected. There is a strong genetic association for IBD. Medical treatment for IBD includes medications to suppress the immune system, antibiotics, and surgery to remove the diseased area. Dietary intake and nutritional health should be closely monitored in those suffering from IBD.

Hemorrhoids

Hemorrhoids, also called piles, are swollen veins of the rectum and anus (like varicose veins in the legs). The blood vessels in this area are subject to intense pressure, especially during bowel movements. Obesity, prolonged sitting, and violent coughing or sneezing add stress to the vessels. Many pregnant women also develop hemorrhoids (see Chapter 16). Hemorrhoids develop unnoticed until a strained bowel movement triggers symptoms, which may include itching, pain, and bleeding.

Itching is caused by moisture, swelling, or other irritation in the anal canal (an approximately 2-inch-long section between the rectum and anus). Pain, if present, is usually a steady ache. Bleeding from a hemorrhoid may appear in the toilet as a bright red streak in the feces. The sensation of a mass in the anal canal after a bowel movement is a symptom of an internal hemorrhoid that protrudes through the anus.

Anyone can develop a hemorrhoid—about half of adults over age 50 do.[39] Pressure from prolonged sitting or exertion is often enough to bring on symptoms, although diet, lifestyle, and possibly heredity play a role. For example, a low-fiber diet can lead to hemorrhoids as a result of constipation and straining during bowel movements. If you think you have a hemorrhoid, you should consult your physician. Rectal bleeding, although usually caused by hemorrhoids, may also indicate other problems, such as cancer.

Take Action

Are You Taking Care of Your Digestive Tract?

All of us need to think about the health of our digestive tracts. To protect our GI tracts, there are symptoms we need to notice and habits we need to practice. Now that you know some basics about how your digestive system functions, use the following questionnaire to assess the health of your digestive tract. Section 4.8, When Digestive Processes Go Awry, can help you understand why these habits are important to examine. Answer each question yes or no.

Yes	No	1.	Are you currently experiencing greater than normal stress and tension?
Yes	No	2.	Do you have a family history of digestive tract problems (e.g., ulcers, hemorrhoids, acid indigestion, constipation, lactose intolerance)?
Yes	No	3.	Do you feel pain in your stomach region about 2 hours after eating?
Yes	No	4.	Do you smoke cigarettes?
Yes	No	5.	Do you take aspirin frequently?
Yes	No	6.	Do you have heartburn at least once per week?
Yes	No	7.	Do you commonly lie down after eating a large meal?
Yes	No	8.	Do you drink alcoholic beverages more than 2 or 3 times per day?
Yes	No	9.	Do you experience abdominal pain, bloating, and gas about 30 minutes to 2 hours after consuming milk products?
Yes	No	10.	Do you often have to strain while having a bowel movement?
Yes	No	11.	Do you consume less than 9 cups (women) to 13 cups (men) of a combination of water and other fluids per day?
Yes	No	12.	Do you perform physical activity (e.g., jog, swim, walk briskly, row, stair climb) less than 30 minutes on fewer than 5 days of the week?
Yes	No	13.	Do you eat a diet relatively low in fiber (significant fiber is found in whole fruits, vegetables, legumes, nuts, seeds, whole-grain breads, and whole-grain cereals)?
Yes	No	14.	Do you frequently have diarrhea?
Yes	No	15.	Do you frequently use laxatives or antacids?

Interpretation

If you answered yes to more than 8 questions, your habits and symptoms may put you at risk of digestive tract problems. Take particular note of the habits to which you answered yes. Consider trying to cooperate more with your digestive tract.

A physician may suggest a variety of self-care measures for hemorrhoids. Pain can be reduced by applying warm, soft compresses or sitting in a tub of warm water for 15 to 20 minutes. Dietary recommendations are the same as those for treating mild constipation, emphasizing the need to exercise every day and consume adequate fiber (25 to 35 grams daily) and fluid. Over-the-counter remedies, such as Preparation H*, offer symptom relief. Some hemorrhoids require removal procedures, usually done in a surgeon's office.

Knowledge Check

1. Which foods or eating practices can increase the risk of heartburn?
2. What is the most common cause of peptic ulcers?
3. What are 2 nutritional factors that can increase the risk of gallstones?
4. What are 3 factors that increase the chances of developing constipation?

▶ Lactose intolerance and diverticulosis are two other common GI tract disorders (these are discussed in Chapter 5).

Summary

4.1 The cell is the basic structural unit of the human body. Cells join together to make up tissues. The 4 primary types of tissues are epithelial, connective, muscle, and nervous. Tissues unite to form organs, and organs work together as an organ system.

4.2 The gastrointestinal (GI) tract includes the mouth, esophagus, stomach, small intestine, and large intestine (colon, rectum, and anus). Sphincters along the GI tract control the flow of digesting food. The accessory organs (liver, gallbladder, and pancreas) are an important part of the digestive system. Movement through the GI tract is mainly through muscular contractions known as peristalsis. GI contents are mixed with segmental contractions. Enzymes are specialized protein molecules that speed up digestion by catalyzing chemical reactions. Most digestive enzymes are synthesized in the small intestine and pancreas. A lack of digestive enzymes can result in poor digestion, poor absorption, malnutrition, and weight loss.

4.3 The mouth chews food to break it into smaller parts and increase its surface area, which enhances enzyme activity. Amylase produced by salivary glands digests a small amount of starch. Chewed food mixed with saliva is called a bolus. When swallowing is initiated, the epiglottis covers the trachea to prevent food from entering it. Peristalsis moves food down the esophagus. There are 5 basic taste sensations perceived by taste cells on taste buds in the mouth, especially the tongue. Genetic variability affects the ability to taste bitter compounds. The sense of smell contributes greatly to flavor perceptions.

4.4 The lower esophageal sphincter protects the esophagus from the backflow of acidic stomach contents. When this sphincter does not work normally, heartburn and GERD may occur. Stomach cells produce gastric juice (HCl, pepsinogen, mucus, and intrinsic factor). Pepsin (from pepsinogen) starts the digestion of protein. Mixing of food and gastric juice results in the production of chyme, the liquid substance released in small amounts into the small intestine.

4.5 The small intestine has 3 sections: duodenum, jejunum, and ileum. Most digestion occurs in the small intestine. Secretions from the liver, gallbladder, and pancreas are released into the small intestine. These secretions contain enzymes, bile, and sodium bicarbonate. Villi in the small intestine greatly increase its surface area, which enhances absorption. Villi are lined by enterocytes that release enzymes. Enterocytes are constantly broken down and replaced. Diseases, such as celiac disease, damage the villi and enterocytes. The liver, gallbladder, and pancreas aid digestion and absorption. The liver produces bile,

which is stored in the gallbladder and used to emulsify fat. Pancreatic juices contain the alkaline sodium bicarbonate and digestive enzymes. Bile and pancreatic juice are released into the small intestine via the pancreatic bile duct. Most nutrients are absorbed primarily in the small intestine. There are 4 main types of absorption: passive diffusion, facilitated diffusion, active absorption, and endocytosis. Hormones regulate digestion and absorption. The 4 major GI-regulating hormones are gastrin, cholecystokinin, secretin, and gastric inhibitory peptide.

4.6 Nutrients absorbed into the absorptive cells are transported in the body via either the cardiovascular or the lymphatic circulation. Water-soluble nutrients entering the cardiovascular system from absorptive cells travel via the hepatic portal vein to the liver, then to the general circulation and body tissues. Fat-soluble and large particles enter the lymphatic system from absorptive cells. Lymphatic vessels drain into the thoracic duct that releases its contents to the bloodstream.

4.7 The large intestine is the last part of the GI tract. It houses over 400 species of beneficial and pathogenic bacteria, absorbs water and electrolytes, and forms and eliminates feces. GI contents entering the large intestine are mainly water, some minerals, fiber, and some starch. Carbohydrates (fiber and starch) can be digested to some extent by bacteria in the large intestine and form short-chain fatty acids, which serve as an energy source for the large intestine and may help prevent and treat diseases. Bacteria in the large intestine also synthesize vitamin K and biotin and produce intestinal gas. Probiotics are live microorganisms found in fermented foods and supplements. They may promote intestinal health, such as preventing diarrhea in children. Prebiotics are nondigestible carbohydrates that promote the growth of beneficial bacteria in the large intestine. It takes 12 to 24 hours for contents to pass through the large intestine. Feces defecated through the rectum contain about 75% water and 25% solids—indigestible plant fibers, tough connective tissues from animal foods, and bacteria.

4.8 Common digestive disorders include heartburn, GERD, peptic ulcers, gallstones, constipation, diarrhea, irritable bowel syndrome, inflammatory bowel disease, and hemorrhoids. These disorders often can be prevented or managed with healthy nutrition and lifestyle habits.

Study Questions

1. What is the smallest functional unit of the human body?

   a. organ
   b. organ system
   c. cell
   d. epithelial tissue

2. Most digestive enzymes are produced in the _____.

   a. mouth and esophagus
   b. esophagus and stomach
   c. small intestine and pancreas
   d. liver and gallbladder

3. The coordinated squeezing and shortening of the muscles of the GI tract is called _____.

   a. enzyme hydrolysis
   b. peristalsis
   c. olfaction
   d. diarrhea

4. Which part of the digestive system normally houses large numbers of bacteria?

   a. large intestine
   b. small intestine
   c. stomach
   d. pancreas

5. The main role of the stomach in digestion and absorption is to _____.

   a. absorb proteins and carbohydrates
   b. digest fats
   c. mix ingested foods to form chyme
   d. produce enzymes that digest carbohydrates and fats

6. Villi are found mainly in the _____.

   a. large intestine
   b. small intestine
   c. esophagus
   d. stomach

7. Which of the following is known to prevent or treat diarrhea in developing countries?

   a. oral rehydration therapy
   b. supplemental zinc
   c. prevention of malnutrition
   d. all of the above

8. Both the _____ empty their contents into the small intestine via the sphincter of Oddi.

   a. stomach and gallbladder
   b. pancreas and stomach
   c. liver and pancreas
   d. gallbladder and stomach

9. The hormone _____ stimulates the release of pancreatic enzymes and bile from the gallbladder.

   a. gastrin
   b. lipase
   c. cholecystokinin
   d. gastric inhibitory peptide

10. The last section of the small intestine, known as the _____, is where _____ is absorbed and recirculated to the liver.

    a. jejunum; fat
    b. ileum; bile
    c. cecum; water
    d. duodenum; carbohydrate

11. _____ are absorbed in the large intestine.

    a. Vitamins and minerals
    b. Vitamins and water
    c. Fatty acids and minerals
    d. Water and electrolytes

12. Probiotics may be most useful in treating _____.

    a. diarrhea
    b. constipation
    c. celiac disease
    d. food intolerance

13. Which of the following digestive disorders is caused by the bacterium *Helicobacter pylori*?

    a. excessive intestinal gas
    b. constipation
    c. diarrhea
    d. peptic ulcer

14. Irritable bowel syndrome (IBS) is caused by flattening of the villi in the small intestine.

    a. true
    b. false

15. Match each secretion with the organ that produces it. Some organs may be selected more than once.

    hydrochloric acid
    sodium bicarbonate
    bile
    CCK
    brush border enzymes

    a. pancreas
    b. liver
    c. stomach
    d. small intestine

16. Consider the digestion and absorption of your evening meal. Write out the steps that occur with each of the digestive organs and secretions.

17. Explain why, after a period of semistarvation, normal amounts of food can be difficult to digest and absorb.

18. Describe how the absorption and transport of water-soluble and fat-soluble nutrients differ.

19. There are more microbes in the gastrointestinal tract than there are cells in the body. Explain their importance to a healthy gastrointestinal tract.

20. Describe the dietary and lifestyle practices that may help prevent or treat the following gastrointestinal problems: gastroesophageal reflux disease, gallstones, constipation, and diarrhea.

21. Differentiate irritable bowel syndrome from inflammatory bowel disease. Which of these conditions is generally regarded as most serious?

Answer Key: 1-c; 2-c; 3-b; 4-a; 5-c; 6-b; 7-d; 8-c; 9-c; 10-b; 11-d; 12-a; 13-d; 14-b. 15. hydrochloric acid-c; sodium bicarbonate-a and d; bile-b; CCK-d; brush border enzymes-d. 16-refer to Sections 4.3, 4.4, 4.5, 4.7; 17-refer to Section 4.5; 18-refer to Section 4.8; 19-refer to Section 4.7; 20-refer to Section 4.8; 21-refer to Section 4.8

Websites

To learn more about the topics covered in this chapter, visit these websites.

Digestion

digestive.niddk.nih.gov

www.acg.gi.org

www.healthfinder.org

Irritable Bowel Syndrome

www.ibsgroup.org

www.aboutibs.org

Celiac Disease and Gluten Sensitivities

digestive.niddk.nih.gov/ddiseases/pubs/celiac/index.htm

consensus.nih.gov/2004/2004CeliacDisease118html.htm

www.celiac.nih.gov

www.gluten.net

www.celiac.org

www.celiac.com

www.celiaccenter.org

www.celiacdiseasecenter.columbia.edu/CF-HOME.htm

celiaccenter.ucsd.edu

Inflammatory Bowel Disease

www.acg.gi.org/patients/cgp/pdf/ibd.pdf

digestive.niddk.nih.gov/ddiseases/pubs/crohns

digestive.niddk.nih.gov/ddiseases/pubs/colitis

www.ccfa.org

References

1. Tepper B. Nutritional implications of genetic taste variation: The role of PROP sensitivity and other taste phenotypes. *Annu Rev Nutr.* 2008;28:367.

2. Tordoff MG and others. Involvement of T1R3 in calcium-magnesium taste. *Physiol Genomics.* 2008;34:338–348.

3. Fushan AA and others. Allelic polymorphism within the TAS1R3 promoter is associated with human taste sensitivity to sucrose. *Curr Biol.* 2009;19:1288.

4. Muller O, Krawinkel M. Malnutrition and health in developing countries. *CMAJ.* 2005;173:279.

5. Glass RI. New hope for defeating rotavirus. *Scientific Am.* 2006; 294:46.

6. UNICEF. Nutrition. 2012; www.unicef.org/nutrition/index.html.

7. United Nations Children's Fund/World Health Organization. *Clinical management of acute diarrhea.* World Health Organization. 2004; rehydrate.org/diarrhoea/acute-diarrhoea.htm.

8. Parashar U, Glass R. Rotavirus vaccines—Early success, remaining questions. *N Engl J Med.* 2009;360:1063.

9. Richardson V and others. Effects of rotavirus vaccination on death from childhood diarrhea in Mexico. *N Engl J Med.* 2010;362:299.

10. Madhi SA and others. Effect of human rotavirus vaccine on severe diarrhea in African infants. *N Engl J Med.* 2010;362:289.

11. Food and Nutrition Board, Institute of Medicine. Dietary Reference Intakes for energy, carbohydrate, fiber, fat, fatty acids, cholesterol, protein and amino acids. Washington, DC: National Academy Press; 2005.

12. Douglas L, Sanders M. Probiotics and prebiotics in dietetics practice. *J Am Diet Assoc.* 2008;108:510.

13. Allen S and others. Probiotics for treating infectious diarrhoea. *Cochrane Database of Systematic Reviews.* 2003, Issue 4. Art No. CD003048. DOI: 10.1002/14651858.CD003048.pub2.

14. Johnston B and others. Probiotics for the prevention of pediatric antibiotic-associated diarrhea. *Cochrane Database of Systematic Reviews.* 2007, Issue 2. Art No. CD004827. DOI: 10.1002/145651858.CD004827.pub2.

15. AlFaleh K, Bassler D. Probiotics for prevention of necrotizing enterocolitis in preterm infants. *Cochrane Database of Systematic Reviews.* 2008, Issue 1. Art No. CD005496. DOI: 10.1002/14561858.CD005496.pub2.

16. National Digestive Diseases Information Clearinghouse. Heartburn, gastroesophageal reflux (GER) and hiatal hernia and gastroesophageal reflux disease (GERD). *Digestive Diseases.* 2007; digestive.niddk.nih.gov/ddiseases/pubs/gerd/index.htm.

17. Hampel H and others. Meta-analysis: Obesity and the risk for gastroesophageal reflux disease and its complications. *Ann Internal Med.* 2005;143:199.

18. Fass R. The pathophysiological mechanisms of GERD in the obese patient. *Dig Dis Sci* 2008;53:2300.

19. Kandulski A, Malfertheiner P. GERD in 2010: diagnosis, novel mechanisms of disease and promising agents. *Nat Rev Gastroent Hepat.* 2011;8:73.

20. American College of Gastroenterology. Ulcers and the treatment of ulcers caused by *H. pylori* infection. 2011; www.acg.gi.org/patients/patientinfo/ulcers.asp.

21. Malfertheiner P and others. Peptic ulcer disease. *Lancet.* 2009;374:1449.

22. Portincaso P and others. Cholesterol gallstone disease. *Lancet.* 2006;368:230.

23. Tsai C and others. Long-term effect of magnesium consumption on the risk of symptomatic gallstone disease among men. *Am J Gastroenterol.* 2008;103:375.

24. Bellows CF and others. Management of gallstones. *Am Family Physician.* 2005;72:637.

25. Tsai C-J and others. Dietary protein and the risk of cholecystectomy in a cohort of US women: The Nurses Health Study. *Am J Epi.* 2004;160:11.

26. National Digestive Diseases Information Clearinghouse. Gallstones. 2007; digestive.niddk.nih.gov/ddiseases/pubs/gallstones/index.htm.

27. National Digestive Diseases Information Clearinghouse. Gas in the digestive tract. *Digestive Diseases.* January 2008; digestive.niddk.nih.gov/ddiseases/pubs/gas/index.htm.

28. Quigley EM. The enteric microbiota in the pathogenesis and management of constipation. *Best Pract Res Clin Gastroent.* 2011;25:119.

29. Liu LW Chronic **constipation:** current treatment options. *Can J Gastroenterol* 2011;25 Suppl B: 22B.

30. Rubio-Tapia A and others. Increased prevalence and mortality in undiagnosed celiac disease. *Gastroenterol.* 2009;137:373.

31. Sabatino A, Corazza GR. Coeliac disease. *Lancet.* 2009;373:1480.

32. Niewinski M. Advances in celiac disease and gluten-free diet. *J Am Diet Assoc.* 2008;108:661.

33. American Academy of Pediatrics. Children's health topics: gastroenterology and hepatology. 2007; www.aap.org/healthtopics/gastroenterology.cfm.

34. Malone MA. Irritable bowel syndrome. *Prim Care* 2011; 38:433.

35. Moynihan NT and others. How do you spell relief for irritable bowel syndrome? *J Fam Pract.* 2008;57:100.

36. Heizer W and others. The role of diet in symptoms of irritable bowel syndrome in adults: A narrative review. *J Am Diet Assoc.* 2009;109:1204.

37. Crohn's and Colitis Foundation of America. 2011; www.ccfa.org.

38. Sharmir R. Nutritional aspects in inflammatory bowel disease. *J Pediatric Gastroenterology and Nutrition.* 2009;48:S86.

39. Harvard Medical Center. Hemorrhoids and what to do about them. *Harvard Women's Health Watch.* 2004;July:4.

40. Insogna KL. The effect of proton pump-inhibiting drugs on mineral metabolism. *Am J Gastroenterol* 2009; 104 Suppl 2: S2.

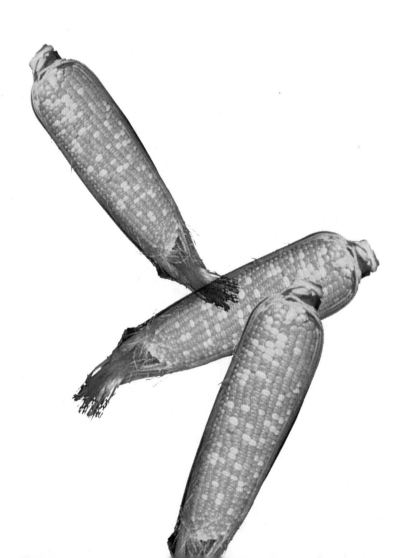

Energy-Yielding Nutrients and Alcohol

Sticky rice was the secret ingredient in super-strong mortar used in tombs, pagodas, and city walls in China 1500 years ago. Amylopectin, a type of complex carbohydrate found in rice, made the mortar strong and durable. Learn more at **pubs.acs.org/doi/abs/10.1021/ar9001944.**

PART 2 Energy-Yielding Nutrients and Alcohol

5 Carbohydrates

Student Learning Outcomes

After studying this chapter, you will be able to

1. Identify the major types of carbohydrates and give examples of food sources for each.

2. List alternative sweeteners that can be used to reduce sugar intake.

3. Describe recommendations for carbohydrate intake and health risks caused by low or excessive intakes.

4. List the functions of carbohydrates in the body.

5. Explain how carbohydrates are digested and absorbed.

6. Explain the cause of, effects of, and dietary treatment for lactose intolerance.

7. Describe the regulation of blood glucose, conditions caused by blood glucose imbalance, types of diabetes, and dietary treatments for diabetes.

8. Describe dietary measures to reduce the risk of developing type 2 diabetes.

FRUITS, VEGETABLES, DAIRY PRODUCTS, CEREALS, breads, pasta, and desserts—all of these supply carbohydrates (i.e., sugar, starch, and fiber). Maybe you've avoided many of these foods in an attempt to lose weight or "bulk up" with muscle. Unfortunately, the benefits of carbohydrates are frequently misunderstood.[1] People often mistakenly think carbohydrate-rich foods are fattening or cause diabetes. However, high-carbohydrate foods—especially fiber-rich foods, such as fruits, vegetables, legumes, and whole-grain breads and cereals—provide essential nutrients and should constitute about 45 to 65% of our daily energy intake.[2] They also add interest to our diets—consider the vivid colors of fruits and vegetables, the crunchiness of cereals, and the delicious flavors of desserts.

Carbohydrates are a primary fuel source for cells, especially the cells of the central nervous system and red blood cells.[3] Muscle cells also rely on carbohydrates to fuel intense physical activity. Yielding an average of 4 kcal/g, carbohydrates are a readily available fuel for all cells in the form of glucose (a sugar) in the blood and glycogen (a starch) in the liver and muscles. Glycogen can be broken down to glucose and released into the blood to maintain blood glucose levels when the diet does not supply enough. Regular intake of carbohydrate is important because glycogen stores in the liver and muscles are exhausted in about 18 hours if no carbohydrate is consumed.[3] After that point, the body is forced to produce glucose from protein or to use fat as the primary source of energy; as you will learn later in this chapter; this eventually leads to health problems.

Figure 5-1 Food sources of carbohydrates. In addition to MyPlate food groups, yellow is used for oils and pink is used for substances that do not fit easily into food groups (e.g., honey and soft drinks).

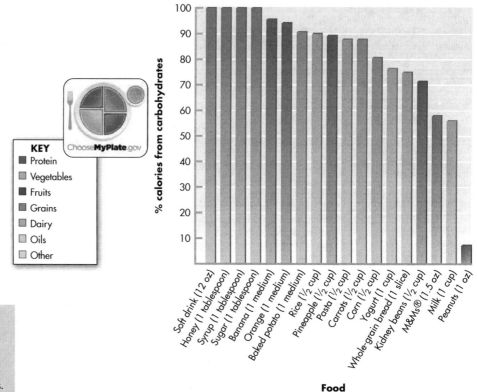

KEY
- Protein
- Vegetables
- Fruits
- Grains
- Dairy
- Oils
- Other

monosaccharide Class of single sugars that are not broken down further during digestion.

disaccharide Class of sugars formed by the chemical bonding of 2 monosaccharides.

polysaccharide Class of complex carbohydrates containing many glucose units, from 10 to 1000 or more.

5.1 Structures of Carbohydrates

The carbohydrate family includes sugar, starch, and fiber (Fig. 5-1). Most forms of carbohydrates are composed of carbon, hydrogen, and oxygen. Plants are the main source of carbohydrates. During photosynthesis, plants produce glucose by using carbon and oxygen from carbon dioxide in the air, hydrogen from water, and energy from the sun (Fig. 5-2). Plants either store the glucose or transform it into starch, fiber, fat, or protein.

The general formula for carbohydrates is $(CH_2O)_n$ or $C_n(H_2O)_n$, where n represents the number of times the formula is repeated. For example, the chemical formula for glucose is $C_6H_{12}O_6$ or $(CH_2O)_6$. The simpler forms of carbohydrates are called **monosaccharides** and **disaccharides.** Monosaccharides are single sugars with the general formula of $(CH_2O)_6$. Disaccharides are double sugars, made of 2 monosaccharide sugars, with the general formula of $(CH_2O)_{12}$. The more complex forms of carbohydrates (i.e., glycogen, starch, and fiber) are called **polysaccharides** and typically contain many glucose molecules linked together.

Monosaccharides: Glucose, Fructose, Galactose, Sugar Alcohols, and Pentoses

The common monosaccharides (*mono* means "one"; *saccharide* means "sugar") are glucose, fructose, and galactose. The structures of these monosaccharides are shown in Figure 5-3. Notice that each of these monosaccharides contains 6 carbon, 12 hydrogen, and 6 oxygen molecules, but in slightly different configurations.

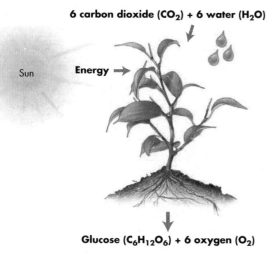

6 carbon dioxide (CO₂) + 6 water (H₂O)

Sun

Energy

Glucose (C₆H₁₂O₆) + 6 oxygen (O₂)

Figure 5-2 A summary of photosynthesis. Plants use carbon dioxide, water, and energy to produce glucose. Glucose is then stored in the leaves but also can undergo further metabolism to form starch and fiber in the plant. With the addition of nitrogen from the soil or air, glucose also can be transformed into protein.

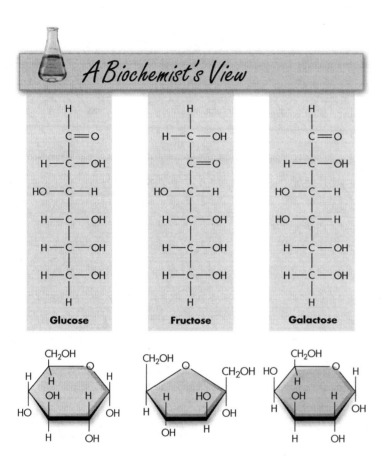

Figure 5-3 The 6-carbon monosaccharides—glucose, fructose, and galactose—shown in the linear form and in their most common form—as a ring (each corner represents a carbon atom unless otherwise indicated). Being familiar with the chemical structures makes it easier to understand how sugars are interrelated, combined, digested, metabolized, and synthesized.

Because each is a 6-carbon sugar, it is classified as a **hexose** (*hex* means "6"; *ose* refers to "sugar" or "carbohydrate").

Glucose is the most abundant monosaccharide, although we eat very little of it as a monosaccharide. Much of the glucose in our diets is linked together with additional sugars to form disaccharides or polysaccharides. In the body, glucose is sometimes called "blood sugar."

The monosaccharide **fructose** is found in fruits, vegetables, honey (which is about 50% fructose and 50% glucose), and high-fructose corn syrup. Because high-fructose corn syrup is sweeter and less expensive than table sugar, it is used to sweeten many food products, especially beverages. The presence of fructose in these products makes it a common sugar in our diets. In most North American diets, fructose accounts for about 9 to 11% of total energy intake.[4]

Galactose is the third major monosaccharide of nutritional importance. A comparison of the structure of this sugar with that of glucose shows that they are almost identical (see Fig. 5-3). Most of the galactose in our diets is found in combination with glucose. When galactose combines with glucose, it forms a disaccharide called **lactose,** which is found in milk and other dairy products.

The sugar alcohols, which are derivatives of monosaccharides, include sorbitol, mannitol, and xylitol. These are used primarily as sweeteners in sugarless gum and dietetic foods.

Two additional monosaccharides found in nature are ribose and deoxyribose. These are classified as "pentoses" because they contain 5 carbons (*penta* means "5"). Although these sugars do not need to be supplied by the diet, they are very important in the body because they are an essential part of the cell's genetic material. Ribose is part of ribonucleic acid (RNA), and deoxyribose is part of deoxyribonucleic acid (DNA).

Simple Forms of Carbohydrates

Monosaccharides: glucose, fructose, galactose

Disaccharides: sucrose, lactose, maltose

Complex Forms of Carbohydrates

Oligosaccharides: raffinose, stachyose

Polysaccharides: starches (amylose and amylopectin), glycogen, fiber

hexose A carbohydrate containing 6 carbons.

glucose Most abundant monosaccharide; also called dextrose.

fructose Monosaccharide found in fruits, vegetables, and honey; also called levulose.

galactose Monosaccharide found most abundantly as a part of lactose (milk sugar).

condensation reaction Chemical reaction in which 2 molecules bond to form a larger molecule by releasing water.

Disaccharides: Maltose, Sucrose, and Lactose

Carbohydrates containing 2 monosaccharides are called disaccharides (*di* means "2"). The linking of 2 monosaccharides occurs in a **condensation reaction.** During this reaction, 1 molecule of water is formed (and released) by taking a hydroxyl group (OH) from 1 sugar and a hydrogen (H) from the other sugar (Fig. 5-4).

One carbon on each monosaccharide participating in the condensation reaction chemically bonds with a single oxygen. Two forms of this C—O—C bond exist in nature:

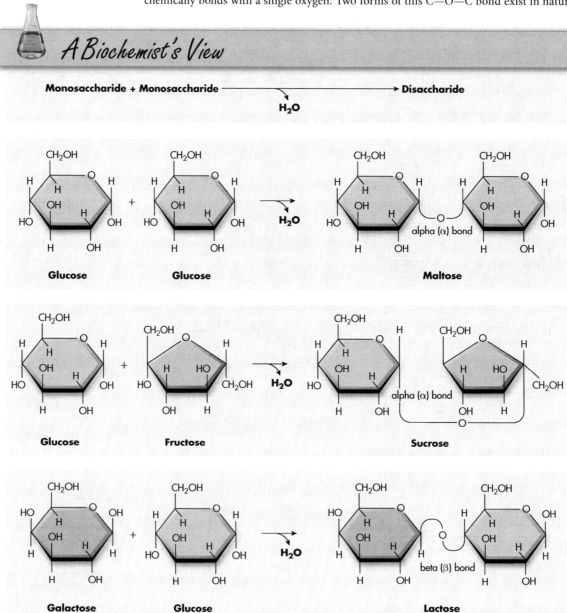

A Biochemist's View

Figure 5-4 Two monosaccharides combine to form a disaccharide.

- Maltose is made up of 2 glucose molecules.
- Sucrose, or common table sugar, is made up of glucose and fructose.
- Lactose, or milk sugar, is made up of glucose and galactose. Note that lactose contains a different type of bond (beta, or β) than maltose and sucrose (alpha, or α); this type of bond makes it difficult for individuals who produce little of the enzyme lactase to digest lactose.

alpha (α) bonds and beta (β) bonds. As shown in Figure 5-4, maltose and sucrose contain the alpha form, whereas lactose contains the beta form. Many carbohydrates contain long chains of glucose with the individual monosaccharides bonded together by either alpha or beta bonds.

Beta bonds differ from alpha bonds in that they cannot be easily broken down by digestive enzymes for absorption in the small intestine. Thus, foods that contain saccharide molecules linked together by beta bonds (e.g., in milk and dietary fiber) are often difficult or impossible for individuals to digest because they lack the enzymes necessary for breaking beta bonds apart.

The disaccharide **maltose** contains 2 glucose molecules joined by an alpha bond. When seeds sprout, they produce enzymes that break down polysaccharides stored in the seed to sugars, such as maltose and glucose. These sugars provide the energy for the plant to grow. Malting, the first step in the production of alcoholic beverages, such as beer, lets grain seeds sprout. Few other food products or beverages contain maltose. In fact, most of the maltose we ultimately digest in the small intestine is produced when we break down longer-chain polysaccharides.

Sucrose, common table sugar, is composed of glucose and fructose linked by an alpha bond. Large amounts of sucrose are found naturally in plants, such as sugarcane, sugar beets, and maple tree sap. The sucrose from these sources can be purified to various degrees. Brown, white, and powdered sugars are common forms of sucrose sold in grocery stores.

Lactose, the primary sugar in milk and milk products, consists of glucose joined to galactose by a beta bond. As discussed later in this chapter, many people are unable to digest large amounts of lactose because they don't produce enough of the enzyme lactase, which is needed to break this beta bond. This can cause intestinal gas, bloating, cramping, and discomfort as the unabsorbed lactose is metabolized into acids and gases by bacteria in the large intestine.[5]

Many terms are used to refer to monosaccharides and disaccharides and products containing these sugars. Monosaccharides and disaccharides often are referred to as *simple sugars* because they contain only 1 or 2 sugar units. Food labels combine all the sugars either naturally present in food products or added during their manufacture into one category, listing them as "sugars."[1]

Beano® contains an enzyme, called alphagalactosidase, that can break apart the bonds in oligosaccharides. This helps reduce the intestinal gas produced when beans and other legumes are eaten.

CRITICAL THINKING

Keith enjoys Mexican food, especially with a generous portion of black or pinto beans. However, he often develops gas and intestinal cramps after these meals. His friends suggest that he try using a product called Beano® to reduce his symptoms. How might it help Keith?

Oligosaccharides: Raffinose and Stachyose

Oligosaccharides are complex carbohydrates that contain 3 to 10 single sugar units (*oligo* means "few"). Two oligosaccharides of nutritional importance are **raffinose** and **stachyose,** which are found in onions, cabbage, broccoli, whole wheat, and legumes, such as kidney beans and soybeans. Oligosaccharides cannot be broken down by our digestive enzymes. Thus, when we eat foods with raffinose and stachyose, these oligosaccharides pass undigested into the large intestine, where bacteria metabolize them, producing gas and other by-products.[6]

Although many people have no symptoms after eating legumes, others experience unpleasant side effects from intestinal gas. An enzyme preparation, such as Beano®, can help prevent these side effects if taken right before a meal. This enzyme preparation works in the digestive tract to break down many of the indigestible oligosaccharides.

Polysaccharides: Starch, Glycogen, and Fiber

Polysaccharides are complex carbohydrates that often contain hundreds to thousands of glucose molecules. The polysaccharides include some that are digestible, such as **starch,** and some that are largely indigestible, such as **fiber.** The digestibility of these polysaccharides is determined mainly by whether the glucose units are linked together by alpha or beta bonds.

raffinose Indigestible oligosaccharide made of 3 monosaccharides (galactose-glucose-fructose).

stachyose Indigestible oligosaccharide made of 4 monosaccharides (galactose-galactose-glucose-fructose).

starch Complex carbohydrate made of multiple units of glucose attached together in a form that the body can digest.

fiber Complex carbohydrate in foods of plant origin that is made of multiple units of glucose attached together in a form that cannot be broken down by digestive processes in the stomach or small intestine.

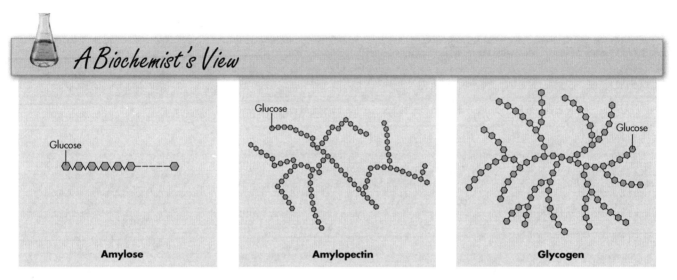

Figure 5-5 Digestible polysaccharides. Amylose and amylopectin are the storage forms of glucose in plants. Glycogen is the storage form of glucose in animals.

As some vegetables age, their sugars are converted to starches, making them taste less sweet.

Digestible Polysaccharides: Starch and Glycogen

Starch, the major digestible polysaccharide in our diets, is the storage form of glucose in plants. There are 2 types of plant starch—**amylose** and **amylopectin**—both of which are a source of energy for plants and for animals that eat plants. Amylose and amylopectin are found in potatoes, beans, breads, pasta, rice, and other starchy products, typically in a ratio of about 1:4.

Amylose and amylopectin contain many glucose units linked by alpha bonds. The primary difference is that amylose is a linear, unbranched chain of glucose molecules that contains only 1 type of alpha bond (called a 1-4 bond), whereas amylopectin is a highly branched–chain structure that links glucose molecules using 2 types of alpha bonds (1-4 bonds link straight chains of glucose and 1-6 bonds link glucose at the branching points) (Fig. 5-5). Alpha 1-4 bonds are broken by amylase enzymes produced in the mouth and pancreas. Alpha 1-6 bonds are broken by an intestinal enzyme called alpha-dextrinase. The more numerous the branches in a starch, the more sites (ends) available for enzyme action. This explains why amylopectin causes blood glucose levels to increase more quickly than amylose.

The properties of amylopectin and amylose make them useful in food manufacturing. The branches in amylopectin allow it to retain water to form a very stable starch gel. Thus, food manufacturers commonly use starches rich in amylopectin to thicken sauces and gravies. Amylopectin also is used in many frozen foods because it remains stable over a wide temperature range. Amylose-rich molecules can be bonded to one another to produce modified food starch, a thickener used in baby foods, salad dressings, and instant puddings.

Glycogen, the storage form of carbohydrate in humans and other animals, also contains many glucose units linked together with alpha bonds. The structure of glycogen is similar to that of amylopectin, but it is even more highly branched. The branched structure of glycogen allows it to be broken down quickly by enzymes in the body cells where it is stored.

Liver and muscle cells are the major storage sites for glycogen. The amount stored in these cells is influenced by the amount of carbohydrate in the diet. Although the amount of glycogen that can be stored is limited, glycogen storage is extremely important.[3] The approximately 90 grams (360 kcal) of glycogen stored in the liver can be converted into blood glucose to supply the body with energy, whereas the 300 grams (1200 kcal) of glycogen stored in muscles supply glucose for muscle use, especially during high-intensity and endurance exercise. (See Chapter 11 for a detailed discussion of carbohydrate use during physical activity.)

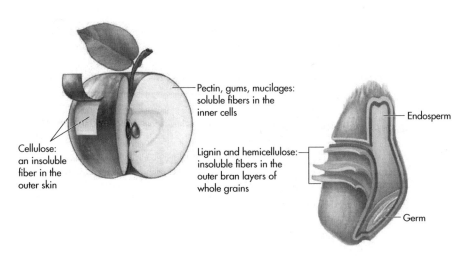

Figure 5-6 Types of dietary fiber. The skin of an apple consists of the insoluble fiber cellulose, which provides structure for the fruit. The soluble fiber pectin "glues" the fruit cells together. The outside covering of a wheat kernel is made of layers of bran—insoluble fibers.

▶ The Food and Nutrition Board has recommended that the terms *soluble* and *insoluble fibers* gradually be replaced by other terms, such as *viscosity* and *fermentability*, which more clearly describe the properties of fibers. The actual terms used may change as scientific knowledge expands.

Indigestible Polysaccharides: Dietary and Functional Fiber

Folklore surrounding fiber, or "roughage," has been a part of American culture since the 1800s, when a minister named Sylvester Graham traveled up and down the East Coast, extolling the virtues of fiber. He left us a legacy—the graham cracker. Although today's graham cracker bears little resemblance to the whole-grain product he promoted, present-day scientific evidence supports this early promotion of fiber as part of a healthy diet.

Total fiber (or just the term *fiber*) refers to the **dietary fiber** that occurs naturally in foods, as well as the **functional fiber** that may be added to food to provide health benefits.[2] Currently, Nutrition Facts labels include only dietary fiber and do not reflect any added functional fiber.

Fibers are composed primarily of the nonstarch polysaccharides **cellulose, hemicelluloses, pectins, gums,** and **mucilages. Lignins** are the only noncarbohydrate components of dietary fibers. Unlike the digestible polysaccharides that contain alpha bonds, the monosaccharide units in fibers are linked by beta bonds. As noted earlier, monosaccharide molecules joined by beta bonds are not broken down by human digestive enzymes. Thus, these undigested fibers pass through the small intestine into the large intestine, where bacteria metabolize some and form short-chain fatty acids and gas. These short-chain fatty acids provide fuel for cells in the large intestine and enhance intestinal health.[7] Pectins, gums, and mucilages are most readily digested by the intestinal bacteria, yielding about 1.5 to 2.5 kcal/g. Cellulose, hemicellulose, and lignins are more resistant to being broken down by bacteria. The body tends to adapt over time to a high-fiber intake, leading to fewer symptoms of bloating, gas, and discomfort.[6]

Cellulose, hemicelluloses, and lignins form the structural part of the plant cell wall in vegetables and whole grains. Bran layers form the outer covering of all seeds; thus, whole grains (those in which the bran and outer layers have not been removed in processing) are good sources of fiber (Fig. 5-6). Because of their chemical structure, these fibers do not dissolve in water. Therefore, they are often referred to as **insoluble fibers.**

In contrast to the insoluble fibers, pectins, gums, mucilages, and some hemicelluloses dissolve easily in water and are classified as **soluble fibers.** In water, they become viscous (gel-like) in consistency. This property makes them useful for thickening jam, jelly, yogurt, and other food products. They also occur naturally inside and around plant cells in oat bran, many fruits, legumes, and psyllium.

total fiber Dietary and functional fiber in food.

dietary fiber Fiber naturally in food.

functional fiber Fiber added to food to provide health benefits.

insoluble fibers Fibers that are not easily dissolved in water or metabolized by bacteria in the large intestine; include cellulose, some hemicelluloses, and lignins.

soluble fibers Fibers that dissolve in water and can be metabolized (fermented) by bacteria in the large intestine; include pectin, gums, and mucilages; also called viscous fibers.

Fruit is a good source of dietary fiber.

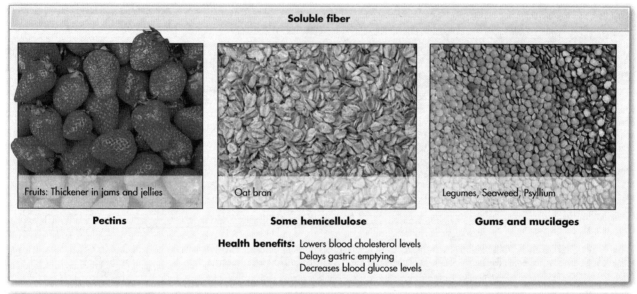

Soluble fiber

Fruits: Thickener in jams and jellies

Pectins

Oat bran

Some hemicellulose

Legumes, Seaweed, Psyllium

Gums and mucilages

Health benefits: Lowers blood cholesterol levels
Delays gastric emptying
Decreases blood glucose levels

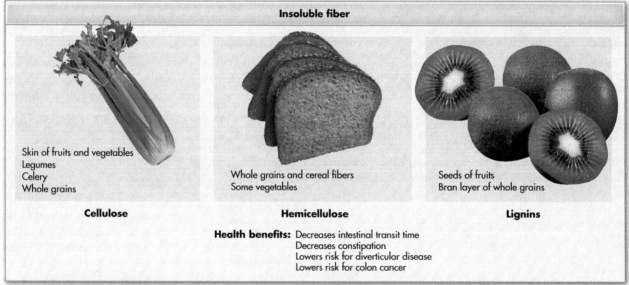

Insoluble fiber

Skin of fruits and vegetables
Legumes
Celery
Whole grains

Cellulose

Whole grains and cereal fibers
Some vegetables

Hemicellulose

Seeds of fruits
Bran layer of whole grains

Lignins

Health benefits: Decreases intestinal transit time
Decreases constipation
Lowers risk for diverticular disease
Lowers risk for colon cancer

Figure 5-7 Soluble and insoluble fibers. Fibers can be classified as either soluble or insoluble based on their properties. Soluble fibers dissolve in water, whereas insoluble fibers do not dissolve in water.

The physical properties of soluble and insoluble fibers provide health benefits (Fig. 5-7). When consumed in adequate quantities, these fibers have been shown to lower blood cholesterol levels and blood glucose levels, thereby reducing risks of cardiovascular disease and diabetes.[8,9] In addition, fiber can decrease intestinal transit time, thus reducing risks of constipation, diverticular disease, and colon cancer.[8, 10–12] The health benefits of fiber are discussed in detail later in the chapter.

Knowledge Check

1. Which sugars are classified as monosaccharides? As disaccharides?
2. Why are foods that contain saccharide units linked by beta bonds difficult to digest?
3. What types of carbohydrates are classified as polysaccharides?

5.2 Carbohydrates in Foods

Carbohydrates are found in a wide variety of foods. Foods such as table sugar, jam, jelly, fruit, fruit juices, soft drinks, baked potatoes, rice, pasta, cereals, and breads are predominantly carbohydrates. Other foods, such as dried beans, lentils, corn, peas, and dairy products (milk and yogurt), also are good sources of carbohydrate, although they contribute protein, and in some cases fat, to our diets as well. Foods with little or no carbohydrate include meats, fish, poultry, eggs, vegetable oils, butter, and margarine.

Starch

Starches contribute much of the carbohydrate in our diets. Recall that plants store glucose as polysaccharides in the form of starches. Thus, plant-based foods—such as legumes, tubers, and the grains (wheat, rye, corn, oats, barley, and rice) used to make breads, cereals, and pasta—are the best sources of starch. A diet rich in these starches provides ample carbohydrate, as well as many micronutrients.

Fiber

Fiber can be found in many of the same foods as starch, so a diet rich in grains, legumes, and tubers also can provide significant amounts of dietary fiber (especially insoluble cellulose, hemicellulose, and lignins). Because much of the fiber in whole grains is found in the outer layers, which are removed in processing, highly processed grains are low in fiber. Soluble fibers (pectin, gums, mucilages) are found in the skins and flesh of many fruits and berries; as thickeners and stabilizers in jams, yogurts, sauces, and fillings; and in products that contain psyllium and seaweed.

For individuals who have difficulties consuming adequate dietary fiber, fiber is available as a supplement or as an additive to certain foods (functional fiber). In this way, individuals with relatively low dietary fiber intakes can still obtain the health benefits of fiber.

Nutritive Sweeteners

The various substances that impart sweetness to foods fall into 2 broad classes: nutritive sweeteners, which can be metabolized to yield energy, and non-nutritive (alternative) sweeteners, which provide no food energy (Table 5-1). The sweetness of sucrose (table sugar)

Breads are a rich source of carbohydrate.

Table 5-1 Typical Sources of Sweeteners

Type of Sweetener	Typical Sources
Nutritive Sweeteners	
Sugars	
Lactose	Dairy products
Maltose	Sprouted seeds, some alcoholic beverages
Glucose	Corn syrup, honey
Sucrose	Table sugar, most sweets
Invert sugar*	Some candies, honey
Fructose	Fruit, honey, some soft drinks, corn syrup
Sugar Alcohols	
Sorbitol	Sugarless candies, sugarless gum
Mannitol	Sugarless candies
Xylitol	Sugarless gum
Non-Nutritive (Alternative) Sweeteners	
Tagatose (Naturlose˚)	Ready-to-eat cereals, diet soft drinks, health bars, frozen yogurt, fat-free ice cream, candies, frosting, sugarless gum
Cyclamate	Not currently in use in the U.S. but available in Canada
Aspartame (Equal˚)	Diet soft drinks, diet fruit drinks, sugarless gum, powdered diet sweetener
Acesulfame-K (Sunette˚)	Sugarless gum, diet drink mixes, powdered diet sweeteners, puddings, gelatin desserts
Saccharin (Sweet'N Low˚)	Diet soft drinks
Sucralose (Splenda˚)	Diet soft drinks, tabletop use, sugarless gum, jams, frozen desserts
Neotame	Tabletop sweetener, baked goods, frozen desserts, diet soft drinks, jams and jellies
Stevia (Truvia˚)	Diet soft drinks

*Sucrose broken down into glucose and fructose.

There are many forms of sugar in our diets.

160   **PART 2**   Energy-Yielding Nutrients and Alcohol

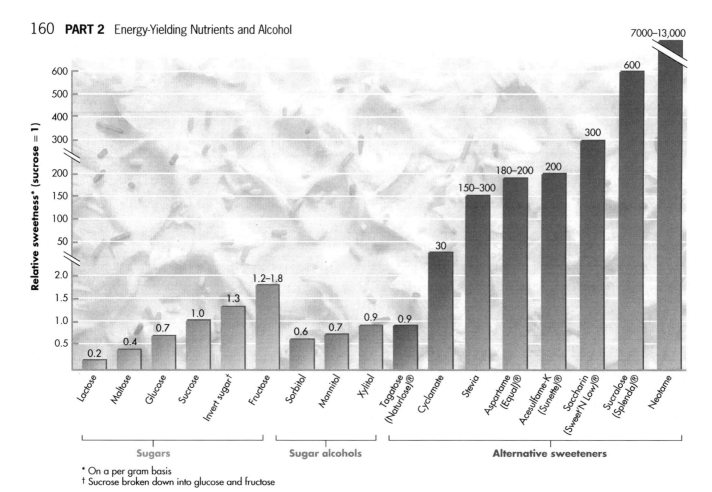

* On a per gram basis
† Sucrose broken down into glucose and fructose

Figure 5-8 Sweetness of sugars and alternative sweeteners compared with sucrose.

makes it the benchmark against which all other sweeteners are measured. As shown in Figure 5-8, the alternative sweeteners are much sweeter on a per gram basis than the nutritive sweeteners.[1]

The monosaccharides (glucose, fructose, and galactose) and disaccharides (sucrose, lactose, and maltose) are classified as nutritive sweeteners (Table 5-2).[1] Sucrose is obtained from sugarcane and sugar beet plants. Most of the sucrose and the other sugars we eat come from foods and beverages to which sugar has been added during processing and/or manufacturing. The major sources are soft drinks, candy, cakes, cookies, pies, fruit drinks, and dairy desserts, such as ice cream. In general, the more processed the food, the more simple sugar it contains. The rest of the sugar in our diets is present naturally in foods such as fruits and juices.

A nutritive sweetener used frequently by the food industry is high-fructose corn syrup. High-fructose corn syrup is made by treating cornstarch with acid and enzymes to break down much of the starch into glucose. Then enzymes convert some of the glucose into fructose. The final syrup is about 55% fructose, although it can range from 40 to 90% fructose. High-fructose corn syrup is similar in sweetness to sucrose, but it is much cheaper to use in food products. High-fructose corn syrup is used in soft drinks, candies, jam, jelly, and desserts (e.g., packaged cookies).[4]

Sugar Alcohols

The sugar alcohols, sorbitol, mannitol, and xylitol, are nutritive sweeteners used in sugarless gum and candies. Sugar alcohols are

Table 5-2 Nutritive Sweeteners Used in Foods	
Sugar	Honey
Sucrose	Corn syrup or sweeteners
Brown sugar	High-fructose corn syrup
Confectioner's sugar (powdered sugar)	Molasses
Turbinado sugar	Date sugar
Invert sugar	Maple syrup
Glucose	Dextrin
Sorbitol	Dextrose
Levulose	Fructose
Polydextrose	Maltose
Lactose	Caramel
Mannitol	Fruit sugar

not readily metabolized by bacteria in the mouth and thus do not promote dental caries as readily as do sugars such as sucrose. Sugar alcohols do contribute energy (about 1.5–3 kcal/g), but they are absorbed and metabolized to glucose more slowly than sugars. In large quantities, sugar alcohols can cause diarrhea, so labels must include this warning.

Sugar alcohols are listed individually on ingredient labels if only 1 sugar alcohol is used in a product; they are grouped together under the heading "sugar alcohols" if 2 or more are used. The calories listed on Nutrition Facts labels account for the calories in each sugar alcohol in the food products.

Non-Nutritive (Alternative) Sweeteners

Non-nutritive (alternative or artificial) sweeteners provide very-low-calorie or noncaloric sugar substitutes for people with diabetes and those trying to lose (or control) body weight. Alternative sweeteners include saccharin, cyclamate, aspartame, neotame, sucralose, acesulfame-K, tagatose, and stevia.[1, 13] Alternative sweeteners yield little or no energy when consumed in amounts typically used in food products and do not promote dental caries. All but cyclamate are currently available in the U.S. Due to concerns about increased cancer risk, cyclamate was banned for use in the U.S. in 1970, although it has never been conclusively shown to cause health problems when used appropriately. Cyclamate is still used in Canada and many other countries as a tabletop sweetener and as a sweetener in certain medications.

The safety of sweeteners is determined by the FDA and is indicated by an **Acceptable Daily Intake (ADI)** guideline.[13] The ADI is the amount of alternative sweetener considered safe for daily use over one's lifetime. ADIs are based on studies in laboratory animals and are set at a level 100 times less than the level at which no harmful effects were noted in animal studies. Alternative sweeteners can be used safely by adults and children. Although general use is considered safe during pregnancy, pregnant women may want to discuss this issue with their health-care providers.[1]

Saccharin

The oldest alternative sweetener, saccharin, is approximately 300 times sweeter than sucrose. Saccharin was once thought to pose a risk of bladder cancer based on studies using laboratory animals. It is no longer listed as a potential cause of cancer in humans because the earlier research is now considered weak and inconclusive.[1] The FDA has set the ADI for saccharin at 5 mg/kg body weight per day. For a 154-pound (70 kg) adult, this equates to approximately three 12-ounce diet soft drinks or nine packets of the sweetener (e.g., Sweet'N Low*) daily.[13] Saccharin is used as a tabletop sweetener and in a variety of foods and beverages. It is not useful in cooking because heating causes it to develop a bitter taste.

Aspartame

Aspartame is used throughout the world to sweeten beverages, gelatin desserts, chewing gum, cookies, and the toppings and fillings of prepared bakery goods. Aspartame breaks down when heated and loses its sweetness when foods are cooked or heated. NutraSweet* and Equal* are brand names for aspartame.

Although aspartame yields about 4 kcal/g (the same calories as sucrose), it is 180 to 200 times sweeter than sucrose. Thus, because only a small amount of aspartame is needed to sweeten a food or beverage, it does not contribute calories to foods. The ADI for aspartame for an adult is 50 mg/kg body weight/day. This is equivalent to about 18 cans of diet soft drink or about 80 packets of Equal*.[13]

Scientific evidence has shown that the use of aspartame is safe for most individuals. However, the FDA has received reports of adverse reactions (headaches, dizziness, seizures, nausea, and other side effects) to aspartame. Although the percentage of people affected is very small, it is important for people who are sensitive to aspartame to avoid it. Those with the genetic disease phenylketonuria (PKU), which interferes with the metabolism of the amino acid phenylalanine, also should avoid aspartame because of its high phenylalanine content.

Soft drinks are common sources of sugars and alternative sweeteners.

INGREDIENTS: SORBITOL, GUM BASE, MANNITOL, GLYCEROL, HYDROGENATED GLUCOSE SYRUP, XYLITOL, ARTIFICIAL AND NATURAL FLAVORS, ASPARTAME, RED 40, YELLOW 6 AND BHT (TO MAINTAIN FRESHNESS). PHENYLKETONURICS: CONTAINS PHENYLALANINE.

Sugar alcohols and the alternative sweetener aspartame are used to sweeten this product. Note the warning for people with phenylketonuria (PKU) that this product is made with aspartame and, thus, contains phenylalanine.

Acceptable Daily Intake (ADI) Estimate of the amount of a sweetener that an individual can safely consume daily over a lifetime. ADIs are given as mg per kg of body weight per day.

162 **PART 2** Energy-Yielding Nutrients and Alcohol

A variety of alternative sweeteners are available.

Neotame

Neotame is approved by the FDA for use as a general purpose sweetener in a wide variety of food products, such as baked goods, nonalcoholic beverages (including soft drinks), chewing gum, confections and frostings, frozen desserts, gelatins and puddings, jams and jellies, processed fruits and fruit juices, toppings, and syrups. Neotame is heat stable and can be used in cooking and as a tabletop sweetener. Neotame is approximately 7000 to 13,000 times sweeter than sucrose. Thus, the small amounts needed to sweeten products do not contribute calories. Although neotame also contains phenylalanine, its bonding to other amino acids differs from that of aspartame and prevents it from being broken down. Therefore, it does not cause a problem for individuals with PKU. The ADI for neotame is 18 mg/kg body weight/day.[13]

Acesulfame-K

The alternative sweetener acesulfame-K (the *K* stands for potassium) is sold for use in the U.S. as Sunette˚. Acesulfame-K is 200 times sweeter than sucrose. It contributes no energy to the diet because it is not digested by the body.[1] Acesulfame-K can be used in baking because it does not lose its sweetness when heated. In the U.S., it is currently approved for use in chewing gum, powdered drink mixes, gelatins, puddings, baked goods, tabletop sweeteners, candy, throat lozenges, yogurt, and nondairy creamers. The ADI for acesulfame-K is 15 mg/kg body weight/day.[13]

Sucralose

Sucralose, sold as Splenda˚, is 600 times sweeter than sucrose. It is the only artificial sweetener made from sucrose. It is made by substituting 3 chlorines (Cl) for 3 hydroxyl groups (–OH) on sucrose.[1] This substitution prevents it from being digested and absorbed. Sucralose is used as a tabletop sweetener and in soft drinks, chewing gum, baked goods, syrups, gelatins, frozen dairy desserts (e.g., ice cream), jams, and processed fruits and fruit juices. Sucralose is heat stable; thus, it can be used in cooking and baking. The ADI for sucralose is 5 mg/kg body weight/day.[13]

Tagatose

Tagatose, sold as Naturlose˚, is an isomer of fructose. It is almost as sweet as sucrose and can be used in cooking and baking. Because it is poorly absorbed by the body, tagatose yields only 1.5 kcal/g. It has a prebiotic effect because it is fermented by bacteria in the large intestine (see Chapter 4). Tagatose is approved for use in ready-to-eat cereals, diet soft drinks, health bars, frozen yogurt, fat-free ice cream, soft and hard confectionary products, frosting, and chewing gum. It is metabolized like fructose, so individuals with disorders of fructose metabolism should avoid using it.

Stevia

Stevia (also called rebiana) is an alternative sweetener derived from a plant from the Amazon rain forest. It is 100 to 300 times sweeter than sucrose but provides no energy.[14] Although it has been used in teas and as a sweetener in Japan since the 1970s, the FDA has only recently approved its use in beverages. Stevia can be purchased as a dietary supplement in natural and health-food stores. In the U.S., it is combined with a sugar alcohol called erythritol and marketed as PureVia™ and Truvia˚. Stevia also is blended with cane sugar and sold as Sun Crystals˚. The ADI for stevia is 4 mg/kg body weight/day.

Knowledge Check

1. Which foods are good sources of starch?
2. List 5 foods that contain soluble fibers.
3. Which sugars are classified as non-nutritive sweeteners?

5.3 Recommended Intake of Carbohydrates

According to the RDA, adults need about 130 g/day of digestible carbohydrate to supply adequate glucose for the brain and central nervous system to prevent the partial replacement of glucose by ketone bodies as an energy source (see Section 5.4). The Food and Nutrition Board recommends that, to provide for total body energy needs, carbohydrate intake should be considerably higher, ranging from 45 to 65% of total energy intake.[2] However, not all diet programs follow the Food and Nutrition Board recommendations.[15] Some diet programs (e.g., the Atkins™ and South Beach™ diets) promote very low carbohydrate intakes, whereas others (e.g., the Pritikin and Eat More, Weigh Less diets) promote very high carbohydrate intakes. Despite these differences in opinion, most scientists and nonscientists agree that carbohydrates in our diets should include mostly fiber-rich fruits, vegetables, and whole grains and little added sugars and caloric sweeteners.[2]

North Americans obtain about 50% of their energy intakes from carbohydrates. The leading carbohydrate sources for U.S. adults are white bread, soft drinks, cookies, cakes, doughnuts, sugars, syrups, jams, and potatoes. Worldwide, carbohydrates account for about 70 to 80% of energy consumed, with much greater intakes of whole grains, fruits, vegetables, and legumes than is typical in North American diets.

The Dietary Guidelines for Americans recommend limiting added sugars to approximately 6% of total energy intake.[16] The World Health Organization suggests that sugars added

▶ The *Healthy People 2020* goals related to carbohydrate intake include:

- Increase the contribution of whole grains to the diets of the population aged 2 years and older

- Increase the contribution of fruits to the diets of the population aged 2 years and older

- Increase the variety and contribution of vegetables to the diets of the population aged 2 years and older

- Increase the contribution of dark green vegetables, orange vegetables, and legumes to the diets of the population aged 2 years and older

- Reduce consumption of calories from added sugars

 *Take Action*

Choose the Sandwich with the Most Fiber

Dietitians and personal nutritionists often are asked to help clients make healthier choices, especially when eating out. Your client has asked you to help him get more fiber in his lunch from the local deli. All the sandwiches on the blackboard provide about 350 kcal. The fiber content ranges from approximately 1 gram to 8 grams. Rank the sandwiches from the highest amount of fiber (1) to the lowest amount (6); then check your answers at the bottom of the page.

Deli Specials

Turkey & Swiss on Rye
Served with tomato slices, sliced cucumbers, romaine lettuce, and mustard

Ham & Swiss on Sourdough
Extra-lean ham served with mayonnaise

Tuna Salad on Whole Wheat
Our tuna salad contains tuna, grated carrots, onions, and mayonnaise, and is served with alfalfa sprouts, romaine lettuce, and cucumber slices

Hot Dog
Served on a white bun with relish, mustard, and catsup

Soyburger
Served on a whole-wheat English muffin with tomato and pickle slices, romaine lettuce, and mayonnaise

PB & J
Soft white bread with strawberry jelly and smooth peanut butter

1. Soyburger: 7.5 g, 2. Tuna Salad on Whole Wheat: 7 g, 3. Turkey & Swiss on Rye: 4 g, 4. PB & J: 3 g, 5. Ham & Swiss on Sourdough: 1.5 g, 6. Hot Dog: 1 g

Answer Key

164   **PART 2**   Energy-Yielding Nutrients and Alcohol

to foods during processing and preparation ("added sugars") should provide no more than about 10% of total daily energy intake. The Institute of Medicine's Food and Nutrition Board set an upper limit of 25% of energy intake for added sugar consumption.[2] Based on new evidence concerning the relationship between sugar intake and increased risk of cardiovascular disease, the American Heart Association has set the prudent upper limit of sugar intake as half of one's discretionary calorie allowance. For most Americans, this is less than 100 calories daily for women and 150 calories for men.[17]

The Adequate Intake for fiber is based on a goal of 14 g/1000 kcal consumed. For adults up to age 50, the Adequate Intake is set at 25 g for women and 38 g for men. After age 50, the Adequate Intake falls to 21 g/day and 30 g/day, respectively.[2] The Adequate Intake for fiber is aimed to reduce the risk of diverticular disease, cardiovascular disease, and other chronic diseases. The Daily Value used for fiber on food and supplement labels is 25 g for a 2000 kcal diet.

To plan a nutritious diet with ample sources of carbohydrate, your daily diet should include approximately 6 ounces of grains, 2.5 cups of vegetables, 2 cups of fruit, and 3 cups of milk. As a protein alternative to meat, include more dried beans and lentils in your diet to increase fiber and total carbohydrate intake. Table 5-3 shows a diet containing the recommended intakes of carbohydrates.

Many of the foods we enjoy contain simple sugars. To improve nutrient intake, limit the consumption of sweets.

Table 5-3 Sample Menus Containing 1600 kcal with 25 g of Fiber and 2000 kcal with 38 g of Fiber*

Menu	25 g Fiber Plan			38 g Fiber Plan		
	Serving Size	Carbohydrate Content (g)	Fiber Content (g)	Serving Size	Carbohydrate Content (g)	Fiber Content (g)
Breakfast						
Muesli cereal	1 cup	60	6	1 cup	60	6
Raspberries	½ cup	11	2	½ cup	11	2
Whole-wheat toast	1 slice	13	2	2 slices	26	4
Margarine	1 tsp	0	0	1 tsp	0	0
Orange juice	1 cup	28	0	1 cup	28	0
1% milk	1 cup	24	0	1 cup	24	0
Coffee	1 cup	0	0	1 cup	0	0
Lunch						
Bean and vegetable burrito	2 small	50	4.5	3 small	75	7
Guacamole	¼ cup	5	4	¼ cup	5	4
Monterey Jack cheese	1 oz	0	0	1 oz	0	0
Pear (with skin)	1	25	4	1	25	4
Carrot sticks	—	—	—	¾ cup	6	3
Sparkling water	2 cups	0	0	2 cups	0	0
Dinner						
Grilled chicken (no skin)	3 oz	0	0	3 oz	0	0
Salad	½ cup red cabbage ½ cup romaine ¼ cup peach slices	7	3	½ cup red cabbage ½ cup romaine 1 cup peach slices	19	6
Toasted almonds	—	—	—	½ oz	3	2
Fat-free salad dressing	2 tbsp	0	0	2 tbsp	0	0
1% milk	1 cup	24	0	1 cup	24	0
Total		247	25		306	38

*The overall diet is based on MyPlate. Breakdown of approximate energy content: carbohydrate 58%; protein 12%; fat 30%.

Table 5-4 Suggestions for Reducing Simple-Sugar Intake

Many foods we enjoy are sweet. These should be eaten in moderation.

At the Supermarket

- Read ingredient labels. Identify all the added sugars in a product. Select items lower in total sugar when possible.
- Buy fresh fruits or fruits packed in water, juice, or light syrup rather than those packed in heavy syrup.
- Buy fewer foods that are high in sugar, such as prepared baked goods, candies, sugared cereals, sweet desserts, soft drinks, and fruit-flavored punches. Substitute vanilla wafers, graham crackers, bagels, English muffins, diet soft drinks, and other low-sugar alternatives.
- Buy reduced-fat microwave popcorn to replace candy for snacks.

In the Kitchen

- Reduce the sugar in foods prepared at home. Try new low-sugar recipes or adjust your own. Start by reducing the sugar gradually until you've decreased it by one-third or more.
- Experiment with spices, such as cinnamon, cardamom, coriander, nutmeg, ginger, and mace, to enhance the flavor of foods.
- Use home-prepared items with less sugar instead of commercially prepared ones that are higher in sugar.

At the Table

- Reduce use of white and brown sugars, honey, molasses, syrups, jams, and jellies.
- Choose fewer foods high in sugar, such as prepared baked goods, candies, and sweet desserts.
- Reach for fresh fruit instead of cookies or candy for dessert and between-meal snacks.
- Add less sugar to foods—coffee, tea, cereal, and fruit. Cut back gradually to a quarter or half the amount. Consider using sugar alternatives to substitute for some sugar.
- Reduce the number of sugared soft drinks, punches, and fruit juices you drink. Substitute water, diet soft drinks, and whole fruits.

Our Carbohydrate Intake

Carbohydrates supply about 50% of the energy intakes of adults in North America. Although the proportion of total energy provided by carbohydrates is in line with recommendations, the types of carbohydrates consumed are not. Added sugars account for almost 16% of total energy intake—nearly triple the 6% of total energy intake recommended by the Dietary Guidelines for Americans.[16] High sugar intakes are, in large part, due to the popularity of sugar-sweetened beverages.[17] Intake of high-fructose corn syrup, the caloric sweetener primarily used in these beverages, adds approximately 300 calories daily to the diets of Americans age 2 years and older.[18] Table 5-4 provides suggestions for reducing sugar intake.

In contrast to high sugar intakes, the dietary fiber intakes of Americans fall well below the recommended 14 grams per 1000 calories. Throughout life, both males and females eat 25 to 50% less fiber than recommended.[8] Insufficient fiber intake is due to low intakes of fruits and vegetables and high consumption levels of refined grains, such as pasta, corn chips, white rice, and white bread. Dietary surveys indicate that Americans age 2 and over eat only 1 fruit serving daily and only 1 serving or less of whole grain daily, usually in the form of breakfast cereals and yeast breads.[19]

Increasing intake of vegetables is a healthful way to include carbohydrates in your diet.

Figure 5-9 The Nutrition Facts panel on food labels can help us choose more nutritious foods. Based on the information from these panels, note which cereal is the better choice for breakfast. When choosing a breakfast cereal, it is generally wise to focus on those that are rich sources of fiber. Sugar content also can be used for evaluation. However, food labels do not distinguish between sugars naturally present in foods (e.g., raisins) and added sugars.

Nutrition Facts

Serving Size: 1 cup (55g/2.0 oz.)
Servings Per Container: 10

Amount Per Serving	Cereal	Cereal with ½ Cup Vitamins A & D Skim Milk
Calories*	170	210
Calories from Fat	10	10
	% Daily Value**	
Total Fat 1.0g	2%	2%
Sat. Fat 0g	0%	0%
Trans Fat 0g		
Cholesterol 0mg	0%	0%
Sodium 300mg	13%	15%
Potassium 340mg	10%	16%
Total Carbohydrate 43g	14%	16%
Dietary Fiber 7g	28%	28%
Sugars 16g		
Other Carbohydrate 20g		
Protein 4g		
Vitamin A	15%	20%
Vitamin C	20%	22%
Calcium	2%	15%
Iron	65%	65%
Vitamin D	10%	25%
Thiamin	25%	30%
Riboflavin	25%	35%
Niacin	25%	25%
Vitamin B$_6$	25%	25%
Folic acid	30%	30%
Vitamin B$_{12}$	25%	35%
Phosphorus	20%	30%
Magnesium	20%	25%
Zinc	25%	25%
Copper	10%	10%

*Amount in cereal. One half cup skim milk contributes an additional 40 calories, 65mg sodium, 6g total carbohydrate (6g sugars), and 4g protein.
**Percent Daily Values are based on a 2000 calorie diet. Your daily values may be higher or lower depending on your calorie needs:

	Calories:	2000	2500
Total Fat	Less than	65g	80g
Sat Fat	Less than	20g	25g
Cholesterol	Less than	300mg	300mg
Sodium	Less than	2400mg	2400mg
Potassium		3500mg	3500mg
Total Carbohydrate		300g	375g
Dietary Fiber		25g	30g

Calories per gram:
Fat 9 • Carbohydrate 4 • Protein 4

Ingredients: Wheat bran with other parts of wheat, raisins, sugar, corn syrup, salt, malt flavoring, glycerin, iron, niacinamide, zinc oxide, pyridoxine hydrochloride (vitamin B₆), riboflavin (vitamin B₂), vitamin A palmitate, thiamin hydrochloride (vitamin B₁), folic acid, vitamin B₁₂, and vitamin D.

Nutrition Facts

Serving Size: ¾ cup (30g)
Servings Per Package: About 17

Amount Per Serving	Cereal	Cereal with ½ Cup Skim Milk
Calories*	170	210
Calories from Fat	0	5
	%Daily Value**	
Total Fat 0g	0%	1%
Saturated Fat 0g	0%	1%
Trans Fat 0g		
Cholesterol 0mg	0%	1%
Sodium 60mg	2%	4%
Potassium 80mg	2%	8%
Total Carbohydrate 35g	9%	11%
Dietary Fiber 1g	4%	4%
Sugars 20g		
Other Carbohydrate 13g		
Protein 3g		
Vitamin A	25%	30%
Vitamin C	0%	2%
Calcium	0%	15%
Iron	10%	10%
Vitamin D	10%	20%
Thiamin	25%	25%
Riboflavin	25%	35%
Niacin	25%	25%
Vitamin B$_6$	25%	25%
Folic acid	25%	25%
Vitamin B$_{12}$	25%	30%
Phosphorus	4%	15%
Magnesium	4%	8%
Zinc	10%	10%
Copper	2%	2%

*Amount in Cereal. One-half cup skim milk contributes an additional 65mg sodium, 6g total carbohydrate (6g sugars), and 4g protein.
**Percent Daily Values are based on a 2000 calorie diet. Your daily values may be higher or lower depending on your calorie needs:

	Calories:	2000	2500
Total Fat	Less than	65g	80g
Sat. Fat	Less than	20g	25g
Cholesterol	Less than	300mg	300mg
Sodium	Less than	2400mg	2400mg
Potassium		3500mg	3500mg
Total Carbohydrate		300g	375g
Dietary Fiber		25g	30g

Calories per gram:
Fat 9 • Carbohydrate 4 • Protein 4

Ingredients: Wheat, Sugar, Corn Syrup, Honey, Caramel Color, Partially Hydrogenated Soybean Oil, Salt, Ferric Phosphate, Niacinamide (Niacin), Zinc Oxide, Vitamin A (Palmitate), Pyridoxine Hydrochloride (Vitamin B₆), Riboflavin, Thiamin Mononitrate, Folic Acid (Folate), Vitamin B₁₂ and Vitamin D.

Many individuals lack knowledge about fiber-rich food sources and their benefits. Also, food ingredient labels can be confusing. For example, manufacturers list enriched white (refined) flour as "wheat flour" on food labels. Most people think that, if "wheat flour" or "wheat bread" is on the label, they are buying a whole-wheat product. However, if the label does not list "whole-wheat flour" first, the product is not truly whole-wheat bread and does not contain as much fiber as it could. Careful label reading is important in the search for

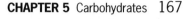

Take Action

Estimate Your Fiber Intake

To roughly estimate your daily fiber consumption, determine the number of servings that you ate yesterday from each food category listed here. Multiply the serving amount by the value listed and then add up the total amount of fiber.

Food	Servings	Grams
Vegetables (Serving size: 1 cup raw leafy greens or ½ cup other vegetables)	_____ × 2	_____
Fruits (Serving size: 1 whole fruit; ½ grapefruit; ½ cup berries or cubed fruit; ¼ cup dried fruit)	_____ × 2.5	_____
Beans, lentils, split peas (Serving size: ½ cup cooked)	_____ × 7	_____
Nuts, seeds (Serving size: ¼ cup; 2 tbsp peanut butter)	_____ × 2.5	_____
Whole grains (Serving size: 1 slice whole-wheat bread, ½ cup whole-wheat pasta, brown rice, or other whole grain; ½ bran or whole-grain muffin)	_____ × 2.5	_____
Refined grains (Serving size: 1 slice bread; ½ cup pasta, rice, or other processed grain; ½ refined bagel or muffin)	_____ × 1	_____
Breakfast cereals (Serving size: check package for serving size and grams of fiber per serving)	_____ × fiber per serving	_____
	Total grams of fiber =	_____

How does your total fiber intake for yesterday compare with the general recommendation of 25 to 38 g of fiber per day for women and men, respectively? If you are not meeting your needs, how could you do so?

more fiber—especially for whole grains. Meeting fiber recommendations is possible if you include whole-wheat bread, fruits, vegetables, and legumes as a regular part of your diet. Eating a high-fiber cereal topped with fruit for breakfast is one way to increase your fiber intake (Fig. 5-9). Use the Take Action activity to estimate the fiber content of your diet. What is *your* fiber score?

Knowledge Check

1. Why is the RDA for carbohydrate intake set at 130 g/day? Is this an optimal intake?
2. What is the Adequate Intake for dietary fiber?
3. Why are the dietary fiber intakes of many North Americans far below the recommended level?

5.4 Functions of Carbohydrates in the Body

The digestible and indigestible carbohydrates in our diets have vital functions in our bodies.[3, 8] These diverse functions are critical to normal metabolism and overall health.

Digestible Carbohydrates

Most of the digestible carbohydrates in our diets are broken down to glucose. As glucose, they provide a primary source of energy, spare protein from use as an energy source, and prevent ketosis.

Providing Energy

The main function of glucose is to act as a source of energy for body cells. In fact, red blood cells and cells of the central nervous system derive almost all of their energy from glucose. Glucose also fuels muscle cells and other body cells, although many of these cells rely on fatty acids to meet energy needs, especially during rest and light activity. Recall that glucose provides 4 kcal of energy per gram.

Sparing Protein from Use as an Energy Source

The amino acids that make up dietary protein are used to build body tissues and to perform other vital functions only when carbohydrate intake provides enough glucose for energy needs. If you do not consume enough carbohydrate to yield glucose, your body is forced to break down amino acids in your muscle tissue and other organs to make glucose. This process is termed **gluconeogenesis,** which means the production of new glucose (see Chapter 9 for details). However, when dietary carbohydrate intake is adequate to maintain blood glucose levels, protein is "spared" from use as energy. Generally, North Americans consume ample protein, so sparing protein is not an important role of carbohydrate in the diet. It does become important in some carbohydrate- and energy-reduced diets and in starvation. (Chapter 7 discusses the specific effects of starvation.)

Preventing Ketosis

A minimal intake of carbohydrates—at least 50 to 100 g/day—is necessary for the complete breakdown of fats to carbon dioxide (CO_2) and water (H_2O) in the body.[3] When carbohydrate intake falls below this level, the release of the hormone **insulin** decreases, resulting in the release of a large amount of fatty acids from adipose tissue to provide energy for body cells. These fatty acids travel in the bloodstream to the liver. The subsequent incomplete breakdown of these fatty acids in the liver results in the formation of acidic compounds called ketone bodies, or keto-acids, and a condition called ketosis, or ketoacidosis (see Chapter 9). Ketone bodies include acetoacetic acid and its derivatives.

Although the brain and other cells of the central nervous system normally cannot utilize energy from fats, these cells can adapt to use ketones for energy when carbohydrate intake is inadequate. This is an important adaptive mechanism for survival during starvation. If the brain could not use ketone bodies, the body would be forced to produce much more glucose from protein to support the brain's energy needs. The resulting breakdown of muscles, heart, and other organs to provide protein for gluconeogenesis would severely limit our ability to tolerate starvation.

Excessive ketone production also can occur in untreated diabetes. This is not usually the result of low carbohydrate intake, however. Diabetic ketosis develops when insulin production is inadequate or cells resist insulin action, thereby preventing glucose from entering body cells. Cells then rely on ketone bodies from the breakdown of fats for energy. The accumulation of these ketones in the blood results in a more acidic pH. This condition, called diabetic ketoacidosis, is a very serious complication of untreated or poorly controlled diabetes.

gluconeogenesis Synthesis of new glucose by metabolic pathways in the cell. Amino acids derived from protein usually provide the carbons for this glucose.

insulin Hormone produced by beta cells of the pancreas. Among other processes, insulin increases the movement of glucose from the bloodstream into body cells, increases the synthesis of glycogen in the liver, and decreases the breakdown of fat (lipolysis).

Many low-carbohydrate/high-fat weight-reduction diets (e.g., the Atkins™ and South Beach™ diets) and fasting regimens promote ketosis as a beneficial state for successful weight loss. Ketosis can suppress one's appetite, resulting in a lower calorie intake. It also can cause increased loss of water from the body, which may be reflected in lower body weight. However, over time, ketosis can lead to serious consequences, such as dehydration, loss of lean body mass, and electrolyte imbalances. If severe, ketosis can even cause coma and death.

Indigestible Carbohydrates

Although fiber is indigestible, it plays an important role in maintaining the integrity of the GI tract and overall health.[8] Fiber helps prevent constipation and diverticular disease and enhances the management of body weight, blood glucose levels, and blood cholesterol levels.[8–12, 20–22]

Promoting Bowel Health

Fiber adds bulk to the feces, making bowel movements easier. When adequate fiber and fluid are consumed, the stool is large and soft because many types of plant fibers absorb water. The larger size stimulates the intestinal muscles, which aids elimination. Consequently, less force is necessary to expel the feces.

When too little fiber is eaten, the opposite can occur: the stool may be small and hard. Constipation may result, causing one to exert excessive force during defecation. Over time, excessive exertion can lead to the development of hemorrhoids. This high pressure from exertion also can cause parts of the large intestine wall to protrude through the surrounding bands of muscle, forming small pouches called **diverticula**.[10] Fibrous material, feces, and bacteria can become trapped in diverticula and lead to inflammation (Fig. 5-10).

Diverticular disease is asymptomatic (without noticeable symptoms) in about 80% of affected people. The asymptomatic form of this condition is called **diverticulosis** and is one of the most common conditions in Western countries.[10] If the diverticula become inflamed and symptomatic, the condition is known as **diverticulitis**. Intake of fiber then should be reduced to limit further bacterial activity and inflammation. Once the inflammation subsides, a high-fiber and high-fluid diet, along with regular physical activity, is advised to restore GI tract motility and reduce the risk of a future attack. Recent studies indicate that nuts, corn, and popcorn can be included in the diet because they do not increase the risk of diverticulitis or diverticular complications, as previously believed.[23]

Over the past 30 years, epidemiological studies have shown an association between increased fiber intake and decreased risk of colon cancer. However, more recently, scientists have questioned these findings.[11, 12] Current studies of diet and colon cancer are focusing on the potential preventive effects of increased intakes of fruits, vegetables, legumes, and whole-grain breads and cereals (rather than fiber per se); regular exercise; and adequate vitamin D, folate, magnesium, selenium, and calcium intakes. Overall, it appears that the potential cancer prevention benefits of a high-fiber diet are, for the most part, due to the nutrients that are commonly part of high-fiber foods, such as vitamins, minerals, and phytochemicals. Thus, it is more advisable to increase fiber intake using fiber-rich foods than to rely on fiber supplements.[8]

Reducing Obesity Risk

A diet high in fiber likely aids weight control and reduces the risk of accumulating body fat and becoming obese.[20–22] The bulky nature of high-fiber foods fills us up without yielding much energy. Fibrous foods also absorb water and expand in the GI tract, which may result in a sense of fullness and contribute to satiety.

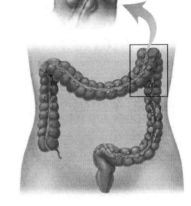

Large intestine (colon)

Diverticula

Figure 5-10 Diverticula in the large intestine. A low-fiber diet increases the risk of developing diverticula. About one-third of people over age 45 have this condition, whereas two-thirds of people over 85 do.

CRITICAL THINKING

Laura has a family history of colon cancer. What dietary advice would you give her to reduce her risk of developing colon cancer?

diverticula Pouches that have extruded through the exterior wall of the large intestine.

diverticulosis Condition of having many diverticula in the large intestine.

diverticulitis Inflammation of the diverticula, caused by acids produced by bacterial metabolism inside the diverticula.

Because oatmeal is rich in soluble fiber, the FDA allows oatmeal package labels to list the benefits of oatmeal in lowering blood cholesterol as a part of a low-fat diet.

Enhancing Blood Glucose Control

When consumed in recommended amounts, soluble fibers slow glucose absorption from the small intestine and decrease insulin release from the pancreas. This contributes to better blood glucose regulation, which can be helpful in the treatment of diabetes. In fact, adults with high-fiber diets are less likely to develop diabetes than are those with low-fiber diets.[8, 9]

Reducing Cholesterol Absorption

A high intake of soluble fiber inhibits the absorption of cholesterol and the reabsorption of bile acids from the small intestine, thereby reducing the risk of cardiovascular disease and gallstones. The short-chain fatty acids resulting from the bacterial degradation of soluble fiber in the large intestine also reduce cholesterol synthesis in the liver. Overall, a fiber-rich diet containing fruits, vegetables, legumes, and whole-grain breads and cereals is advocated as part of a strategy to reduce the risk of cardiovascular disease.[8] Recall from Chapter 2 that the FDA has approved the claims that diets rich in whole-grain foods and other plant foods and low in total fat, saturated fat, and cholesterol may decrease the risk of cardiovascular disease and certain cancers.

Knowledge Check

1. What are 3 functions of digestible carbohydrates?
2. How does carbohydrate spare protein from use as an energy source?
3. Why are indigestible carbohydrates an important component of our diets?

5.5 Carbohydrate Digestion and Absorption

The goal of carbohydrate digestion is to break down starch and sugars into monosaccharide units that are small enough to be absorbed. Food preparation can be viewed as the start of carbohydrate digestion because cooking softens the tough, fibrous tissues of vegetables, fruits, and grains. When starches are heated, the starch granules swell as they soak up water, making them much easier to digest. All these effects of cooking generally make these foods easier to chew, swallow, and break down during digestion.

Digestion

The enzymatic digestion of some carbohydrates begins in the mouth. Saliva contains an enzyme called salivary **amylase,** which mixes with starch containing amylose when the food is chewed. Amylase breaks down the starch into smaller polysaccharides (called dextrins) and disaccharides (Fig. 5-11). Because food is in the mouth for such a short amount of time, this phase of digestion is only a minor part of the overall digestive process.

When food reaches the stomach, the salivary enzyme is inactivated by the acidity of the stomach. Thus, the digestion of carbohydrate stops until it passes into the small intestine. In the small intestine, the polysaccharides in the food that were first acted on in the mouth now are digested further by pancreatic amylase and dextrinase. Disaccharides are digested to their monosaccharide units by specialized enzymes in the absorptive cells of the small intestine. The disaccharides include maltose from starch breakdown, lactose mainly from dairy products, and sucrose from sweetened foods. The enzyme **maltase** acts on maltose to produce 2 glucose molecules. **Sucrase** breaks down sucrose to produce glucose and fructose. **Lactase** digests lactose to produce glucose and galactose. Monosaccharides that occur in food (usually as glucose or fructose) do not require further digestion in the small intestine. The indigestible carbohydrates (dietary fibers and a small portion of starch in whole grains and some fruits, called resistant starch) cannot be broken down by the digestive enzymes of

Carbohydrates

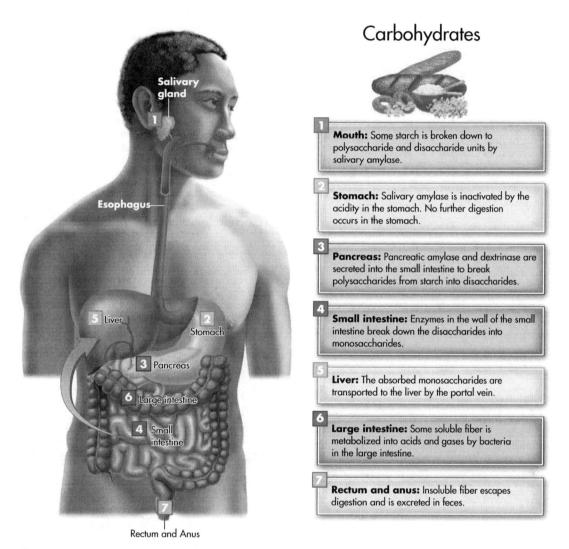

1. **Mouth:** Some starch is broken down to polysaccharide and disaccharide units by salivary amylase.

2. **Stomach:** Salivary amylase is inactivated by the acidity in the stomach. No further digestion occurs in the stomach.

3. **Pancreas:** Pancreatic amylase and dextrinase are secreted into the small intestine to break polysaccharides from starch into disaccharides.

4. **Small intestine:** Enzymes in the wall of the small intestine break down the disaccharides into monosaccharides.

5. **Liver:** The absorbed monosaccharides are transported to the liver by the portal vein.

6. **Large intestine:** Some soluble fiber is metabolized into acids and gases by bacteria in the large intestine.

7. **Rectum and anus:** Insoluble fiber escapes digestion and is excreted in feces.

Figure 5-11 Carbohydrate digestion and absorption. Enzymes made by the salivary glands, pancreas, and small intestine participate in the process of digestion. Most carbohydrate digestion and absorption take place in the small intestine (see Chapter 4 for details).

the small intestine. As discussed previously, they pass into the large intestine, where they are fermented by bacteria into acids and gases or are excreted in fecal waste.[6,7]

Intestinal diseases can interfere with the digestion of carbohydrates, such as lactose, and prevent their breakdown and absorption. When unabsorbed carbohydrates reach the large intestine, bacteria there digest them, producing acids and gases as by-products (see Fig. 5-11). If produced in large amounts, these gases can cause abdominal discomfort. People recovering from intestinal disorders, such as diarrhea, may need to avoid lactose for a few weeks or more because of temporary lactose maldigestion and malabsorption. A few weeks is often sufficient time for the small intestine to resume producing enough lactase enzyme to allow for more complete lactose digestion (see the discussion of lactose intolerance in Section 5.6).[24]

Absorption

With the exception of fructose, monosaccharides are absorbed by an active absorption process. Recall from Chapter 4 that this process requires a specific carrier and energy input for the substance to be taken up by the absorptive cells in the small intestine. Following digestion,

172   **PART 2**   Energy-Yielding Nutrients and Alcohol

Figure 5-12 Active absorption of glucose in the absorptive cells that line the villi in the small intestine (see Fig. 4-14 for a diagram of villi). Glucose and sodium pass across the absorptive cell membrane in a carrier-dependent, energy-requiring process. Once inside the absorptive cell, glucose can exit by facilitated diffusion and enter the bloodstream. Sodium is pumped out of the absorptive cell to maintain a low concentration in the absorptive cell and a high concentration in the extracellular fluid.

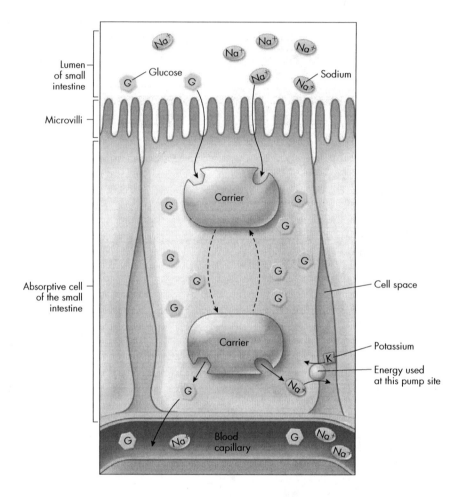

glucose and galactose are pumped into the absorptive cells, along with sodium (Fig. 5-12). The ATP energy used in the process pumps sodium back out of the absorptive cell.

Fructose is taken up by the absorptive cells via facilitated diffusion. In this case, a carrier is used, but no energy input is needed. This absorptive process is slower than that of glucose or galactose. Once glucose, galactose, and fructose enter the intestinal cells, glucose and galactose remain in that form, whereas some fructose is converted to glucose. These monosaccharides are then transported via the portal vein to the liver. In the liver, fructose and galactose are converted to glucose. Glucose is transported through the bloodstream for use by the cells of the body. If blood glucose levels are adequate to meet the energy needs of body cells, the liver stores additional glucose as glycogen. (Muscle cells also can store glycogen.) Although the liver's capacity to store glycogen is limited, glycogen storage provides an important reserve of energy to maintain blood glucose levels and cellular function. When carbohydrates are consumed in very high amounts, the glycogen storage capacity of the liver (and muscles) often is exceeded. The liver then converts the excess glucose to fat for storage in adipose tissue.

Knowledge Check

1. What enzymes are involved in the digestion of carbohydrates?
2. Why do some individuals with intestinal diseases need to temporarily restrict their consumption of foods containing lactose?
3. How are monosaccharides absorbed?

Expert Perspective from the Field

Taxing Sugar-Sweetened Beverages

Many nutrition and health experts are concerned about the large increase in consumption of sugar-sweetened beverages that has occurred over the last few decades. For example, in the U.S., intake of these beverages doubled between 1977 and 2002. This increase added an extra 175 calories to our daily diets!

Sugar-sweetened beverages are associated with an increased risk of obesity, diabetes, and heart disease.[37] Thus, to reduce intake and raise money for nutrition and health programs, researchers, such as Dr. Kelly Brownell,* are proposing to tax these beverages.[38] Dr. Brownell and colleagues estimate that a tax of 1 cent per ounce of sugar-sweetened beverages could generate about $15 million each year.[39] In addition, research indicates that taxing less healthy foods, such as sugar-sweetened beverages, reduces calorie intake.[40]

Many individuals and groups, especially in the beverage industry, strongly oppose taxing sugar-sweetened beverages. They argue that it would unfairly burden the poor and would not help solve the obesity epidemic. They believe that the increase in obesity rate is not related to sugar-sweetened beverages, but is the result of inactivity and poor overall dietary habits. In response, Dr. Brownell points out that "sweetened beverages are

the single largest source of added sugar in the American diet. Discouraging soft drink purchases could improve health by reducing empty calorie intake."

Dr. Brownell also noted that public health advocates encountered similar resistance when they proposed increasing taxes on tobacco. Thus, he and other public health advocates plan to continue campaigning for a sugar-sweetened beverage tax as a means of helping reduce the incidence of obesity and related diseases.

Kelly Brownell, Ph.D., is Professor of Psychology and of Epidemiology and Public Health and Director of the Rudd Center on Food Policy and Obesity at Yale University. Time magazine named him one of the "World's 100 Most Influential People." He is a member of the Institute of Medicine. He has received the James Mckeen Cattell Award from the New York Academy of Sciences, the Outstanding Contribution to Health Psychology Award from the American Psychological Association, the Lifetime Achievement Award from Rutgers University, and the Distinguished Alumni Award from Purdue University.

 ## 5.6 Health Concerns Related to Carbohydrate Intake

As a part of a nutritious diet, adequate carbohydrate intake is important for maintaining health and decreasing the risk of chronic disease. However, as with many nutrients, excessive intakes of different forms of carbohydrate can be harmful to overall health. The following discussions will help you understand the risks of high intakes of different types of carbohydrates.

Very-High-Fiber Diets

Adequate fiber intake provides many health benefits. However, very high intakes of fiber (i.e., above 50 to 60 g/day) can cause health risks. For example, high fiber consumption combined with low fluid intake can result in hard, dry stools that are painful to eliminate. Over time, this may cause hemorrhoids, as well as rectal bleeding, from increased exertion and pressure. In severe cases, the combination of excess fiber and insufficient fluid may contribute to blockages in the intestine, requiring surgery.

Very-high-fiber diets also may decrease the absorption of certain minerals and increase the risk of deficiencies. This occurs because some minerals can bind to fiber, which prevents them from being absorbed. In countries where fiber intake is often greater than 60 g/day, deficiencies of zinc and iron have been reported.

High-fiber diets can be of concern in young children, elderly persons, and malnourished individuals, all of whom may not eat adequate amounts of foods and nutrients. For these individuals, high fiber intakes may cause a sense of fullness and reduce their overall intake of foods, energy, and nutrients.

HISTORICAL PERSPECTIVE

Photographing Atoms

Discovering the molecular layout of biologically important molecules is critical to understanding their function and treating disease. The biochemist and crystallographer Dorothy Crowfoot Hodgkin developed new x-ray techniques that permitted her to determine the structure of over 100 molecules including insulin, vitamin B-12, vitamin D, and penicillin. Her work with insulin improved treatment of diabetes. Knowing the structure of vitamin B-12 advanced our knowledge of its role in blood health. Learn more about this Nobel Prize winner at: www.nobelprize.org/nobel_prizes/chemistry/laureates/1964/hodgkin.html

174 **PART 2** Energy-Yielding Nutrients and Alcohol

High-carbohydrate beverages can contribute to tooth decay.

Figure 5-13 Dental caries. Bacteria in the mouth metabolize sugars in food and create acids that can dissolve tooth enamel. This leads to the development of caries. If the caries progress into the pulp cavity, damage to the nerve and pain are likely.

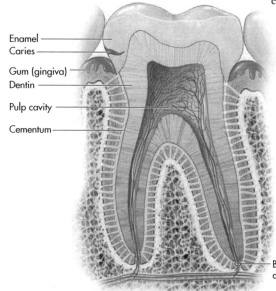

Enamel
Caries
Gum (gingiva)
Dentin
Pulp cavity
Cementum
Blood vessels and nerves

High-Sugar Diets

For many Americans, sugars constitute a large part of their daily diets. In fact, on average, North Americans eat about 22 teaspoons (355 kcal) of sugars daily.[17] Recall that most of the sugar we eat comes from foods and beverages to which sugar has been added during processing and/or manufacturing. Major sources of added sugar are soft drinks, cakes, cookies, fruit punch, and dairy desserts, such as ice cream. Although sugars supply calories, they usually provide little else and often replace the intake of more nutritious foods. Children and adolescents are typically at greatest risk of overconsuming sugar and empty calories. Dietary surveys indicate that many children and adolescents are drinking an excess of sugar-sweetened beverages and much less milk than ever before. In fact, between 1970 and 2000, consumption of caloric soft drinks increased 70% and has resulted in an intake of 34 teaspoons (549 kcal) of added sugar daily in children 14 to 18 years old.[17] Milk contains calcium and vitamin D, both of which are essential for bone health. Thus, replacing sugared drinks for milk can compromise bone development and health.

High intakes of sugars also can increase the risk of weight gain and obesity. (However, it is important to note that, although obesity is a risk factor for type 2 diabetes, high-sugar diets do not directly cause diabetes.) The "supersizing" trend noted in food and beverage promotions is contributing to this concern. For example, in the 1950s, a typical soft drink serving was a 6.5-ounce bottle. Today, a 20-ounce bottle is a typical serving. This change alone contributes 170 extra calories of sugar to the diet. Drinking 1 bottle per day for a year amounts to 62,050 extra calories and a 17- to 18-pound (7.75–8.25 kg) weight gain.

The sugar in cakes, cookies, and ice cream also supplies extra energy, which promotes weight gain. Although dieters may be choosing more low-fat and fat-free snack products, these usually are made with substantial amounts of added sugar in order to produce a dessert with an acceptable taste and texture. The resulting product often is a high-calorie food that equals or even exceeds the energy content of the original high-fat food product it was designed to replace.

High intakes of sugar (especially fructose) have been associated with conditions that increase the risk of cardiovascular disease—namely, increased blood levels of triglycerides and LDL-cholesterol and decreased levels of HDL-cholesterol.[17] To date, scientists do not have enough evidence to conclude that increased sugar intake is a risk factor for cardiovascular disease. However, as mentioned earlier in this chapter, the American Heart Association recommends limiting intake to about half of one's discretionary calorie allowance.

Diets high in sugar have been reported to cause hyperactivity in children. However, scientists have determined that hyperactivity and other behavioral problems are likely due to a variety of non-nutritional factors. Although eating a nutritious diet is important for a child's overall health and well-being, it will not prevent hyperactivity, behavioral problems, or learning disabilities.

High-sugar diets increase the risk of developing dental caries (cavities).[25] Dental caries can develop when bacteria in the mouth metabolize sugars into acids (Fig. 5-13). The acids gradually dissolve the tooth enamel and the underlying structure, causing decay, discomfort, and even nerve damage. Sugar from any source can lead to caries. Sticky and gummy foods that are high in sugar and adhere to teeth, such as caramels, licorice, and gummy bears, are the most likely to promote dental caries. Starches that are readily fermented in the mouth, such as crackers and white bread, also increase the risk of dental caries. Sipping fruit juices, soft drinks, and milk (which contains lactose) throughout the day bathes the teeth in sugar and can increase the risk of caries. Thus, parents should be cautioned against serving infants and young children these beverages to sip on between meals.

Lactose Intolerance

The amount of the enzyme lactase produced in the small intestine often begins to decrease after early childhood. The insufficiency of lactase, referred to as *primary* lactose intolerance, can cause symptoms of abdominal pain, bloating, gas, and diarrhea after consuming lactose, especially in large amounts. The bloating and gas are caused by the bacterial fermentation of undigested lactose in the large intestine. The undigested lactose also draws water into the large intestine, causing diarrhea.

Primary lactose intolerance may occur in up to 75% of the world's population.[26] In North America, approximately 25% of adults show signs of decreased lactose digestion. Those who have Asian, African, or Latino/Hispanic backgrounds are more likely to experience lactose intolerance than Caucasians. Some people with primary lactose intolerance do not experience symptoms. In addition, many are able to consume moderate amounts of lactose with little or no intestinal discomfort because bacteria in the large intestine break down the lactose.[26] In fact, recent studies have shown that nearly all individuals with decreased lactase production can tolerate ½ to 1 cup of milk with meals. Hard cheese, yogurt, and acidophilus milk also are well tolerated because much of the lactose in these foods has been converted to lactic acid. Thus, it is unnecessary for many with lactose intolerance to greatly restrict their intakes of lactose-containing foods, such as milk and other dairy products.

Another type of lactose intolerance, called *secondary* lactose intolerance, occurs when conditions of the small intestine, such as Crohn's disease and severe diarrhea, damage the cells that produce lactase. Secondary lactose intolerance also can cause gastrointestinal symptoms, but the symptoms are usually temporary and cease when the intestine recovers and lactase production normalizes.

Yogurt helps those with lactose intolerance meet their calcium needs.

Glucose Intolerance

Maintaining blood glucose levels within normal ranges is important for providing adequate glucose for body functions and for preventing the symptoms associated with changes in blood glucose levels. Abnormal regulation of blood glucose can lead to either **hyperglycemia** (high blood glucose) or **hypoglycemia** (low blood glucose). Hyperglycemia is a more common condition than hypoglycemia and is most commonly associated with diabetes (technically, *diabetes mellitus*) and Metabolic Syndrome.

Regulation of Blood Glucose

Under fasting conditions (at least several hours after eating), blood glucose normally varies between about 70 and 100 mg/dl of blood. However, if a fasting blood glucose level is above 126 mg/dl, it is classified as diabetes. The symptoms of diabetes include hunger, thirst, frequent urination, and weight loss. When blood glucose falls below 50 mg/dl, the condition is classified as hypoglycemia. A person with hypoglycemia may experience hunger, shakiness, irritability, weakness, and headache as energy availability decreases.

CASE STUDY

Myeshia, a 19-year-old female, recently read about the health benefits of calcium and decided to increase her intake of dairy products by drinking milk. Not long afterward, she experienced bloating, cramping, and gassiness. She suspected that the source of this discomfort was the milk she consumed, especially because her parents and sister had complained of the same problem. She wanted to determine if the milk was, in fact, the cause of her gastrointestinal discomfort, so the next day she substituted yogurt for the milk in her diet. Subsequently, she did not have any symptoms. What component of milk likely caused the problem? Why was she able to tolerate yogurt but not milk?

hyperglycemia High blood glucose, above 126 mg/dl of blood on a fasting basis.

hypoglycemia Low blood glucose, below 50 mg/dl of blood.

MEDICAL PERSPECTIVE

Diabetes Mellitus

As mentioned previously, an inability to regulate glucose metabolism can result in diabetes. Diagnosis of diabetes is based on a **fasting blood glucose** level above 126 mg/dl. Diabetes affects about 6% of North Americans and leads to over 200,000 deaths each year. An additional 15% of our population shows evidence of pre-diabetes (indicated by a borderline high blood glucose level between 100 and 126 mg/dl).

There are two major forms of diabetes: **type 1 diabetes** (formerly called insulin-dependent or juvenile-onset diabetes) and **type 2 diabetes** (formerly called non-insulin-dependent or adult-onset diabetes) (Table 5-5). The change in names to type 1 and type 2 diabetes stems from the fact that many with type 2 diabetes eventually must rely on insulin injections as a part of their treatment.[27] Approximately 90% of individuals with diabetes have type 2 diabetes.

In type 1 diabetes, individuals develop the classic symptoms of hyperglycemia (increased hunger, thirst, urination, and weight loss). However, in type 2 diabetes, 30 to 50% of individuals may not have any symptoms and are not aware that they have diabetes until diagnosed in routine health screening tests. Thus, new guidelines promote testing fasting blood glucose levels in adults over age 45 every 3 years to avoid missing cases and to prevent related morbidity and mortality.[27]

A third form of diabetes is called gestational diabetes. Gestational diabetes occurs in approximately 7% of all pregnancies. It is usually treated with insulin and dietary modification, and it resolves after delivery of the baby. However, pregnant women who develop gestational diabetes are at high risk of developing type 2 diabetes later in life.

Type 1 Diabetes

Although type 1 diabetes can occur at any age, it often begins in late childhood, between 8 and 12 years of age. The disease runs in families, suggesting a genetic link. Thus, children and siblings of those with diabetes are at increased risk. Most cases of type 1 diabetes begin as an autoimmune disorder that destroys the insulin-producing cells in the pancreas. As the pancreas loses its ability to synthesize insulin and thus regulate blood glucose levels, the clinical symptoms of the disease develop.

The onset of type 1 diabetes is associated with decreased release of insulin from the pancreas and increased blood glucose, especially after eating. When blood glucose exceeds the kidney's threshold for returning it to the bloodstream, the excess glucose ends up in the urine—hence the

▶ The classic symptoms of diabetes include polyuria (excessive urination), polydipsia (excessive thirst), and polyphagia (excessive hunger). No one symptom is diagnostic of diabetes. Other symptoms—such as unexplained weight loss, exhaustion, and blurred vision—may accompany these symptoms.[27]

▶ A common clinical method to determine a person's success in controlling blood glucose is to measure glycated (or glycosylated) hemoglobin (hemoglobin A1c). Over time, blood glucose attaches to (glycates) hemoglobin in red blood cells, especially when blood glucose remains elevated. Hemoglobin A1c values over 6.5 to 7% indicate poor blood glucose control.

fasting blood glucose Measurement of glucose levels in the blood taken after an 8- to 12-hour or overnight period without any food or caloric beverages (a fast).

type 1 diabetes Autoimmune disease causing failure of the pancreas to produce insulin and an inability to control blood glucose levels.

type 2 diabetes Progressive disease characterized by insulin resistance or loss of responsiveness of body cells to insulin, resulting in hyperglycemia.

Table 5-5 Comparison of Type 1 and Type 2 Diabetes

	Type 1 Diabetes	**Type 2 Diabetes**
Occurrence	5–10% of cases of diabetes	90% of cases of diabetes
Cause	Autoimmune attack on the pancreas	Insulin resistance
Risk Factors	Moderate genetic predisposition	Strong genetic predisposition Obesity and physical inactivity Ethnicity Metabolic Syndrome Pre-diabetes
Characteristics	Distinct symptoms (frequent thirst, hunger, and urination) Ketosis Weight loss	Mild symptoms, especially in early phases of the disease (fatigue and nighttime urination) Ketosis does not generally occur
Treatment	Insulin Diet Exercise	Diet Exercise Oral medications to lower blood glucose Insulin (in advanced cases)
Complications	Cardiovascular disease Kidney disease Nerve disease Blindness Infections	Cardiovascular disease Kidney disease Nerve damage Blindness Infections
Monitoring	Blood glucose Urine ketones HbA1c*	Blood glucose HbA1c*

*Hemoglobin A1c

term *diabetes mellitus*, which means "flow of much urine" (*diabetes*) that is "sweet" (*mellitus*). Figure 5-14 shows a typical glucose tolerance curve observed in a patient with type 1 diabetes, after eating a test load of about 20 teaspoons (75 grams) of glucose.

Before 1921, if a person had type 1 diabetes, a high-fat, low-calorie diet was recommended. This approach was somewhat effective but resulted in poor growth in childhood and was difficult to follow. The isolation of insulin by Banting and Best in 1921, and the first use of it soon after by children, opened a new door in diabetes care.

Type 1 diabetes is treated by insulin therapy, either with injections several times per day or with an insulin pump. The pump dispenses insulin at a steady rate into the body, with greater amounts delivered after a meal. Dietary therapy includes 3 regular meals and 1 or more snacks (including a bedtime snack), as well as a regulated ratio of carbohydrate:protein:fat to maximize insulin action and minimize swings in blood glucose. The diet also should include ample fiber, supply energy in balance with expenditure, be low in saturated fats and cholesterol, and meet overall nutritional needs.[28, 29]

Carbohydrate counting and the diabetic exchange system are useful tools for balancing carbohydrate intake and improving blood glucose control while eating a wide selection of foods. The carbohydrate counting method awards 1 point to approximately 12 to 15 g of carbohydrate. The exchange system is described in Appendix E.

Poorly controlled diabetes can lead to short-term and long-term health problems. The hormone imbalances that occur in people with uncontrolled type 1 diabetes lead to the breakdown of body fat for energy. Ketosis develops as fat is converted to ketone bodies. Ketones can increase to high levels in the blood, eventually ending up in the urine. Ketones also pull sodium and potassium ions with them into the urine, leading to dehydration, ion imbalance, coma, and even death. Treatment includes insulin and fluids, as well as sodium, potassium, and chloride.[27]

Over time, poorly controlled diabetes can cause degenerative conditions, such as blindness, cardiovascular disease, and kidney disease.[27, 30] Nerves also can deteriorate, resulting in decreased nerve stimulation throughout the body (called neuropathy).[31] When this occurs in the intestinal tract, intermittent diarrhea and constipation result. Because of nerve deterioration in the arms, hands, legs, and feet, many people with diabetes lose the sensation of pain associated with injuries and infections. Without normal pain sensations, they often delay treatment. This delay, combined with an environment rich in glucose that readily supports bacterial growth, sets the stage for damage to and the death of tissues in the extremities, sometimes even leading to the need for amputation. Poorly controlled diabetes also contributes to a rapid

Checking blood glucose regularly is an important part of diabetes therapy.

buildup of fats in blood vessel walls, which increases the risk of cardiovascular disease.[30]

The Diabetes Control and Complications Trial (DCCT) and other recent studies have shown that the development of diabetes-related cardiovascular disease and nerve damage can be delayed with aggressive treatment directed at keeping blood glucose within the normal range.[30, 31] The therapy poses some risks of its own, however, such as hypoglycemia, so it must be implemented under the close supervision of a physician.

A person with diabetes should work regularly with a physician and dietitian to monitor and adjust (when necessary) diet, medications, and physical activity. Physical activity enhances glucose uptake by muscles independent of insulin action, which in turn can lower blood glucose.[32] This outcome is beneficial, but people with diabetes need to be aware of their own blood glucose response to physical activity and plan appropriately to avoid hypoglycemia.

Type 2 Diabetes

Type 2 diabetes is a progressive disease characterized by insulin resistance or loss of responsiveness by body cells to insulin. As a result,

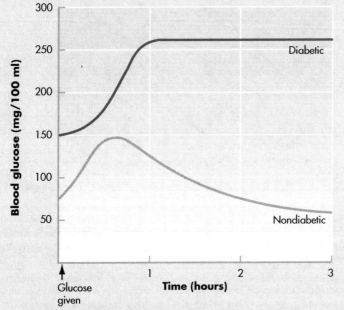

Figure 5-14 Glucose tolerance test: a comparison of blood glucose concentrations in untreated diabetic and healthy, nondiabetic persons after consuming a 75 g test load of glucose.

CRITICAL THINKING

Marc and Dan are twins who like the same activities and foods. At a recent doctor's appointment, Dan was told that he has type 2 diabetes. He has been feeling good and has not noticed any changes in his health. He does not understand why he has diabetes but his brother does not and why he has not had any noticeable symptoms. How would you explain this to him?

(continued)

continued

glucose is not readily transferred into cells and builds in the bloodstream, causing hyperglycemia. In type 2 diabetes, insulin production may be low, normal, or at times even elevated. However, regardless of the amount of insulin produced, cells are less responsive to its actions.

Type 2 diabetes is the most common type, accounting for about 90% of the cases diagnosed in North America. Those over age 45 and with Latino/Hispanic, African, Asian, Native American, or Pacific Island backgrounds are at particular risk. The number of people with type 2 diabetes is on the rise, primarily because of widespread inactivity and obesity. There also has been a substantial increase in type 2 diabetes in children, mainly due

Regular exercise has a key role in decreasing the risk of type 2 diabetes. For individuals with type 2 diabetes, exercise also can be an important part of managing the disease.

to an increase in overweight coupled with limited physical activity in this population. Type 2 diabetes is genetically linked, so family history is a very important risk factor. Because of this genetic link, those with a family history should be careful to avoid other risk factors, such as obesity, inactivity, and diets rich in saturated fats, cholesterol, and high-glycemic-load foods.[27-29]

Treatments for type 2 diabetes are aimed at maintaining normal ranges of blood glucose through lifestyle modification and medication use. Adhering to a nutritious diet plan and a regular physical activity program is an important component of therapy. Consistent exercise and an energy-controlled, nutritious diet eaten at regular mealtimes promote a healthy body weight, enhance the uptake of glucose by muscle cells, lower blood lipids and cardiovascular risk, and help achieve normal blood sugar levels. For overweight or obese individuals, even a modest weight loss can improve blood glucose control.[27, 32]

Many with type 2 diabetes need medications in addition to diet modification and regular activity to control blood glucose. Oral medications that reduce glucose production by the liver, increase insulin synthesis by the pancreas, slow intestinal absorption of glucose, or decrease cellular resistance to insulin are used by many with type 2 diabetes to regulate blood glucose. However, when oral medications fail to normalize blood glucose levels, insulin injections are necessary.[27]

Moderate amounts of alcohol (1 serving/day) can be allowed in the diets of those with both type 1 and type 2 diabetes. In fact, for some individuals, small amounts of alcohol may help increase HDL-cholesterol and reduce cardiovascular disease risk. However, alcohol intake, especially without adequate food intake, can lead to severe hypoglycemia. Thus, those with diabetes need to use alcohol cautiously and monitor blood glucose levels closely to avoid hypoglycemia.

Decreasing the Risk of Diabetes and Protecting Health if Diabetes Is Diagnosed

There are many lifestyle modifications that individuals with an increased risk of type 2 diabetes can adopt to decrease their likelihood of developing the disease. Obesity and inactivity are common risk factors associated with type 2 diabetes. Thus, maintaining a healthy weight, staying physically active, and following the Dietary Guidelines can decrease one's risk. For those with a family history of diabetes and for women with a history of gestational diabetes, regular testing of fasting blood glucose levels or screening through glucose tolerance testing is an important part of personal health care.

Although diabetes is not yet a curable disease, it can be controlled through diet, exercise, and medications. Maintaining good glucose control is critical to prevent the long-term, diabetes-related complications of cardiovascular disease, renal disease, blindness, and nerve damage. Diabetes education, lifestyle modification, medication management, and self-monitoring of blood glucose levels are essential in maintaining overall health for those with all types of diabetes.

The liver is important in controlling the amount of glucose in the bloodstream. As the first organ to screen the sugars absorbed from the small intestine, the liver helps determine the amount of glucose that enters the bloodstream after a meal (see Fig. 5-11) and the amount that is stored as glycogen for later use.[3]

The pancreas also is important in blood glucose control. The pancreas releases small amounts of insulin as soon as a person starts to eat. Following carbohydrate digestion and absorption, blood glucose levels rise, signaling the pancreas to release large amounts of insulin. Insulin promotes increased glucose uptake by muscle, nerve, adipose, and other body cells. In addition, insulin promotes the storage of excess glucose as glycogen. These actions lower blood glucose to the normal fasting range within a few hours after a person eats.

Other hormones in the body counteract the effects of insulin. When a person has not eaten carbohydrates for a few hours, the amount of glucose in the blood is maintained by another pancreatic hormone, called glucagon. Glucagon is secreted in response to a decrease in blood glucose. It prompts the breakdown of glycogen in the liver and promotes gluconeogenesis, resulting in the release of glucose to the bloodstream and the normalization of blood glucose levels (Fig. 5-15).

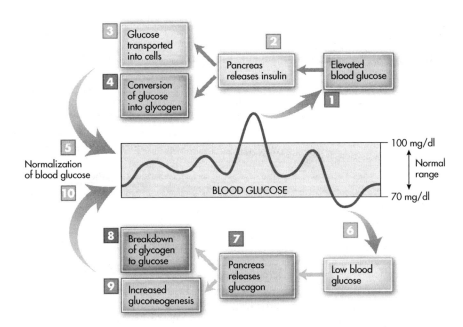

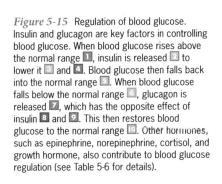

Figure 5-15 Regulation of blood glucose. Insulin and glucagon are key factors in controlling blood glucose. When blood glucose rises above the normal range **1**, insulin is released **2** to lower it **3** and **4**. Blood glucose then falls back into the normal range **5**. When blood glucose falls below the normal range **6**, glucagon is released **7**, which has the opposite effect of insulin **8** and **9**. This then restores blood glucose to the normal range **10**. Other hormones, such as epinephrine, norepinephrine, cortisol, and growth hormone, also contribute to blood glucose regulation (see Table 5-6 for details).

The hormones epinephrine (adrenaline) and norepinephrine, from the adrenal glands, also trigger the breakdown of glycogen in the liver and result in glucose release into the bloodstream. These hormones are responsible for the "fight-or-flight" reaction that we sometimes experience. They are released in large amounts in response to a perceived threat, such as a car approaching head-on. The resulting rapid release of glucose into the bloodstream promotes quick mental and physical reactions. The hormones cortisol and growth hormone also help regulate blood glucose by decreasing glucose use by muscle (Table 5-6).

In essence, the actions of insulin on blood glucose are balanced by the actions of glucagon, epinephrine, norepinephrine, cortisol, and growth hormone. If hormonal balance is not maintained, as during overproduction or underproduction of insulin or glucagon, major changes in blood glucose concentrations occur. This system of checks and balances allows blood glucose to be maintained within fairly narrow ranges.

Metabolic Syndrome

Over 50 million American adults have a condition known as Metabolic Syndrome. **Metabolic Syndrome** is characterized by a group of factors that increase the risk of type 2 diabetes and cardiovascular disease, including insulin resistance or glucose intolerance (causing high blood glucose), abdominal obesity, high blood triglycerides and LDL-cholesterol with low HDL-cholesterol, elevated blood pressure, increased inflammatory blood proteins (e.g., C-reactive protein), and higher concentrations of oxidized LDL-cholesterol

Table 5-6 Roles of Various Hormones in the Regulation of Blood Glucose

Hormone	Source	Target Organ or Tissue	Overall Effects on Organ or Tissue	Effect on Blood Glucose
Insulin	Pancreas	Liver, muscle, adipose tissue	Increases glucose uptake by muscles and adipose tissue, increases glycogen synthesis, suppresses gluconeogenesis	Decrease
Glucagon	Pancreas	Liver	Increases glycogen breakdown and release of glucose by the liver, increases gluconeogenesis	Increase
Epinephrine, norepinephrine	Adrenal glands	Liver, muscle	Increases glycogen breakdown and release of glucose by the liver, increases gluconeogenesis	Increase
Cortisol	Adrenal glands	Liver, muscle	Increases gluconeogenesis by the liver, decreases glucose use by muscles and other organs	Increase
Growth hormone	Pituitary gland	Liver, muscle, adipose tissue	Decreases glucose uptake by muscles, increases fat mobilization and utilization, increases glucose output by the liver	Increase

(see Chapter 6).[33] Metabolic Syndrome also is associated with overall obesity, physical inactivity, genetic predisposition, and aging.

To date, there have been no fully established criteria for diagnosing Metabolic Syndrome. The American Heart Association and National Heart, Lung, and Blood Institute suggest that 3 or more of the following criteria be present for diagnosing Metabolic Syndrome: a waist circumference greater than 35 inches for women and 40 inches for men, a fasting triglyceride level above 150 mg/dl, blood HDL-cholesterol below 40 mg/dl for men and below 50 mg/dl for women, elevated blood pressure above 130/85 mm Hg, and fasting blood glucose above 110 mg/dl. Lifestyle modification (focusing on weight loss, decreased dietary fat intake, and increased physical activity) is fundamental to decreasing the health risks associated with Metabolic Syndrome.

Hypoglycemia

Hypoglycemia, or low blood sugar, is a condition that can occur in people with or without diabetes. In those with diabetes, hypoglycemia can occur if they inject too much insulin, if they don't eat frequently enough, and if they exercise without eating additional carbohydrate.

In nondiabetics, 2 types of hypoglycemia have been reported: **reactive hypoglycemia** and **fasting hypoglycemia.** Reactive (postprandial) hypoglycemia is caused by an exaggerated insulin response after eating. Symptoms of irritability, sweating, anxiety, weakness, headache, and confusion may develop 2 to 5 hours after a meal, especially one high in sugars. Fasting hypoglycemia is a condition of low blood glucose after fasting for 8 or more. However, it usually is caused by an underlying serious medical condition, such as cancer, liver disease, or renal disease, rather than by simply fasting.

The diagnosis of hypoglycemia requires the simultaneous presence of a blood glucose level below 50 mg/dl and classic hypoglycemic symptoms. Although healthy people may occasionally experience some hypoglycemic symptoms if they have not eaten for a prolonged period of time, this usually is not true hypoglycemia. However, these individuals also benefit from the nutritional recommendations given to individuals diagnosed with hypoglycemia. Regular meals consisting of a balance of protein, fat, and low-glycemic-load carbohydrates, plus ample soluble fiber, help prevent hypoglycemia. Individuals also should substitute protein-containing snacks for those that contain mostly sugar and aim to spread carbohydrate intake throughout the day. Finally, limiting caffeine and alcohol intake can be beneficial in preventing symptoms of hypoglycemia.

Glycemic Index and Glycemic Load

Our bodies react uniquely to different sources of carbohydrates. For example, a serving of high-fiber brown rice results in lower blood glucose levels compared with the same-size serving of mashed potatoes. As researchers investigated the glucose response to various foods, they noted that it was not always as predicted. Thus, they developed 2 tools, the glycemic index and the glycemic load, to indicate how blood glucose responds to various foods (Table 5-7).[34]

The **glycemic index (GI)** is a ratio of the blood glucose response of a given food compared with a standard (typically, glucose or white bread).[34] Glycemic index is influenced by a food's starch structure (amylose vs. amylopectin), fiber content, food processing, physical structure (small vs. large surface area), and temperature, as well as the amount of protein and fat in a meal.[34] Foods with particularly high glycemic index values are potatoes, breads, Gatorade°, short-grain white rice, honey, and jelly beans. A major shortcoming of the glycemic index is that it is based on a serving of food that would provide 50 grams of carbohydrate. However, this amount of food may not reflect the amount typically consumed.

Glycemic load (GL) takes into account the glycemic index and the amount of carbohydrate consumed, so it better reflects a food's effect on blood glucose than does the glycemic index alone. To calculate the glycemic load of a food, the number of grams of carbohydrate in 1 serving is multiplied by the food's glycemic index, then divided by 100 (because the glycemic index is a percentage). For

► For more information on diabetes, consult this website: www.diabetes.org.

reactive hypoglycemia Low blood glucose that may follow a meal high in simple sugars, with corresponding symptoms of irritability, headache, nervousness, sweating, and confusion; also called postprandial hypoglycemia.

fasting hypoglycemia Low blood glucose that occurs after 8 hours or more of fasting.

glycemic index (GI) Blood glucose response of a given food, compared with a standard (typically, glucose or white bread).

glycemic load (GL) Amount of carbohydrate in a food multiplied by the glycemic index of that food. The result is then divided by 100.

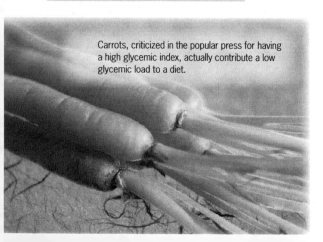

Carrots, criticized in the popular press for having a high glycemic index, actually contribute a low glycemic load to a diet.

example, vanilla wafers have a glycemic index of 77, and a serving of 5 wafers contains 15 g of carbohydrate. This yields a glycemic load of approximately 12:

$$(77 \times 15) / 100 = 12$$

Even though the glycemic index of vanilla wafers is considered high, the glycemic load calculation shows that the impact of this food on blood glucose levels is fairly low.

Table 5-7 Glycemic Index (GI) and Glycemic Load (GL) of Common Foods

Reference food glucose = 100
Low-GI foods—below 55
Intermediate-GI foods—between 55 and 69
High-GI foods—more than 70

Low-GL foods—below 10
Intermediate-GL foods—between 11 and 19
High-GL foods—more than 20

	Serving Size	Glycemic Index (GI)*	Carbohydrate (grams)	Glycemic Load (GL)
Pastas/Grains				
Brown rice	1 cup	55	46	25
White rice, short-grain	1 cup	72	53	38
Vegetables				
Carrots, boiled	1 cup	49	16	8
Sweet corn	1 cup	55	39	21
Potato, baked	1 cup	85	57	48
Dairy Foods				
Milk, fat-free	1 cup	32	12	4
Yogurt, low-fat	1 cup	33	17	6
Ice cream	1 cup	61	31	19
Legumes				
Baked beans	1 cup	48	54	26
Kidney beans	1 cup	27	38	10
Lentils	1 cup	30	40	12
Sugars				
Honey	1 tsp	73	6	4
Sucrose	1 tsp	65	5	3
Lactose	1 tsp	46	5	2
Breads and Muffins				
Whole-wheat bread	1 slice	69	13	9
White bread	1 slice	70	10	7
Fruits				
Apple	1 medium	38	22	8
Banana	1 medium	55	29	16
Orange	1 medium	44	15	7
Peach	1 medium	42	11	5
Beverages				
Orange juice	1 cup	46	26	13
Gatorade	1 cup	78	15	12
Coca-Cola	1 cup	63	26	16
Snack Foods				
Potato chips	1 oz	54	15	8
Chocolate	1 oz	49	18	9
Jelly beans	1 oz	80	26	21

*Based on a comparison with glucose.
Source: Foster-Powell K and others. International table of glycemic index and glycemic load. *Am J Clin Nutr.* 2002;76:5.

▶ You might wonder why the glycemic index and glycemic load of white bread and whole-wheat bread are similar. This is because whole-wheat flour typically is ground so finely that it is quickly digested and absorbed. Thus, experts suggest we focus on more minimally processed grains, such as coarsely ground whole-wheat flour and steel-cut oats, to get the full benefits of these fiber sources in reducing blood glucose levels.

▶ A term you might see on food labels is *net carbs*. Although this term is not FDA approved, sometimes it is used to describe the carbohydrates that increase blood glucose. Fiber and sugar alcohol content are subtracted from the total carbohydrate content to yield net carbs because they have a negligible effect on blood glucose.

Why should we be concerned with the effects of various foods on blood glucose? Foods with a high glycemic load elicit an increased insulin response from the pancreas and a resulting drop in blood glucose. These dramatic fluctuations in blood glucose can cause short- and long-term consequences in individuals with diabetes. Chronically high insulin output leads to many harmful effects on the body, such as high blood triglycerides, increased fat deposition in the adipose tissue, increased fat synthesis in the liver, and a more rapid return of hunger after a meal. Thus, increasing intakes of lower-glycemic-load foods is often recommended as a part of a healthful diet.[35] Because many foods with a low glycemic load contain higher amounts of dietary fiber, increasing one's intake of these foods will, in turn, increase fiber intake and may help reduce risk of cardiovascular disease, Metabolic Syndrome, and certain cancers.[35, 36]

The use of the glycemic index and glycemic load remains somewhat controversial. Many researchers question their benefits. Nutritionally, neither tool indicates blood glucose responses when individual foods are eaten as a part of mixed meals. Because most high-glycemic foods are eaten in combination with low-glycemic foods (e.g., rice cereals with milk, macaroni with cheese, bread with peanut butter), the glycemic index and glycemic load are often lower than the value given for these foods individually.

Knowledge Check

1. How do insulin and glucagon regulate blood glucose levels?
2. How does type 1 diabetes differ from type 2 diabetes?
3. What are the health risks associated with poorly controlled diabetes?
4. How does the glycemic index differ from the glycemic load?

CASE STUDY FOLLOW-UP

Myeshia suspected she had a problem with milk because, when she consumed it she developed bloating and gas. She was successful in reducing these symptoms by replacing milk with yogurt. As you have learned, yogurt is tolerated better than milk by people with lactose intolerance because the bacteria in yogurt digest much of the lactose. Note, however, that many people with lactose intolerance can consume small to moderate amounts of milk with few or no symptoms from the lactose that is present.

Summary

5.1 The general formula for carbohydrates is $(CH_2O)_n$, where n represents the number of times the ratio is repeated. The common monosaccharides are glucose, fructose, and galactose. Sugar alcohols are derivatives of monosaccharides. Additional monosaccharides found in nature are ribose and deoxyribose. Carbohydrates containing 2 monosaccharides are called disaccharides. Disaccharides include maltose, sucrose, and lactose. Oligosaccharides are complex carbohydrates that contain 3 to 10 single sugar units. Polysaccharides are complex carbohydrates that often contain hundreds to thousands of glucose molecules. Digestible polysaccharides are starch and glycogen. Dietary and functional fibers are indigestible polysaccharides.

5.2 Carbohydrates are found in a wide variety of foods, including table sugar, jam, jelly, fruits, soft drinks, rice, pasta, cereals, breads, dried beans, lentils, corn, peas, and dairy products. Starches contribute much of the carbohydrate in our diets. A diet rich in grains, legumes, and tubers also can provide significant amounts of dietary fiber (especially insoluble cellulose, hemicellulose, and lignins). Substances that impart sweetness to foods fall into 2 broad classes: nutritive sweeteners, which can be metabolized to yield energy, and non-nutritive (alternative) sweeteners, which provide no food energy. The sugar alcohols, sorbitol, mannitol, and xylitol, are nutritive sweeteners used in sugarless gum and candies. Non-nutritive (alternative or artificial) sweeteners provide noncaloric or very-low-calorie sugar substitutes.

5.3 Adults need about 130 g/day of digestible carbohydrate to supply adequate glucose for the brain and central nervous system, without having to rely on partial replacement of glucose by ketone bodies as an energy source. In North America, carbohydrates supply about 50% of energy intakes in adults. The Dietary Guidelines for Americans recommend limiting added sugars to approximately 6% of total energy intake. The Institute of Medicine's Food and Nutrition Board set an upper limit of 25% of energy intake for added sugar consumption. The Adequate Intake for fiber is based on a goal of 14 g/1000 kcal consumed. For adults up to age 50 years, the Adequate Intake is set at 25 g for women and 38 g for men. After age 50, the Adequate Intake falls to 21 g/day and 30 g/day, respectively. In North America, carbohydrates supply about 50% of the energy intakes of adults. Sugar intake tends to be higher than recommended and fiber intake lower than recommended.

5.4 Most of the digestible carbohydrates in our diets are broken down to glucose. As glucose, they provide a primary source of energy, spare protein for vital processes, and prevent ketosis. Fiber helps prevent constipation and diverticular disease and enhances the management of body weight, blood glucose levels, and blood cholesterol levels.

5.5 During digestion, starch and sugars are broken into monosaccharide units that are small enough to be absorbed. The enzymatic digestion of some carbohydrates begins in the mouth with the action of an enzyme called salivary amylase. Salivary enzyme is inactivated by the acidity of the stomach. In the small intestine, polysaccharides are digested further by pancreatic amylase and specialized enzymes in the absorptive cells of the small intestine. Glucose and galactose are absorbed by an active absorption process. Fructose is taken up by the absorptive cells via facilitated diffusion. Monosaccharides are transported via the portal vein to the liver. Within the liver, fructose and galactose are converted to glucose. Glucose is transported through the bloodstream for use by the cells of the body.

5.6 Adequate carbohydrate intake is important for maintaining health and decreasing the risk of chronic disease. Very high intakes of fiber (i.e., above 50 to 60 g/day) combined with low fluid intake can result in hard, dry stools that are painful to eliminate. Very high fiber intakes also may decrease the absorption of several trace minerals. High intakes of sugars can displace more nutritious foods and increase the risk of weight gain, obesity, and dental caries. Lactose intolerance can cause symptoms of abdominal pain, bloating, gas, and diarrhea after consuming lactose, especially in large amounts. An inability to regulate glucose metabolism can result in diabetes, the major forms of which are type 1 diabetes and type 2 diabetes. Type 1 diabetes often begins as an autoimmune disorder in late childhood and runs in families, suggesting a genetic link. The onset of type 1 diabetes is caused by insufficient insulin release by the pancreas, which results in increased blood glucose levels. Type 1 diabetes is treated by insulin and diet therapy. Poorly controlled diabetes can cause blindness, cardiovascular disease, kidney disease, and nerve deterioration. A person with diabetes should work regularly with a physician and dietitian to monitor and adjust his or her diet, medications, and physical activity. Type 2 diabetes is a progressive disease characterized by insulin resistance or loss of responsiveness by body cells to insulin. As a result, glucose is not readily transferred into cells and builds up in the bloodstream, causing hyperglycemia. Treatments for type 2 diabetes are aimed at maintaining normal ranges of blood glucose through lifestyle modification and medication use. Glycemic index is a ratio of the blood glucose response of a given food, compared with a standard, such as white bread. Glycemic load takes into account the glycemic index and the amount of carbohydrate consumed.

Study Questions

1. Which of the following is a monosaccharide?

   a. lactose   **c.** fructose
   b. raffinose   **d.** maltose

2. Which of the following is classified as a digestible form of polysaccharide?

   a. cellulose   **c.** lignin
   b. raffinose   **d.** pectin

3. Carbohydrates are involved in all of the following functions *except* _____.

   a. providing energy
   b. preventing ketosis
   c. promoting bowel health
   d. promoting cell differentiation

4. Individuals with lactose intolerance have difficulty digesting milk products because they lack the enzyme needed to break apart the beta bond linkages.

   a. true
   b. false

5. The Adequate Intake for dietary fiber is set at 14 g/1000 kcal.

   a. true
   b. false

6. Which of the following sweeteners is classified as a non-nutritive sweetener?

   a. sorbitol   **c.** aspartame
   b. honey   **d.** mannitol

184 **PART 2** Energy-Yielding Nutrients and Alcohol

7. Which of the following is a poor source of dietary fiber?

   a. whole-grain oats   **c.** low-fat yogurt
   b. fresh blueberries   **d.** dried lentils

8. Which of the following is a good source of starch?

   a. citrus fruits   **c.** enriched grains
   b. dark, leafy greens   **d.** barbequed chicken

9. Which of the following terms is used to describe an elevated blood sugar level?

   a. glucosuria   **c.** hyperlipidemia
   b. hypoglycemia   **d.** hyperglycemia

10. Which of the following is *not* a classic symptom of type 1 diabetes?

    a. polyuria   **c.** hunger
    b. polydipsia   **d.** rapid weight gain

11. Which of the following population groups is at lowest risk of diabetes?

    a. college athletes
    b. obese individuals
    c. individuals of Hispanic/Latino heritage
    d. adults over 45 years of age

12. High-fiber diets can impair the absorption of trace minerals.

    a. true
    b. false

13. Which of the following is associated with low-fiber diets?

    a. diverticulosis   **c.** diarrhea
    b. dental caries   **d.** lactose intolerance

14. Diabetic exchanges and carbohydrate counting are effective ways for individuals with diabetes to monitor their daily carbohydrate intake.

    a. true
    b. false

15. The glycemic index is a ratio of the blood glucose response of a given food compared with a standard.

    a. true
    b. false

16. Describe how each of the 3 major dissacharides plays a part in the human diet.

17. How do amylose, amylopectin, and glycogen differ from each other?

18. Compare the sweetness and food uses of nutritive and non-nutritive (alternative) sweeteners.

19. Compare the recommended intakes of carbohydrate with the typical intakes in North America.

20. What health benefits do indigestible carbohydrates offer?

21. Explain the main steps in carbohydrate digestion and absorption.

22. What are the possible effects of a diet too high in fiber?

23. How do type 1 and type 2 diabetes differ?

Answer Key: 1-c; 2-d; 3-d; 4-a; 5-a; 6-c; 7-c; 8-c; 9-d; 10-d; 11-a; 12-a; 13-a; 14-a; 15-a; 16-refer to Section 5.1; 17-refer to Section 5.1; 18-refer to Section 5.2; 19-refer to Section 5.3; 20-refer to Section 5.4; 21-refer to Section 5.5; 22-refer to Section 5.6; 23-refer to Medical Perspective.

Websites

To learn more about the topics covered in this chapter, visit these websites.

www.ific.org

www.cancer.gov/cancertopics/factsheet/Risk/artificial-sweeteners

www.fda.gov/Food

www.diabetes.org

www.eatright.org

www.ada.org

www.nidcr.nih.gov

www.niddk.nih.gov

References

1. ADA Reports. Position of the American Dietetic Association. Use of nutritive and nonnutritive sweeteners. *J Am Diet Assoc.* 2004;104:225.

2. Food and Nutrition Board. *Dietary Reference Intakes for energy, carbohydrate, fiber, fat, fatty acids, cholesterol, protein, and amino acids.* Washington, DC: National Academy Press; 2002.

3. Keim NL and others. Carbohydrates. In: Shils ME and others, eds. *Modern nutrition in health and disease.* 10th ed. Philadelphia: Lippincott Williams & Wilkins; 2006.

4. Marriott BP and others. National estimates of dietary fructose intake increase from 1977 to 2004 in the United States. *J Nutr.* 2009;139:1228S.

5. Skypala I. Adverse food reactions—an emerging issue for adults. *J Am Diet Assoc.* 2011;111:1877.

6. Grabitske H, Slavin J. Gastrointestinal effects of low-digestible carbohydrates. *Crit Rev Food Sci Nutr.* 2009;49:327.

7. Murphy MM and others. Resistant starch intakes in the U.S., *J Am Diet Assoc.* 2008;108:67.

8. Anderson JW and others. Health benefits of dietary fiber. *Nutr Rev.* 2009;67:188.

9. Wolfram T, Ismail-Beigi F. Efficacy of high-fiber diets in the management of type 2 diabetes mellitus. *Endocr Pract.* 2011;17:132.

10. Sheth AA and others. Diverticular disease and diverticulitis. *Am J Gastroenterol.* 2008;103:1550.

11. Jonnalagadda SS and others. Putting the whole grain puzzle together: health benefits associated with whole grains—summary of Amercian Society for Nutrition 2010 Satellite Symposium. *J Nutr.* 2011;141:1011S.

12. Aune D and others. Dietary fibre, whole grains and risk of colorectal cancer: systematic review and dose-response meta-analysis of prospective studies. *BMJ.* 2011;343:d6617.

13. Mattes RD, Popkin BM. Nonnutritive sweetener consumption in humans: Effects on appetite and food intake and their putative mechanisms. *Am J Clin Nutr.* 2009;89:1.

14. Mogra R, Dashora V. Exploring the use of *Stevia rebaudiana* as a sweetener in comparison with other sweeteners. *J Hum Ecol.* 2009;25:117.

15. Sacks FM and others. Comparison of weight-loss diets with different compositions of fat, protein and carbohydrates. *JAMA.* 2009;360:859.

16. USDHHS/USDA. *Dietary Guidelines for Americans.* 7th ed. 2010; www.dietaryguidelines.gov.

17. Johnson RK and others. Dietary sugar intake and cardiovascular health: A scientific statement from the American Heart Association. *Circulation.* 2009;120:1011.

18. Stanhope KL, Havel PJ. Fructose consumption: recent results and their potential implications. *Ann NY Acad Sci.* 2010;1190:15.

19. Murphy MM and others. Phytonutrient intake by adults in the United States in relation to fruit and vegetable consumption. *J Am Diet Assoc.* 2011;112:222.

20. Tucker LA, Thomas KS. Increasing total fiber intake reduces risk of weight and fat gains in women. *J Nutr.* 2009;139:546.

21. Davis JN and others. Inverse relation between dietary fiber intake and visceral adiposity in overweight Latino youth. *Am J Clin Nutr.* 2009;90:1160.

22. Ventura E and others. Reduction in risk factors for type 2 diabetes in response to a low-sugar, high-fiber dietary intervention in overweight Latino youth. *Arch Pediatr Adolesc Med.* 2009;163:320

23. Strate LL and others. Nut, corn, and popcorn consumption and the incidence of diverticular disease. *JAMA.* 2008;300:907.

24. Shaukat A and others. Systematic review: Effective management strategies for lactose intolerance. *Ann Int Med.* 2010;152:797.

25. Sweeteners can sour your health. *Consumer Reports on Health.* 2005;January:8.

26. Krebs JR. The gourmet ape: Evolution and human food preferences. *Am J Clin Nutr.* 2009;90:707S.

27. American Diabetes Association. Standards of medical care in diabetes. *Diabetes Care.* 2012;35:S11.

28. American Diabetes Association. Nutritional recommendations and invervention for diabetes. *Diabetes Care.* 2008;31:S61.

29. Franz MJ and others. Evidence-based nutrition practice guidelines for diabetes and scope and standards of practice. *J Am Diet Assoc.* 2008;108:S52.

30. Diabetes Control and Complications Trial/Epidemiology of Diabetes Interventions and Complications Research Study Group. Intensive diabetes treatment and cardiovascular disease in patients with type 1 diabetes. *N Engl J Med.* 2005;353:2643.

31. Tesfaye S and others. Vascular risk factors and diabetic neuropathy. *N Engl J Med.* 2005;352:341.

32. Hayes C, Kriska A. Role of physical activity in diabetes management and prevention. *J Am Diet Assoc.* 2008;108:S19.

33. Holvoet P and others. Association between circulating oxidized low-density lipoprotein and incidence of the metabolic syndrome. *JAMA.* 2008;299:2287.

34. Wheeler ML, Pi-Sunyer X. Carbohydrate issues: Type and amount. *J Am Diet Assoc.* 2008;108:S34.

35. Esfahani A and others. The application of the glycemic index and glycemic load in weight loss: A review of the clinical evidence. *IUBMB Life.* 2011;63:7.

36. Grau K and others. Overall glycaemic index and glycaemic load of habitual diet and risk of heart disease. *Pub Health Nutr.* 2011;14:109.

37. Vasanti S and others. Sugar-sweetened beverages, obesity, type 2 diabetes mellitus, and cardiovascular disease risk. *Circ.* 2010;121:1356.

38. Brownell KD and others. The public health and economic benefits of taxing sugar-sweetened beverages. *New Eng J Med.* 2009; 361:1599.

39. Brownell KD and Frieden TR. Ounces of prevention—The public policy case for taxes on sugared beverages. *N Engl J Med.* 2009;60:18

40. Epstein L and others. The influence of taxes and subsidies on energy purchased in an experimental purchasing study. *Psychol Sci.* 2010;21:406.

The Mediterranean Diet, rich in olive oil, is an eating pattern that promotes lifelong good health. Learn more at **www.oldwayspt.org.**

6 Lipids

Student Learning Outcomes

After studying this chapter, you will be able to

1. Describe the basic chemical structure of fatty acids and explain how they are named.

2. Explain the functions of triglycerides, fatty acids, phospholipids, and sterols in the body.

3. Classify and evaluate the different fatty acids based on their health benefits or consequences.

4. Identify food sources of triglycerides, fatty acids, phospholipids, and sterols.

5. Discuss the recommended intake of lipids.

6. Identify strategies for modifying total fat, saturated fat, and *trans* fat intake.

7. Explain the digestion, absorption, and transport of lipids in the body.

8. Discuss health concerns related to dietary fat intake.

9. Describe dietary measures to reduce the risk of developing cardiovascular disease.

FATS (TECHNICALLY, LIPIDS) GIVE FOOD a creamy, luscious mouthfeel. They also add a great deal of flavor to foods—think about the buttery taste of croissants or the savory flavor of beef. Nearly every food we eat contains at least some fat. The foods richest in fat are vegetable oils, margarine, butter, avocado, and nuts (Fig. 6-1). All contain close to 100% of energy as fat. Many protein-rich foods, such as meat, cheese, and peanut butter, are high in fat, too. Cakes, pies, cookies, muffins, chocolate, ice cream, and snack foods, such as chips and crackers, also contain sizeable amounts of fat. In addition to providing flavor, texture, and energy, dietary fats supply fat-soluble vitamins (vitamins A, D, E, and K). They also are a compact source of calories—gram for gram, fats supply more than twice as many calories as carbohydrates and proteins. Fat insulates the body and pads its organs to protect them from injuries. We also use fat to make hormones.

As you can see, fats are essential for good health, so why do fats have such a bad reputation? It's because not all fats are created equal from a health perspective. Exploring the characteristics of the lipid family members will clarify this often misunderstood nutrient.

Figure 6-1 Food sources of fat. In addition to MyPlate food groups, yellow is used for oils and pink is used for substances that do not fit easily into food groups (e.g., candy, salty snacks).

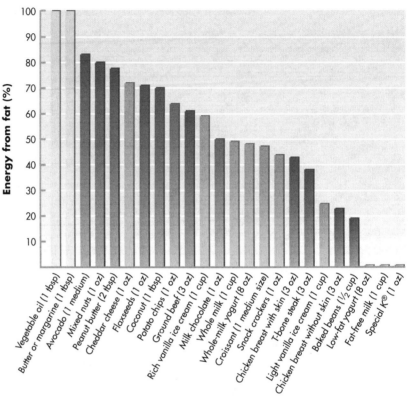

KEY
- ■ Protein
- ■ Vegetables
- ■ Fruits
- ■ Grains
- ■ Dairy
- □ Oils
- □ Other

Types of Lipids

- Triglycerides

- Phospholipids

- Sterols

▶ Fat in foods has been considered the most satiating of all the macronutrients. However, studies show that protein and carbohydrate probably provide more satiety (gram for gram). High-fat meals do provide satiety, but primarily because they are high in calories.

The term *fat* typically refers to lipids that are solid at room temperature. *Oil* refers to lipids that are liquid at room temperature.

6.1 Triglycerides

When you hear the word *lipid,* you may think of butter, lard, olive oil, and margarine. We usually refer to lipids simply as *fats and oils;* however, the lipid family includes more than that—it includes triglycerides, phospholipids, and sterols. Although these diverse family members differ in their structures and functions, they all contain carbon, hydrogen, and oxygen, and none of them dissolve in water. However, they do dissolve in organic solvents, such as chloroform, benzene, and ether. Think of oil and vinegar salad dressing. No matter how long or hard you shake the dressing, when you stop shaking, the vinegar and oil quickly separate into layers, with the oil floating on the vinegar. This insoluble property sets lipids apart from carbohydrates and proteins.

Triglycerides are the most common type of lipid found in foods and in the body. About 95% of the fats we eat and 95% of the fat stored in the body are in the form of triglycerides.

Structure

Each **triglyceride** molecule consists of 3 fatty acids attached (bonded) to a glycerol, which serves as a backbone for the fatty acids (Fig. 6-2). A triglyceride is built by attaching a fatty acid to each of glycerol's 3 hydroxyl groups (–OH). The fatty acids can be all the same fatty acid or they can be different. One water molecule is released when each fatty acid bonds to glycerol. The process of attaching fatty acids to glycerol is called **esterification.** The release of fatty acids from glycerol is called **de-esterification.** Fatty acids released from the glycerol backbone are called **free fatty acids** to emphasize that they are unattached. A triglyceride that loses a fatty acid is a **diglyceride**. A **monoglyceride** results when 2 fatty acids are lost. The process of reattaching a fatty acid to glycerol that has lost a fatty acid is known as **re-esterification.**

Free fatty acids are chains of carbons linked together and surrounded by hydrogens. The many kinds of free fatty acids have similar structures: long chains of carbon atoms linked together and surrounded by hydrogens. Free fatty acids have an acid (carboxyl) group at one end of the chain and a methyl group at the opposite end (Fig. 6-3). Their carbon chains can vary in 3 ways: the number of carbons in the chain, the extent to which the chain is saturated with hydrogen, and the shape of the chain (straight or bent).

Carbon Chain Length

Fatty acid chains usually have between 4 and 24 carbons. **Long-chain fatty acids** have 12 or more carbon atoms. Fats from beef, pork, and lamb and most plant oils are long chain. Long chains of carbon atoms take the longest to digest and are transported via the lymphatic system. **Medium-chain fatty acids** are 6 to 10 carbons in length, are digested almost as rapidly as glucose, and are transported via the circulatory system. Coconut and palm kernel oils are examples of medium-chain fatty acids. **Short-chain fatty acids** are usually less than 6 carbons in length. The fat in dairy products, such as butter and whole milk, are short chain. They are rapidly digested and transported via the circulatory system.

Saturation

Fatty acids can be saturated, monounsaturated, or polyunsaturated. To understand saturation, it is important to note that, at a maximum, a carbon atom can form 4 chemical bonds, an oxygen atom can form 2 bonds, and a hydrogen atom can form only 1 bond. Each atom always tries to form the maximum number of bonds possible, but it cannot form more than the maximum.

Figure 6-3 shows a **saturated fatty acid (SFA)**. Notice that every carbon in the chain has formed the maximum of 4 bonds. Also note that each bond is formed with a separate atom (2 different carbons and 2 different hydrogens). It is a saturated fatty acid because all the bonds between the carbons are single connections and the other carbon bonds are filled with hydrogens. To understand this concept, picture a school bus with a child in every seat. The school bus is "saturated" with children—there are no empty seats. A **monounsaturated fatty acid (MUFA)** is shown in Figure 6-4. Notice how carbons 8 and 9 in the chain are each missing 1 hydrogen. These carbons formed a double bond between each other by each giving up 1 hydrogen. (Remember, carbons can form only 4 bonds.) Fatty acids that have 1 double bond in the carbon chain are called monounsaturated fatty acids. They have 1 (*mono*) location in the carbon chain that is not saturated with hydrogen. Using the school bus example, a MUFA is like having 1 empty seat.

A Biochemist's View

Building, Breaking Down, and Rebuilding Triglycerides
(Esterifying, De-esterifying, and Re-esterifying Fatty Acids)

Triglycerides are built from a glycerol backbone and 3 fatty acids. Glycerol (in white) has 3 carbons in its chain. A triglyceride forms when each hydroxyl (–OH) group on the glycerol backbone bonds with the hydrogen atom from the acid (carboxyl) end of a fatty acid.

The bond between a fatty acid and glycerol is called an ester bond. One molecule of water (H_2O) forms each time an ester bond forms (this is called **esterification**). Thus, when a diglyceride (2 fatty acids attached to a glycerol backbone) forms, 2 molecules of water form. Similarly, forming a triglyceride will generate 3 water molecules.

A molecule of water is used when a fatty acid breaks away from a glycerol backbone (called **de-esterification**). Reattaching the fatty acid to a glycerol backbone (called **re-esterification**) will produce a water molecule.

Figure 6-2 Triglycerides are made of 3 fatty acids attached to a glycerol backbone. Diglycerides have only 2 of the 3 fatty acids, and monoglycerides have just 1 of the 3 fatty acids.

▶ Chemists classify triglycerides as esters. Triacylglyceride is the chemical name for triglyceride. *Acyl* refers to a fatty acid that has lost its hydroxyl group (–OH). A fatty acid loses its hydroxyl group when it attaches to glycerol.

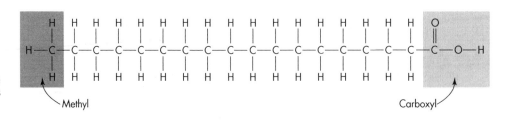

Figure 6-3 A saturated fatty acid has no carbon-carbon double bonds. This saturated fatty acid is called stearic acid.

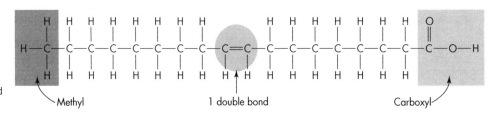

Figure 6-4 A monounsaturated fatty acid has 1 carbon-carbon double bond. This monounsaturated fatty acid is called oleic acid.

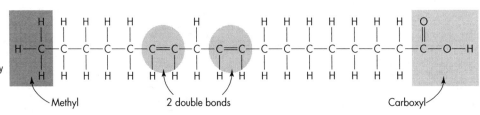

Figure 6-5 A polyunsaturated fatty acid has 2 or more carbon-carbon double bonds. This polyunsaturated fatty acid is called linoleic acid.

A **polyunsaturated fatty acid (PUFA)** has at least 2 double bonds in its carbon chain (Fig. 6-5). If the school bus were a PUFA, it would have 2 or more empty seats.

▶ Why are some fats solid at room temperature and others liquid? The fat's carbon chain shape and length determine this. Like crumpled paper, the kinked carbon chains of unsaturated fatty acids do not pack tightly together. This "loose" packing causes them to be soft or liquid at room temperature. In contrast, saturated fatty acids, with their straight carbon chain, like unfolded paper, pack tightly together. This tight packing helps them stay firm (not melt) at room temperature. However, the effect of the straight chain shape on saturated fats (but not unsaturated fats) can be overridden by chain length. That is, only saturated fatty acids with a long carbon chain, such as beef fat, are solid at room temperature. Medium- and short-chain saturated fats are soft or liquid at room temperature.

Shape

The shape of the carbon chain varies with saturation. Saturated and *trans* fatty acids have straight carbon chains, and unsaturated *cis* fatty acids have bent or kinked carbon chains. In *cis* **fatty acids,** the hydrogens attached to the double-bonded carbons are on the same side of the carbon chain (see Fig. 6-5). In *trans* **fatty acids** (also called *trans* fats), the hydrogens attached to the double-bonded carbons zigzag back and forth across the carbon chain (Fig. 6-6). In Figure 6-7, notice how the *cis* fatty acid, which has the hydrogens next to the double bonds on the same side of the carbon chain, bends. The *trans* fatty acid, which has the hydrogens next to the double bonds on opposite sides of the carbon chain, is straight and resembles a saturated fatty acid.

Most unprocessed unsaturated fatty acids, such as oils freshly pressed from nuts and seeds, are in the *cis* form. *Trans* fatty acids are found mostly in the polyunsaturated oils modified by food manufacturers using a process called hydrogenation.

Hydrogenation adds hydrogen to the carbon chain of unsaturated fats. As the amount of added hydrogen increases, the unsaturated fat becomes more and more saturated (until it is totally saturated) and increasingly solid. For instance, corn oil, which is polyunsaturated and liquid at room temperature, can be hydrogenated: a little to make squeeze margarine, some to make tub margarine, and a lot to make stick margarine.

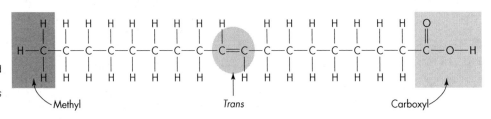

Figure 6-6 This monounsaturated fatty acid is a *trans* fat. It is called elaidic acid, which is the major *trans* fatty acid found in processed fats.

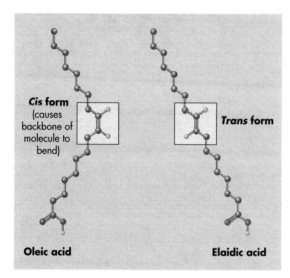

Figure 6-7 *Cis* and *trans* fatty acids. *Cis* fatty acids are more common in foods than *trans* fats. *Trans* fats are primarily found in foods containing hydrogenated fats, such as margarine, shortening, and deep fat–fried foods.

▶ Ball-and-stick models (e.g., Fig. 6-7) show the spatial arrangement of atoms in a molecule. The blue balls are carbon, white hydrogen, and red oxygen. The lines between the balls represent bonds.

Hydrogenation is like putting children in some of the empty bus seats except, when the children are added to the bus, it changes the shape of the bus. The shape change occurs because hydrogenation creates *trans* fatty acids that have a straighter shape than *cis* fatty acids.

hydrogenation Addition of hydrogen to some carbon-carbon double bonds and producing some *trans* fatty acids. This process is used to convert liquid oils into more solid fats.

Naming Fatty Acids

Two systems are commonly used to name fatty acids. Both are based on the numbers of carbon atoms and the location of double bonds in a fatty acid's carbon chain. The omega (ω or n) system indicates where the first double bond closest to the methyl (omega) end of the chain occurs. For example, the fatty acid linoleic acid is named 18:2 ω6 (18:2 n6). This means that linoleic acid, shown on the right in Figure 6-8, has 18 carbons in its carbon chain and 2 double bonds, and the first double bond starts at the 6th carbon from the omega end (orange boxed area of Fig. 6-8). The delta (Δ) system describes fatty acids in relation to the carboxyl end of the carbon chain (blue boxed area of Fig. 6-8) and indicates the location of all double bonds. Thus, in the delta system, linoleic acid is written 18:2 $\Delta^{9,12}$. Whereas the scientific community uses both of these systems nearly equally, the popular media use the omega system, as does this text.

▶ Alpha is the first letter of the Greek alphabet and omega is the last letter. Alpha looks like this: α. Omega looks like this in Greek: ω. In English, a lowercase *n* is sometimes used in place of the Greek letter for omega.

Omega-3 (alpha-linolenic acid)

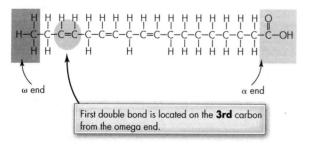

Omega-6 (linoleic acid)

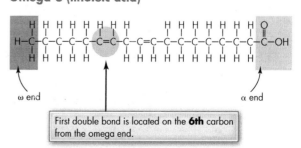

Figure 6-8 Omega-3 fatty acids have their first double bond 3 carbons in from the methyl (omega) end of the carbon chain. Likewise, omega-6 fatty acids have their first double bond 6 carbons in from the omega end. How would alpha-linolenic acid be named using the omega and delta systems?

192   **PART 2**   Energy-Yielding Nutrients and Alcohol

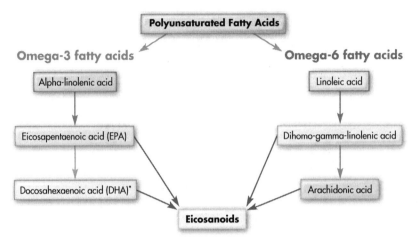

*Technically, DHA yields docosanoids, which are similar to eicosanoids.

Figure 6-9   The essential fatty acids alpha-linolenic acid and linoleic acid are used to make other important fatty acids.

On food packages, hydrogenated fats appear in the ingredient list as partially hydrogenated fat or hydrogenated fat. Food manufacturers can call a food "*trans* fat free" if it contains 0.5 gram or less of *trans* fats.

Essential Fatty Acids

Humans can synthesize a wide variety of fatty acids, but we *cannot* make 2 PUFAs: alpha-linolenic acid (the major omega-3 fatty acid in food) and linoleic acid (the major omega-6 fatty acid in food). Alpha-linolenic acid and linoleic acid are **essential fatty acids (EFAs).** We must get EFAs from foods because our bodies are unable to synthesize essential fatty acids with a double bond before the 9th carbon in the chain, counting from the omega end (see Fig. 6-8).

The location of the double bond closest to the omega carbon (methyl end) of the fatty acid identifies the fatty acid's family. If the first double bond of a polyunsaturated fatty acid occurs after the 3rd carbon from the methyl end, it is called an omega-3 fatty acid (ω−3). If the first double bond occurs after the 6th carbon on a polyunsaturated fatty acid, it is called an omega-6 fatty acid (ω−6).

As you can see in Figure 6-9, the fatty acids eicosapentaenoic acid (EPA) and, subsequently, docosahexaenoic acid (DHA) are made from alpha-linolenic acid. Likewise, the fatty acids dihomo-gamma-linolenic acid and, subsequently, arachidonic acid are made from linoleic acid.

Different eicosanoids are produced from dihomo-gamma-linolenic acid, arachidonic acid, and eicosapentaenoic acid. **Eicosanoids** are hormonelike compounds, such as **prostaglandins,** prostacyclins, thromboxanes, leukotrienes, and lipoxins, that affect the body in the region where they are produced. (They are called *local* hormones because, unlike typical hormones, they are made *and* used in the same area of the body.)

eicosanoids Hormonelike compounds synthesized from polyunsaturated fatty acids, such as omega-3 fatty acids and omega-6 fatty acids.

prostaglandins Potent eicosanoid compounds that produce diverse effects in the body.

Knowledge Check

1. What characteristics do all lipids have?
2. How do saturated, monounsaturated, and saturated fats differ?
3. What are the differences between *cis* and *trans* fats?
4. How do the omega and delta systems for naming fatty acids differ?
5. Why must essential fatty acids be provided by the diet?

6.2 Food Sources of Triglycerides

Almost all foods provide at least some triglycerides. Certain foods, such as animal fat and vegetable oils, are primarily triglycerides. Bakery items, snack foods, and dairy desserts also contain significant amounts of fat. In contrast, fat-free milk and yogurt, as well as many breakfast cereals and yeast breads, contain little or no fat. Other than coconut and avocados, fruits and vegetables are low in fat.

Table 6-1 lists the main sources of each type of fatty acid. For instance, fats from animal sources and tropical oils (coconut, palm, palm kernel) are rich in saturated fatty acids. Omega-3 fatty acid sources include cold-water fish (salmon, tuna, sardines, mackerel), walnuts, and flaxseed. Fish oil and flaxseed oil supplements are another source of omega-3 fatty acids.

Flax is a common plant that produces seeds high in omega-3 fats. The seeds can be ground and used as a meal in baked goods. They also can be pressed to extract the oil, which is sold as a nutritional supplement.

Table 6-1 Main Sources of Fatty Acids and Their State at Room Temperature			
Type and Health Effects	**Double Bonds**	**Main Sources**	**State at Room Temperature**
Saturated Fatty Acids *Increase blood levels of cholesterol*	0		
Long-chain	0	Lard; fat in beef, pork, and lamb	Solid
Medium- and short-chain	0	Milk fat (butter), coconut oil, palm oil, palm kernel oil	Soft or liquid
Monounsaturated Fatty Acids *Decrease blood levels of cholesterol*	1	Olive oil, canola oil, peanut oil	Liquid
Polyunsaturated Fatty Acids *Decrease blood levels of cholesterol*	2 or more	Sunflower oil, corn oil, safflower oil, fish oil	Liquid
Essential Fatty Acids Omega-3: alpha-linolenic acid *Reduces inflammation responses, blood clotting, and plasma triglycerides*	3	Cold-water fish (salmon, tuna, sardines, mackerel), walnuts, flaxseed, hemp oil, canola oil, soybean oil	Liquid
Omega-6: linoleic acid *Regulates blood pressure and increases blood clotting*	2	Beef, poultry, safflower oil, sunflower oil, corn oil	Solid to liquid
***Trans* Fatty Acids** *Increase blood cholesterol more than saturated fat*	Less than the PUFA used to make *trans* fat	Margarine (squeeze, tub, stick), shortening	Soft to very solid

Cold-water fish are high in essential fatty acids, but are fish safe to eat? Some people worry about potential health risks related to fish and fish oil supplements, such as carcinogens (e.g., DDT, dieldrin, heptachlor, PCBs, dioxin) and toxins (e.g., methylmercury). Although these contaminants are present in low levels in fresh and salt water, they can be concentrated in fish. To minimize exposure, select small, nonpredatory fish; vary the type of fish you eat; buy fish from reputable markets; and discard fatty portions of fish, where toxins concentrate. If you catch your own fish, always check local advisories to be sure that the water you plan to fish in is safe. You can call your local health department or visit your state government's website to learn about fishing advisories.

Cut away fat along the back.

Remove the skin.

Cut away the dark, fatty tissue along the side of the fillet.

Trim off the belly fat.

194 **PART 2** Energy-Yielding Nutrients and Alcohol

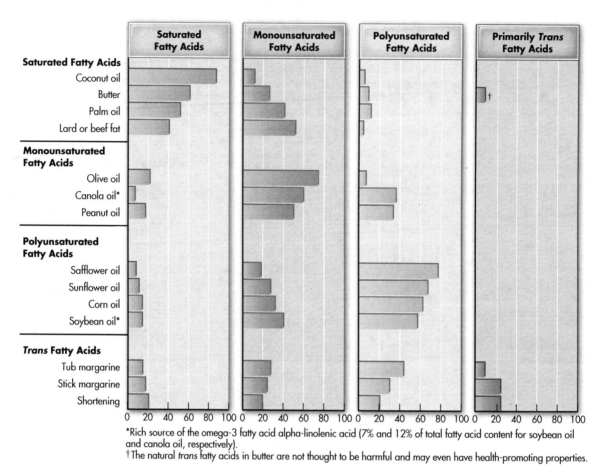

*Rich source of the omega-3 fatty acid alpha-linolenic acid (7% and 12% of total fatty acid content for soybean oil and canola oil, respectively).

†The natural *trans* fatty acids in butter are not thought to be harmful and may even have health-promoting properties.

Figure 6-10 Saturated, monounsaturated, polyunsaturated, and *trans* fatty acid composition of common fats and oils (expressed as % of all fatty acids in the product).

▶ A "reduced-fat" food may not be lower in calories than its full-fat counterpart. That's because, when fat is removed from a product, something must be added—commonly, sugars—in its place.

Most triglyceride-rich foods contain a mixture of fatty acids. As you can see in Figure 6-10, butter contains saturated, monounsaturated, and polyunsaturated fatty acids. Saturated fats are the predominant fatty acid in butter, so it is referred to as a saturated fat. Similarly, olive oil contains saturated, monounsaturated, and polyunsaturated fatty acids, but monounsaturated fat predominates. Thus, it is referred to as a monounsaturated fat.

Hidden Fats

The fat in some foods is visible: butter on bread, mayonnaise in potato salad, and marbling in raw meat. In many foods, however, fat is hidden, as is the fat in whole milk, cheese, pastries, cookies, cake, hot dogs, crackers, french fries, and ice cream. Nutrition Facts labels can help you learn more about the quantity of fat in the foods you eat (Fig. 6-11).

Fat Replacements

To help consumers trim their fat intake and still enjoy the mouthfeel sensations fat provides, food companies offer low-fat versions of many foods. To lower the fat in foods, manufacturers may replace some of the fat with water, protein (Dairy-Lo˙), or forms of carbohydrates such as starch derivatives (Z-trim˙), fiber (Maltrin˙, Stellar™, Oatrim), and gums. Manufacturers also may use engineered fats, such as olestra (Olean˙) and salatrim (Benefat˙), which are made with fat and sucrose (table sugar) but provide few or no calories because they cannot be digested and/or absorbed well.

CRITICAL THINKING

Martin wants to cut back on the saturated and *trans* fat in his diet. He mentions to you that he is still going to eat hamburgers and fries, but now he will order the burger without cheese and dip his fries in ketchup instead of Ranch dressing. Has he really reduced his fat intake?

Fat replacements, such as gum fiber, are often used in soft serve ice cream.

Take Action

Is Your Diet High in Saturated and *Trans* Fat?

Instructions: In each row of the following list, circle your typical food selection from column A or B.

Column A		Column B
Bacon and eggs	or	Ready-to-eat whole-grain breakfast cereal
Doughnut or sweet roll	or	Whole-wheat roll, bagel, or bread
Breakfast sausage	or	Fruit
Whole milk	or	Reduced-fat, low-fat, or fat-free milk
Cheeseburger	or	Turkey sandwich, no cheese
French fries	or	Plain baked potato with salsa
Ground chuck	or	Ground round
Soup with cream base	or	Soup with broth base
Macaroni and cheese	or	Macaroni with marinara sauce
Cream/fruit pie	or	Graham crackers
Cream-filled cookies	or	Granola bar
Ice cream	or	Frozen yogurt, sherbet, or reduced-fat ice cream
Butter or stick margarine	or	Vegetable oils or soft margarine in a tub

Interpretation

The foods listed in column A tend to be high in saturated fat, *trans* fatty acids, cholesterol, and total fat. Those in column B generally are low in these dietary components. If you want to help reduce your risk of cardiovascular disease, choose more foods from column B and fewer from column A.

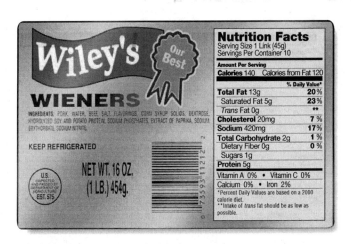

Figure 6-11 Reading labels helps you locate hidden fat. Who would think that wieners (hot dogs) can contain about 86% of energy content as fat? Looking at the hot dog itself does not suggest that almost all its energy content comes from fat, but the label shows otherwise. Do the math: 120 kcal from fat / 140 kcal = 0.86, or 86%.

▶ Olestra binds fat-soluble vitamins and reduces their absorption. To compensate, the manufacturer adds these vitamins to foods containing olestra. At first, olestra was suspected of causing GI tract discomfort; however, careful research indicates this is not the case, and warning labels on olestra-containing foods are no longer required.

▶ Table 2-3 in Chapter 2 defines the fat claims that are permitted on food labels, such as "low-fat," "fat-free," and "reduced-fat."

So far, fat replacements have had little impact on our diets, partly because the currently approved forms are either not very versatile or not used extensively by manufacturers. In addition, fat replacements are not practical for use in the foods that provide the most fat in our diets—beef, cheese, whole milk, and pastries.

Knowledge Check

1. What are 3 sources of each type of fatty acid?
2. What are examples of foods that contain hidden fats?
3. What types of fat replacements are currently available?

6.3 Functions of Triglycerides

Triglycerides are essential for optimal health. They provide a concentrated source of energy, insulate and cushion vital organs, and help transport essential nutrients in the bloodstream. However, high intakes, especially of saturated and *trans* fat, and imbalances of EFAs can present health challenges.

Provide Energy

▶ A triglyceride's glycerol backbone can be used as a fuel for the nervous system. Another brain fuel that originates with triglycerides is ketones—compounds formed when fatty acids do not metabolize completely; large amounts of ketones form when carbohydrate (glucose) intake is restricted or insulin is low. (See Chapter 9.)

Triglycerides in food and body fat cells are a rich source of energy, with each gram providing about 9 calories. Triglycerides are the main fuel source for all body cells, except the nervous system and red blood cells. When you are resting or engaging in light physical activity, triglycerides provide 30 to 70% of the energy you burn. The exact amount depends on how well fed you are before exercise, how physically fit you are, and the intensity and duration of the exercise.

Provide Compact Energy Storage

Triglycerides are the body's main storage form of energy. Excess calories from carbohydrate, fat, protein, and alcohol can be converted to fatty acids and then to triglycerides. Triglycerides make an excellent energy "savings account" because they are stable (don't react with other cell parts) and calorie dense. Fat cells contain about 80% lipid and only 20% water and protein. Muscle cells also contain fat and protein but are 73% water. This difference means that the lipid-rich fat cells can deliver much more energy than the water-rich muscle cells. Another reason triglycerides make an excellent storage form of energy is that the amount we can store is nearly limitless. A single adipose (fat) cell can increase in weight about 50 times. When adipose cells are maxed out with fat, new fat cells can form. Although it is important to have some body fat stores, very small and large stores can pose numerous health risks. (Chapter 10 discusses the health issues associated with underweight, overweight, and obesity.)

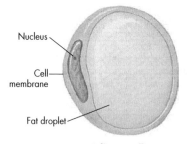

Nucleus

Cell membrane

Fat droplet

Adipose cell

Insulate and Protect the Body

The insulating layer of fat just beneath the skin (called subcutaneous fat) is made mostly of triglycerides. By insulating the body, subcutaneous fat helps keep body temperature at a constant level. Visceral fat is packed around some organs—kidneys, for example—to cushion them and keep them from jostling around and getting injured. We usually do not notice the insulating function of subcutaneous fat because we wear clothes and add more when needed. However, people who are starving lose most of their body fat and, as a result, feel chilled even when the environment is warm.

Aid Fat-Soluble Vitamin Absorption and Transport

Fats found in food carry fat-soluble vitamins (vitamins A, D, E, and K) to the small intestine. Once there, dietary fat assists in the absorption of these vitamins. Fat-soluble vitamins are transported in the bloodstream in the same manner as dietary fat (see Chapter 4). Those who eat an extremely low-fat diet, use mineral oil as a laxative, take certain medications (e.g., the weight-loss medication orlistat), or have diseases that affect fat absorption (e.g., cystic fibrosis) may be unable to absorb sufficient amounts of fat-soluble vitamins.

Essential Fatty Acid Functions

Essential fatty acids, along with phospholipids and cholesterol, are important structural components of cell walls.[1] They also keep the cell wall fluid and flexible, so that substances can flow into and out of the cell. The omega-3 fatty acid docosahexaenoic acid (DHA) is needed during fetal life and infancy for normal development and function of the retina (the part of the eye that senses light). Starting in the first few weeks of embryonic life, DHA is vital for normal development and maturation of the nervous system. Throughout life, DHA helps regulate nerve transmission and communication.

Eicosanoids, which are made from essential fatty acids, have over 100 different actions, such as regulating blood pressure, blood clotting, sleep/wake cycles, body temperature, inflammation or hypersensitivity reactions (e.g., asthma), stomach secretions, labor during child birth, and immune and allergic responses. For example, some types of eicosanoids cause inflammation, whereas other types prevent the inflammation associated with inflammatory diseases and allergic reactions. Other eicosanoids help the blood form clots, whereas other types help prevent clots. Still other eicosanoids from omega-6 fats constrict blood vessels and raise blood pressure, yet other omega-6 eicosanoids, along with the omega-3 eicosanoids, lower blood pressure by dilating blood vessels.

Eicosanoids also have other important roles in the body, many of which are only just being discovered. For example, they assist in

- Regulating cell division rates, which may help prevent certain cancers or slow the growth of existing tumors and help prevent cancer from spreading to other parts of the body
- Maintaining normal kidney function and fluid balance
- Directing hormones to their target cells
- Regulating the flow of substances into and out of cells
- Regulating ovulation, body temperature, immune system function, and hormone synthesis

When at rest or during light activity, the body uses mostly fatty acids for fuel.

CRITICAL THINKING

Advertisements claim that omega-3 fatty acids are good for you. Your roommate says, "If omega-3's are so good, then consuming a lot of them would be even better for us." What would be your answer?

Knowledge Check

1. What are 3 functions of triglycerides?
2. When is fat used as the main fuel in the body?
3. What roles do essential fatty acids play in the body?

198 **PART 2** Energy-Yielding Nutrients and Alcohol

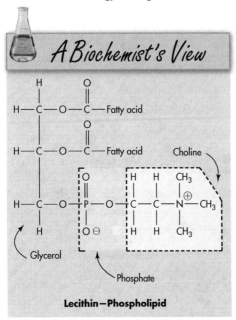

A Biochemist's View

Lecithin—Phospholipid

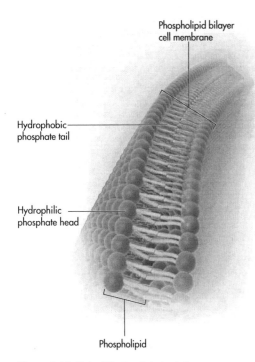

Phospholipid bilayer
cell membrane

Hydrophobic
phosphate tail

Hydrophilic
phosphate head

Phospholipid

Figure 6-12 Hydrophilic phosphate heads from the outer and inside edges of cell membranes. The hydrophobic tails point away from the heads.

emulsifier Compound that can suspend fat in water by isolating individual fat droplets using a shell of water molecules or other substances to prevent the fat from coalescing.

 6.4 Phospholipids

Many types of phospholipids are found in food and the body, especially the brain. The structure of these lipids is very similar to that of triglycerides—with one exception. One fatty acid is replaced with a compound (phosphate) that contains the mineral phosphorus and often has nitrogen attached. Phosphate gives phospholipids an important quality—it lets these fats function in a watery environment (e.g., the blood) without clumping together.

Here's how phospholipids work. The phosphate end (head) of the phospholipid is hydrophilic (water loving) and will mix with water. The fatty acid end (tail) of the phospholipid is hydrophobic (water fearing) and is attracted to fats. When placed in water, phospholipids cluster together, with their hydrophilic phosphate heads facing outward in contact with the water and their hydrophobic tails extending into the cluster away from the water.

Phospholipid Functions

In the body, phospholipids have 2 major roles: as a cell membrane component and an emulsifier. Phospholipids, along with fatty acids and cholesterol, are a primary component of cell membranes (Fig. 6-12). A cell membrane is the double-layered outer covering of a cell that corrals the cell's contents and regulates the movement of substances into and out of the cell. Imagine the cell membrane as being like corrugated cardboard. The cardboard has a smooth outside edge and a smooth inside edge, and the corrugated area fills in the space between the 2 edges. The hydrophilic phosphate heads of phospholipids orient themselves to form the cell membrane's outside edge (the part that is exposed to the blood) or inside edge (the part that is exposed to the watery cell components). Regardless of whether the hydrophilic heads are facing toward the inside or outside of the cell, their hydrophobic tails point away from the heads—so they form the "corrugation." Because the heads and tails orient themselves in this way, the cell membrane remains fluid, so that compounds can move into and out of the cell.

Phospholipids also serve as emulsifiers in the body. Bile and lecithins are the body's main emulsifiers. An **emulsifier** is a compound that forms a shell around fat droplets, so that the droplets can be suspended in water and not clump together (Fig. 6-13). The hydrophobic tails of the phospholipids reach toward fat droplets and form the inside of the shell. The outside of the shell is made of the hydrophilic heads that extend away from the fat droplet. With the hydrophilic heads on the outside, fat droplets mix with water (stay suspended) and "repel" other fat droplets (don't clump together). Emulsifiers are essential for fat to be digested and transported through the bloodstream.

The phospholipids in food often are used as an emulsifier in food preparation and manufacturing. Their ability to emulsify fats works the same in foods as it does in the body. For example, eggs are used in many muffin recipes. The lecithins in yolks emulsify fat in muffin batter and keep it suspended in the other ingredients. Mayonnaise is thick because phospholipids in egg yolks and mustard emulsified the oil and vinegar used to make this food. Food manufacturers add emulsifiers to keep the fat and watery compounds in them from separating. Emulsifying fats in foods such as cakes, muffins, and salad dressings gives them body and a smooth texture. Without emulsifiers, these foods would seem oily and have a sandy or rough texture.

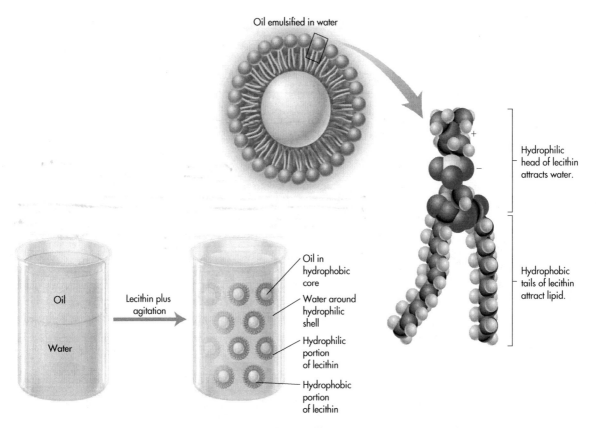

Oil emulsified in water

Hydrophilic head of lecithin attracts water.

Hydrophobic tails of lecithin attract lipid.

Oil

Water

Lecithin plus agitation

Oil in hydrophobic core

Water around hydrophilic shell

Hydrophilic portion of lecithin

Hydrophobic portion of lecithin

Figure 6-13 When an emulsifier, such as lecithin, is added to water and oil and agitated, the two solutions (oil and water) form an emulsion.

Sources of Phospholipids

Phospholipids can be synthesized by the body or supplied by the diet. For example, lecithins are found in foods such as egg yolks, wheat germ, and peanuts. Although lecithin supplements are available, they are not needed because the liver can produce sufficient amounts of phospholipids. Lecithin supplements have been promoted as a way to lose weight, lower cholesterol, and reduce the risk of Alzheimer disease. However, studies indicate that lecithin has no effect on weight loss. Data are conflicting when it comes to lecithin's ability to lower cholesterol or Alzheimer disease risk.[2, 3] It is important to note that high doses of lecithin can cause gas, diarrhea, and weight gain.

Lecithins are a family of phospholipids synthesized by the body and found in foods such as peanuts, wheat germ, soybeans, egg yolks, and liver.

Knowledge Check

1. What is the main structural difference between phospholipids and triglycerides?
2. What are the main functions of phospholipids?
3. How are phospholipids used in the food industry?

6.5 Sterols

Sterols are the last type of lipid. Sterols are a type of steroid. The structure of sterols is very different from that of the long carbon chains seen in fatty acids and phospholipids. Instead, the carbons are mostly arranged in many rings (Fig. 6-14).

Sterol Functions

From a nutrition perspective, cholesterol is the most well known sterol. This waxy substance is required to synthesize many compounds. For instance, our bodies use cholesterol to make steroid hormones, such as testosterone, estrogens, the active form of vitamin D hormone, and corticosteroids (cortisone). Cholesterol also is used to make bile, which is required to emulsify fats, so that they can be digested normally.

In addition, cholesterol, along with phospholipids, forms cell membranes and allows fat-soluble substances to move into and out of the cell. Cholesterol, along with phospholipids and proteins, also forms the shell covering chylomicrons (droplets that transport lipids). This shell is what allows fat droplets to float through the water-based bloodstream (see Section 6.8).

Sources of Sterols

Cholesterol is found in foods of animal origin, such as meat, fish, poultry, eggs, and dairy products. (Foods of plant origin do not contain cholesterol.) Most people get about one-third of their cholesterol from the foods they eat and the rest is manufactured by their bodies. Of the approximately 875 mg of cholesterol produced daily by our bodies, about 400 mg is used to replenish bile stores and about 50 mg is used to make steroid hormones. On average, American diets supply about 180 to 325 mg of cholesterol per day.[4] Of that, we absorb about 40 to 60%. Cholesterol does not need to be supplied by the diet because the body can synthesize all the cholesterol it needs.

Although plants do not contain or produce cholesterol, they do make other sterols, such as ergosterol (a form of vitamin D) and sitostanol (added to some margarines, such as Take Control). Eating margarine that contains sitostanol can reduce the body's absorption of cholesterol and bile, which is made from cholesterol, thereby reducing blood cholesterol levels, which decreases the risk of heart disease.

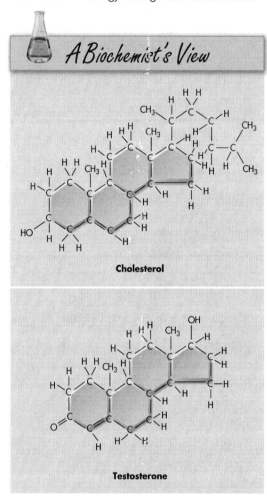

A Biochemist's View

Cholesterol

Testosterone

Figure 6-14 The carbons in sterols are arranged in rings. There is a carbon on each corner of this structural drawing of cholesterol and testosterone.

Eggs are the main source of cholesterol in the North American diet. The Food and Nutrition Board suggests limiting intake of high-cholesterol foods.

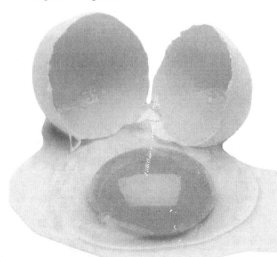

Knowledge Check

1. What is the main structural difference between sterols and triglycerides?
2. What are the main functions of sterols?
3. What are 2 dietary sources of cholesterol?

6.6 Recommended Fat Intakes

Fats are an essential part of a healthful diet but, for optimal health, the total amount and type of fat consumed need careful attention. There is no RDA for fat, but there is an Adequate Intake for infants. As you can see in Table 6-2, the Institute of Medicine's Acceptable Macronutrient Distribution Range for total fat is 20 to 35% of calories for most age groups. A total fat intake that exceeds 35% of calories often means saturated fat intake is too high. A low intake of total fat (less than 20% of calories) increases the chances of getting too little vitamin E and essential fatty acids and may adversely affect blood levels of triglycerides and a type of cholesterol called high-density lipoprotein (HDL) cholesterol, which is sometimes called "good" cholesterol (see Section 6.7).

The Institute of Medicine also recommends that saturated fat intake, including *trans* fats, and cholesterol levels be kept as low as possible while still consuming a nutritionally adequate diet. *Healthy People 2020* and other expert groups, such as the Academy of Nutrition and Dietetics, American Heart Association, and Dietary Guidelines for Americans committee, also suggest that healthy people limit saturated fats and *trans* fat intake.[5–8] Most experts recommend that, when fat calories exceed 30% of total calories, monounsaturated fats supply the extra calories. In addition, cholesterol intake should be limited to about 300 mg daily. The intake levels recommended by these expert groups meet or exceed the body's daily needs while minimizing the risk of chronic disease.

Fat intake recommendations are lower for those at risk of heart disease, such as people with high blood levels of low-density lipoprotein (LDL) cholesterol, the so-called bad cholesterol. For example, the American Heart Association recommends that these individuals restrict dietary fat to 20% of total calories, saturated fat to 7% of total calories, and cholesterol to 200 mg or less daily. Even more stringent is Dr. Dean Ornish's recommendation that dietary fat be limited to 10% of total calories.[9] Low-fat diets can help lower the risk of heart disease and, in some cases, partly reverse damage already done to arteries. However, many low-fat diets are high in carbohydrates, which may increase blood triglyceride levels and raise the risk of heart disease. As a result, it's best for those getting less than 20% of total calories from fat to be monitored by a physician. Elevated blood triglycerides often decline over several months, especially if carbohydrate choices are high in fiber, weight is kept at a healthy level, and regular exercise is included.

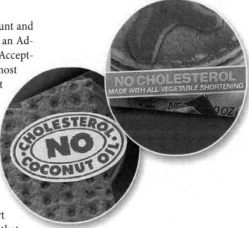

Products with reduced or no cholesterol can help keep cholesterol intake under control.

▶ Infants and children younger than 2 years need to get about half of their total calories from fat to meet calorie needs and to obtain sufficient fat for normal brain development. For children 2 to 3 years of age, keep total fat intake between 30 and 35% of calories. Between the ages of 4 and 18 years, keep fat intake between 25 and 35% of calories.

Cholesterol Content of Foods

3 oz beef brains	2635 mg
3 oz beef liver	337 mg
1 large egg yolk*	209 mg
3 oz shrimp	166 mg
3 oz beef*	75 mg
3 oz pork	75 mg
3 oz chicken or turkey (white meat)*	75 mg
1 cup ice cream	63 mg
3 oz trout	60 mg
3 oz tuna	45 mg
3 oz hot dog	38 mg
1 oz cheddar cheese*	30 mg
1 cup whole milk*	24 mg
1 cup 1% milk	12 mg
1 cup fat-free milk	5 mg
1 large egg white	0 mg

*Leading dietary sources of cholesterol in American diets.

Table 6-2 Institute of Medicine (IOM) Recommended Daily Fat Intakes[4]

Fat Component	IOM Recommendations
Total Dietary Fat	20 to 35% of calories
Saturated fat	As low as possible
Trans fat	As low as possible
Unsaturated fat	Most of fat intake
Omega-6: linoleic acid	5% of calories
Omega-3: alpha-linolenic acid	0.6 to 1.2% of calories
Cholesterol*	**As low as possible**

*National Cholesterol Education Program daily recommendation for cholesterol is 200 mg or less.

Followers of the traditional Mediterranean Diet, which is rich in olive oil, have low rates of chronic diseases.

The importance of consuming eicosanoids was discovered many years ago in studies of Greenland Eskimos. Their diet is very high in EPA-rich fish oils, and they exhibit diminished blood clotting and lower risks of heart disease.

Mediterranean Diet

There is some evidence that up to 40% of calories from fat can be healthy if monounsaturated fats account for most of the fat. The first evidence that a diet high in monounsaturated fats can be heart healthy was reported over 60 years ago in the 7 countries study conducted by Ancel Keys and colleagues[10]—this study led to today's popular Mediterranean Diet. Those who follow the traditional Mediterranean Diet enjoy some of the lowest recorded rates of chronic disease in the world. In years gone by, Greek farmers in Crete drank a glass of monounsaturated fat–rich olive oil for breakfast! Even today, the average consumption of olive oil in Greece is 20 liters per person per year.

The traditional Mediterranean Diet features the following:

- Olive oil as the main fat
- Abundant daily intake of fruits, vegetables (especially leafy greens), whole grains, beans, nuts, and seeds
- An emphasis on minimally processed and, wherever possible, seasonally fresh and locally grown foods
- Daily intake of small amounts of cheese and yogurt
- Weekly intake of low to moderate amounts of fish
- Limited use of eggs and red meat
- Regular exercise
- Moderate drinking of wine at mealtime

Essential Fatty Acid Needs

The Institute of Medicine has set Adequate Intakes for essential fatty acids. These recommendations add up to less than 120 calories daily for women and 170 calories for men—that's about 2 to 4 tablespoons daily of oils rich in these fatty acids. A deficiency of essential fatty acids is very unlikely to occur, but insufficient intake for many weeks can lead to diarrhea, slowed growth, delayed healing of wounds and infections, and flaky, itchy skin. Although the Institute of Medicine has not yet set an Upper Level for safe intake of omega-3 fats, Greenland Eskimos safely consume about 6.5 g/day, which is 3 to 5 times higher than the Adequate Intake.

Our Fat Intake

Most North Americans get more than enough total dietary fat. In fact, during the last century, our fat intake has doubled. Added fats are those that we add to food, such as butter on bread and shortenings used to make cookies, pastries, and fried foods. In terms of types of fat, many people get too much saturated fat and too little monounsaturated and polyunsaturated fat.

Dairy products (whole milk, cheese, ice cream, butter), beef, chicken, mayonnaise, and margarine are the main contributors of saturated fat. The major *trans* fat sources are margarine and baked goods made with shortening, such as cakes, cookies, crackers, pies, and breads. Vegetable oils are the prime contributors of polyunsaturated fat. Figure 6-15 compares the fat content of a high-fat meal with one lower in fat. What changes can you make to bring your fat intake under control?

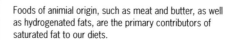

Foods of animal origin, such as meat and butter, as well as hydrogenated fats, are the primary contributors of saturated fat to our diets.

1/4 lb cheeseburger = 31 g fat

Sandwich with 2 slices ham = 6 g fat

Figure 6-15 Knowing the fat content of foods can help you plan a healthy diet.

Adequate Intake

Linoleic acid

Men: 14–17 g/day

Women: 11–12 g/day

Alpha-linolenic acid

Men: 1.6 g/day

Women: 1.1 g/day

Omega-6 fatty acid intakes are usually plentiful, but omega-3 intakes often are lower than optimal. Omega-3 fat needs can be met by eating at least 2 portions of cold-water fish each week. For individuals who do not eat fish regularly, walnuts, flaxseeds, and canola, soybean, and flaxseed oils also supply omega-3 fatty acids. Supplements also are an option. The National Institutes of Health recommends choosing a fish oil supplement that has 650 mg of EPA and 650 mg of DHA. Those who have bleeding disorders, are scheduling surgery, or are taking anticoagulants (e.g., aspirin, warfarin [Coumadin˚], or the herb ginkgo biloba) should check with their physician to minimize the risk of harmful side effects from an omega-3 supplement, which can prolong bleeding time.

Knowledge Check

1. What are the recommendations regarding total fat intake?
2. What are the main characteristics of the traditional Mediterranean Diet?
3. How does our fat intake compare with recommendations?
4. What are some steps you can take to ensure a sufficient intake of omega-3 fatty acids?

Two servings of cold-water fish, such as salmon, each week can meet omega-3 fatty acid needs.

CASE STUDY

Jessica, a college freshman, is not crazy about dorm food. As a matter of fact, she only eats breakfast in the school cafeteria. Her breakfast typically includes chocolate milk and a 2-egg cheese omelet with either ham or bacon. Her other meals are generally at fast-food restaurants and consist of cheeseburgers and fries, tacos, or fried chicken sandwiches and Tater Tots®. What type of fat is she mostly eating? Even though she is young and not at risk for a heart attack, what concerns do you have about her eating habits? What changes would you recommend?

6.7 Fat Digestion and Absorption

The body is very efficient at digesting and absorbing dietary fat (Fig. 6-16). (For a complete review of the digestive process, see Chapter 4.)

Digestion

Fat digestion begins in the mouth, where lingual lipase is secreted. This enzyme helps break down triglycerides with short- and medium-chain fatty acids that are found in milk fat. Although this enzyme is active during infancy, it plays only a minor role in fat digestion in adulthood.

In the stomach, gastric lipase helps break triglycerides into monoglycerides, diglycerides, and free fatty acids. Fat floats on top of the watery contents of the stomach, which limits the extent of lipid digestion in the stomach.

Fat digestion occurs mostly in the small intestine. Recall that the presence of fat in the small intestine triggers the release of the hormone cholecystokinin (CCK) from intestinal cells. CCK stimulates the release of bile from the gallbladder and lipase and colipase from the pancreas, all of which are delivered to the small intestine by the common bile duct. Bile emulsifies fats. That is, it breaks fat into many tiny droplets, called **micelles,** and forms a shell around the micelles that keeps the fat droplets suspended in the water-based intestinal contents. Emulsification increases the surface area of lipids and allows pancreatic lipase to efficiently break triglycerides into monoglycerides and free fatty acids. Fat digestion is very rapid and thorough because the amount of pancreatic lipase released usually is much greater than the amount needed. In addition, colipase helps lipase latch onto micelles.

Phospholipids and cholesterol also are digested mostly in the small intestine. Phospholipase enzymes from the pancreas and enzymes from the small intestine mucosa break phospholipids into their basic parts: glycerol, fatty acids, phosphoric acid, and other components (e.g., choline). Cholesterol esters (cholesterol with a fatty acid attached) are broken down to cholesterol and free fatty acids by a pancreatic enzyme called cholesterol esterase.

> **micelle** Water-soluble, spherical structure formed by lecithin and bile acids in which the hydrophobic parts face inward and hydrophilic parts face outward.

Fats

1 Mouth

2 Stomach

3 Liver

4 Pancreas

5 Small intestine

6 Large intestine

1 Mouth: Lingual lipase is secreted. Little or no fat is digested.

2 Stomach: Gastric lipase is secreted. Little fat is digested.

3 Liver: The liver produces bile, which is stored and released by the gallbladder into the common bile duct, which empties into the small intestine. Bile emulsifies fat.

4 Pancreas: The pancreas secretes pancreatic lipase, phospholipase, and cholesterol esterase into the common bile duct, which empties into the small intestine. Pancreatic lipase digests triglycerides. Phospholipase digests phospholipids. Cholesterol esterase digests cholesterol.

5 Small intestine: Fat is digested and absorbed in the duodenum and jejunum. Bile is reabsorbed in the ileum.

6 Large intestine: Less than 5% of fat passes through the large intestine and is excreted.

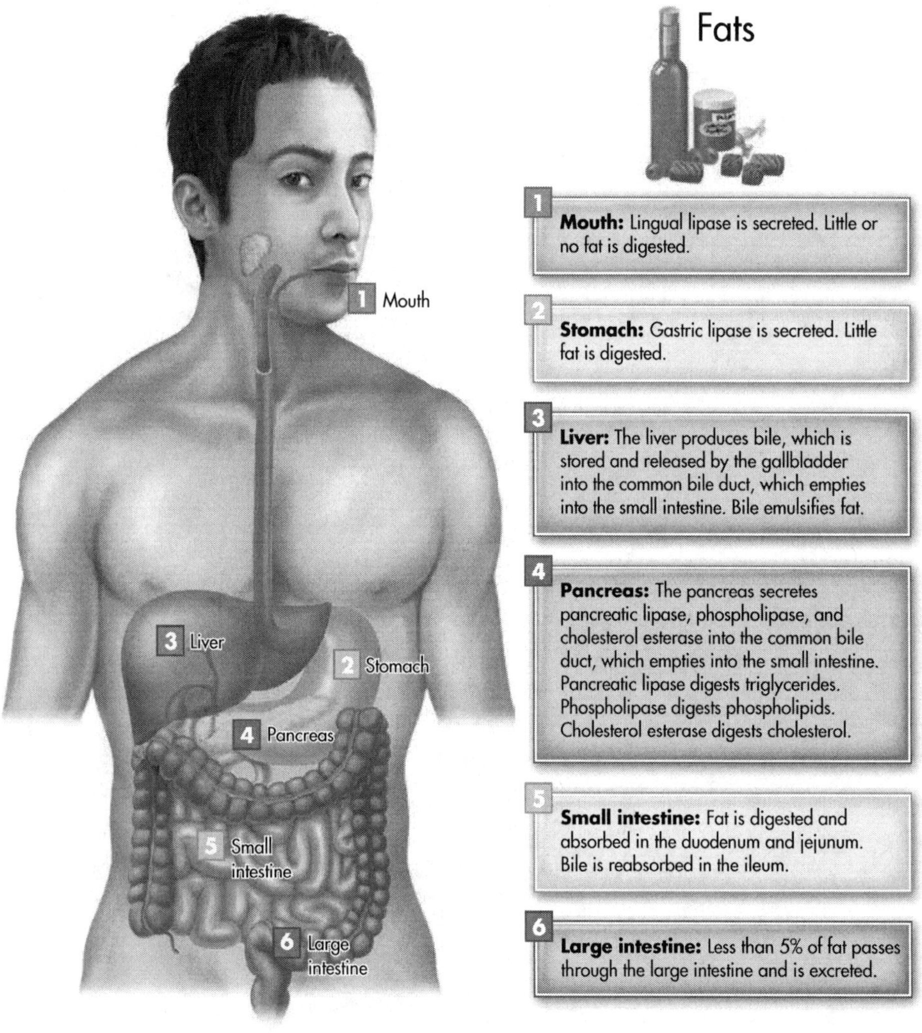

Figure 6-16 Lipid digestion and absorption. Enzymes made by the mouth, stomach, pancreas, and small intestine, as well as bile from the liver, participate in the process of digestion. Lipid digestion and absorption mostly take place in the small intestine (see Chapter 4 for details).

Absorption

The lipid portion of the micelles is absorbed by the brush border of the absorptive cells lining the duodenum and jejunum sections of the small intestine (Fig. 6-17). About 95% of dietary fat is absorbed. The carbon chain length of a fatty acid or monoglyceride determines whether it is absorbed by the cardiovascular or the lymphatic system. After absorption,

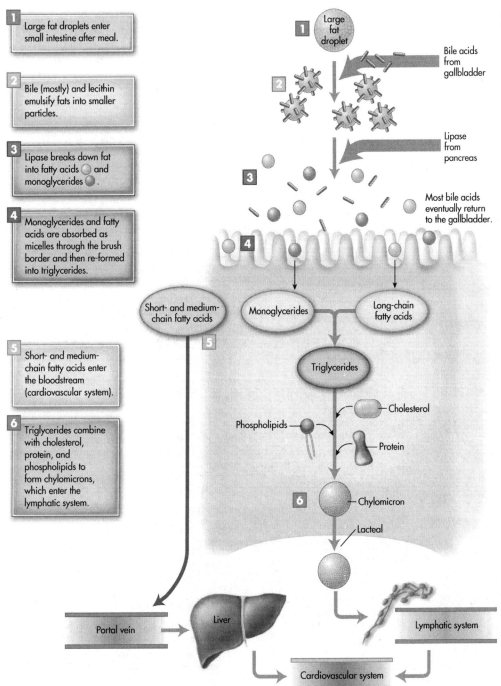

1. Large fat droplets enter small intestine after meal.

2. Bile (mostly) and lecithin emulsify fats into smaller particles.

3. Lipase breaks down fat into fatty acids ◯ and monoglycerides ●.

4. Monoglycerides and fatty acids are absorbed as micelles through the brush border and then re-formed into triglycerides.

5. Short- and medium-chain fatty acids enter the bloodstream (cardiovascular system).

6. Triglycerides combine with cholesterol, protein, and phospholipids to form chylomicrons, which enter the lymphatic system.

Figure 6-17 A simplified look at absorption of triglycerides.

Bile acids from gallbladder

Lipase from pancreas

Most bile acids eventually return to the gallbladder.

Short- and medium-chain fatty acids

Monoglycerides

Long-chain fatty acids

Triglycerides

Cholesterol

Phospholipids

Protein

Chylomicron

Lacteal

Portal vein

Liver

Lymphatic system

Cardiovascular system

short- and medium-chain fatty acids (<12 carbons) mostly enter the cardiovascular system via the portal vein, which leads directly to the liver. Long-chain fatty acids (≥12 carbons) are re-esterified into triglycerides in the absorptive cell. After further packaging (described in Section 6.8), they enter the lymphatic circulation, along with fat-soluble vitamins and dietary cholesterol.

Recall that bile, and the cholesterol it contains, is recycled by enterohepatic circulation. That is, bile is reabsorbed in the ileum and returned to the liver (via the portal vein) to be used again in fat digestion. About 98% of bile is recycled, and the rest is eliminated in the feces. Increasing the amount of bile that is excreted can help lower blood cholesterol levels because, when less is recycled, the liver takes more cholesterol out of the blood to restore the bile supply. Certain medications and diets rich in soluble fiber, which binds bile and carries it out with the feces, reduce the amount of recycled bile, thus lowering blood cholesterol.

> *Knowledge Check*
>
> 1. What is the role of cholecystokinin in the digestion of lipids?
> 2. What is the role of bile in fat digestion?
> 3. How does the chain length of a fatty acid affect absorption?

 ## 6.8 Transporting Fat in the Blood

Transporting fats through the water-based blood and lymphatic system presents a challenge because water and fat do not mix. Fats are transported in the blood as lipoproteins called chylomicrons, very-low-density lipoproteins, intermediate-density lipoproteins, low-density lipoproteins, and high-density lipoproteins. **Lipoproteins** have a core, made of lipids, that is covered with a shell composed of protein, phospholipid, and cholesterol. The shell lets the lipoprotein circulate in the blood. Figure 6-18 and Table 6-3 show the composition role of these lipoproteins.

Transporting Dietary Fats Utilizes Chylomicrons

Triglycerides that are re-formed in the absorptive cells of the intestine are packaged with other lipids, such as cholesterol and phospholipids, into lipoproteins called **chylomicrons**. These large lipid droplets are surrounded by a thin shell of phospholipid, cholesterol, and protein, which allows the chylomicrons to float freely in the blood

lipoprotein Compound containing a core of lipids with a shell composed of protein, phospholipid, and cholesterol.

chylomicron Lipoprotein made of dietary fats surrounded by a shell of cholesterol, phospholipids, and protein.

Table 6-3 Composition and Roles of the Major Lipoproteins in the Blood

Lipoprotein	Primary Component	Key Role
Chylomicron	Triglyceride	Carries dietary fat from the small intestine to cells
VLDL	Triglyceride	Carries lipids both taken up and made by the liver to cells
LDL	Cholesterol	Carries cholesterol made by the liver and from other sources to cells
HDL	Protein	Helps remove cholesterol from cells and, in turn, excrete cholesterol from the body

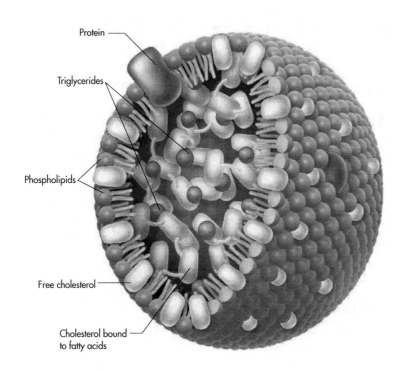

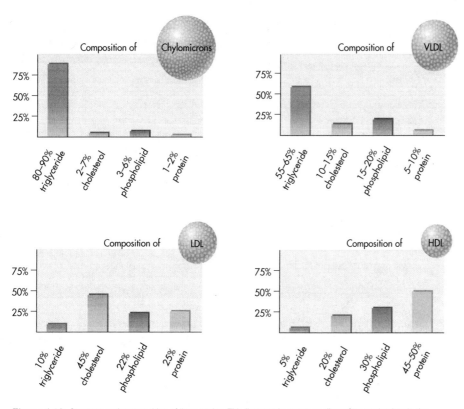

Figure 6-18 Structure and composition of lipoproteins. This lipoprotein structure allows fats to circulate in the bloodstream. Note that, for each class of lipoprotein, there are various subclasses of slightly different composition.

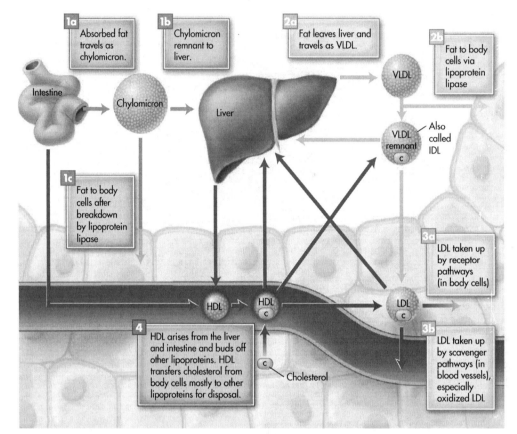

Figure 6-19 Lipoprotein interactions. ▮ Chylomicrons carry absorbed fat to body cells ▮ VLDL carries fat taken up from the bloodstream by the liver, as well as any fat made by the liver, to body cells. ▮ LDL arises from VLDL and carries mostly cholesterol to cells. ▮ HDL arises from body cells, mostly in the liver and intestine, as well as from particles that bud off other lipoproteins. HDL carries cholesterol from cells to other lipoproteins and to the liver for excretion.

Within the figure:

- **1a** Absorbed fat travels as chylomicron.
- **1b** Chylomicron remnant to liver.
- **2a** Fat leaves liver and travels as VLDL.
- **2b** Fat to body cells via lipoprotein lipase
- **1c** Fat to body cells after breakdown by lipoprotein lipase
- VLDL remnant — Also called IDL
- **3a** LDL taken up by receptor pathways (in body cells)
- **3b** LDL taken up by scavenger pathways (in blood vessels), especially oxidized LDL
- **4** HDL arises from the liver and intestine and buds off other lipoproteins. HDL transfers cholesterol from body cells mostly to other lipoproteins for disposal.
- Cholesterol
- Intestine, Chylomicron, Liver, VLDL, HDL, LDL

apolipoprotein Protein attached to the surface of a lipoprotein or embedded in its outer shell.

antioxidant Compound that protects other compounds, such as unsaturated fats, and body tissues from the damaging effects of oxygen (*anti* means "against"; *oxidant* means "oxygen").

(Fig. 6-19). The protein portion of the shell lipoproteins contains **apolipoproteins.** A series of letters (A through E) with subclasses are used to identify apolipoproteins. For convenience, they are abbreviated "apo," followed by an identifying letter—that is, apo A, apo B-48, apo C-II, and so on. Apolipoproteins can turn on a lipid transfer enzyme (e.g., apo C-II turns on lipoprotein lipase), assist in binding a lipoprotein to a receptor on cell surfaces (e.g., apo B-48 binds chylomicrons to the liver), or assist enzymes (e.g., apo A-I activates lecithin:cholesterol acyltransferase).

Chylomicrons are secreted from the intestinal cells into the lymphatic system via the lacteals (special lymphatic vessels) in the intestinal villi. Recall that lacteals connect to larger lymphatic vessels, which then connect to the thoracic duct. The thoracic duct extends from the abdomen to the neck, where it connects to the bloodstream at a large vein called the left subclavian vein. Once in the blood, nutrients originally absorbed by the lymphatic system are transported to body tissues in the vascular system.

The enzyme lipoprotein lipase (LPL) is attached to the inside wall of most cells, including those in blood vessels, muscles, fat tissue, and other cells. When LPL is activated by apo C-II, it transfers triglycerides from the chylomicrons to the cells where LPL is attached. Cells can immediately use transferred triglycerides for energy or store them for later use. Certain cells, such as muscles, tend to use the triglycerides as energy, whereas adipose cells tend to store them.

After a meal, the whole process of removing chylomicrons from the blood via LPL activity takes from 2 to 10 hours, depending partly on how much fat was in the meal. After 12 to 14 hours of fasting, no chylomicrons should be in the blood. It is a good idea for people to fast 12 to 14 hours before having blood lipid profiles because the presence of chylomicrons can affect the results.

Transporting Lipids Mostly Made by the Body Utilizes Very-Low-Density Lipoproteins

The liver makes some fat and cholesterol using carbon, hydrogen, and energy from the carbohydrate, protein, and free fatty acids it takes from the blood. Free fatty acids are the major source of "ingredients" for triglyceride synthesis. The liver coats the cholesterol and triglycerides that collect in that organ with a shell of protein and lipids and produces what are called **very-low-density lipoproteins (VLDLs).**

When VLDLs from the liver enter the circulatory system, the enzyme LPL in the lining of blood vessels transfers the triglycerides in VLDLs to body cells, including adipose tissue for fat storage and muscle tissue for energy. As triglycerides are released, VLDLs get more and more dense and become **intermediate-density lipoproteins (IDLs).** IDLs lose additional triglycerides by activating an enzyme called hepatic triglyceride lipase (HTGL) found on the endothelial surface of the liver. HTGL and LPL remove triglycerides from IDLs, causing the proportions of triglyceride to decrease and cholesterol to increase. As more triglycerides are removed, the IDLs become **low-density lipoproteins (LDLs).** LDLs are composed primarily of cholesterol.

Fried foods are a rich source of fat and *trans* fats. Reducing the intake of these foods can help lower blood lipid levels.

Pathways for Cholesterol Uptake

In the **receptor pathway for cholesterol uptake,** LDL is removed from the blood by cells with the LDL receptor called B-100. The liver, as well as other cells, has this receptor (Fig. 6-20). Once inside a cell, LDL is broken down to protein and free cholesterol. These LDL components are used for maintaining the cell membrane or synthesizing specialized compounds, such as estrogen, testosterone, and vitamin D. When the free cholesterol concentration inside the cell increases to the point at which the cell can no longer take up any more LDL, the B-100 receptor stops taking LDL from the blood. When this occurs, the concentration of LDL increases in the blood. LDL that remains in the blood becomes damaged (oxidized) by free radicals, although a diet rich in **antioxidants** can help reduce LDL oxidation. Recall that oxidized LDL increases the risk of cardiovascular disease and Metabolic Syndrome.[11]

The oxidized LDL is removed from circulation by the **scavenger pathway for cholesterol uptake.** In this pathway, certain "scavenger" white blood cells leave the bloodstream and embed themselves in blood vessels. The scavenger cells detect oxidized LDL, then engulf and digest it. Once engulfed, oxidized LDL generally is prevented from re-entering the bloodstream. Scavenger cells are able to pick up enormous amounts of oxidized LDL.

Cholesterol builds up in the scavenger cells and eventually kills them. They are replaced with new scavenger cells, which also eventually die. Over time, the cholesterol-filled scavenger cells build up on the inner blood vessel walls—especially in the arteries—and plaque develops. Diets rich in saturated fat, *trans* fat, and cholesterol encourage this process. The plaque eventually mixes with connective tissue (collagen) and

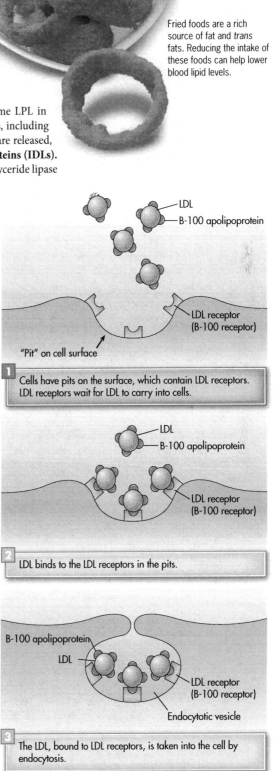

1 Cells have pits on the surface, which contain LDL receptors. LDL receptors wait for LDL to carry into cells.

2 LDL binds to the LDL receptors in the pits.

3 The LDL, bound to LDL receptors, is taken into the cell by endocytosis.

Figure 6-20 Receptor Pathway for Cholesterol Uptake. **1** LDL receptors wait for LDL to carry into cells. **2** LDL receptors capture circulating LDL and **3** release it inside the cell to be metabolized. Once free of their load, LDL receptors return to the cell surface to await new LDL.

Expert Perspective from the Field

Omega-6 Fatty Acids: Harmful or Healthful?

Omega-6 fatty acids are essential fatty acids used to produce a wide array of eicosanoids. Linoleic acid is the main omega-6 fatty acid in the diet, accounting for about 90% of total polyunsaturated fat intake. For some time, it was thought that linoleic acid played a key role in the production of eicosanoids that cause inflammation and, as a result, promoted the onset and progression of heart disease. However, new evidence indicates that omega-6 intake has little effect on the production of these inflammatory eicosanoids. Additionally, the eicosanoids that are produced from omega-6's can be converted into a variety of anti-inflammatory or pro-inflammatory compounds. According to Dr. Penny Kris-Etherton,* all metabolites derived from omega-6 fatty acids need to be considered when evaluating their health benefits.[15]

Dr. Kris-Etherton also points out that several studies have reported that low omega-6 intakes were associated with an increased risk of heart disease and that replacing saturated fat with omega-6 fatty acids reduced that risk. She stated, "Omega-6 fatty acids have independent cholesterol-lowering properties beyond the simple removal of saturated fats." Omega-6 fatty acids clearly provide health benefits. For instance, replacing saturated fatty acids with omega-6's reduces heart disease risk.[30] For optimal heart health, the American Heart Association recommends that omega-6 fatty acid intake account for at least 5 to 10% of calorie intake. Reducing omega-6 intake below this level likely would increase the risk of heart disease.[31]

*Penny Kris-Etherton, PhD, RD is Distinguished Professor of Nutrition in the Department of Nutritional Sciences at Pennsylvania State University and a Fellow of the American Heart Association. She is the recipient of the Lederle Award for Human Nutrition Research from the American Society for Nutritional Sciences and the Foundation Award for Excellence in Research and the Marjorie Hulsizer Copher Award from the American Dietetic Association (now called Academy of Nutrition and Dietetics). She has served on the National Academies Panel on Macronutrients, American Heart Association Nutrition Committee, National Cholesterol Education Program Second Adult Treatment Panel, and the 2005 Dietary Guidelines for Americans Advisory Committee.

Menus incorporating food sources of omega-6 polyunsaturated fatty acids (PUFAs)[15] (Used with permission)

Menu 1 ~6% PUFA, 33% Total Fat, 11% Saturated Fat				Menu 2 ~10% PUFA, 33% Total Fat, 7% Saturated Fat			
Foods	kcal	PUFA (g)	SFA (g)	Foods	kcal	PUFA (g)	SFA (g)
Breakfast				**Breakfast**			
Coffee	2	0.0	0.0	Coffee	2	0.0	0.0
Orange juice (8 oz)	110	0.16	0.07	Orange juice (8 oz)	110	0.16	0.07
Corn flakes, 1 cup	100	0.09	0.05	Granola, ½ cup	180	1.0	0.0
Blueberry mini muffin (2)	134	3.3	1.21	Blueberry mini muffin (2)	134	3.3	1.21
				Margarine, 1 tsp	34	1.27	0.67
Fat-free milk, 1 cup	90	0.0	0.0	Fat-free milk, 1 cup	90	0.0	0.0
Breakfast total	437	3.55	1.33	**Breakfast total**	539	5.72	1.95
Lunch				**Lunch**			
Cheeseburger (fast food)	343	1.93	7.36	3 oz tuna, 1 tbsp mayo	134	1.88	0.69
French fries, medium	385	5.35	4.06	7-grain bread, 2 slices	138	0.98	0.46
Soda, 12 oz	142	0.0	0.0	Low-fat American cheese, 1 oz	51	0.06	1.25
				Sun Chips`, 1.5 oz	210	2.77	1.38
				Grapes, 1 cup	62	0.09	0.0
Lunch total	869	7.28	11.42	**Lunch total**	594	5.78	3.78
Afternoon snack				**Afternoon snack**			
				Trail mix with sunflower seeds, ¼ cup	190	4.58	2.28
Dinner				**Dinner**			
Meatloaf, 1 piece	231	0.7	4.94	Pork chop, 1 piece	147	0.7	3.19
Mashed potatoes, ½ cup	110	0.39	0.64	Mashed potatoes, ½ cup	110	0.39	0.64
Green peas, ½ cup	57	0.14	0.05	Spinach salad with vinaigrette dressing, 1 tbsp	92	3.86	1.46
Dinner roll	133	1.08	0.59	Dinner roll	133	1.08	0.59
Butter, 1 tsp	34	0.14	2.43	Margarine, 1 tsp	34	1.27	0.67
Chocolate chip cookie, 2	137	1.05	2.22	Applesauce, ½ cup	52	0.02	0.01
Dinner total	703	3.50	10.87	**Dinner total**	569	7.32	6.56
Evening snack				**Evening snack**			
				Fat-free chocolate pudding	100	0.0	0.0
Daily Total	2002	14.33	23.62	**Daily Total**	1993	23.40	14.57

is covered with a cap of smooth fibrous muscle cells and calcium. **Atherosclerosis,** also referred to as hardening of the arteries, develops as plaque thickens in the vessel (Fig. 6-21). This thickening eventually chokes off the blood supply to organs, setting the stage for a heart attack and other problems, or it breaks apart and causes a clot to form in an artery.

A final critical participant in this extensive process of fat transport is **high-density lipoprotein (HDL).** Its high proportion of protein makes it the heaviest (most dense) lipoprotein. The liver and intestine produce most of the HDL found in the blood. HDL roams the bloodstream, picking up cholesterol from dying cells and other sources. HDL donates the cholesterol to other lipoproteins for transport back to the liver to be excreted. Some HDL travels directly back to the liver. Another beneficial function of HDL is that it blocks the oxidation of LDL.

Many studies have demonstrated that the amount of HDL in the blood can closely predict the risk of cardiovascular disease. Risk increases with low HDL levels because little blood cholesterol is transported back to the liver and excreted. Women tend to have high amounts of HDL, especially before menopause, whereas low amounts are more common in men.

Because high amounts of HDL slow the development of cardiovascular disease, any cholesterol carried by HDL is considered "good" cholesterol. In contrast, cholesterol carried by LDL is termed "bad" cholesterol because high amounts of LDL speed the development of cardiovascular disease. Still, some LDL is needed for normal body functions; LDL is only a problem when there is too much in the blood.

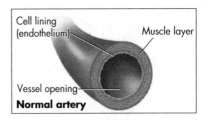

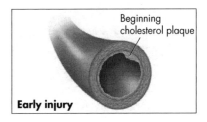

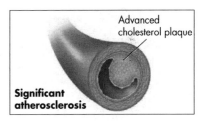

> ### Knowledge Check
>
> 1. How are fats carried in the blood?
> 2. How do chylomicrons, LDL, VLDL, and HDL differ in their composition?
> 3. What role do apolipoproteins play in fat metabolism?
> 4. What determines if LDL is metabolized by the receptor pathway or the scavenger pathway?
> 5. What role does HDL play in cardiovascular disease?

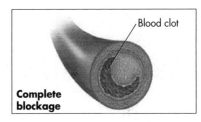

Figure 6-21 Progression of atherosclerosis.

 ## 6.9 Health Concerns Related to Fat Intake

Dietary fat is essential for good health. However, high intakes can adversely affect health status.

High Polyunsaturated Fat Intake

Intakes of polyunsaturated fats greater than 10% of total calorie intake seem to increase the amount of cholesterol deposited in arteries, which raises the chances of developing cardiovascular disease. High intakes also may impair the immune system's ability to fight disease.

Excessive Omega-3 Fatty Acid Intake

Diets that include fish rich in omega-3 fatty acids twice a week (8 ounces/week) can reduce blood clotting abilities and may favorably affect heart rhythm in some people—both of these effects help lower the chances of having a heart attack. Larger intakes of fish (4 to 8 ounces/ day) further reduce the risk of heart disease by lowering blood triglyceride levels in those whose levels are high. However, an excessive intake of omega-3 fatty acids may impair the function of the immune system, allow uncontrolled bleeding, and cause hemorrhagic stroke (bleeding in the brain that damages it). Excessive levels of omega-3's are usually the result of supplement use.

atherosclerosis Buildup of fatty material (plaque) in the arteries, including those surrounding the heart.

MEDICAL PERSPECTIVE

Cardiovascular Disease (CVD)

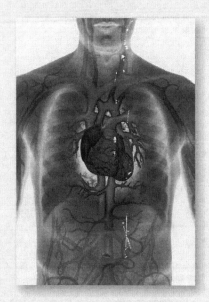

Cardiovascular disease (CVD) is the major killer of North Americans. Each year, about 500,000 people die of CVD in the U.S., about 60% more than die of cancer. The figure rises to almost 1 million if strokes and other circulatory diseases are included. About 1.5 million people in the U.S. each year have a heart attack. The overall male-to-female ratio for heart disease is about 2:1. Women generally lag about 10 years behind men in developing the disease. Still, it eventually kills more women than any other disease—twice as many as cancer. And, for each person in North America who dies of CVD, 20 more (over 13 million people) have symptoms of the disease.

▶ A *Healthy People 2020* goal is to reduce death from coronary heart disease and stroke.

▶ CVD typically involves the coronary arteries and thus is frequently termed *coronary heart disease (CHD)* or *coronary artery disease (CAD)*.

homocysteine Amino acid not used in protein synthesis but, instead, produced during metabolism of the amino acid methionine. Homocysteine is likely toxic to many cells, such as those lining the blood vessels.

High-fat diets, especially those rich in saturated and *trans* fats, increase the risk of CVD. (Recall that the vascular system includes the blood, heart, arteries, and veins.) The symptoms develop over many years and often do not become obvious until old age. Nonetheless, autopsies of those under 20 years of age have shown that many already had atherosclerotic plaque in their arteries.

Development of CVD

Atherosclerotic plaque is probably first deposited to repair injuries in the lining in any artery. The damage that starts plaque formation can be caused by smoking, diabetes, hypertension, **homocysteine** (likely, but not a major factor), and LDL.[20–22] Viral and bacterial infections and ongoing blood vessel inflammation also may promote plaque formation.[23]

As atherosclerosis progresses, plaque thickens over time, causing arteries to harden, narrow, and become less elastic. This makes them unable to expand to accommodate the normal ups and downs of blood pressure. Affected arteries are further damaged as blood pumps through them and pressure increases. In the final phase, a clot or spasm in a plaque-clogged artery blocks the flow of blood and leads to a heart attack (myocardial infarction) or stroke (cerebrovascular accident).

Recall that blood supplies the heart muscle and brain—and other body organs—with oxygen and nutrients. When blood flow via the coronary arteries surrounding the heart is interrupted, a heart attack may occur, which damages the heart muscle. If blood flow to parts of the brain is interrupted long enough, part of the brain dies, causing a stroke. Factors that typically bring on a heart attack in a person at risk include dehydration, severe emotional stress, strenuous physical activity when not otherwise physically fit, sudden awakening during the night or just getting up in the morning (linked to an abrupt increase in blood pressure and stress), and high-fat meals, which increase blood clotting.

Risk Factors for CVD

In addition to a high-fat diet, the American Heart Association has identified several other factors that affect the risk of heart disease. The more risk factors a person has, the greater the risk of CVD. Some of the risk factors cannot be changed, but

others can. The risk factors that cannot be changed are age, gender, genetics, and race.

- *Age.* The risk of CVD increases with age. Over 83% of people who die of CVD are at least 65 years old.
- *Gender.* Men have a greater chance of having a heart attack than women do, and they have attacks earlier in life. Even after menopause, when women's death rate from heart disease increases,[24] it's not as great as the risk men face.
- *Genetics.* Having a close relative who died prematurely from CVD, especially before age 50, may increase the risk. Those with the highest risk of premature CVD have genetic defects that block the removal of chylomicrons and triglycerides from the blood, reduce the liver's ability to remove LDL-cholesterol from the blood, limit the synthesis of HDL-cholesterol, or increase blood clotting.
- *Race.* Race may affect CVD risk. For example, those of African heritage have more severe high blood pressure levels compared with Caucasians, which puts them at higher risk of CVD. Heart disease risk also is higher among those of Hispanic/Latino, Native American, and native Hawaiian descent, as well as some Asian groups, which is partly due to higher rates of obesity and diabetes in these groups.

The risk factors that can be modified are blood cholesterol levels, blood triglyceride levels, hypertension, smoking, physical inactivity, obesity, diabetes, liver and kidney disease, and low thyroid hormone levels.

- *Blood cholesterol levels.* A total blood cholesterol level over 200 mg/dl (especially when greater than 240 mg/dl), along with an LDL-cholesterol level of 160 mg/dl or higher, increases the risk of CVD. When high blood cholesterol levels accompany other risk factors (e.g., high blood pressure and smoking), CVD risk increases even more. Reducing dietary intakes of cholesterol, saturated fat, and total fat; keeping weight under control; and exercising can help lower blood cholesterol levels, as can prescription medications.
- *Blood triglyceride levels.* Fasting blood triglyceride levels should be below 150 mg/dl. Excess triglycerides in the blood is called

hypertriglyceridemia. Blood triglycerides are derived from fats in the foods we eat. In some individuals, simple carbohydrates and alcohol raise plasma triglyceride levels. A high triglyceride level in combination with a low HDL and high LDL may speed up atherosclerosis. Individuals with a high triglyceride level should lower their saturated fat intake and increase monounsaturated fat and omega-3 fatty acids.

- *Hypertension.* Hypertension (high blood pressure) damages the heart muscle by making it thicker and stiffer. This damage causes the heart to work harder than normal. It also increases the risk of stroke, heart attack, kidney failure, and congestive heart failure. Hypertension accompanied by high blood cholesterol levels, smoking, obesity, or diabetes raises the risk of heart attack or stroke by several times. Reducing sodium intake, losing weight, and taking medication can help bring hypertension under control. Exercise also may help.

- *Smoking.* Smokers have a 2 to 4 times greater risk of CVD than nonsmokers. Even exposure to secondhand smoke can increase the risk of CVD. Smoking boosts a person's genetically linked risk of CVD, increases risk even when blood lipids are low, and makes blood more likely to clot. Smoking also tends to negate the lower CVD risk that females have compared with males. In fact, smoking is the main cause of about 20% of the CVD cases in women. In addition, women who smoke and take oral contraceptives are at even greater risk of CVD.

- *Physical inactivity.* Lack of exercise increases the risk of CVD. Regular moderate to vigorous physical activity lowers CVD risk, helps control blood cholesterol levels, reduces the risk of diabetes and obesity, and may even reduce blood pressure.

- *Obesity.* Many adults gain weight as they grow older. This weight gain, especially if it is around the waist, is a chief contributor to the increases in LDL blood cholesterol levels common in older

adults. Obesity increases inflammation in the body and reduces the adipose cells' production of the hormone adiponectin. The reduced level of this hormone in the blood elevates the risk of having a heart attack. Obesity also leads to insulin resistance in many people, creating a risk of diabetes.

- *Diabetes.* Diabetes greatly increases the risk of developing CVD. Even when blood glucose (sugar) levels are well controlled, diabetes increases the risk of heart attack and stroke, but the risks are even greater when blood glucose levels are not well controlled. About 75% of those with diabetes die of some form of CVD. Diabetes also negates the female advantage of reduced CVD risk.

- *Liver and kidney disease and low thyroid hormone levels.* Certain forms of liver and kidney disease and low concentrations of thyroid hormone can increase blood LDL-cholesterol and thus increase the risk of CVD. Medical treatment can help control these conditions and lower CVD risk.

Assessing CVD Risk

The National Cholesterol Education Program (NCEP) suggests that all adults age 20 years or older have a blood lipoprotein profile done every 5 years. This profile is most useful when the person fasts for 12 to 14 hours before the test. (Only total cholesterol and HDL values are accurate if the person has not fasted.) Table 6-4 shows how blood lipoprotein levels are interpreted.

▶ **Systolic blood pressure** over 140 mm (millimeters of mercury) and **diastolic blood pressure** over 90 mm indicate hypertension. Healthier blood pressure values are 120 mm and 80 mm, respectively. (Systolic blood pressure is the maximum pressure in the arteries when the heart beats. Diastolic blood pressure is the pressure in the arteries when the heart is between beats.)

▶ The values in Table 6-4 are for adults. Age-specific values for adolescents, which take their growth and maturation differences into account, have been published.[23, 29]

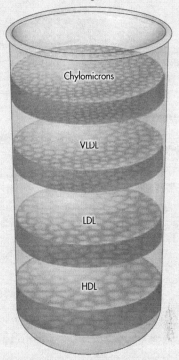

Centrifuge tube

One way to measure the amount of chylomicrons, VLDL, LDL, and HDL particles in the bloodstream is to centrifuge the serum portion of the blood at high speed for about 24 hours in a sucrose-rich solution. The lipoproteins settle out in the centrifuge tube based on their density, with chylomicrons at the top and HDL at the bottom.

Table 6-4 Ratings of Blood Lipoprotein Levels (mg/dl)

Lipoprotein (mg/dl)	Rating
Total Cholesterol	
<200	Desirable
200–239	Borderline high
≥240	High
LDL-Cholesterol	
<100	Optimal
100–129	Near optimal
130–159	Borderline high
160–189	High
≥190	Very high
HDL-Cholesterol	
<40	Low
≥60	High
Triglycerides	
<100	Optimal
100–149	Near optimal
150–199	Borderline high
200–499	High
≥500	Very high

(continued)

continued

The NCEP also has developed tables to help you calculate your risk of developing heart disease in the next 10 years. The risk is based on age, total and HDL blood cholesterol levels, blood pressure, and whether you smoke. Knowing your score can help you and your health-care provider determine if you need to make lifestyle changes, go on medication, or both.

Preventing CVD

The following are lifestyle changes that can lower LDL blood cholesterol levels and reduce health risks.

- Keep total fat intake between 20 and 35% of total calories.
- Keep saturated fat intake to less than 7% of total calories.
- Keep *trans* fat intake low.
- Keep polyunsaturated fat under 10% of total calories.
- Keep monounsaturated fat under 20% of total calories.
- Lower cholesterol intake to less than 200 mg per day.
- Include 2 grams of plant stanols/sterols in your daily diet to help reduce cholesterol absorption in the small intestine and lower its return to the liver.
- Increase soluble fiber intake to 20 to 30 grams per day.
- Moderate sugar intake.[25]
- Keep body weight at a healthy level.
- Increase physical activity.

Frequently eating fruits, vegetables, nuts, and plant oils also can help reduce plaque buildup in arteries and slow the progression of cardiovascular disease.[26] That's because these foods are rich in antioxidants, which likely reduce LDL oxidation and slow the need for scavenger cells to pick up

oxidized LDL. Supplements of antioxidant nutrients, such as vitamins C and E, may help. However, large studies of people with CVD have shown no benefit from megadoses of vitamin E (200–400 mg/day, equaling about 400–800 IU/day).[27, 28] Still, some experts suggest that vitamin E supplements (up to 200 mg [400 IU] per day) may be helpful for *preventing* CVD; these should be taken under a physician's guidance, however. Note that antioxidant supplements can be harmful to some, especially those taking certain medications that reduce blood clotting (anticoagulants) because vitamin E also reduces blood clotting. High intakes of iron probably speed LDL oxidation, making it unwise to take an iron supplement unless a physician prescribes it. To learn more, visit www.nhlbi.nih.gov/guidelines/cholesterol.

Heart Attack Symptoms

A heart attack can strike with the sudden force of a sledgehammer, with pain radiating up the neck or down the arm. It can sneak up at night, masquerading as indigestion, with slight pain or pressure in the chest. Many times, the symptoms are so subtle in women that it often is too late once she or health professionals realize that a heart attack is taking (or has recently taken) place. If there is any suspicion at all that a heart attack is occurring, the person should first chew an aspirin (325 mg) thoroughly and then call 911. Aspirin helps reduce the blood clotting that precipitates a heart attack. The typical warning signs are

- Intense, prolonged chest pain or pressure, sometimes radiating to other parts of the upper body (men and women)
- Shortness of breath (men and women)
- Sweating (men and women)

- Weakness (men and women)
- Nausea and vomiting (especially women)
- Dizziness (especially women)
- Jaw, neck, and shoulder pain (especially women)
- Irregular heartbeat (men and women)

Symptoms of Stroke

Each year, 700,000 North Americans suffer strokes, and almost 25% of them die. Over 90% of strokes (i.e., ischemic strokes) occur when a blood clot blocks blood flow to the brain—think of a stroke as a "brain attack," similar to a heart attack. The other 10% are hemorrhagic strokes, occurring when a blood vessel bursts. The major risk factor for stroke is high blood pressure. Individuals experiencing any of the following symptoms of stroke should seek immediate treatment because physicians can administer drugs that can limit the further death of brain cells and reduce the extent of the damage caused by most ischemic strokes. The stroke warning signs are

- Sudden numbness or weakness of the face, arm, or leg, especially on one side of the body
- Sudden confusion and/or trouble speaking or understanding
- Sudden trouble seeing in one or both eyes
- Sudden trouble walking, dizziness, and/or loss of balance or coordination
- Sudden, severe headache with no known cause

▶ Benecol® and Take Control® margarines contain plant stanols/sterols.

▶ The soluble fiber in 1½ cups of oatmeal a day will reduce blood cholesterol levels by about 15%.

CRITICAL THINKING

As part of his annual health checkup, Juan has a blood sample drawn for the measurement of cholesterol values. The results of the test indicate that his total cholesterol is 210 mg/dl, his HDL-cholesterol is 65 mg/dl, and his triglycerides are 100 mg/dl. Juan has read that total cholesterol should be less than 200 mg/dl to minimize cardiovascular problems. However, he is happy with the result of the blood test. How would Juan explain his satisfaction to his parents?

Imbalances in Omega-3 and Omega-6 Fatty Acids

On average, Americans consume 20 times more omega-6 fatty acids than omega-3's. Both fatty acids use the same metabolic pathways; as a result, they compete with one another. Thus, the body may not have enough of some compounds and too much of others. For example, as you saw in Figure 6-9, omega-6 fatty acids can be converted to arachidonic acid, which then can be used to make inflammation-causing eicosanoids called prostaglandins. In contrast, the omega-3 fatty acids EPA and DHA can be made into substances that help decrease inflammation, pain, and blood triglycerides.[12] Low intakes of omega-3's may worsen inflammatory diseases, such as arthritis. Although it is not known what causes or cures arthritis, an imbalance in the intakes of omega-3 and omega-6 fatty acids may play a role.[12-15] (See Expert Perspective from the Field.)

Intake of Rancid Fats

Rancid (spoiled) fats smell and taste bad. They also contain compounds (peroxides and aldehydes) that can damage cells. Polyunsaturated fats go rancid fairly easily because their double bonds are easily damaged (broken) by oxygen, heat, metals, or light (sunlight or artificial light). The broken double bonds cause the polyunsaturated fats to decompose. (Saturated and *trans* fats are less susceptible to rancidity because they have no or few double bonds in their carbon chains.)

The foods most likely to become rancid are those high in polyunsaturated fats (e.g., fish and vegetable oils), packaged fried foods (e.g., potato chips), and fatty foods with a large surface area (e.g., powdered egg yolks). To prevent rancidity, food manufacturers can break the double bonds and add hydrogen (hydrogenate them). Or they can protect the double bonds in fats by sealing foods in airtight packages or adding antioxidants, such as certain nutrients (vitamin E, vitamin C), or additives, such as butylated hydroxyanisol (BHA) and butylated hydroxytolune (BHT). (See Chapter 15 to learn more about the antioxidant functions of vitamins and Chapter 3 to learn about additives.)

Trimming the fat off meats can help reduce saturated fat intake. Limiting intake of meat that is highly marbled with fat (streaks of fat running through the lean) helps, too.

Diets High in *Trans* Fat

Trans fatty acids from hydrogenated fats have harmful health effects. Hydrogenated fats were popular for many years because they helped food manufacturers produce high-quality baked and fried products. For example, some foods are more pleasing when made with solid fats. Pastries and pies made with oil tend to be oily and mealy, whereas those made with solid fats are flaky and crispy. Although solid fat from animals, such as butter or lard, could be used instead of hydrogenated fat, hydrogenated fat is cholesterol free. Another advantage of hydrogenation is that it delays fat decomposition and spoilage (rancidity) in packaged foods.

Despite any advantages of hydrogenation, in recent years scientists have learned that consuming *trans* fatty acids raises blood cholesterol levels, which increases the risk of heart disease. In addition, *trans* fats lower HDL (good) cholesterol and increase inflammation in the body. Studies with monkeys indicated that diets rich in *trans* fats raise body weight and the amount of body fat stored in the abdomen, even when calories are at levels that should only maintain weight. Much of the stored abdominal fat was visceral fat, which increases the risk of type 2 diabetes.[16]

To help people control *trans* fat intake, the FDA now requires *trans* fats to be on Nutrition Facts labels (food labels in Canada also must list *trans* fats in foods, as well as their negative health effects). To lower the *trans* fat levels in foods, food manufacturers have reformulated many products to make them *trans* fat free (less than 0.5 g/serving is defined by the FDA as *trans* fat free). The reformulated products often use interesterified fats, which are made by interchanging the fatty acids in solid fats and liquid oils. This interchange creates a fat with properties similar to *trans* fats—that is, it is solid at room temperature, stands up to high-temperature cooking methods, and stays fresh a long time. Interesterified fats appear to be healthier than *trans* fats, but more research is needed.

Both *trans* and interesterified fat intake can be kept to a minimum when eating out by limiting fried (especially deep fat–fried) foods, pastries, flaky bread products (e.g., pie crusts, crackers, croissants, and biscuits), and cookies. At home, keep intake of these fats under control by using little or no stick margarine or shortening. Instead, substitute vegetable oils and softer tub or squeeze margarine. Applesauce and fruit purees can be substituted for shortening in many baked goods. Also, to avoid deep-fat frying in shortening, try baking, pan-frying, broiling, steaming, grilling, or stir frying. Most nondairy creamers are rich in hydrogenated vegetable oils, so replace them with reduced-fat milk or nonfat dry milk.

Choosing low-fat dairy products can help keep fat intake under control.

216 **PART 2** Energy-Yielding Nutrients and Alcohol

Take Action

What Is Your 10-Year Risk of Cardiovascular Disease?

During the past 2 decades, researchers have identified a number of factors that can contribute to an increased risk of cardiovascular disease. You can estimate your risk of developing cardiovascular disease if you know your blood pressure and blood lipid levels.

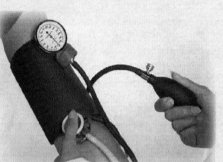

1. Select the chart for your gender.

2. Find your age group and circle your age, smoker, and total cholesterol scores.

3. Circle your systolic blood pressure score.

4. Circle your HDL-cholesterol score.

5. Add all your scores and compare them with the risk chart.

   For example, a 21-year-old male smoker with a total cholesterol of 245, untreated systolic blood pressure of 145, and HDL-cholesterol less than 40 has a score of 11. He has an 8% risk of cardiovascular disease in the next 10 years. A 35-year-old female nonsmoker with a total cholesterol of 180, untreated systolic blood pressure of 125, and HDL-cholesterol of 55 has a score of 2. She has a less than 1% risk of cardiovascular disease in the next 10 years.

10-Year Cardiovascular Disease Risk for Women

	Age Group									
	20–34	35–39	40–44	45–49	50–54	55–59	60–64	65–69	70–74	75–79
Age Score	–7	–3	0	3	6	8	10	12	14	16
Smoker Score	9	9	7	7	4	4	2	2	1	1
Total Cholesterol Score										
<160	0	0	0	0	0	0	0	0	0	0
160–199	4	4	3	3	2	2	1	1	1	1
200–239	8	8	6	6	4	4	2	2	1	1
240–279	11	11	8	8	5	5	3	3	2	2
≥280	13	13	10	10	7	7	4	4	2	2

Systolic Blood Pressure Score					
	<120	120–129	130–139	140–159	≥160
Untreated	0	1	2	3	4
Treated	0	3	4	5	6

HDL-Cholesterol Score	
<40	2
40–49	1
50–59	0
≥60	–1

Total Cardiovascular Disease Risk Score _____

Risk Chart for Women	
Score	10-Year Risk (%)
<9	<1
9–12	1
13–14	2
15	3
16	4
17	5
18	6
19	8
20	11
21	14
22	17
23	22
24	27
≥25	≥30

10-Year Cardiovascular Disease Risk for Men

	Age Group									
	20–34	35–39	40–44	45–49	50–54	55–59	60–64	65–69	70–74	75–79
Age Score	–9	–4	0	3	6	8	10	11	12	13
Smoker Score	8	8	5	5	3	3	1	1	1	1
Total Cholesterol Score										
<160	0	0	0	0	0	0	0	0	0	0
160–199	4	4	3	3	2	2	1	1	1	1
200–239	7	7	5	5	3	3	1	1	0	0
240–279	9	9	6	6	4	4	2	2	1	1
≥280	11	11	8	8	5	5	3	3	1	1

Systolic Blood Pressure Score

	<120	120–129	130–139	140–159	≥160
Untreated	0	0	1	1	2
Treated	0	1	2	2	3

HDL-Cholesterol Score

<40	2
40–49	1
50–59	0
≥60	–1

Total Cardiovascular Disease Risk Score _____

Risk Chart for Men

Score	10-Year Risk (%)
<0	<1
0–4	1
5–6	2
7	3
8	4
9	5
10	6
11	8
12	10
13	12
14	16
15	20
16	25
≥17	≥30

CASE STUDY FOLLOW-UP

Jessica's diet is high in saturated fat and *trans* fat. Even though she is female and young, she is increasing her risk of heart disease, especially if she continues to eat this way and not exercise. Jessica could make improvements by eating a breakfast rich in fiber and nutrients, such as whole-grain cereal, fat-free milk, and fruit juice. Instead of fatty burgers and fast foods, she should choose lean meat, chicken, and fish. To round out meals, she needs to add several servings of fruits and vegetables. To improve her intake of monounsaturated fats, she could eat a small handful of peanuts each day as a snack. Jessica could either choose cold-water fish for dinner more often or take an omega-3 fatty acid supplement. She should also think about adding a consistent exercise program to her daily routine.

Many manufacturers offer products that are lower in fat than traditional products. Even though these products are lower in fat, portion size and total calories provided still must be considered.

Diets High in Total Fat

Diets high in total fat increase the risk of obesity (see Chapter 10), certain types of cancer (see Chapter 12), and cardiovascular disease.

Diets high in fat, especially saturated fat, may increase the risk of colon, prostate, and breast cancer.[17-19] Although it isn't known how high-fat diets increase risk, one theory related to colon cancer is that bile, which is secreted into the intestine to emulsify dietary fat, may irritate colon cells. As fat intake rises, more bile is secreted, which then irritates the cells more intensely and frequently, perhaps damaging them and causing them to become cancerous. In the case of breast and prostate cancer, the risk of both climbs as blood levels of estrogen hormones rise. High-fat diets elevate blood lipid levels, which in turn raise blood estrogen levels. In contrast, low-fat diets seem to lower blood estrogen levels. Another possible explanation of the relationship between high-fat diets and cancer is that high-fat diets usually are low in fiber and other phytonutrients—thus, high-fat diets may lack the protective plant compounds that help prevent certain cancers.

Lowering the intake of dietary fat is one way to help control calorie intake and avoid being overfat. Obesity is linked with a greater risk of cancer of the colon, breast, and uterus. (The risks associated with obesity are discussed in Chapter 10.)

Knowledge Check

1. What is the risk of eating a diet that is low or high in omega-3 fatty acids?
2. What risk factors for cardiovascular disease can be modified by lifestyle changes?
3. What are the risks and benefits of *trans* fatty acids?
4. What health conditions are associated with diets high in total fat?

Summary

6.1 Triglycerides are the most common type of lipid found in foods and in the body. Each triglyceride molecule consists of 3 fatty acids attached to a glycerol. A triglyceride that loses a fatty acid is a diglyceride. A monoglyceride results when 2 fatty acids are lost. The carbon chains of fatty acids can vary in 3 ways: the number of carbons in the chain, the extent to which the chain is saturated with hydrogen, and the shape of the chain (straight or bent). Hydrogenation adds hydrogen to the carbon chain of unsaturated fats. The systems commonly used to name fatty acids, omega and delta, are based on the numbers of carbon atoms and the location of double bonds in a fatty acid's carbon chain. Essential fatty acids (alpha-linolenic acid and linoleic acid) must be obtained from the diet because humans cannot synthesize them.

6.2 Triglycerides are the main fuel source for all body cells, except the nervous system and red blood cells. Triglycerides are the body's main storage form of energy. The insulating layer of fat just beneath the skin is made mostly of triglycerides. Fats in food carry fat-soluble vitamins (vitamins A, D, E, and K) to the small intestine. Essential fatty acids, along with phospholipids and cholesterol, are important structural components of cell walls. They also keep the cell wall fluid and flexible, so that substances can flow into and out of the cell. Eicosanoids, which are made from essential fatty acids, have over 100 different actions, such as regulating blood pressure, blood clotting, sleep/wake cycles, and body temperature.

6.3 Almost all foods provide at least some triglycerides. Most triglyceride-rich foods contain a mixture of fatty acids. The fat in some foods is visible; however, fat is hidden in many foods. Fat replacements help consumers trim fat intake and still enjoy the mouthfeel sensations fat provides.

6.4 The structure of phospholipids is very similar to that of triglycerides, except a fatty acid is replaced with a compound that contains the mineral phosphorus and often has nitrogen attached. Phospholipids function in a watery environment without clumping together. The hydrophilic head of phosphate is attracted to water, and the fatty acid tail of phospholipids is attracted to fats. When placed in water, phospholipids cluster together, with their hydrophilic phosphate heads facing outward in contact with water and their hydrophobic tails extending into the cluster away from the water. In the body, phospholipids have 2 major roles: cell membrane component and emulsifier. Phospholipids can be synthesized by the body or supplied by the diet.

6.5 The carbons in the structure of sterols are mostly arranged in many rings. Cholesterol, the most well-known sterol, is used in the body to make bile and steroid hormones, such as testosterone, estrogens, the active form of vitamin D hormone, and corticosteroids. Cholesterol is found in foods of animal origin, such as meat, fish, poultry, eggs, and dairy products. Foods of plant origin do not contain cholesterol.

6.6 The Acceptable Macronutrient Distribution Range for total fat is 20 to 35% of calories for most age groups. Saturated fat intake, including *trans* fats, and cholesterol should be kept as low as possible while still consuming a nutritionally adequate diet. Cholesterol intake should be limited to about 300 mg daily. Fat intake recommendations are lower for those at risk of heart disease. Adequate Intakes for essential fatty acids equal less than 120 calories daily for women and 170 calories for men—that's about 2 to 4 tablespoons daily of oils rich in these fatty acids. Most North Americans get too much saturated and too little monounsaturated and polyunsaturated fat. Omega-6 fatty acid intake is usually plentiful, but omega-3 intakes often are lower than optimal.

6.7 Fat digestion occurs mostly in the small intestine. The presence of fat in the small intestine triggers the release of cholecystokinin from intestinal cells. Cholecystokinin stimulates the release of bile and pancreatic enzymes. Bile emulsifies fats and allows enzymes to efficiently break triglycerides into monoglycerides and free fatty acids. Phospholipids and cholesterol are digested mostly in the small intestine. After absorption, short- and medium-chain fatty acids mostly enter the circulatory system. Long-chain fatty acids enter the lymphatic circulation.

6.8 Fats are transported in the blood as lipoproteins called chylomicrons, very-low-density lipoproteins (VLDLs), intermediate-density lipoproteins (IDLs), low-density lipoproteins (LDLs), and high-density lipoproteins (HDLs). Lipoproteins have a core, made of lipids, that is covered with a shell composed of protein, phospholipid, and cholesterol. The shell lets the lipoprotein circulate in the blood. The receptor pathway for cholesterol uptake removes LDL from the blood, breaks it down, and uses the component parts for maintaining the cell membrane or synthesizing compounds. Oxidized LDL is removed from the blood by the scavenger pathway for cholesterol uptake. Over time, cholesterol builds up in the scavenger cells. When scavenger cells have collected and deposited cholesterol for many years at a heavy pace, plaque builds up on the inner blood vessel walls. HDL roams the bloodstream, picking up cholesterol from dying cells and other sources, and donates the cholesterol to other lipoproteins for transport back to the liver to be excreted.

6.9 Intakes of polyunsaturated fats greater than 10% of total calorie intake seem to increase the amount of cholesterol deposited in arteries. Diets that include fish rich in omega-3 twice a week can reduce blood clotting abilities and may favorably affect heart rhythm. Omega-6 and omega-3 fatty acids use the same metabolic pathways; as a result, imbalances in intake of these fatty acids may cause health problems. Rancid fats contain compounds that can damage cells. *Trans* fatty acids raise blood cholesterol levels, lower HDL-cholesterol levels, and increase inflammation in the body. Diets high in total fat increase the risk of obesity; colon, prostate, and breast cancer; and cardiovascular disease (CVD). Atherosclerotic plaque is probably first deposited to repair injuries in the lining in any artery. As atherosclerosis progresses, plaque thickens over time, causing arteries to harden, narrow, and become less elastic. CVD risk factors are age, gender, genetics, race, blood cholesterol levels, blood triglyceride levels, hypertension, smoking, physical inactivity, obesity, and diabetes. All adults age 20 years or older should have a blood lipoprotein profile done every 5 years. Lifestyle changes can lower blood LDL-cholesterol levels and reduce health risks.

220 **PART 2** Energy-Yielding Nutrients and Alcohol

Study Questions

1. All of the following are ways in which fatty acids can differ from one another *except* _____.

   a. number of double bonds
   b. degree of saturation
   c. carbon chain length
   d. number of calories provided

2. Triglycerides consist of _____.

   a. glycerol
   b. cholesterol
   c. 3 fatty acids
   d. a and b
   e. a and c

Match the fat-related terms on the right to their definitions on the left.

3. _____A_____ lipid that is solid at room temperature

4. _____E_____ chief form of fat in food

5. _____B_____ sterol manufactured in the body

6. _____D_____ similar to triglycerides, except a fatty acid has been replaced by a phosphorus

7. _____C_____ lipid that is liquid at room temperature

a. fat
b. cholesterol
c. oil
d. phospholipid
e. triglyceride

8. *Trans* fatty acids tend to _____ blood cholesterol.

   a. raise
   b. lower
   c. have no effect on

9. Chylomicrons are the principal transport vehicle for _____.

   a. glucose
   b. triglycerides
   c. cholesterol
   d. free fatty acids

10. Which of the following lipoproteins is responsible for transporting cholesterol from the liver to tissues?

    a. chylomicrons
    b. low-density lipoprotein (LDL)
    c. high-density lipoprotein (HDL)
    d. very-low-density lipoprotein (VLDL)

11. Which essential fatty acid can help lower the risks of coronary heart disease?

    a. omega-3   c. omega-9
    b. omega-6   d. both a and b

12. Mike has been told to reduce his fat intake to less than 25% of his total calories (2500 per day). How many grams of fat should he consume?

    a. 69 grams or less   c. 89 grams or less
    b. 76 grams or less   d. 93 grams or less

13. Monounsaturated fatty acids _____.

    a. are liquid at room temperature
    b. have 1 double bond in the fatty acid chain
    c. are provided by plants
    d. lower blood cholesterol levels
    e. all of the above

14. Fats liquid at room temperature can be made more solid by the process of _____.

    a. esterification   c. emulsification
    b. hydrogenation   d. calcification

15. The Dietary Guidelines recommend that no more than _____ of total calories be consumed as polyunsaturated fat and that no more than _____ of total calories be consumed in the form of saturated fat.

    a. 20%; 5%   c. 45%; 25%
    b. 10%; 10%   d. 50%; 10%

16. Describe the chemical structures of saturated and polyunsaturated fatty acids and their different effects in the human body.

17. Relate the need for omega-3 fatty acids in the diet to the recommendation to consume fish twice a week.

18. What are the functions of lipids in the human body?

19. What are the recommendations of health-care professionals regarding fat intake? What do these recommendations mean in terms of actual food choices?

20. Trace the digestion of fat from the beginning to end of the digestive tract.

21. Describe the structures, origins, and roles of the 4 major lipoproteins.

22. List the main risk factors for the development of cardiovascular disease.

Answer Key: 1-d; 2-e; 3-a; 4-e; 5-b; 6-d; 7-c; 8-a; 9-b; 10-b; 11-d; 12-a; 13-e; 14-b; 15-b; 16-refer to Sections 6.1 to 6.4; 17-refer to Sections 6.1 and 6.2; 18-refer to Sections 6.3 to 6.5; 19-refer to Section 6.6; 20-refer to Section 6.7; 21-refer to Section 6.8; 22-refer to Section 6.9 and Medical Perspective.

Websites

To learn more about the topics covered in this chapter, visit these websites.

www.nhlbi.nih.gov/guidelines/cholesterol/index.htm

www.heart.org

www.webmd.com/cholesterol-management

www.healthypeople.gov/hp2020

www.fns.usda.gov/fdd/facts/nutrition/TransFatFactSheet
.pdf

www.eatright.org

www.oldwayspt.org

References

1. Riediger ND and others. A systemic review of the roles of n-3 fatty acids in health and disease. *J Am Diet Assoc.* 2009;109:668.

2. Higgins JP, Flicker L. Lecithin for dementia and cognitive treatment. *Cochrane Database Syst Rev.* 2003;(3)CD 001015.

3. Mourad AM and others. Influence of soy lecithin administration on hypercholesterolemia. *Cholesterol.* 2010:Article ID 824813

4. Food and Nutrition Board. *Dietary Reference Intakes for energy, carbohydrate, fiber, fat, fatty acids, cholesterol, protein, and amino acids.* Washington, DC: National Academy Press; 2002.

5. Gidding SS and others. Implementing American Heart Association pediatric and adult nutrition guidelines. *Circ.* 2009;119:1161.

6. American Dietetic Association. Position of the American Dietetic Association and Dietitians of Canada: Dietary fatty acids. *J Am Diet Assoc.* 2007;107:1599.

7. USDA/USDHHS. *Dietary Guidelines for Americans.* 5th ed. 2010; www.dietaryguidelines.gov.

8. USDHHS. *Healthy People 2020.* HealthyPeople.gov.

9. Dod HS and others. Effect of intensive lifestyle changes on endothelial function and on inflammatory markers of atherosclerosis. *Am J Cardiol.* 2010;105:362.

10. Vanitallie TB. Ancel Keys: A tribute. *Nutr Metab.* 2005;14:4.

11. Sigurdardottir V and others. Circulating oxidized low-density lipoprotein (LDL) is associated with risk factors of the metabolic syndrome and LDL size in clinically healthy 58-year-old men (AIR study). *J Int Med.* 2010;152:440.

12. Shearer GC and others. Fish Oil—How does it reduce plasma triglycerides? *Biochim Biophys Acta* 2012; 1821:843.

13. Simopoulos AP. Importance of the omega-6/omega-3 balance in health and disease: evolutionary aspects of diet. *World Rev Nutr Diet.* 2011;10210.

14. Mozaffarian D and Wu JHY. Omega 3 fatty acids and cardiovascular disease. *J Am Coll Cardio.* 2011;58:2047.

15. Kris-Etherton K and others. The debate about n-6 polyunsaturated fatty acid recommendations for cardiovascular health. *J Am Diet Assoc.* 2010;110:201.

16. Kavanagh K and others. Trans fat diet induces abdominal obesity and changes in insulin sensitivity in monkeys. *Obesity.* 2007;15:1675.

17. Howard BV and others. Low-fat dietary pattern and lipoprotein risk factors: The Women's Health Initiative Dietary Modification Trial. *Am J Clin Nutr.* 2010;91:860.

18. Thiébaut ACM and others. Dietary fatty acids and pancreatic cancer in the NIH-AARP diet and health study. *JNCI.* 2009;101:1010.

19. Lophatananon A and others. Dietary fat and early-onset prostate cancer risk. *Br J Nutr.* 2010;103:1375.

20. Wijeysundera HC and others. Association of temporal trends in risk factors and treatment uptake with coronary heart disease mortality, 1994–2005. *JAMA.* 2010;303:1841.

21. Wilson PW. Prediction of cardiovascular disease events. *Cardiol Clin.* 2011;29:1.

22. Millen BE and others. Dietary patterns, smoking, and subclinical heart disease in women. *J Am Diet Assoc.* 2004;104:208.

23. Rosenfeld ME and Campbell LA. Pathogens and atherosclerosis: update on the potential contribution of multiple infectious organisms to the pathogenesis of atherosclerosis. *Thromb Haemo.* 2011;106:858

24. Karim R and others. Relationship between serum levels of sex hormones and progression of subclinical atherosclerosis in postmenopausal women. *J Clin Endocrin Metab.* 2008;93:131.

25. Welsh JA and others. Caloric sweetener consumption and dyslipidemia among US adults. *JAMA* 2010;303:1490.

26. Sabaté J and others. Nut consumption and blood lipid levels. A pooled analysis of 25 intervention trials. *Arch Intern Med.* 2010;170:821.

27. Kris-Etherton PM and others. Antioxidant vitamin supplements and cardiovascular disease. *Circ.* 2004;110:637.

28. Lonn E and others. Effects of long-term vitamin E supplementation on cardiovascular events and cancer: A randomized trial. *JAMA.* 2005;293:1338.

29. Jolliffe C, Janssen I. Age-specific lipid and lipoprotein thresholds for adolescents. *J Cardio Nurs.* 2008;23:56.

30. Mozaffarian D and others. Effects on coronary heart disease of increasing polyunsaturated fat in place of saturated fat: A systematic review and meta-analysis of randomized controlled trials. *PLoS Med.* 2010;7(3):e1000252.

31. Harris WS and others. Omega-6 fatty acids and risk for cardiovascular disease. science advisory from the American Heart Association Nutrition Subcommittee of the Council on Nutrition, Physical Activity, and Metabolism; Council on Cardiovascular Nursing; and Council on Epidemiology and Prevention. *Circ.* 2009;119:902.

Many cultures around the world enjoy the flavors of insects and benefit from the protein they provide—3 ounces of the locusts in this stir-fry provide about 11 grams of protein! Learn more about entomophagy at **www.food-insects.com.**

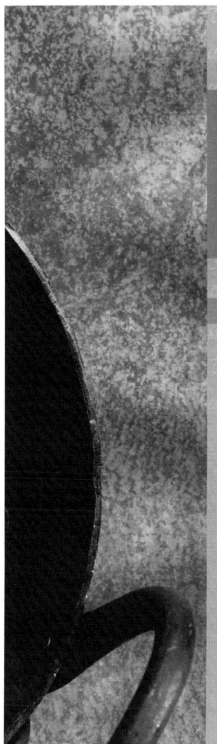

7 Proteins

Student Learning Outcomes

After studying this chapter, you will be able to

1. Describe how amino acids form proteins.

2. Define *essential* and *nonessential amino acids* and explain why adequate amounts of each of the essential amino acids are required for protein synthesis.

3. Distinguish between high-quality and low-quality proteins and list sources of each.

4. Describe how 2 low-quality proteins can be complementary to each other to provide the required amounts of essential amino acids.

5. Explain the methods used to measure the protein quality of foods.

6. List the factors that influence protein needs.

7. Calculate the RDA for protein for a healthy adult with a given body weight.

8. Explain positive nitrogen balance, negative nitrogen balance, and nitrogen equilibrium and list the conditions under which they occur.

9. Describe how protein is digested and absorbed in the body.

10. List the primary functions of protein in the body.

11. Describe the types of protein-energy malnutrition.

12. Describe the symptoms and treatment of food allergies.

13. Develop a vegetarian diet plan that meets the body's protein needs.

THE TERM PROTEIN COMES FROM the Greek word *protos*, which means "to come first." This is an appropriate name, given that proteins are a primary component of all cells throughout the body. In fact, aside from water, proteins form the major part of lean body tissue, totaling about 17% of body weight.[1] Many of our body proteins are found in muscle, connective tissue, organs, DNA, hemoglobin, antibodies, hormones, enzymes, and other vital compounds.

Proteins are crucial to the regulation and maintenance of essential body functions. For example, maintenance of fluid balance, hormone and enzyme production, cell synthesis and repair, and vision each requires specific proteins. The body synthesizes proteins in many sizes and configurations, so that they can serve these greatly varied functions.[1]

224 **PART 2** Energy-Yielding Nutrients and Alcohol

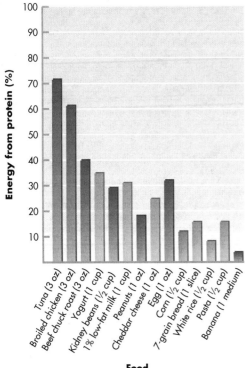

Figure 7-1 Protein content of foods. In addition to MyPlate food groups, yellow is used for oils and pink is used for substances that do not fit easily into food groups (e.g., candy, salty snacks).

nonessential amino acids Amino acids that the human body can synthesize in sufficient amounts.

In industrialized countries, such as the U.S. and Canada, most people consume diets rich in protein. In contrast, diets in developing countries often contain insufficient amounts of protein. As you'll see, consuming inadequate amounts of protein can impair many metabolic processes because the body is unable to build the proteins it needs. For example, the immune system no longer functions efficiently when it lacks key proteins, which leads to an increased risk of infection, disease, and, if severe, even death. This chapter will examine the functions of protein, its metabolism, the sources of protein, and the consequences of eating diets that are too low or too high in protein.

7.1 Structure of Proteins

Like carbohydrates and lipids, proteins are made of the elements carbon, hydrogen, and oxygen. However, all proteins also contain the element nitrogen. Some proteins also contain the mineral sulfur. Together, these elements form various amino acids, which serve as the building blocks for protein synthesis.

Amino Acids

The amino acids needed to make body proteins are supplied by the protein-containing foods we eat and through cell synthesis (Fig. 7-1). Each amino acid is composed of a central carbon bonded to 4 groups of elements: a nitrogen (amino) group, an acid (carboxyl) group, hydrogen, and a side chain (often signified by the letter *R*). The basic, or "generic," model of an amino acid and the structures of 2 amino acids, glycine and alanine, are shown in Figure 7-2. (The chemical structures of the rest of the amino acids are shown in Appendix B.)

The side chain makes each amino acid unique and determines the structure, function, and name of the amino acid. For example, if R is a hydrogen, the amino acid is glycine; if R is a methyl group ($-CH_3$), the amino acid is alanine. Some amino acids have chemically similar side chains. These related amino acids form special classes, such as acidic amino acids, basic amino acids, and branched-chain amino acids. For instance, the acidic amino acids lose a hydrogen in reactions and become negatively charged, whereas the basic amino acids gain a hydrogen and become positively charged. This allows them to participate in different enzymatic reactions in the body.

The body needs 20 different amino acids to function. Although all amino acids are important, 11 of them do not need to be obtained from the diet. They are classified as **nonessential** (or *dispensable*) **amino acids** because our bodies make them, using other amino acids we consume (Table 7-1). The 9 amino acids the body cannot make are known as

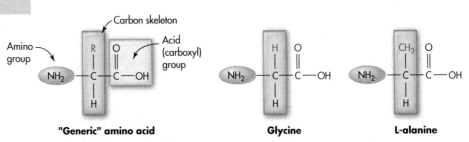

Figure 7-2 Amino acid structure. The side chain (R) differentiates glycine from alanine.

essential (or *indispensable*) **amino acids** because they must be obtained from foods. Essential amino acids cannot be synthesized in the body because body cells cannot make the **carbon skeleton** of the amino acid, cannot attach an amino group to the carbon skeleton, or cannot do the whole process fast enough to meet the body's needs.

Several nonessential amino acids may be classified as "conditionally essential" amino acids during infancy, disease, or trauma.[1] For example, a person with the genetic disease phenylketonuria (PKU) has a limited ability to metabolize the essential amino acid phenylalanine due to a deficiency of the enzyme phenylalanine hydroxylase. This enzyme is needed to convert phenylalanine to the nonessential amino acid tyrosine. As a result, individuals with PKU cannot produce sufficient tyrosine, thereby making tyrosine a "conditionally" essential amino acid because it must be obtained from the diet. Following trauma and infection, the amino acids glutamine and arginine may be considered conditionally essential because supplemental amounts have been shown to promote recovery.

Synthesis of Nonessential Amino Acids

Nonessential amino acids can be synthesized through a process called transamination. **Transamination** involves the transfer of an amino group from 1 amino acid to a carbon skeleton to form a new amino acid. As illustrated in Figure 7-3, glutamic acid donates its amino group to the carbon skeleton of pyruvic acid to become the nonessential amino acid alanine.

Glutamic acid (and several other amino acids) also can lose an amino group without transferring it to another carbon skeleton. This process is called **deamination.** The amino group (in the form of ammonia) is incorporated into **urea** in the liver, transported via the bloodstream to the kidneys, and excreted in the urine. Once an amino acid breaks down to its amino-free carbon skeleton, the carbon skeleton can be used for energy or synthesized into other compounds, such as glucose (see Chapter 9).

Table 7-1	Classification of Amino Acids
Essential Amino Acids	**Nonessential Amino Acids**
Histidine	Alanine
Isoleucine*	Arginine
Leucine*	Asparagine
Lysine	Aspartic acid
Methionine	Cysteine
Phenylalanine	Glutamic acid
Threonine	Glutamine
Tryptophan	Glycine
Valine*	Proline
	Serine
	Tyrosine

*Branched-chain amino acids.

essential amino acids Amino acids that the human body cannot synthesize in sufficient amounts or at all and therefore must be included in the diet.

carbon skeleton Amino acid without the amino group.

urea Nitrogenous waste product of protein metabolism and the major source of nitrogen in the urine; chemically depicted as this:

$$NH_2-\overset{\overset{\textstyle O}{\|}}{C}-NH_2$$

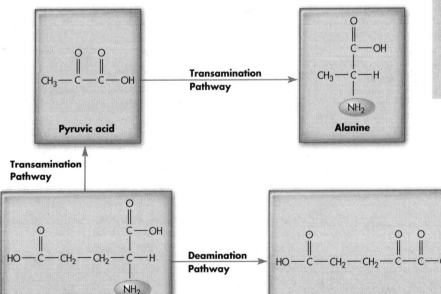

Figure 7-3 In **transamination,** the pathway allows cells to synthesize nonessential amino acids. In this example, pyruvic acid gains an amino group from glutamic acid to form the amino acid alanine. In **deamination,** the pathway allows for loss of an amino group without transferring it to another carbon skeleton. In this example, glutamic acid loses its amino group to form alpha-ketoglutaric acid.

Amino Acid Composition: Complete and Incomplete Proteins

Animal and plant proteins can differ greatly in their proportions of essential and nonessential amino acids. Animal proteins, such as meat, poultry, fish, eggs, and milk, contain ample amounts of all 9 essential amino acids. (Gelatin—made from the animal protein collagen—is an exception because it loses an essential amino acid during processing and is low in several essential amino acids.) In contrast, plant proteins do not contain the needed amounts of essential amino acids. With the exception of quinoa and soy protein, they are low in at least 1 of the 9 essential amino acids.

Dietary proteins are classified according to their amino acid composition. Because they contain sufficient amounts of all the essential amino acids, animal proteins (except gelatin) are classified as complete, or high-quality, proteins. Plant proteins (except soybeans and quinoa) are classified as incomplete, or low-quality, proteins because they contain limited amounts of 1 or more of the essential amino acids.

Cells require a **pool** of essential amino acids for the synthesis of body proteins. Thus, a single plant protein, such as wheat (which is low in the amino acid lysine), cannot support the synthesis of body protein if it is the sole source of dietary protein. Even a variety of low-quality proteins may not provide sufficient amounts of essential amino acids for protein synthesis if food choices are not carefully planned. When this occurs, proteins cannot be made and the remaining amino acids may be used for energy or converted to carbohydrate or fat.

The essential amino acid in smallest supply in a food or diet in relation to body needs is called the **limiting amino acid** because it limits the amount of protein the body can synthesize. For example, assume the letters of the alphabet represent the 20 different amino acids we need. If *A* represents an essential amino acid, we need 4 of these letters to spell the hypothetical protein *ALABAMA*. If the body had an *L*, a *B*, and an *M*, but only 3 *A*s, the "synthesis" of *ALABAMA* would not be possible. *A* would be the limiting amino acid, preventing the synthesis of the protein *ALABAMA*.

When 2 or more plant proteins are combined to compensate for deficiencies in essential amino acid content in each protein, the proteins are called **complementary proteins** (Table 7-2). When complementary protein sources are combined, the amino acids in one

High-protein foods, such as meat, can provide all the essential amino acids needed by our bodies.

pool Amount of a nutrient found within the body that can be easily mobilized when needed.

Food	Primary Limiting Amino Acid	Create a Complete Protein By Combining It With	Complementary Food Protein Combinations
Legumes (peanuts and dry beans, such as navy, black, and kidney beans)	Methionine Tryptophan	Grains, nuts, or seeds	Hummus and pita bread Bean burrito White beans and pasta Bean and barley stew Pinto beans and polenta Black-eyed pea croquettes
Nuts and seeds (cashews, walnuts, almonds, sunflower seeds)	Lysine	Legumes	Vegetarian chili with kidney beans and cashews Sesame, buckwheat, and bean bread Walnut and baked bean casserole
Grains (wheat, rice, oats, corn)	Lysine	Legumes	Red beans and rice Lentil soup and cornbread Barley and black beans

Table 7-2 Limiting Amino Acids in Plant Sources of Protein

Biological Value *peptide* *saa + pro* *edema*

source can make up for the limiting amino acid in the other sources to yield a high-quality (complete) protein for the diet. Mixed diets generally provide high-quality protein because these diets often contain complementary proteins. Complementary proteins need not be consumed at the same meal but can be balanced over the course of a day to provide a sufficient supply of amino acids for body cells. For nonvegetarians, adding a small amount of animal protein to a plant-based dish (e.g., pizza with cheese or spaghetti with meatballs) is a way of providing adequate essential amino acids.

> ### Knowledge Check
>
> 1. Why are some amino acids classified as essential and others as nonessential?
> 2. What are complementary proteins? Give 2 examples.
> 3. What does the term *limiting amino acid* mean?

Small amounts of animal protein in a meal quickly add up to meet daily protein needs.

 ## 7.2 Synthesis of Proteins

Within body cells, amino acids can be linked together by a chemical bond, called a peptide bond, to form needed proteins (Fig. 7-4). **Peptide bonds** form between the amino group of 1 amino acid and the acid (carboxyl) group of another. Through peptide bonding of amino acids, cells can synthesize dipeptides (joining of 2 amino acids), tripeptides (joining of 3 amino acids), oligopeptides (joining of 4 to 9 amino acids), and polypeptides (joining of 10 or more amino acids). Most proteins are polypeptides, ranging from approximately 50 to 2000 amino acids. The body can synthesize many different proteins by joining different combinations of amino acids with peptide bonds.

Transcription and Translation of Genetic Information

The synthesis of body proteins is determined through a process called gene expression. Gene expression begins when deoxyribonucleic acid (DNA) replicates, making an exact copy of the gene. Thus, each gene serves as a template to guide the duplication of genetic information carried by the DNA.

As you know, DNA is a double-stranded molecule in a helical form. Each strand of DNA is composed of 4 nucleotides (building blocks of DNA): adenine (A), guanine (G), cytosine (C), and thymine (T). Each of the nucleotides is complementary to (binds to) another nucleotide; A and T are complementary, as are C and G.

DNA-coded instructions for protein synthesis consist of a sequence of 3 nucleotides per unit of instruction (e.g., CTC), which dictate where each amino acid is to be placed in a protein and in which order. These nucleotide units are called

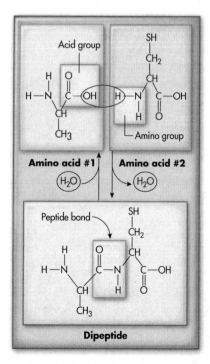

Figure 7-4 Peptide bonds link amino acids.

THINKING

Landon has heard that he should be certain to include complementary proteins in his vegetarian diet. What food combinations would you suggest to him?

228 PART 2 Energy-Yielding Nutrients and Alcohol

codons, and each represents a specific amino acid. For example, the codon CTC represents the amino acid glutamic acid. Some amino acids have only 1 possible codon, whereas others have as many as 6. For instance, the amino acid glutamic acid actually has 2 codons: CTC and CTT. Having the correct codons in the right sequence is critical for producing the needed amino acid and a normal protein. DNA with mistakes in the order or types of

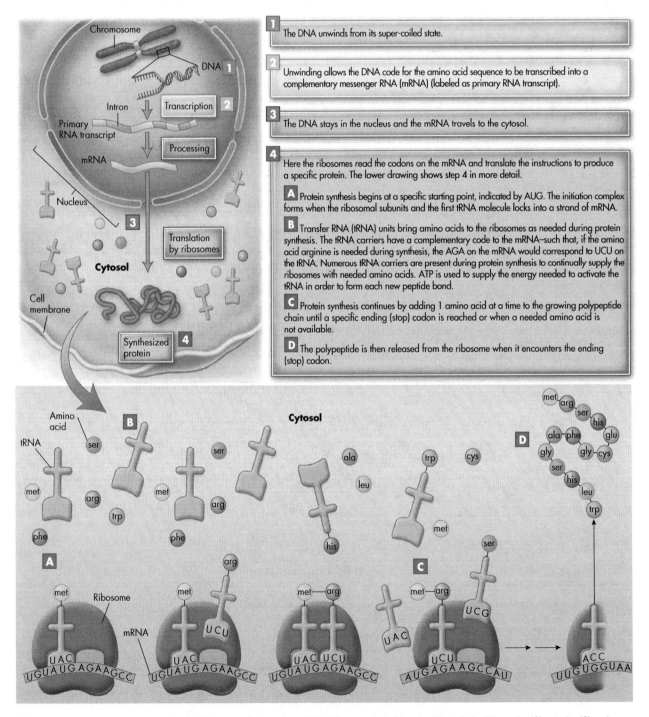

1 The DNA unwinds from its super-coiled state.

2 Unwinding allows the DNA code for the amino acid sequence to be transcribed into a complementary messenger RNA (mRNA) (labeled as primary RNA transcript).

3 The DNA stays in the nucleus and the mRNA travels to the cytosol.

4 Here the ribosomes read the codons on the mRNA and translate the instructions to produce a specific protein. The lower drawing shows step 4 in more detail.

A Protein synthesis begins at a specific starting point, indicated by AUG. The initiation complex forms when the ribosomal subunits and the first tRNA molecule locks into a strand of mRNA.

B Transfer RNA (tRNA) units bring amino acids to the ribosomes as needed during protein synthesis. The tRNA carriers have a complementary code to the mRNA–such that, if the amino acid arginine is needed during synthesis, the AGA on the mRNA would correspond to UCU on the tRNA. Numerous tRNA carriers are present during protein synthesis to continually supply the ribosomes with needed amino acids. ATP is used to supply the energy needed to activate the tRNA in order to form each new peptide bond.

C Protein synthesis continues by adding 1 amino acid at a time to the growing polypeptide chain until a specific ending (stop) codon is reached or when a needed amino acid is not available.

D The polypeptide is then released from the ribosome when it encounters the ending (stop) codon.

Figure 7-5 **Summary of protein synthesis.** DNA present in the nucleus of the cell is composed of 4 nucleotides: adenine (A), guanine (G), cytosine (C), and thymine (T). The DNA code is read 3 nucleotides at a time, with each specific unit being called a codon. Each DNA codon represents a specific amino acid.

	Complementary mRNA	Complementary tRNA
Table 7-3 DNA, mRNA, and tRNA Complementary Nucleotides		
DNA Nucleotides	**Nucleotides**	**Nucleotides**
Adenine	Uracil	Adenine
Cytosine	Guanine	Cytosine
Thymine	Adenine	Uracil
Guanine	Cytosine	Guanine

The double stranded, helical-shaped DNA located in the cell nucleus contains the genetic codes for the synthesis of proteins.

amino acids can result in profound health consequences (see the discussion of sickle-cell disease later in this section).

Protein synthesis takes place in the ribosomes, which are located in the cytosol of the cell. Because DNA is in the nucleas, the DNA code used for the synthesis of a specific protein must be transferred from the nucleus to the cytosol to allow for such synthesis. This transfer is the job of messenger RNA (mRNA). To produce mRNA, the DNA unwinds from its super-coiled state. Enzymes read the code on the DNA and transcribe that code into a complementary single-stranded mRNA molecule, called the primary transcript (Fig. 7-5). This process is called **DNA transcription.** The nucleotides of mRNA are A, G, C, and U (uracil, which replaces the thymine of DNA) and are organized in complement to the DNA (Table 7-3). Thus, a DNA code of ACTGAT yields an mRNA of UGACUA.

The primary transcript mRNA undergoes processing in the cell nucleus to remove any parts of the DNA code that do not code for protein synthesis. These parts are called introns and actually make up much of the DNA. The mRNA then travels to the ribosomes. The ribosomes read the codons on the mRNA and translate those instructions to produce a specific protein. This is the **mRNA translation** phase of protein synthesis. Amino acids are added 1 at a time to the polypeptide chain as directed by the instructions on the mRNA. Protein synthesis begins at a specific starting point on the mRNA (indicated by AUG) and continues until a specific ending (stop) codon is reached, such as UAA, UAG, or UGA. Energy input from ATP is needed to add each amino acid to the growing polypeptide chain, making protein synthesis very "costly" to the body in terms of energy use.

One key participant in protein synthesis in the cytosol is transfer RNA (tRNA). The tRNA units take amino acids to the ribosomes as needed during protein synthesis. The tRNA carriers have a complementary code to the mRNA. For example, if the amino acid arginine were needed during synthesis, the AGA on the mRNA would correspond to UCU on the tRNA. Numerous tRNA carriers are present during protein synthesis to continually supply the ribosomes with needed amino acids.

Once synthesis of the polypeptide is completed, indicated by the ending codon, it is released from the ribosome, as is the mRNA. The polypeptide now twists and folds into a very complex 3-dimensional structure (see the section Protein Organization). The DNA code determines not only the shape but also the function of the protein. Thus, if the DNA contains errors, an incorrect mRNA will be produced. The ribosomes, in turn, will read this incorrect message and produce an abnormal polypeptide.

The genetic disorder sickle-cell anemia illustrates what can happen when amino acid sequencing errors occur.[2] In this disease, the amino acid valine replaces glutamic acid in the DNA sequence of half of the 4 polypeptide chains of hemoglobin. This error produces a profound change in hemoglobin structure (Fig. 7-6). Instead of forming normal, doughnut-shaped discs, the red blood cells collapse into crescent, or sickle, shapes. This limits their ability to carry oxygen to tissues effectively, resulting in many serious health concerns. The disease can lead to severe bone and joint pain, abdominal pain, headache, convulsions,

(b)

(a)

Figure 7-6 An example of the consequences of errors in DNA coding of proteins. (a) Normal red blood cell; (b) red blood cell from a person with sickle-cell anemia—note its abnormal crescent (sicklelike) shape.

codon Specific sequence of 3 nucleotide units within DNA that codes particular amino acids needed for protein synthesis.

DNA transcription Process of forming messenger RNA (mRNA) from a portion of DNA.

mRNA translation Synthesis of polypeptide chains by the ribosome according to information contained in strands of messenger RNA (mRNA).

230   **PART 2**   Energy-Yielding Nutrients and Alcohol

Synopsis of the Steps in Protein Synthesis

Part of DNA code (gene) is transcribed to mRNA in the nucleus.

↓

mRNA leaves the nucleus and travels to cytosol.

↓

Ribosomes in the cytosol read the mRNA code and translate it into directions for a specific sequence of amino acids in a polypeptide chain.

↓

To produce the polypeptide, tRNA takes the appropriate amino acid to the ribosome as dictated by the mRNA code. The amino acid is added to the existing amino acid chain, which begins with the amino acid methionine.

↓

When synthesis of the polypeptide is complete, it is released from the ribosome.

↓

The polypeptide folds into its active 3-dimensional form.

▶ Sulfur-containing amino acids stabilize many compounds, such as the hormone insulin. Sulfur atoms can bond together (—S—S—), creating a bridge between 2 protein strands or 2 parts of the same strand. This stabilizes the structure of the molecule and helps create the *secondary structure.*

paralysis, and even death when the sickled cells clump in the capillary beds and impede blood flow. Treatment usually involves blood transfusions, medications to increase red blood cell synthesis, and bone marrow transplants.

Protein Organization

The sequential order and strong peptide bonding of the amino acids in the polypeptide chain, called the *primary structure,* determines a protein's shape. Amino acids must be accurately positioned in order for the amino acids to interact and fold correctly into the intended shape for the protein. This, in turn, allows weaker chemical bonds to form between amino acids near each other and stabilizes the structure. This creates a spiral-like or pleated sheet shape called the *secondary structure.* The unique 3-dimensional folding of a protein, called *tertiary structure,* determines the protein's overall shape and physiological function. Thus, if a protein fails to form the appropriate configuration, it cannot function. In some cases, 2 or more separate polypeptides interact to form a large, new protein, with *quaternary structure* (Fig. 7-7). In this way, a protein may be active when the units are joined but inactive when the units are separate. Hemoglobin is an example of a protein with quaternary structure.

Denaturation of Proteins

Exposure to acid or alkaline solutions, enzymes, heat, or agitation can change a protein's structure, leaving it in a denatured state (Fig. 7-8). Alteration of a protein's 3-dimensional structure is called **denaturation.** Although denaturation does not affect the protein's primary structure, unraveling a protein's shape often destroys its normal biological function.

Sometimes the denaturation of proteins is beneficial. For example, the secretion of hydrochloric acid in the stomach during digestion denatures food proteins, which increases their exposure to digestive enzymes and aids in the breakdown of polypeptide chains. The heat produced during cooking also can denature proteins, making them safer to eat (e.g., when harmful bacterial protein is denatured) and more pleasing to eat (e.g., when eggs solidify in

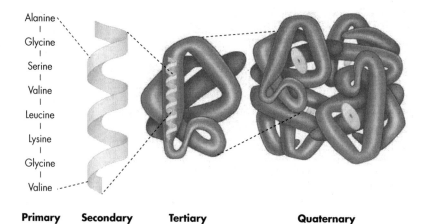

Alanine
|
Glycine
|
Serine
|
Valine
|
Leucine
|
Lysine
|
Glycine
|
Valine

Primary   **Secondary**   **Tertiary**   **Quaternary**

Figure 7-7 **Protein organization.** Four different levels of structure are found in proteins. The primary structure of a protein is the linear sequence of amino acids in the polypeptide chain. Secondary structure consists of areas in the polypeptide chain that have a specific shape stabilized by hydrogen and sulfur bonds. The 3-dimensional shape of proteins is called tertiary structure. It determines the function of the protein. Some proteins also show quaternary structure where 2 or more protein units join together to form a larger protein, such as hemoglobin, depicted in the figure.

cooking). However, denaturation also can be harmful to physiological function and overall health. During illness, changes in gastrointestinal acidity, body temperature, or body pH can cause essential proteins to denature and lose their function.

Adaptation of Protein Synthesis to Changing Conditions

Most vital body proteins are in a constant state of breakdown, rebuilding, and repair. This process, called protein turnover, allows cells to adapt to changing circumstances. For example, when we eat more protein than necessary for health, the liver makes more enzymes to process the waste product from the resulting amino acid metabolism—namely, ammonia—into urea. Overall, protein turnover is a process by which a cell can respond to its changing environment by increasing the production of needed proteins while reducing the production of proteins not currently needed.[1]

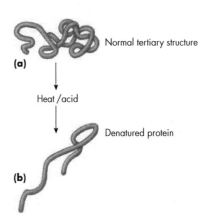

Figure 7-8 **Denaturation.** (a) Protein in a typical coiled state. (b) Protein is now partly uncoiled, exhibiting a denatured state. This uncoiling typically reduces or eliminates biological activity and is usually caused by treatment by heat, enzymes, acid or alkaline solutions, or agitation.

Knowledge Check

1. How are the amino acids in a protein linked together?
2. Why is the structure of a protein important?
3. What effects does denaturation have on a protein?

 7.3 Sources of Protein

Proteins and amino acids are supplied by the diet as well as by the recycling and reutilization of amino acids released during the breakdown of body protein. For example, the intestinal tract lining is constantly sloughed off. The digestive tract treats sloughed cells just like food particles and absorbs their amino acids released during digestion. In fact, most protein breakdown products—amino acids—released throughout the body can be recycled and added to the pool of amino acids available for future protein synthesis. By comparing the 250 to 300 g of protein an adult makes and degrades each day with the 65 to 100 g of protein typically consumed by adults, you can see how important recycled amino acids are as a protein source for the body.[3] Nonetheless, dietary protein is needed to replenish and maintain an adequate amino acid pool for protein synthesis and repair.

In typical North American diets, about 70% of dietary protein is supplied by meat, poultry, fish, milk, cheese, legumes, and nuts (Fig. 7-9).[4] Worldwide, only 35% of protein comes from animal sources. Plants are the major source of protein in many areas of the world.

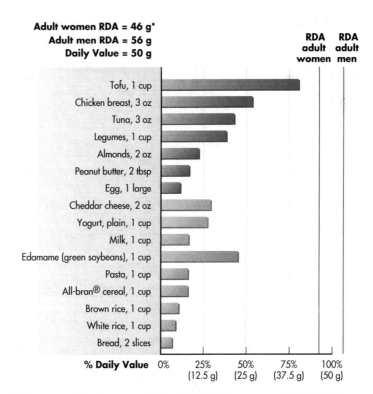

Adult women RDA = 46 g*
Adult men RDA = 56 g
Daily Value = 50 g

*RDA based on 0.8 g/kg body weight for 125-lb (57-kg) woman and 154-lb (70-kg) man

Figure 7-9 Food sources of protein.

232 **PART 2**   Energy-Yielding Nutrients and Alcohol

Table 7-4   Protein Content of Sample Menus Containing 1600 kcal and 2000 kcal

	Menu	1600 kcal Serving Size	Protein (g)	2000 kcal Serving Size	Protein (g)
Breakfast	Low-fat granola	²/₃ cup	5	²/₃ cup	5
	Blueberries	1 cup	1	1 cup	1
	Fat-free (skim) milk	1 cup	8.5	1 cup	8.5
	Coffee	1 cup	0	1 cup	0
Lunch	Broiled chicken breast	3 oz	25	4 oz	33
	Salad greens	3 cups	5	3 cups	5
	Baked taco shell strips	½ cup	2	½ cup	2
	Low-fat salad dressing	2 tbsp	0	2 tbsp	0
	Fat-free (skim) milk	1 cup	8.5	1 cup	8.5
Dinner	Yellow rice	1¼ cups	5	2½ cups	10
	Shrimp	4 large	5	6 large	7
	Mussels	4 medium	8	6 medium	12
	Clams	5 small	12	10 small	24
	Peas	¼ cup	4	½ cup	4
	Sweet red pepper	¼ cup	0	½ cup	0
Snack	Muffin	1 small	4	1 small	4
	Swiss cheese	1 oz	7.5	1 oz	7.5
	Banana	½ small	0.5	½ small	0.5
	Total		101		132

As shown in Table 7-4, plants can provide ample amounts of dietary protein in addition to providing fiber and a variety of vitamins, minerals, and phytochemicals. Unlike animal proteins, plant proteins contain no cholesterol and little saturated fat, unless added during processing. North Americans might benefit from adding soy and other plant proteins to their diets because higher intakes of these proteins may help decrease the risk of cardiovascular disease, certain cancers, obesity, and diabetes.[5-8] In fact, the FDA has approved a health claim regarding the benefits of soy protein in lowering blood cholesterol levels.

As a way to add more plant proteins to your diet, consider these suggestions:

- At your next cookout, try a veggie burger instead of a hamburger. These are available in the frozen foods section of the grocery store. Many restaurants have veggie burgers on their menus.
- Sprinkle sunflower seeds or chopped walnuts on top of a salad to add taste and texture.
- Mix chopped pecans or almonds into the batter of banana bread, muffins, or pancakes to boost your intake of monounsaturated fats and protein.

- Eat edamame (green soybeans) or roasted soy nuts as a snack.
- Spread peanut butter, instead of butter or cream cheese, on bagels.
- Consider using soy milk, especially if you have lactose intolerance. Look for varieties that are fortified with calcium.
- Substitute black beans or vegetarian refried beans for the meat or fish in your tacos.
- Make a stir-fry with tofu, cashew nuts, and a variety of vegetables.

Evaluation of Food Protein Quality

Scientists use various measures to evaluate the protein quality of a food. These measures indicate a food protein's ability to support body growth and maintenance. Protein quality is determined primarily by the food's digestibility (amount of amino acids absorbed) and amino acid composition compared with a reference protein (e.g., egg white protein) that provides the essential amino acids in amounts needed to support growth. The digestibility of animal proteins is relatively high (90–100%), in contrast to that of plant proteins (70%).

It is important to note that the concept of protein quality applies only under conditions in which protein intakes are equal to or less than the amount of protein needed to meet the requirement for essential amino acids. When protein intake exceeds this amount, the efficiency of protein use is decreased, even with the highest-quality proteins. This occurs because, once essential amino acid needs have been met, the remaining amino acids (both essential and nonessential) are mostly degraded for use as energy.

Biological Value (BV)

The **biological value (BV)** of a protein is a measure of how efficiently the absorbed food protein is converted into body tissue protein. If a food possesses adequate amounts of all 9 essential amino acids, it should allow a person to efficiently incorporate amino acids from food protein into body protein.

To determine the BV, nitrogen retention in the body is compared with the nitrogen content of the food protein. More nitrogen is retained when a food's amino acid pattern closely matches the amino acid pattern of body protein. The better the match, the higher the BV. In contrast, if the amino acid pattern in a food is quite unlike body tissue amino acid patterns, more nitrogen is excreted because many of the amino acids in the food will not be incorporated into body protein. The BV of such a food protein is low, as little of the nitrogen is retained in body tissues.

Egg white protein has a BV of 100, the highest BV of any single food protein. This means that essentially all the nitrogen absorbed from egg protein is retained and incorporated into body tissue protein. Most animal proteins have a high BV, reflecting a tissue amino acid composition similar to that of human tissues. Plants have amino acid patterns that differ greatly from those of humans. Therefore, the BV of plant proteins is usually much lower than that of animal proteins.

Protein Efficiency Ratio (PER)

Protein efficiency ratio (PER) is another method for assessing a food's protein quality. The PER compares the amount of weight gain by a growing laboratory animal consuming a standardized amount of the protein being studied with the weight gain by an animal consuming a standardized amount of a reference protein, such as casein (milk protein). The PER of a food reflects its biological value because the weight gain and growth measured in the PER are dependent on the incorporation of food protein into body tissue. Thus, animal proteins with a high BV also yield a high PER, whereas plant proteins generally yield a lower BV and PER because they are incomplete proteins. The FDA uses the PER to set standards for the labeling of foods intended for infants.

Legumes are rich sources of protein. One-half cup meets about 10% of protein needs but contributes only about 5% of energy needs.

$$BV = \frac{\text{Nitrogen retained (g)}}{\text{Nitrogen absorbed (g)}} \times 100$$

$$PER = \frac{\text{Weight gain (g)}}{\text{Protein consumed}}$$

$$\text{Chemical score} = \frac{\text{mg of limiting amino acid per g of protein}}{\text{mg of limiting amino acid per g of an "ideal" protein}}$$

$$PDCAAS = \text{Chemical score} \times \text{Digestibility}$$

▶ The concept of biological value has clinical importance whenever protein intake must be limited. This is because it is important that the small amount of protein consumed be used efficiently by the body. For example, protein intake during liver disease and kidney disease may need to be controlled to lessen the effects of the disease. In these cases, most of the protein consumed should be of high biological value, such as eggs, milk, and meat.

Meat, fish, and poultry are primary sources of high biological value protein.

CASE STUDY

Bethany is a college freshman. She lives in a campus residence hall and teaches aerobics in the afternoon. She eats 2 or 3 meals a day at the residence hall cafeteria and snacks between meals. Bethany decided to become a vegetarian after reading an article describing the health benefits of a vegetarian diet. Yesterday, her diet consisted of a café latte and Danish pastry for breakfast; a vegetarian tomato-rice dish, pretzels, and a diet soft drink for lunch; 2 cookies in the afternoon after aerobics class; and a vegetarian sub sandwich with 2 glasses of fruit punch for dinner. In the evening, she had a bowl of popcorn. What is missing from Bethany's current diet? How can she improve her new diet to meet her nutrient needs? What foods would Bethany need to include in her diet to increase her protein intake?

Chemical Score

The protein quality of a food also can be evaluated by its chemical score. To calculate a **chemical score,** the amount of each essential amino acid in a gram of the food protein being tested is divided by the "ideal" amount for that amino acid in a gram of the reference protein (usually egg protein). The lowest (limiting) amino acid ratio that is calculated for the essential amino acids of the test protein is the chemical score of that protein. Chemical scores range from 0 to 1.0.

Protein Digestibility Corrected Amino Acid Score (PDCAAS)

The most widely used measure of protein quality is called the **Protein Digestibility Corrected Amino Acid Score (PDCAAS).** This score is derived by multiplying a food's chemical score by its digestibility. For example, to determine the PDCAAS of wheat, multiply its chemical score (0.47) by its digestibility (0.90). This gives a PDCAAS of approximately 0.40. The highest PDCAAS is 1.0, which is the score for soy protein and most animal proteins. A protein missing any of the 9 essential amino acids (e.g., gelatin) has a PDCAAS of 0 because its chemical score is 0.

For nutrition labeling purposes, protein content (when listed as % Daily Value) is reduced if the PDCAAS is less than 1.0. For example, if the protein content of ½ cup of spaghetti noodles is 3 g, only 1.2 g are counted when calculating % Daily Value, since the PDCAAS of wheat is 0.40 (3 g × 0.40 = 1.2). Other PDCAAS values are egg white, 1.0; soy protein, 0.92 to 0.99; beef, 0.92; and black beans, 0.53. Currently, the Nutrition Facts panel rarely contains the % Daily Value for protein because manufacturers do not want to spend the money needed to determine the PDCAAS.

Knowledge Check

1. What are 3 good sources of protein?
2. What are 3 ways of assessing protein quality?
3. What are 2 examples of proteins with high biological value (BV)?
4. What factors affect the protein quality of a food?

7.4 Recommended Intakes of Protein

The Institute of Medicine recommends a protein intake equaling 10 to 35% of total calories. Healthy individuals who are not in periods of growth or recovering from illness or injury need to consume protein in an amount that replaces the protein lost in urine, feces, sweat, skin cells, hair, and nails. When protein intake equals the amount in losses, protein balance (equilibrium) is maintained as long as energy intake is adequate to prevent the use of protein for energy.

When protein intake is less than losses, an individual is in negative protein balance (negative nitrogen balance). Negative protein balance often develops in individuals eating inadequate protein accompanied by a serious, untreated illness or injury (see Section 7.7) and in those with diseases that increase protein breakdown. For example, individuals with untreated acquired immune deficiency syndrome (AIDS) synthesize protein at rates similar to those of healthy people, but they often break down body protein at much higher rates. Over time, the increased rates of protein breakdown result in wasting of lean body mass. Negative protein balance eventually causes loss of proteins in skeletal muscles, blood, the heart, the liver, and other organs.

When protein intake is greater than losses, a state of positive protein balance is attained. During periods of growth and recovery from injury, trauma, or illness, positive protein balance is required to supply sufficient materials for building and repairing tissues. In addition,

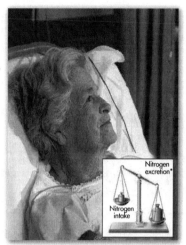

Positive Nitrogen Balance	Nitrogen Equilibrium	Negative Nitrogen Balance
Situations when positive nitrogen balance occur: Growth Pregnancy Recovery stage after illness/injury Athletic training resulting in increased lean body mass Increased secretion of certain hormones, such as insulin, growth hormone, and testosterone	**Situation when nitrogen equilibrium occurs:** Healthy adult meeting protein and energy needs	**Situations when negative nitrogen balance occur:** Inadequate intake of protein Inadequate energy intake Conditions such as fevers, burns, and infections Bed rest (for several days) Deficiency of essential amino acids (e.g., poor-quality protein consumed) Increased protein loss (as in some forms of disease) Increased secretion of certain hormones, such as thyroid hormone and cortisol

*Based on losses of urea and other nitrogen-containing compounds in the urine as well as protein losses in feces, skin, hair, nails, and other minor routes.

Figure 7-10 Determining nitrogen balance requires measuring nitrogen intake and loss.

the hormones insulin, growth hormone, and testosterone all stimulate protein synthesis for the building of new tissue. Merely eating more protein does not build additional body protein; one must be in a situation requiring positive nitrogen balance for this to occur.

Researchers and clinicians can measure dietary protein intake and body losses of protein to determine protein balance. Because nitrogen is a component of protein and can be more easily quantified, nitrogen, rather than protein, is measured. Figure 7-10 provides examples of the states of nitrogen (protein) balance. Nitrogen makes up approximately 16% of the weight of an amino acid (16/100 = 6.25). Therefore, nitrogen intake multiplied by 6.25 provides an estimate of protein intake:

$$\text{Nitrogen (g)} \times 6.25 = \text{Protein (g)}$$

Nitrogen balance studies are difficult to conduct because an accurate measure of all sources of nitrogen intake and loss over a 24-hour period is needed. Outside of hospital and research environments, this is not usually feasible. Thus, it is easier to calculate protein needs based on the RDA.

Dietary Reference Intakes for Protein

The RDAs for protein are listed on the inside back cover of this textbook. These guidelines provide recommendations for healthy individuals during periods of growth and development (infancy, childhood, pregnancy, lactation), as well as during normal adulthood.

Legumes, such as cannellini beans, boost the protein content of meals.

The amount of protein fed to infants should closely follow RDA guidelines. At intakes in excess of the Adequate Intake, their kidneys may have difficulty excreting the large amounts of urea formed in metabolizing the protein. The quantity of protein in breast milk and formula is well matched to infant needs.

For most adults, the RDA for protein is 0.8 g/kg body weight. Healthy weight is used as a baseline for the RDA because excess fat storage doesn't contribute much to protein needs. As noted in the following equations, the RDAs for adults are 56 g/day for a 154 lb (70 kg) man and 46 g/day for a 125 lb (57 kg) woman.

Convert weight from pounds to kg:

$$\frac{154 \text{ pounds}}{2.2 \text{ pounds/kg}} = 70 \text{ kg} \quad (\text{man})$$

$$\frac{125 \text{ pounds}}{2.2 \text{ pounds/kg}} = 57 \text{ kg} \quad (\text{woman})$$

Calculate RDA:

$$70 \text{ kg} \times \frac{0.8 \text{ g protein}}{\text{kg body weight}} = 56 \text{ g} \quad (\text{man})$$

$$57 \text{ kg} \times \frac{0.8 \text{ g protein}}{\text{kg body weight}} = 46 \text{ g} \quad (\text{woman})$$

The RDA for protein does not address the additional protein amounts needed during recovery from illness or injury or that might be required to support the needs of highly trained athletes.[3] During these conditions, protein needs can range from approximately 0.8 to 2.0 g/kg body weight. Mental stress, physical labor, and routine weekend sports activities do not require an increase in the protein RDA.[3]

For many North Americans, protein needs are easily met through our typical diets. In fact, North Americans typically consume protein in amounts exceeding the RDA, equaling about 100 g of protein daily for men and 65 g daily for women.[3] Excess protein—whether from dietary sources of protein or amino acid supplements—cannot be stored as such, so the carbon skeletons are metabolized for energy needs or used for other purposes.

Knowledge Check

1. When is it important to be in positive nitrogen balance?
2. What situations increase the risk of being in negative nitrogen balance?
3. During what stage of the life cycle are people generally in nitrogen equilibrium?

Take Action

Meeting Protein Needs When Dieting to Lose Weight

Your father has been gaining weight for the last 5 years. His physician has suggested that he lose 20 pounds to decrease his risk of heart disease and type 2 diabetes. You know that it will be important for your father to meet his protein needs as he tries to lose weight. Design a 1-day diet for him that contains about 1500 kcal with 15% of energy intake as protein. A nutrient database (see Appendix N), a nutrient analysis computer program, or a website (www.nal.usda.gov/fnic/foodcomp/search/) will provide some help. Does your diet plan meet the RDA for protein and follow MyPlate guidelines?

7.5 Protein Digestion and Absorption

For some foods, the first step in protein breakdown takes place during cooking. Cooking unfolds (denatures) proteins and softens the tough connective tissues in meat. This can make many protein-rich foods easier to chew and aids in breakdown during digestion and absorption in the GI tract.

The enzymatic digestion of protein begins in the stomach with the secretion of hydrochloric acid. Once proteins are denatured by stomach acid, **pepsin,** a major enzyme produced by the stomach, begins to break the long polypeptide chains into shorter chains of amino acids through hydrolysis reactions (Fig. 7-11). Pepsin does not completely separate proteins into amino acids because it can break only a few of the many peptide bonds found in these large molecules.

The release of pepsin is controlled by the hormone **gastrin.** Thinking about food or chewing food stimulates gastrin-producing cells of the stomach to release the hormone. Gastrin also strongly stimulates the stomach's parietal cells to produce acid, which aids in digestion and the activation of pepsin. Pepsin is actually stored as an inactive enzyme (called pepsinogen) to prevent it from digesting the stomach lining. Once pepsinogen enters the stomach's acidic environment (pH between 1 and 2), part of the molecule is split off, forming the active enzyme pepsin.

From the stomach, the partially digested proteins move with the rest of the nutrients and other substances in a meal (called chyme) into the duodenum. In the small intestine, chyme triggers the release of the hormones secretin and cholecystokinin (CCK) from the walls of the small intestine. These, in turn, stimulate the pancreas to release the protease or protein-splitting enzymes trypsin, chymotrypsin, and carboxypeptidase into the small intestine. Together, these enzymes

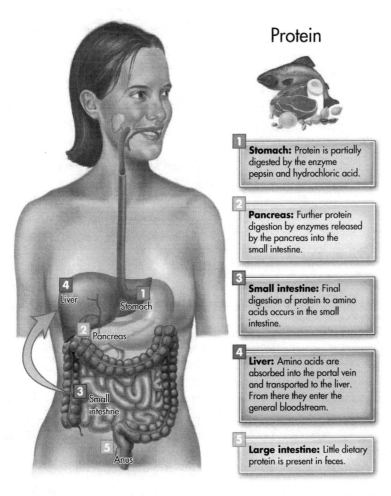

Protein

1 Stomach: Protein is partially digested by the enzyme pepsin and hydrochloric acid.

2 Pancreas: Further protein digestion by enzymes released by the pancreas into the small intestine.

3 Small intestine: Final digestion of protein to amino acids occurs in the small intestine.

4 Liver: Amino acids are absorbed into the portal vein and transported to the liver. From there they enter the general bloodstream.

5 Large intestine: Little dietary protein is present in feces.

Figure 7-11 A summary of protein digestion and absorption. Enzymatic protein digestion begins in the stomach and ends in the absorptive cells of the small intestine, where the last peptides are broken down into single amino acids.

238   PART 2   Energy-Yielding Nutrients and Alcohol

Figure 7-12 Protein digestion takes place in the stomach **1**, the lumen of the small intestine **2**, and the absorptive cells of the small intestine **3**. Absorption of amino acids from the lumen into the intestinal cells requires transporters. Most amino acids are transported by sodium-dependent transporters in an energy-requiring process (active absorption). Any remaining peptides are broken down to amino acids within the absorptive cell. The amino acids are then transported out of the cell and released into the bloodstream **4**.

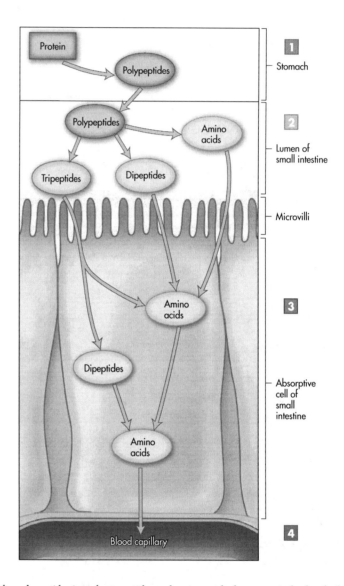

digest the polypeptides into short peptides and amino acids that are actively absorbed into the cells of the small intestine (Fig. 7-12). Any remaining short peptides are broken down to individual amino acids by peptidase enzymes. Amino acids then travel via the portal vein to the liver for use in protein synthesis, energy needs, conversion to carbohydrate or fat, or release into the bloodstream for transport to other cells.

Except during infancy, it is uncommon for intact proteins to be absorbed from the digestive tract. However, in early infancy (up to 4 to 5 months of age), the gastrointestinal tract is somewhat permeable to small proteins, so some whole proteins can be absorbed. Because proteins from foods such as cow's milk and egg white may predispose an infant to food allergies, pediatricians and registered dietitians recommend waiting until an infant is 12 months of age or older before introducing common allergenic foods (see Section 7.8).[9]

Knowledge Check

1. Name 4 enzymes that are involved in protein digestion and absorption.
2. What are the end products of polypeptide digestion?
3. How is the absorption of proteins different in early infancy?

7.6 Functions of Proteins

Proteins function in many crucial ways in metabolism and in the formation of essential compounds and structures (Fig. 7-13). Recall that the amino acids needed for the synthesis of proteins are supplied by the diet as well as by the recycling of body protein. However, if we do not eat adequate amounts of carbohydrate and fat, some amino acids will be used to produce energy, rendering them unavailable to build body proteins for other essential functions.

Producing Vital Body Structures

One of the primary functions of protein is to provide structural support to body cells and tissues. The key structural proteins (collagen, actin, and myosin) constitute more than a third of body protein and provide a matrix for muscle, connective tissue, and bone. During periods of growth, new proteins are synthesized to support the development of vital body tissues and structures. In periods of malnutrition or disease, body proteins are often broken down to

CRITICAL THINKING

Krista eats twice as much protein as her body needs. What happens to this extra protein?

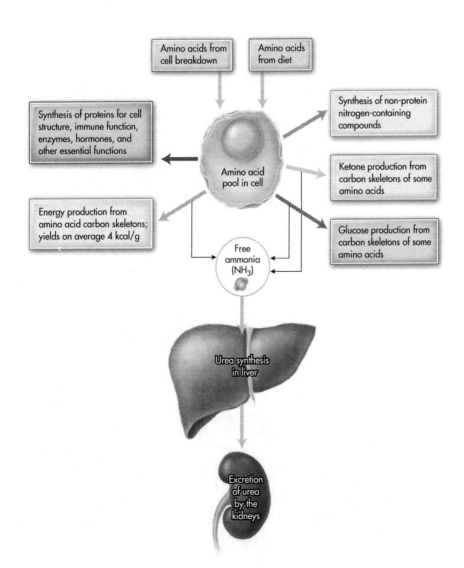

Figure 7-13 The amino acid pool supplies amino acids for varied protein functions. The nitrogen-containing ammonia (NH_3) released during amino acid breakdown is converted to urea and excreted in the urine.

supply energy. Thus, the synthesis of protein for vital tissues drops below normal rates, eventually resulting in protein wasting and the development of a condition known as kwashiorkor (see Section 7.7).

Maintaining Fluid Balance

The blood proteins albumin and globulin are important in maintaining fluid balance between the blood and the surrounding tissue space. Normal blood pressure in the arteries forces blood into **capillary beds.** The blood fluid then moves from the capillary beds into the spaces between nearby cells (interstitial spaces) to provide nutrients to those cells (Fig. 7-14). Proteins such as albumin are too large, however, to move out of the capillary beds into the tissues. The presence of these proteins in the capillary beds attracts the right amount of fluid back to the blood, partially counteracting the force of blood pressure to maintain fluid balance.

When protein consumption is inadequate, the concentration of proteins in the blood eventually decreases. Excessive fluid then builds up in the surrounding tissues because the amount of blood protein is inadequate to pull enough of the fluid back from the tissues into the bloodstream. As fluid builds up in the interstitial spaces, the tissues swell with excess fluid, resulting in **edema.** This can be a sign of a serious medical condition, so it is important for physicians to determine the underlying cause of edema.

capillary beds Minute blood vessels, 1 cell thick, that create a junction between arterial and venous circulation. Gas and nutrient exchange occurs here between body cells and the blood. Figure A-6 in Appendix A provides a detailed view of a capillary bed.

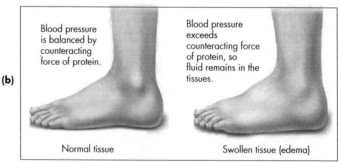

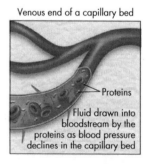

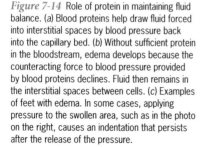
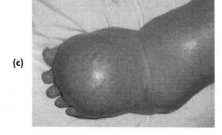
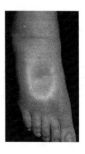

Figure 7-14 Role of protein in maintaining fluid balance. (*a*) Blood proteins help draw fluid forced into interstitial spaces by blood pressure back into the capillary bed. (*b*) Without sufficient protein in the bloodstream, edema develops because the counteracting force to blood pressure provided by blood proteins declines. Fluid then remains in the interstitial spaces between cells. (*c*) Examples of feet with edema. In some cases, applying pressure to the swollen area, such as in the photo on the right, causes an indentation that persists after the release of the pressure.

Contributing to Acid-Base Balance

The acid-base balance in the body is expressed in terms of pH, which reflects the concentration of hydrogen ions [H]. A solution with a high hydrogen ion concentration has a low pH and is therefore more acidic, whereas a solution with a low hydrogen ion concentration has a high pH and is more alkaline (see Appendix B for additional information). Proteins play an important role in regulating acid-base balance and body pH. For example, proteins located in cell membranes pump chemical ions into and out of cells. The ion concentrations that result from the pumping action help keep the blood slightly alkaline (pH = 7.35–7.45). In this way, proteins act as **buffers**—compounds that help maintain acid-base balance within a narrow range. Proteins are especially good buffers for the body because they have negative charges, which attract positively charged hydrogen ions. This allows them to accept and release hydrogen ions as needed to prevent detrimental changes in pH.

Forming Hormones, Enzymes, and Neurotransmitters

Amino acids are required for the synthesis of most hormones in the body. Some hormones, such as the thyroid hormones, are made from only 1 amino acid, whereas others, such as insulin, are composed of many amino acids. Hormones act as messengers in the body and aid in regulatory functions, such as controlling the metabolic rate and the amount of glucose taken up from the bloodstream. Amino acids also are required for the synthesis of enzymes. Cells contain thousands of enzymes that facilitate chemical reactions fundamental to metabolism. Many neurotransmitters, released by nerve endings, also are derivatives of amino acids. This is true for dopamine (synthesized from the amino acid tyrosine), norepinephrine (synthesized from the amino acid tyrosine), and serotonin (synthesized from the amino acid tryptophan).

Contributing to Immune Function

Antibody proteins are a key component of the immune system. Antibodies bind to foreign proteins (called antigens) that invade the body and prevent their attack on target cells. In a normal, healthy individual, antibodies are very efficient in combating these antigens to prevent infection and disease. However, without sufficient dietary protein, the immune system lacks the material needed to build this defense. Thus, immune incompetence (called **anergy**) develops and reduces the body's ability to fight infection. Anergy can turn measles into a fatal disease for a malnourished child. It also increases the risk of illness and infection in protein-deficient adults.

Transporting Nutrients

Many proteins function as transporters for other nutrients, carrying them through the bloodstream to cells and across cell membranes to sites of action. For instance, the protein hemoglobin carries oxygen from the lungs to cells. Lipoproteins transport large lipid molecules from the small intestine, through the lymph and blood to body cells. Some vitamins and minerals also have specific protein carriers that aid in their transport into and out of tissues and storage proteins. Examples include retinol-binding protein (a carrier protein for vitamin A), transferrin and ferritin (carrier and storage proteins, respectively, for iron), and ceruloplasmin (a carrier protein for copper).

buffers Compounds that help maintain acid-base balance within a narrow range.

anergy Lack of an immune response to foreign compounds entering the body.

Expert Perspective from the Field

Nutrition and Immunity

The immune system is a complex network of organs, tissues, cells, and secretions that protects the body from foreign organisms (pathogens), such as bacteria, viruses, parasites, fungi, and toxins. When the body detects the presence of these "non-self" cells or antigens, innate and acquired immune responses attempt to destroy the antigens.

Innate (nonspecific) immunity is present at birth and provides the first barrier of protection against invading antigens. Innate immunity includes *physical barriers,* provided by the skin and mucous membranes, that prevent access to the inside of the body; *chemical secretions,* such as the hydrochloric acid secreted by the stomach, that destroy antigens; *physiological barriers,* such as fever, that prevent the growth of antigens; and *phagocytic cells* that engulf and destroy antigens. Innate immunity provides a general, nonspecific response, as it has a limited ability to recognize antigens that have previously attacked the body.

Acquired (specific) immunity provides an immune response that is initiated by the recognition of a specific antigen. Acquired immunity develops over a person's lifetime. Acquired immunity also is referred to as *adaptive immunity* because after exposure to an antigen the immune system can recognize the antigen and adapt its response to it. When the acquired immune system is triggered, the bone marrow and thymus are stimulated to produce *antibodies* (*immunoglobulins*) and other specialized immune cells that destroy the specific antigens.

Because infants have limited acquired immunity at birth, nutrition experts recommend breastfeeding. Dr. Stephanie Atkinson* is one of many scientists whose research has shown that human milk has high concentrations of many protective immune components, such immunoglobulins and lactoferrin (see Chapter 17). These immune components from the mother can be absorbed by infants and help protect them while their own immune systems are maturing. Although the immune components in human milk benefit all infants, for infants born in underdeveloped countries where exposure to pathogens is much greater than in North America, it can be life saving.

Nutrition is an important part of maintaining both innate and acquired immunity. According to Dr. Atkinson, nutritional deficiencies can suppress the immune system's ability to prevent infection and disease. Malnutrition results in loss of immune tissue, decreased production of immune cells, decreased number and effectiveness of antibodies, and breakdown of physical barriers to antigens. This increases risk of infection, disease, and death.

Severe protein-energy malnutrition (PEM) has profound effects on immune function. Dr. Atkinson indicated that this is of particular concern in infants and children with PEM, because they have increased nutritional needs to support growth and often have simultaneous micronutrient deficiencies (e.g., zinc deficiency), infections, and diarrhea, which result in even greater impairment to immune responses. The severity of the nutrient deficiencies and the child's overall health determine whether the impairment can be reversed by supplementing the diet with the deficient nutrients.

Specific nutrients can increase immune protection during critical illness and trauma. For example, the amino acids arginine and glutamine are considered "immunomodulators" because they promote protein synthesis and immune responses during illness. Glutamine also is important in maintaining the integrity of the intestinal mucosa, thereby preventing bacteria in the GI tract from entering the bloodstream. Studies of omega-3 and omega-6 polyunsaturated fatty acids suggest that these essential fatty acids also may be immunomodulators. Specialized nutritional formulas can provide these key nutrients during times of increased nutritional need, such as during disease or injury.

The study of nutrition and immune function is a relatively new field. Thus, scientists' understanding of how nutritional deficiencies and interventions affect immune responses is far from complete. However, it is clear that maintaining optimal nutritional status is an important way to support immune function and reduce the risk of infection and disease.

Stephanie Atkinson, Ph.D., is Professor, Department of Pediatrics; Associate Chair of Pediatrics (Research); Associate Member, Department of Biochemistry and Biomedical Sciences; and Faculty in the McMaster Medical Sciences Graduate Program and Health Sciences at McMaster University in Hamilton, Ontario, Canada. She directs an internationally recognized research program focused on pediatric nutrition. Among the many honors she has received are a Career Scientist Award from the Ministry of Health in Ontario, the McHenry Award from the Canadian Society for Nutritional Sciences, and a distinguished service award from the Dietitians of Canada.

Forming Glucose

The body must maintain a fairly constant concentration of blood glucose to supply energy, especially for red blood cells, brain cells, and other nervous tissue cells that rely almost exclusively on glucose for energy. If carbohydrate intake is inadequate to maintain blood glucose levels, the liver (and kidneys, to a lesser extent) is forced to make glucose from the amino acids present in body tissues (see Fig. 7-13). This process is called gluconeogenesis (see Chapter 9).

Making glucose from amino acids is a normal backup system the body utilizes to supply needed glucose. For example, when you skip breakfast and haven't eaten since 7 P.M. the preceding evening, glucose must be synthesized from amino acids. However, when this occurs chronically, as in starvation, the conversion of amino acids into glucose results in the development of widespread muscle wasting in the body (called cachexia).

Providing Energy

Proteins supply very little energy for healthy individuals. Under most conditions, body cells use primarily fats and carbohydrates for energy. Although proteins and carbohydrates contain the same amount of usable energy—on average, 4 kcal/g—proteins are a very costly source of energy, considering the amount of metabolism and processing the liver and kidneys must perform to use this energy source (see Fig. 7-13).

$F + C = E$

> *Knowledge Check*
>
> 1. What are 3 functions of proteins?
> 2. How do proteins help maintain fluid balance?
> 3. How do proteins contribute to immune function?

 ## 7.7 Health Concerns Related to Protein Intake

Many people living in developing countries suffer from malnutrition and disease because dietary protein supplies are limited.[10] In contrast, the residents of developed countries tend to eat more protein than they need and may boost their intake even higher by consuming protein or amino acid supplements.[3] As you know, getting sufficient amounts of protein is required for good health, but getting too little or too much can have serious health consequences.[10, 11]

Protein-Energy Malnutrition

Protein deficiency rarely develops as an isolated condition. It most often occurs in combination with a deficiency of energy (and other nutrients) and results in a condition known as **protein-energy malnutrition (PEM),** or protein-calorie malnutrition (PCM). In many developing areas of the world where diets are often low in protein and energy, PEM is a very serious public health concern. Although PEM can affect people of all ages, its most devastating consequences are seen in children. Without adequate protein and energy, children fail to grow normally, and many develop diarrhea, infections, and diseases and die early in life. Of the 55,000 people who die of hunger each day, nearly two-thirds are children.[10]

PEM usually occurs as either marasmus or kwashiorkor. These conditions differ in the severity of the overall energy and protein deficit and the related clinical characteristics

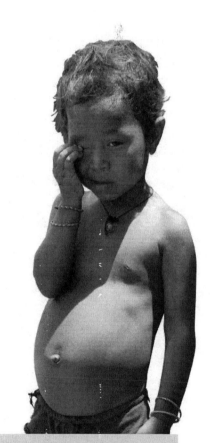

protein-energy malnutrition (PEM) Condition resulting from insufficient amounts of energy and protein, which eventually result in body wasting and an increased susceptibility to infection and disease.

244   **PART 2**   Energy-Yielding Nutrients and Alcohol

Figure 7-15 Classification of undernutrition in children.

Protein-Energy Malnutrition

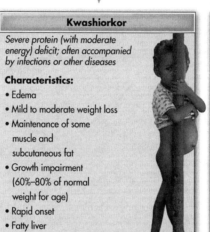

Kwashiorkor

Severe protein (with moderate energy) deficit; often accompanied by infections or other diseases

Characteristics:
- Edema
- Mild to moderate weight loss
- Maintenance of some muscle and subcutaneous fat
- Growth impairment (60%–80% of normal weight for age)
- Rapid onset
- Fatty liver

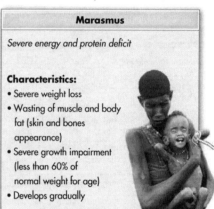

Marasmus

Severe energy and protein deficit

Characteristics:
- Severe weight loss
- Wasting of muscle and body fat (skin and bones appearance)
- Severe growth impairment (less than 60% of normal weight for age)
- Develops gradually

HISTORICAL PERSPECTIVE

Flaky Paint Skin and Bloated Bellies

For centuries, kwashiorkor has sickened and killed millions of young children. Its cause remained elusive until Cicely Williams carefully observed and listened to parents in western Africa where she was working in the 1930s. She discovered that this condition was the result of severe malnutrition that occurred when toddlers were weaned from breast milk, which is rich in protein and other nutrients, to a nutrient poor starchy gruel. This physician's description of kwashiorkor is still valid today. Learn more at: http://www.who.int/bulletin/volumes/81/12/PHCCommentary%20.pdf

---

marasmus Condition that results from a severe deficit of energy and protein, which causes extreme loss of fat stores, muscle mass, and body weight.

kwashiorkor Condition occurring primarily in young children who have an existing disease and consume a marginal amount of energy and severely insufficient protein. It results in edema, poor growth, weakness, and an increased susceptibility to further infection and disease.

(Fig. 7-15). **Marasmus** develops slowly from a severe deficiency of energy (and, in turn, protein and micronutrients). Over time, this leads to extreme weight loss, muscle and fat loss, and growth impairment. **Kwashiorkor** occurs more rapidly in response to a severe protein deficit, typically accompanied by underlying infections or disease. Kwashiorkor is characterized by edema, mild to moderate weight loss, growth impairment, and the development of a fatty liver (excess accumulation of fat in the liver).

PEM is most prevalent in parts of Africa, Southeast Asia, Central America, and South America.[1] However, it also is seen in some population groups in industrialized countries. Those at greatest risk are individuals living in poverty and/or isolation and those with substance abuse problems, anorexia nervosa, or debilitating diseases (e.g., AIDS or cancer). Some hospitalized patients also are at increased risk of PEM because of poor prior health, low dietary intakes, and increased protein needs for recovery from surgery, trauma, and/or disease. Malnourished patients face a much greater risk of complications and even death. Consequently, hospitals have developed nutrition support teams to ensure appropriate nutritional care for at-risk patients.

Kwashiorkor

Kwashiorkor is a word from Ghana that means "the disease that the first child gets when the new child comes." From birth, an infant in developing areas of the world is usually breastfed. Often by the time the child is 12 to 18 months old, the mother is pregnant or has already given birth again. The mother's diet is usually so marginal that she cannot produce sufficient milk to continue breastfeeding the older child. This child's diet then abruptly changes from nutritious human milk to starchy roots and gruels. These foods have low protein densities compared with their energy content. Additionally, the foods are usually high in plant fibers and bulk, making it difficult for the child to consume enough to meet energy needs and nearly impossible to meet protein needs. Many children in these areas also have infections and parasites that elevate protein and energy needs and often precipitate the development of kwashiorkor.

The presence of edema in a child who still has some subcutaneous fat is the hallmark of kwashiorkor (see Fig. 7-15). Other major symptoms of kwashiorkor are apathy, diarrhea, listlessness, failure to grow and gain weight, infections, and withdrawal from the environment. These symptoms also complicate other diseases that may be present. For example, measles, a disease that normally makes a healthy child ill for only a week or so, can become severely debilitating and even fatal in a child with kwashiorkor.

Many symptoms of kwashiorkor can be explained based on our knowledge of proteins. Proteins play important roles in fluid balance, growth, immune function, and the transport of other nutrients. Thus, protein deficiency can severely compromise these functions.

If children with kwashiorkor are helped in time—infections are treated and a diet ample in protein, energy, and other essential nutrients is provided—the disease process often reverses and they begin to grow again. Unfortunately, by the time many of these children reach a hospital or care center, they already have severe infections. Thus, despite good medical care, many still die. Those who survive often continue to battle chronic infections and diseases.[10]

Marasmus

Marasmus is the result of chronic PEM. It is caused by diets containing minimal amounts of energy, protein, and other nutrients. The word *marasmus* means "to waste away." Over time, the severe lack of energy and protein results in a "skin and bones" appearance, with little or no subcutaneous fat (see Fig. 7-15).

Marasmus usually develops in infants who either are not breastfed or have stopped breastfeeding in the early months. Often, the weaning formula used is incorrectly prepared because of unsafe water and because the parents cannot afford sufficient infant formula for the child's needs. The latter problem may lead the parents to dilute the formula to provide more feedings, not realizing that this deprives the infant of essential calories, protein, and other nutrients.

An infant with marasmus requires large amounts of energy and protein to restore growth, development, and overall health. Unless the child receives adequate nutrition, full recovery from the disease may never occur. Most brain growth occurs between conception and the child's first birthday. If the diet does not support brain growth during the first months of life, the brain may not fully develop, resulting in poor cognitive and intellectual growth.

High-Protein Diets

In addition to recommending adequate protein consumption, the Food and Nutrition Board also suggests that protein intake not exceed 35% of energy intake.[3] Diets containing an excessive or disproportionate amount of protein do not provide additional health benefits. Instead, high protein intakes may increase health and disease risks. One area of concern is the effect of excess protein on the kidneys.[12, 13] Recall that the kidneys are responsible for excreting excess nitrogen as urea. Thus, high-protein diets may overburden the kidneys' capacity to excrete nitrogen wastes. Additionally, because water is needed to dilute and excrete urea, inadequate fluid intake can increase the risk of dehydration as the kidneys use body water to dispose of the urea. These concerns are greatest for people who already have impaired kidney function. A lower-protein diet with adequate fluid intake is recommended for these individuals to help preserve kidney health.[13]

When excess protein is primarily from a high intake of animal proteins, the overall diet is likely to be low in plant-based foods and consequently low in fiber, some vitamins (vitamins C and E and folate), minerals (magnesium and potassium), and beneficial phytochemicals. Animal proteins are often rich in saturated fat and cholesterol. As a result, these diets can increase the risk of cardiovascular disease.[5, 6, 8] Diets that also contain high amounts of red meat (especially in cured forms, such as hot dogs, ham, salami, and luncheon meats) have been associated with an increased risk of certain cancers.[14]

High-protein diets also may increase urinary calcium loss and eventually lead to a loss of bone mass and an increased risk of osteoporosis.[5] These findings are somewhat controversial, however, and are less of a concern for individuals with adequate calcium intakes.

Other concerns, particularly with athletes, are the health risks associated with excess protein and amino acid supplementation. As described earlier, our bodies are designed to obtain amino acids from dietary sources of whole proteins. This assures a supply of amino acids in proportions needed for body functions and prevents amino acid toxicity, especially for methionine, cysteine, and histidine—the most toxic amino acids.[11] When individual amino acid supplements are taken, chemically similar amino acids can compete for absorption, resulting in amino acid imbalances and toxicity risk.

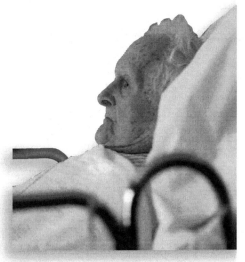

Some hospitalized patients are at risk of protein-energy malnutrition (PEM) because of poor dietary intakes and increased needs for recovery from surgery, trauma, or disease.

C. E. Folate

GLBAL PERSPECTIVE

How big is your foot print?

Growing evidence indicates that what we eat may affect not only our personal health but also that of the environment. Many scientists believe that meat-rich diets and the agricultural practices that support the production of food for these diets negatively affect the environment. For instance, producing food for nonvegetarian diets (especially beef-based diets) uses more water, fossil fuel energy, fertilizer, pesticides, and acres of farmland than vegetarian diets.[29] Meat-rich diets also cause greater emissions of greenhouse gases, such as carbon dioxide, methane, and nitrous oxide, which are associated with global warming.[30] Scientists are concerned that continued global warming may, in turn, decrease agricultural productivity, reduce farmers' incomes, and increase global food insecurity.[31]

Not all scientists agree with these findings and concerns, however. Some believe that consuming a small amount of dairy and/or meat may actually increase land use efficiency, thereby protecting environmental resources and promoting food security.[32] They point out that high-quality farmland is required to grow fruits, vegetables, and grains, whereas meat and dairy products can be produced on the more widely available, lower-quality land. Even though diets containing meat use more land, they can feed more people because of the greater availability of lower-quality farmland. It appears that diets have different "agricultural land footprints," depending on the amount of plant-based and animal-based food they contain. Supporters of mixed animal/vegetable–based diets point out that vegetarian diets often include tofu and other meat substitutes produced from soy, chickpeas, and lentils. Many meat substitutes are highly processed and require energy-intensive production methods. Thus, including small amounts of meat may offer both environmental and nutritional benefits.

Knowledge Check

1. How does kwashiorkor differ from marasmus?
2. Which individuals might be at greatest risk of PEM in the U.S.?
3. What areas of the world have the highest incidence of PEM?
4. Why might an excessive protein intake be harmful?

 ## 7.8 Food Protein Allergies

Allergies, including food allergies, involve responses of the immune system designed to eliminate foreign proteins (antigens). Food allergy responses occur when the body mistakenly reacts to a food as though it were a harmful invader. In some people, certain food components, typically proteins (called **allergens**), cause hypersensitivity reactions and trigger this response. These allergens stimulate white blood cells to produce antibodies (mostly the **immunoglobulin** IgE) that bind to antigens and cause the symptoms associated with an allergic reaction.[15]

Fortunately, most allergic reactions are mild, such as a runny nose, sneezing, itching skin, hives, or digestive upset (indigestion, nausea, vomiting, diarrhea). For those who are severely allergic, exposure to the allergenic food may cause a generalized life-threatening reaction involving all body systems (known as **anaphylaxis** or anaphylactic shock). Anaphylaxis causes decreased blood pressure and respiratory distress so severe that the person cannot breathe—death will occur without immediate medical help. In the U.S., allergic reactions result in 30,000 emergency room visits and 150 to 200 deaths per year.

The protein in any food can trigger an allergic reaction. However, 8 foods account for 90% of all food allergies: peanuts, tree nuts (e.g., walnuts and cashews), milk, eggs, fish, shellfish, soy, and wheat (Fig. 7-16). Other foods frequently identified as causing allergic reactions are meat and meat products, fruits, and cheese.

The only way to prevent allergic reactions is to avoid foods known to trigger reactions. Carefully reading food labels and asking questions when eating out are essential, perhaps lifesaving, steps for those with food allergies.[15] In addition, individuals preparing foods at home or in restaurants need to know their menu ingredients and take steps to ensure that foods

allergen Components, typically proteins (e.g., those in food), that induce a hypersensitive response, with excess production of certain immune system antibodies. Subsequent exposure to the same protein leads to allergic symptoms.[15]

immunoglobulins Proteins (also called antibodies) in the blood that are responsible for identifying and neutralizing antigens as well as pathogens that bind specifically to antigens.

that cause an allergic reaction in a person do not come in contact with the food to be served to that individual. Even trace amounts of an allergen can cause a reaction. To prevent cross-contact, anything that will be used to prepare an allergen-free meal (i.e., hands, workspace, pans, utensils, plates) should be washed thoroughly before preparing the allergen-free meal. Unlike foodborne illness pathogens, such as bacteria and viruses, cooking an allergenic food often does not render its allergens harmless.[16]

The prevalence of food allergies has increased in the last 20 years.[15] Although difficult to estimate, it appears that approximately 6 to 7% of children and 1 to 2% of adults have food allergies.[15] It is unclear why some people develop allergies and what steps might help decrease the risk of developing food allergies. Although some studies have shown that women can help prevent or delay the onset of food allergies in their child by avoiding peanuts and tree nuts during their pregnancy and lactation, currently it appears that maternal dietary restrictions do not play a significant role in preventing food allergies in their children.[15, 17] After the child is born, the following steps may help prevent food allergies.[9] These guidelines are especially important for families with a history of any type of allergy.

- Feed babies only breast milk or infant formula until they are at least 6 months old.
- Delay feeding infants cow's milk and milk products until infants are at least 1 year of age.
- Serve egg whites only after children reach age 2 years.
- Keep diets free of peanuts, tree nuts, fish, and shellfish until children are at least 3 years old.

Many young children with food allergies outgrow them.[15, 18] Thus, parents should not assume that the allergy will be long-lasting. Allergies to certain foods (e.g., milk, egg, soy, wheat) are more likely to be outgrown than are allergies to other foods (e.g., peanuts, tree nuts, fish, and shellfish).[15] Those with allergies may be tested by physicians periodically to determine whether they have outgrown the allergy. If so, the food(s) can be reintroduced into the diet and eaten safely.

CRITICAL THINKING

Jocelyn developed hives and swelling of her lips, tongue, and throat after eating her friend's homemade chili. She learned that her friend used peanut butter as a special ingredient. How could this have caused Jocelyn's symptoms?

People with hypersensitivity to certain foods can be tested to determine which food allergens cause their symptoms.

Figure 7-16 These foods account for the vast majority of all food allergies.

Peanut/tree nuts

Milk products

Soy

Wheat

Eggs

Fish/shellfish

▶ Food allergies and food intolerances are not the same. Food allergies cause an immune response as a result of exposure to certain food components, typically proteins. In contrast, food intolerances (see Chapter 4) are caused by an individual's inability to digest certain food components, usually due to low amounts of specific enzymes. Generally, larger amounts of an offending food are required to produce the symptoms of food intolerance than to trigger allergic symptoms. Food allergies tend to be far more life threatening than food intolerances.

▶ The American Academy of Allergy and Immunology has a 24-hour toll-free hot line (800-822-2762) to answer questions about food allergies and help direct people to specialists who treat allergy problems. Free information on food allergies is available by contacting The Food Allergy & Anaphylaxis Network at www.foodallergy.org.

7.9 Vegetarian Diets

Vegetarianism has evolved over the centuries from a necessity into an option. Today, approximately 2.5% of adults in the U.S. and 4% of adults in Canada follow a vegetarian diet. Additionally, 20 to 25% of Americans report that they eat at least 4 meatless meals a week.[5] Most people choose vegetarian diets for religious, philosophical, ecological, or health-related reasons. For example, Hindus, Seventh-Day Adventists, and Trappist monks follow vegetarian diets as a part of their religious practices. Others adopt vegetarian practices because they are concerned with the economic and ecological impact of eating meat-based diets. They recognize that meat is not an efficient way of obtaining protein because it requires the use of approximately 40% of the world's grain production to raise meat-producing animals. Diets rich in fruits, vegetables, legumes, and grains frequently result in increased intakes of antioxidant nutrients (e.g., vitamins C and E and carotenoids), dietary fiber, and healthful phytochemicals and decreased intakes of saturated fat and cholesterol. Vegetarianism also may offer protection against obesity. Thus, the American Cancer Society, the World Cancer Research Fund, the American Heart Association, and the Heart and Stroke Foundation of Canada encourage plant-based diets to promote health and reduce risk of chronic disease.[5, 19-23]

The eating patterns of vegetarians can vary considerably, depending on the extent to which animal products are excluded. Vegans follow the most restrictive diet, as they eat only plant foods. Because they do not eat any animal foods, their diets may be low in high biological value protein, riboflavin, vitamin D, vitamin B-12, calcium, and zinc unless carefully planned.[5] Lacto-vegetarians are similar to vegans, because their diets exclude meat,

The amino acids in legumes are best used when combined with nuts, seeds, or grains.

Table 7-5 Food Plan for Vegetarians Based on MyPlate

| Food Group | MyPlate Servings | | Key Nutrients Supplied[c] |
	Lacto-vegetarian[a]	Vegan[b]	
Grains	5	6	Protein, thiamin, niacin, folate, vitamin E, zinc, magnesium, iron, fiber
Protein Foods (beans, nuts, seeds)	5	5	Protein, vitamin B-6, zinc, magnesium, fiber
Vegetables	2 (include 1 dark green daily)	2½ (include 1 dark green daily)	Vitamin A, vitamin C, folate, vitamin K, potassium, magnesium
Fruit	1½	1½	Vitamin A, vitamin C, folate
Milk Dairy	3	—	Protein, riboflavin, vitamin D, vitamin B-12, calcium
Fortified soy milk	—	3	Protein, riboflavin, vitamin D, vitamin B-12, calcium

[a]This plan contains about 75 grams of protein in 1650 kcal.

[b]This plan contains about 79 grams of protein in 1800 kcal.

[c]One serving of vitamin- and mineral-enriched ready-to-eat breakfast cereal is recommended to fill possible nutrient gaps. Alternatively, a balanced multivitamin and mineral supplement can be used. Vegans also may benefit from the use of fortified soy milk to provide calcium, vitamin D, and vitamin B-12.

poultry, eggs, and fish but differ in that they include dairy products in their diets. Lacto-ovo-vegetarians include eggs in their diets but avoid meat, poultry, and fish. These last 2 groups eat some animal foods, so their diets often contain ample amounts of nutrients that may be low or missing in strictly plant-based diets. However, to reduce the risk of nutrient deficiencies, all vegetarians need to follow nutritional recommendations (Table 7-5) when making daily food choices.[7, 24, 25]

Vegetarian diets require knowledge and creative planning to yield high-quality protein and other key nutrients without animal products. Earlier in this chapter, you learned about complementary proteins, whereby the essential amino acids deficient in one protein source are supplied by those of another consumed at the same meal or the next. Recall that many legumes are deficient in the essential amino acid methionine, whereas cereals are limited in lysine. Thus, eating a combination of legumes and cereals, such as beans and rice, will supply the body with adequate amounts of all essential amino acids. Variety is an especially important characteristic of a nutritious vegan diet.[25]

At the forefront of nutritional concerns for vegetarians are riboflavin, vitamins D and B-12, calcium, iron, and zinc.[5, 26, 27] A major source of riboflavin, vitamin D, and calcium in the typical North American diet is milk, which is omitted from the vegan diet. However, riboflavin can be obtained from green leafy vegetables, whole-grain breads and cereals, yeast, and legumes—components of most vegan diets. Alternate sources of vitamin D include fortified foods (e.g., soy milk) and dietary supplements, as well as regular sun exposure (see Chapter 15).

Calcium-fortified foods are the vegan's best option for obtaining calcium. These include fortified soy milk, fortified orange juice, calcium-rich tofu (check the label), and certain ready-to-eat breakfast cereals, breads, and snacks. Green leafy vegetables also contain calcium, but it is not well absorbed.[28] Dietary supplements provide another option for meeting calcium needs (see Chapter 12). It is important to read supplement labels and to plan supplement use carefully because a typical multivitamin and mineral supplement supplies only 25 to 45% of daily calcium needs.

Vitamin B-12 occurs naturally only in animal foods. Plants can contain soil or microbial contaminants that provide trace amounts of vitamin B-12, but these are negligible sources of the vitamin. Therefore, vegans need to eat food fortified with vitamin B-12 or take supplements to protect against deficiency.[26]

To obtain iron, vegans can consume whole-grain breads and cereals, dried fruits and nuts, and legumes.[5, 25] The iron in these foods is not absorbed as well as the iron in animal foods, but eating a good source of vitamin C with these foods enhances iron absorption (see Chapter 14).

Vegans can obtain zinc from whole-grain breads and cereals, nuts, and legumes. However, phytic acid and other substances in these foods limit zinc absorption. Grains are most nutritious when consumed as breads, because the leavening (rising of the bread dough) reduces the influence of phytic acid.[5]

Special Concerns for Infants and Children

Infants and children are at highest risk of nutrient deficiencies as a result of poorly planned vegetarian diets.[5] However, with the use of complementary proteins and good sources of the problem nutrients discussed earlier, the energy, protein, vitamin, and mineral needs of vegetarian and vegan infants and children can be met. The most common nutritional concerns for infants and children following vegetarian and vegan diets are deficiencies of iron, vitamin B-12, vitamin D, zinc, and calcium.[5, 7, 27]

Vegetarian and vegan diets tend to be high in bulky, high-fiber, low-calorie foods that cause fullness. Although this side effect can be a welcome advantage for adults, children have a small stomach volume and relatively high nutrient needs for their size and may feel full before their energy needs are met. For this reason, the fiber content of a child's diet may need to be decreased by replacing high-fiber sources with some refined grain products, fruit juices,

Vegetarian versions of common foods are becoming more readily available in groceries and restaurants.

CASE STUDY FOLLOW-UP

Bethany's dietary intake for this day is not as healthy as it could be because it does not come close to following recommendations. Many of the components of a healthy vegetarian diet—whole grains, nuts, soy products, beans, 2 to 4 servings of fruit, and 3 to 5 servings of vegetables per day—are missing. With so few fruits and vegetables, her diet also is low in the many phytochemicals that may provide numerous health benefits. It is apparent that Bethany has not yet learned to implement the concept of complementary proteins, so the quality of the protein in her diet is low. Unless she makes a more informed effort at diet planning, Bethany will not reap the health benefits she had hoped for when she chose to follow a vegetarian diet.

250　**PART 2**　Energy-Yielding Nutrients and Alcohol

Take Action

Protein and the Vegan

Alana is excited about the possible health benefits of her new vegan diet. However, she is concerned that her diet may not contain enough protein, vitamins, and minerals. Use a nutrient database (see Appendix N), a nutrient analysis computer program, or a website (www.nal.usda.gov/fnic/foodcomp/search) to calculate her protein intake and see if her concerns are valid.

Breakfast	**Protein (g)**
Calcium-fortified orange juice, 1 cup	
Soy milk, 1 cup	
Fortified bran flakes, 1 cup	
Banana, medium	
Snack	
Calcium-enriched granola bar	
Lunch	
Garden Veggie Burger, 4 oz	
Whole-wheat bun	
Mustard, 1 tbsp	
Soy cheese, 1 oz	
Apple, medium	
Green leaf lettuce, 1½ cups	
Peanuts, 1 oz	
Sunflower seeds, ¼ cup	
Tomato slices, 2	
Mushrooms, 3	
Vinaigrette salad dressing, 2 tbsp	
Iced tea	
Dinner	
Kidney beans, ½ cup	
Brown rice, ¾ cup	
Fortified margarine, 2 tbsp	
Mixed vegetables, ¼ cup	
Hot tea	
Snack	
Strawberries, ½ cup	
Angel food cake, 1 small slice	
Soy milk, ½ cup	
Total Protein: _____	

> Alana's diet contained 2150 kcal, with _____ g (you fill in) of protein (is this adequate for her?), 57 g of total dietary fat (only 9 g of which came from saturated fat), and 50 g of fiber. Her vitamin and mineral intake with respect to those of concern to vegetarians—vitamin B-12, vitamin D, calcium, iron, and zinc—met her needs.

and peeled fruit. Including concentrated sources of energy, such as fortified soy milk, nuts, dried fruits, and avocados, can help meet calorie and nutrient needs.

Overall, vegetarian and vegan diets can be appropriate during infancy and childhood. However, to achieve normal growth and ensure adequate intake of all nutrients, these diets must be implemented with knowledge and, ideally, professional guidance.[5, 25]

Knowledge Check

1. How does a vegan diet differ from a lacto-vegetarian diet?
2. Which nutrients are likely to be low in a vegan diet?
3. What are 2 nutritional risks for children on vegetarian diets?

Summary

7.1   Amino acids, the building blocks of proteins, contain a usable form of nitrogen for humans. Of the 20 amino acids needed by the body, 9 must be provided in the diet (essential). The other 11 can be synthesized by the body (nonessential) from amino acids in the body's amino acid pool. High-quality, also called complete, proteins contain ample amounts of all 9 essential amino acids. Foods derived from animal sources provide high-quality, or complete, protein. Lower-quality, or incomplete, proteins lack sufficient amounts of 1 or more essential amino acids. This is typical of plant foods. Different types of plant foods eaten together often complement each other's amino acid deficits, thereby providing high-quality protein in the diet.

7.2   Individual amino acids are linked together to form proteins. The sequential order of amino acids determines the protein's ultimate shape and function. This order is directed by DNA in the cell nucleus. Diseases, such as sickle-cell anemia, can occur if the amino acids are incorrect in a polypeptide chain. When the 3-dimensional shape of the protein is unfolded(denatured) by treatment with heat, acid or alkaline solutions, or other processes, the protein also loses its biological activity.

7.3   Almost all animal products are rich sources of protein. The high quality of these proteins means that they can be easily converted into body proteins. Legumes, nuts, seeds, and grains are good sources of plant protein. Protein quality can be measured by determining the extent to which the body can retain the nitrogen contained in the amino acids absorbed. This is called biological value. In addition, the balance of essential amino acids in a food can be compared with an ideal pattern to determine chemical score. When multiplied by the degree of digestibility, the chemical score yields the Protein Digestibility Corrected Amino Acid Score (PDCAAS).

7.4   The adult RDA for protein is 0.8 g per kg of healthy body weight. For a typical 154 lb (70 kg) person, this corresponds to 56 g of protein daily; for a 125 lb (57 kg) person, this corresponds to 46 g/day. The North American diet generally supplies plenty of protein: men typically consume about 100 g

of protein daily, and women consume about 65 g. These intakes are also of sufficient quality to support body functions.

7.5   Protein digestion begins in the stomach, where proteins are broken down into shorter polypeptide chains of amino acids. In the small intestine, these polypeptide chains are digested into dipeptides and amino acids, which are absorbed by the small intestine, where any remaining peptides are broken down into amino acids. Absorbed amino acids then travel via the portal vein to the liver.

7.6   Important body components—such as muscles, connective tissue, transport proteins, enzymes, hormones, and antibodies—are made of proteins. Proteins also provide carbon skeletons, which can be used to synthesize glucose when necessary.

7.7   Undernutrition can lead to protein-energy malnutrition in the form of kwashiorkor or marasmus. Kwashiorkor results primarily from an inadequate energy intake with a severe protein deficit, often accompanied by disease and infection. Kwashiorkor frequently occurs when a child is weaned from human milk and fed mostly starchy gruels. Marasmus results from extreme starvation—a negligible intake of both protein and energy. Marasmus commonly occurs during famine, especially in infants. These conditions have been noted in some North Americans with cancer, AIDS, malabsorption disease, anorexia nervosa, alcoholism, or limited income and resources to obtain food. High-protein diets (above 35% of energy intake) do not provide additional health benefits. They are associated with dehydration, overburdening of the kidneys' capacity to excrete nitrogen wastes, increased risk of cardiovascular disease and certain cancers, increased urinary calcium loss, and risk of amino acid imbalance and toxicity.

7.8   Food allergies involve immune system responses designed to eliminate allergens that the body mistakenly reacts to as though they were harmful invaders. Symptoms range from mild to life threatening. The only way to prevent reactions is to avoid foods known to trigger allergic reactions.

252   **PART 2** Energy-Yielding Nutrients and Alcohol

7.9 Vegetarian diets are becoming more popular as individuals recognize the possible health benefits of plant-based diets. Low intakes of riboflavin, vitamins D and B-12, calcium, iron, and zinc are of greatest concern in vegetarian diets. Vegetarian diets require knowledge and creative planning to obtain high-quality protein and other key nutrients but can be nutritionally adequate when guidelines are followed.

Study Questions

1. Essential amino acids must be supplied by the diet because the body cannot synthesize them in adequate amounts.

   a. true   **b.** false

2. A process involved in the synthesis of nonessential amino acids is called _____.

   a. ketogenesis   **c.** transamination
   b. gluconeogenesis   **d.** supplementation

3. The carbon skeleton of an amino acid is the portion remaining after an amino group has been removed.

   a. true   **b.** false

4. Which of the following is classified as a complete protein?

   a. kidney beans   **c.** whole-grain bread
   b. fat-free milk   **d.** corn tortillas

5. The sequential order of amino acids in a polypeptide chain is called the _____.

   a. primary structure   **c.** tertiary structure
   b. secondary structure   **d.** quaternary structure

6. Which of the following is a rich source of protein?

   a. citrus fruits   **c.** enriched grains
   b. dark, leafy greens   **d.** barbequed chicken

7. Which of the following is *not* a means of determining the protein quality of a food?

   a. biological value   **c.** protein efficiency ratio
   b. chemical score   **d.** complementary score

8. Hospitalized patients recovering from illness or trauma usually need additional protein to attain positive nitrogen balance.

   a. true   **b.** false

9. Proteins are involved in all of the following functions *except*

   _____.

   a. providing energy   **c.** promoting bowel health
   b. aiding in immune function **d.** providing cell structure

10. Which of the following population groups is at increased risk of PEM?

    a. college athletes   **c.** the elderly
    b. obese individuals   **d.** adolescents

11. Many children with kwashiorkor maintain some muscle and subcutaneous fat.

    a. true   **b.** false

12. Which of the following is *not* a usual characteristic of marasmus?

    a. edema   **c.** impaired growth
    b. severe weight loss **d.** muscle wasting

13. Which of the following is associated with excessive protein intakes?

    a. dehydration   **c.** diarrhea
    b. anemia   **d.** diabetes

14. Which of the following foods is a common cause of food allergies?

    a. peanuts   **c.** eggs
    b. shellfish   **d.** all of the above

15. Which of the following nutrients would most likely be low in a vegan diet?

    a. vitamin C   **c.** vitamin B-12
    b. thiamin   **d.** dietary fiber

16. Why is it important for essential acids lost from the body to be replaced by the diet?

17. Explain the process for synthesizing nonessential amino acids.

18. What is a limiting amino acid? Explain why this concept is a concern in a vegetarian diet.

19. Describe factors that determine whether a person is in nitrogen equilibrium.

20. Describe the process of protein digestion from ingestion to excretion.

21. Describe the functions of protein.

22. Outline the major differences between kwashiorkor and marasmus.

23. What is a food allergy?

Answer Key: 1-a; 2-c; 3-a; 4-b; 5-a; 6-d; 7-d; 8-a; 9-c; 10-c; 11-a; 12-a; 13-a; 14-d; 15-c; 16-refer to Section 7.1; 17-refer to Section 7.2; 18-refer to Sections 7.3 and 7.9; 19-refer to Section 7.4; 20-refer to Section 7.5; 21-refer to Section 7.6; 22-refer to Section 7.7; 23-refer to Section 7.8

Websites

To learn more about the topics covered in this chapter, visit these websites.

Food Allergies

www.foodallergy.org

www.foodallergy.rutgers.edu

Vegetarianism

www.ivu.org

www.vrg.org

www.vegetariannutrition.net

fnic.nal.usda.gov

www.vegdining.com

References

1. Gropper SS and others. Protein. 5th ed. In: *Advanced nutrition and human metabolism.* Belmont, CA: Wadsworth, Cengage Learning; 2009.

2. Balke E , Scherer A. Sickle cell disease. *CMAJ.* 2012;184:E201.

3. Institute of Medicine, Food and Nutrition Board. *Dietary Reference Intakes for energy, carbohydrate, fiber, fat, fatty acids, cholesterol, protein, and amino acids.* Washington, DC: National Academy Press; 2002.

4. U.S. Department of Agriculture. *Nutrient content of the U.S. food supply.* Research Report 57. Washington, DC: U.S. Department of Agriculture; 2007.

5. Marsh K and others. Health implications of a vegetarian diet: a review. *Am J Lifestyle Med.* 2011: DOI: 10.1177/1559827611425762.

6. Wu AH and others. Epidemiology of soy exposures and breast cancer risk. *Br J Cancer.* 2009;98:9.

7. Craig WJ, Mangels AR. Position of the American Dietetic Association: Vegetarian diets. *J Am Diet Assoc.* 2009;109:1266.

8. Rimbach G and others. Dietary isoflavones in the prevention of cardiovascular disease—A molecular perspective. *Food Chem Toxicol.* 2009;46:1308.

9. Sicherer SH, Sampson H. Food allergy. *J Allergy Clin Immunol.* 2010;125:S116.

10. Christian P. Impact of the economic crisis and increase in food prices on child mortality: Exploring nutritional pathways. *J Nutr.* 2010;140:177S.

11. Pencharz PB and others. An approach to defining the upper safe limits of amino acid intake. *J Nutr.* 2008;138:1996S.

12. Aparicio M. Protein intake and chronic kidney disease: Literature review, 2003 to 2008. *J Renal Nutr.* 2009;19:5S.

13. Frank H and others. Effect of short-term high-protein compared with normal-protein diets on renal hemodynamics and associated variables in healthy young men. *Am J Clin Nutr.* 2009;90:1509.

14. Bastide NM and others. Heme iron from meat and risk of colorectal cancer: a metab-analysis and a review of the mechanisms involved. *Cancer Prev Res.* 2011;4:177.

15. Boyce JA and others. Guidelines for the diagnosis and management of food allergy in the United States. Report of the NIAID-sponsored Expert Panel. *J Am Diet Assoc.* 2011;111:117.

16. Kim SS, Sicherer SH. Living with food allergy: allergen avoidance. *Food Allergy Child.* 2011;59:459.

17. Greer FR and others. Effects of early nutritional interventions on the development of atopic disease in infants and children: The role of maternal dietary restriction, breastfeeding, timing of introduction of complementary foods, and hydrolyzed formulas. *Pediatrics.* 2008;121:183.

18. Slomski A. Treatment rather than avoidance may be within reach for children with food allergies. *JAMA.* 2012;307:345.

19. Appel LJ and others. ASH Position: Dietary approaches to lower blood pressure. *J Clin Hyperten.* 2009;11:358.

20. Jenkins DJA and others. The effect of a plant-based low-carbohydrate ("Eco-Atkins") diet on body weight and blood lipid concentrations in hyperlipidemic subjects. *Archives Intern Med.* 2009;169:1046.

21. Stitcher MA and others. Reducing heart disease through the vegetarian diet using primary prevention. *J Am Acad Nurs Pract.* 2010;22:134.

22. Thedford K and Sudha R. A vegetarian diet for weight management. *J Am Diet Assoc.* 2011;111:816.

23. Sabate J, Wein M. Vegetarian diets and childhood obesity prevention. *Am J Clin Nutr.* 2010;91:1525S.

24. Morgan SL. Nutrition and bone: It is more than calcium and vitamin D. *Women's Health.* 2009;5:727.

25. School of Public Health. *Vegetarian Food Pyramid.* Loma Linda, CA: Loma Linda University; 2008.

26. Herrmann W and others. Enhanced bone metabolism in vegetarians—The role of vitamin B12 deficiency. *Clin Chem Lab Med.* 2009;47:1381.

27. Sanders TA. DHA status of vegetarians. *Prostaglandins Leukot Essent Fatty Acids.* 2009;81:137.

28. Weaver CM. Should dairy be recommended as part of a healthy vegetarian diet? *Am J Clin Nutr.* 2009; 89:1634S.

29. Marlow HJ and others. Diet and the environment: Does what you eat matter? *Am J Clin Nutr.* 2009;89:1699S.

30. Carlsson-Kanyama A, Gonzalez AD. Potential contributions of food consumption patterns to climate change. *Am J Clin Nutr.* 2009;89:1704S.

31. Battisti DS, Naylor RL. Historical warnings of future food insecurity with unprecedented seasonal heat. *Science.* 2009;323:240.

32. Peters CJ and others. Testing a complete-diet model for estimating the land resource requirements of food consumption and agricultural carrying capacity: The New York State example. *Renew Ag Food Sys.* 2007;22:145.

Malaysia's tiny pen-tailed tree-shrew lives on bertam palm nectar, which naturally ferments into a frothy, beer-like beverage with an alcohol content as high as 3.8%. These animals consume enough to be considered legally drunk but do not become intoxicated. Scientists believe this shrew must have an effective mechanism for metabolizing alcohol and may provide insights into how alcohol tolerance in humans first evolved. Plantain squirrels, several types of rats, and slow lorises also consume this fermented nectar. Learn more at **www.pnas.org/content/105/30/10426.abstract.**

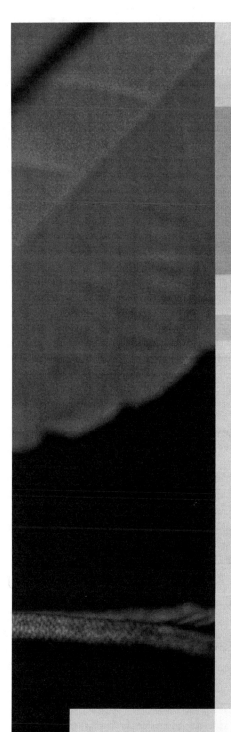

8 *Alcohol*

Student Learning Outcomes

After studying this chapter, you will be able to

1. Describe the sources of alcohol and the calories it provides.

2. Define standard sizes of alcoholic beverages and the term
   moderate drinking.

3. Summarize how alcoholic beverages are produced.

4. Outline the process of alcohol absorption, transport, and metabolism.

5. Define binge drinking and explain how it increases the risk of
   alcohol poisoning.

6. Explain how alcohol consumption affects blood alcohol concentration.

7. Describe guidelines for using alcohol safely.

8. Discuss potential benefits of using alcohol.

9. Summarize the risks of alcohol consumption.

10. Describe the effects of chronic alcohol use on the body
    and nutritional status.

11. List the signs of alcohol dependency and abuse.

12. Outline the methods used to diagnose alcohol abuse.

13. List the strategies and resources available for the treatment
    of alcoholism.

BEER, WINE, AND HARD LIQUOR, or spirits, are consumed by about 60% of the adult population in North America.[1] The alcohol in these beverages, when averaged across the population, provides about 3% of the total energy intake. Although not an essential nutrient, alcohol contributes about 7 kcal/g of energy to the diet.

For some individuals, alcohol adds to the enjoyment of a meal or social times shared with friends and family. For others, moderate alcohol use may help relieve tensions and enhance relaxation. In middle-aged and older adults, moderate alcohol consumption may even reduce the risk of cardiovascular disease. Unfortunately, moderate use of alcohol can escalate to alcohol dependence and abuse in susceptible individuals.

Alcohol is a **narcotic,** an agent that reduces sensations and consciousness, and a central nervous system depressant. It is the most commonly abused drug in North America. The harmful effects of alcohol are well known. Alcohol abuse can cause motor vehicle accidents, destroy families and friendships, and encourage violence, suicide, rape, and other aggressive behaviors. It also can cause multiple nutrient deficiencies. Although too much alcohol damages almost every organ in the body, the liver and brain are especially vulnerable to its toxic effects.

256 **PART 2** Energy-Yielding Nutrients and Alcohol

The following servings of each type of alcoholic beverage provide the same amount of alcohol (about 15 g): wine—5 oz, hard liquor—1.5 oz, beer or wine cooler—12 oz. In determining a safe level of intake, it is important to observe these standard serving sizes.

▶ A survey of 80 restaurants and bars showed that wine, beer, and mixed drinks often were at least 50% larger than standard sizes.[2] This can make it difficult to keep alcohol intake at a safe level.

Alcohol abuse, behind smoking and obesity, is the third leading cause of preventable death in adults. Because alcohol is so widely consumed and its abuse touches many lives, this chapter will examine this substance in detail. It will explore the sources of alcohol, the production of alcohol, the metabolism of alcohol, and the health concerns related to intakes of alcohol.

8.1 Sources of Alcohol

The form of alcohol we consume, chemically known as ethanol (CH_3CH_2OH), is supplied mostly by beverages such as beer, wine, distilled spirits (hard liquor, such as vodka, tequila, and rum), liqueurs, cordials, and hard cider. It also is sometimes used as an ingredient in foods, such as chicken cooked in wine (coq au vin), flaming desserts, and chocolate candy filling.

As shown in Table 8-1, beverages vary in alcohol and calorie content. Most beers are about 5% alcohol or less, although some beers exceed 11% alcohol. Wines generally range in alcohol content from approximately 5 to 14%. Fortified wines (wines that have spirits added to increase their alcohol content) typically contain 15 to 22% alcohol. Distilled wine spirits, such as brandy, contain more than 22% alcohol. For hard liquor (distilled spirits), alcohol content is listed by "proof" rather than by percentage. The proof is actually twice the percentage of alcohol content. Thus, an 80-proof vodka or gin is 40% alcohol.

A standard drink is usually defined as the size that provides approximately 15 g of alcohol. In general, this equates to a 12-ounce beer, 10-ounce wine cooler, 5-ounce glass of wine, or 1.5-ounce pour of hard liquor. These serving sizes are used as the basis for recommendations of moderate and excessive drinking. Many individuals are not aware of these definitions of

Table 8-1 Alcohol and Energy Content of Alcoholic Beverages			
Beverage	**Amount (fl oz)**	**Alcohol (g)**	**Energy (kcal)**
Beer			
Regular	12	12	150
Light	12	10	75–100
Distilled Spirits			
Gin, rum, vodka, bourbon, tequila, whiskey (80 proof)	1.5	14	95
Liqueurs	1.5	14	160
Wine			
Red	5	14	100
White	5	14	100
Dessert, sweet	5	23	225
Rose	5	14	100
Mixed Drinks			
Martini	3.5	32	220
Manhattan	3.5	30	225
Whiskey sour	3.5	17	135
Margarita (frozen)	8	20	175
Rum and cola	8	15	170

serving sizes—some may consider a 20-ounce glass of beer or an 8-ounce glass of wine to be a "drink," when, in fact, these servings are both closer to 2 drinks. Drinks served in bars and restaurants may vary considerably from the defined standard drink serving.

Most guidelines for "moderate alcohol intake" suggest no more than 1 standard-size drink per day for women and no more than 2 per day for men. This does not mean that one can abstain from drinking during the week and then safely consume 7 or more drinks on a single day. As discussed in a later section, this is defined as binge drinking, and it can have serious consequences.

Production of Alcoholic Beverages

The alcohol we consume is produced by fermentation. The process of fermenting foods to produce mead (fermented honey), beer, wine, and other alcoholic products dates back thousands of years. Grains, cereals, fruits, honey, milk, potatoes, and other carbohydrate-rich foods can be used to make alcoholic beverages.

Fermentation occurs when yeast, a microorganism, converts carbohydrates to alcohol and carbon dioxide. The carbohydrate must be in the form of simple sugars, such as maltose or glucose, for yeast to use it as food. If the carbohydrate is a starch, such as that found in cereal grain seeds (e.g., barley), it must be broken down to simpler forms, or "malted," before fermentation can occur. During malting, the grain seeds are allowed to sprout; the sprouting process produces enzymes in the seed that break starches into simple sugars. Each molecule of glucose that is fermented produces 2 molecules of ethanol, 2 molecules of carbon dioxide, and 2 molecules of water. Additionally, the reaction yields energy that the yeast can use.

Fermentation begins when a food rich in simple sugars, yeast, and water are combined and left at room temperature. During the first stage, the yeast cells multiply, using the sugars for energy, and produce small amounts of alcohol. When the oxygen in the container holding the mixture of water, yeast, and sugars is depleted, the second stage begins, during which the yeast ferments the remaining sugar to produce alcohol and carbon dioxide under anaerobic (without oxygen) conditions. After fermentation has ceased (when the sugar is used up or the alcohol content is high enough to inactivate the yeast), the product can be finished in a variety of ways, or the alcohol itself can be recovered from the product by **distilling** it into spirits, such as gin or whiskey.

A Biochemist's View

Ethanol

Distilled spirits, used to make many popular drinks, have the highest alcohol content of the alcohol-containing beverages.

Knowledge Check

1. What amounts of beer, wine, and hard liquor each contain 15 g of alcohol?
2. What ingredients are required for fermentation?
3. How does the proof of an alcoholic beverage (e.g., vodka or tequila) relate to its alcohol content?

CASE STUDY

Charles, a college student, has noticed that his pants are getting hard to button. A quick check on the scale in the gym confirms a 7-pound weight gain over the last 12 weeks. The main change in Charles's diet is his alcohol intake—he now typically drinks 5 or 6 12-ounce beers on Friday and Saturday nights and drinks another 3 or 4 beers during the week. How many extra calories per week is Charles consuming? If each pound of weight gain results from a surplus of 3500 kcal, can Charles's weight gain be explained by his beer consumption?

distill To separate 2 or more liquids that have 2 different boiling points. Alcohol is boiled off and the vapors are collected and condensed. Distillation produces a high alcohol content in hard liquor.

8.2 Alcohol Absorption and Metabolism

Alcohol, unlike carbohydrates, protein, and fat, requires no digestion. It also does not need specific transport mechanisms or receptors to enter cells. Therefore, it is absorbed rapidly throughout the digestive tract by simple diffusion. The stomach absorbs about 20% of ingested alcohol, with the remainder being absorbed in the duodenum and jejunum. When food is consumed with alcohol, absorption is slowed. Larger meals with a high fat content leave the stomach more slowly, thereby slowing the absorption of any alcohol consumed. In contrast, alcohol consumed on an empty stomach is absorbed quickly from the stomach and small intestine into the bloodstream.

Alcohol is readily dispersed throughout the body because alcohol is found wherever water is distributed in the body. Alcohol moves easily through the cell membranes; however, as it does, it damages proteins in the membranes.[3]

Alcohol Metabolism

Because alcohol cannot be stored in the body, it has absolute priority in metabolism as a fuel source, taking precedence over other energy sources, such as carbohydrate. At low to moderate intakes, alcohol is metabolized through a series of reactions called the alcohol dehydrogenase (ADH) pathway.[4] This pathway uses 2 enzymes (alcohol dehydrogenase and aldehyde dehydrogenase) to convert ethanol to the toxic intermediate compound acetaldehyde and then to acetyl-CoA. Acetyl-CoA is converted to carbon dioxide and water or can be used for fatty acid synthesis (see Chapter 9). Although the cells lining the stomach metabolize 10 to 30% of alcohol via the ADH pathway, the liver is the chief site for alcohol metabolism. When a person drinks moderate to excessive amounts of alcohol, the ADH pathway cannot keep up with the demand to metabolize all the alcohol. Under these circumstances, the liver activates the microsomal ethanol oxidizing system (MEOS) to help metabolize alcohol. The MEOS pathway produces the same intermediates as the ADH pathway, but it requires energy to function (see Chapter 9). As a person's alcohol intake increases over time, the MEOS becomes increasingly active, allowing for more efficient metabolism of alcohol and a greater tolerance to alcohol. This means that increasing amounts of alcohol are necessary to produce the same effects.[4]

The MEOS also metabolizes drugs and other substances foreign to the body. Activation of the MEOS by excessive alcohol intake reduces the liver's capacity for metabolizing drugs because the metabolism of alcohol takes priority.[3] Thus, MEOS activation by alcohol increases the potential for drug interactions and toxicities.

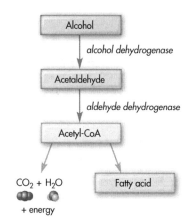

The alcohol dehydrogenase pathway of alcohol metabolism.

Women are smaller, have less body water, and have less alcohol dehydrogenase in their stomachs. This makes them more susceptible than men to the detrimental effects of alcohol.

Table 8-2 Alcohol Metabolism Summary

Alcohol Metabolic Pathway	Main Location of Pathway Activity	Alcohol Intake That Activates Pathway	Extent of Participation in Alcohol Metabolism
Alcohol dehydrogenase pathway (ADH)	Stomach Liver (mostly)	Low to moderate intake	Major role (metabolizes about 90% of alcohol)
Microsomal ethanol oxidizing system (MEOS)	Liver	Moderate to excessive intake	Role increases in importance with increasing alcohol intake levels
Catalase pathway	Liver Other cells	Moderate to excessive intake	Minor

The third metabolic pathway for metabolizing alcohol—the catalase pathway—in the liver and other cells makes a minor contribution to alcohol metabolism in comparison with the alcohol dehydrogenase pathway and the MEOS. Table 8-2 summarizes alcohol metabolism.

The 3 metabolic pathways (ADH, MEOS, and catalase) metabolize nearly all the alcohol consumed. Only a small percentage (2%–10%) of alcohol intake is excreted unmetabolized through the lungs, urine, and sweat.[4]

Factors Affecting Alcohol Metabolism

The key to alcohol metabolism lies in one's ability to produce the enzymes used in the alcohol dehydrogenase pathway because this pathway metabolizes about 90% of the alcohol consumed.[4] Ethnicity, gender, and age affect the production and activity of enzymes in the alcohol dehydrogenase pathway. For instance, many individuals of Asian descent have normal to high alcohol dehydrogenase enzyme activity, allowing a very rapid conversion of alcohol by the first enzyme (alcohol dehydrogenase), but they have very low activity of the second enzyme (aldehyde dehydrogenase) needed to complete alcohol breakdown. The resulting buildup of acetaldehyde commonly causes flushing, dizziness, nausea, headaches, rapid heartbeat (tachycardia), and rapid breathing (hyperventilation). These reactions can be so severe that it's uncomfortable to drink more or even at all.[4, 5]

Compared with men, women produce less of the alcohol dehydrogenase enzyme in the cells that line their stomachs—as a result, women absorb about 30 to 35% more unmetabolized alcohol from the stomach directly into the bloodstream. Another gender-related factor is that, in comparison with men, women are generally smaller in body size, have more body fat, and have less total body water. As a result, alcohol becomes more concentrated in the blood and body tissues of a woman than in a similar-size man because alcohol can be diluted by water, but not by adipose tissue. For these reasons, a woman becomes intoxicated on less alcohol than a similar-size man.

Other factors that can affect alcohol metabolism include the alcohol content of the beverage, the amount of alcohol consumed, and the individual's usual alcohol intake.[5] Compared with an occasional drinker, the MEOS is more active in individuals who drink large amounts of alcohol regularly, which increases the chronic drinker's alcohol metabolism as well as tolerance.

Rate of Alcohol Metabolism

The body is fairly well equipped to metabolize moderate amounts of alcohol. A social drinker who weighs 150 pounds (about 70 kg) and has normal liver function metabolizes about 5 to 7 g of alcohol per hour. This is the amount in about half of a standard-size drink. When the rate of alcohol consumption exceeds the liver's metabolic capacity, blood alcohol levels rise and the symptoms of intoxication appear as the brain and central nervous system are exposed to alcohol (Table 8-3).[6]

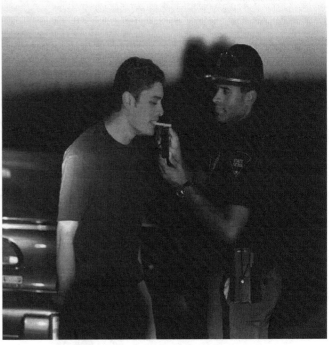

One is legally intoxicated at a blood alcohol concentration of 0.08% in the U.S. and Canada. However, for many individuals, driving is often noticeably impaired at blood alcohol concentrations of 0.02% to 0.05%.

Table 8-3 **Blood Alcohol Concentration (BAC) and Symptoms**		
BAC	**Behaviors**	**Impairments**
.01–.06	• Relaxation • Sense of well-being • Loss of inhibition • Lowered alertness • Joy	• Thought • Judgment • Coordination • Concentration
.06–.10	• Blunted feelings • Disinhibition • Extroversion • Diminished sexual pleasure	• Reflexes • Reasoning • Depth perception • Distance acuity • Peripheral vision • Glare recovery

.11–.20	• Overexpression of emotions
	• Emotional swings
	  • Angry or sad
	  • Boisterous
		• Reaction time
		• Gross motor control
		• Walking (staggering)
		• Speech (slurred)

.21–.29	• Stupor • Loss of understanding • Loss of sensations	• Gross motor control • Consciousness loss • Memory (blackouts)
.30–.39	• Severe depression • Unconsciousness • Possible death	• Bladder function • Breathing • Heart rate
>.40	• Unconsciousness • Death	• Breathing • Heart rate

260 **PART 2** Energy-Yielding Nutrients and Alcohol

	Effect on Women									Drinks	Effect on Men								
Body weight in pounds	90	100	120	140	160	180	200	220	240		100	120	140	160	180	200	220	240	**Body weight in pounds**
ONLY SAFE DRIVING LIMIT	.00	.00	.00	.00	.00	.00	.00	.00	.00	0	.00	.00	.00	.00	.00	.00	.00	.00	**ONLY SAFE DRIVING LIMIT**
DRIVING SKILLS SIGNIFICANTLY AFFECTED	.05	.05	.04	.03	.03	.03	.02	.02	.02	1	.04	.03	.03	.02	.02	.02	.02	.02	**DRIVING SKILLS SIGNIFICANTLY AFFECTED**
LEGALLY INTOXICATED	.10	.09	.08	.07	.06	.05	.05	.04	.04	2	.08	.06	.05	.05	.04	.04	.03	.03	
	.15	.14	.11	.11	.09	.08	.07	.06	.06	3	.11	.09	.08	.07	.06	.06	.05	.05	
	.20	.18	.15	.13	.11	.10	.09	.08	.08	4	.15	.12	.11	.09	.08	.08	.07	.06	
	.25	.23	.19	.16	.14	.13	.11	.10	.09	5	.19	.16	.13	.12	.11	.09	.09	.08	**LEGALLY INTOXICATED**
DEATH POSSIBLE	.30	.27	.23	.19	.17	.15	.14	.12	.11	6	.23	.19	.16	.14	.13	.11	.10	.09	
	.35	.32	.27	.23	.20	.18	.16	.14	.13	7	.26	.22	.19	.16	.15	.13	.12	.11	
	.40	.36	.30	.26	.23	.20	.18	.17	.15	8	.30	.25	.21	.19	.17	.15	.14	.13	**DEATH POSSIBLE**
	.45	.41	.34	.29	.26	.23	.20	.19	.17	9	.34	.28	.24	.21	.19	.17	.15	.14	
	.51	.45	.38	.32	.28	.25	.23	.21	.19	10	.38	.31	.27	.23	.21	.19	.17	.16	

Approximate blood alcohol percentage   Approximate blood alcohol percentage

Figure 8-1 Approximate relationship between alcohol consumption and blood alcohol concentration (units are % or mg of alcohol per 100 ml of blood). Note that effects can vary among people and whether food also is consumed. A blood alcohol concentration of 0.02 begins to impair driving. One is legally intoxicated at a blood alcohol concentration of 0.08 in the U.S. and Canada. Blood alcohol concentrations exceeding 0.30 can cause death.

CRITICAL THINKING

Kevin went out with his friends to celebrate the end of the semester. Over an hour's time, he had 4 beers. Kevin weighs approximately 160 lb. According to Figure 8-1, what would Kevin's blood alcohol level be? Is this within a legally safe limit to drive?

Blood alcohol concentrations can be determined by measuring the amount of alcohol excreted through the lungs because the alcohol content of exhaled air and blood are directly related (Fig. 8-1). The constant relationship between the alcohol content of blood and that of exhaled air makes it possible to use breathalyzer tests as a legal basis for defining alcohol impairment and intoxication.

If blood alcohol levels rise high enough, the person experiences acute alcohol toxicity, also known as alcohol poisoning (Table 8-4). This dangerous condition requires immediate medical treatment—left untreated, alcohol poisoning can cause respiratory failure and death. Inhalation of vomit also can result in death

Although many young adults do not recognize the true impact of binge-drinking habits, it poses a risk to their nutritional status, overall health, and safety.

Table 8-4 Signs and Symptoms of Alcohol Poisoning

- Confusion, stupor
- Vomiting
- Low blood sugar (hypoglycemia)
- Severe dehydration
- Seizures
- Slow or irregular breathing and heartbeat
- Blue-tinged or pale skin
- Low body temperature (hypothermia)
- Unconsciousness

Call 911 or your local emergency number if you suspect alcohol poisoning and the person cannot be roused or is unconscious. If the person is conscious, you can call 1-800-222-1222 to be routed to your local poison control center for further instructions.

and has occurred at levels lower than those that cause alcohol poisoning. The risk of consuming toxic levels of alcohol is greater when drinking distilled spirits because the higher alcohol content makes it easier to ingest more alcohol in less volume and less time than with beer or wine. **Binge drinking,** defined as having 4 or more drinks for females and 5 or more drinks for males on a single occasion, also increases the risk of alcohol poisoning.

▶ The narcotic effects of alcohol begin soon after it enters the bloodstream. Within minutes, alcohol inhibits nerve cells in the brain. If drinking continues, rising blood alcohol impairs speech, vision, balance, and judgment. Extremely high blood alcohol content can lead to cardiac and respiratory failure.

Knowledge Check

1. How does the body metabolize low to moderate amounts and large amounts of alcohol?
2. What factors affect alcohol metabolism?
3. How quickly can most people metabolize 1 alcoholic beverage?
4. Why does binge drinking increase the risk of alcohol poisoning?

8.3 Alcohol Consumption

About 62% of North American adults consume alcohol. Approximately 44% are light drinkers (consuming 3 or fewer drinks per week), 15% have moderate alcohol consumption (no more than 7 or 14 drinks per week for women and men, respectively), and 5% consume alcohol excessively (more than 7 to 14 drinks weekly). Thirty-six percent abstain from consuming alcohol.[1]

The largest drinking population in North America consists of young, White college students, many of whom are not yet of legal drinking age. College students are drinking more heavily and more frequently than ever before. In fact, excessive alcohol consumption is a bigger problem than illicit drug use on most college campuses. Many young adults consider drinking alcohol to be a "rite of passage" into adulthood and incorporate drinking competitions into initiations to clubs and social circles. Alcohol producers also target college students with advertising and other marketing efforts. Drinks that combine alcohol and stimulants, such as caffeine and guarana, are popular on college campuses, but they often lead to excess alcohol intake because individuals are less able to judge their degree of intoxication. In one study, college students consuming "caffeinated cocktails" drank more, were intoxicated more often, and reported more sexual misconduct, physical injuries, and need for medical assistance.[8] Unfortunately, many drinkers have little or no knowledge of the potentially harmful acute and chronic effects of alcohol.

Of the 70% of college students who report using alcohol, approximately 45% or more engage in binge drinking. Binge drinking is associated with vandalism, violent crime, traffic accidents and injuries, sexual abuse, suicide, hazing deaths, and serious acute health risks.[9, 10]

CRITICAL THINKING

Imagine that you are president of a sorority or fraternity where there is a tradition of the "4th-year 5th," a long-standing practice of seniors to consume a 5th of liquor during the semester prior to graduation. Every weekend, between 3 and 10 students arrive in the local emergency room with alcohol poisoning or alcohol-related injuries, and there are several alcohol-related deaths each year. As the president of the organization, what might you recommend to prevent alcohol-related accidents and deaths?

Many colleges require students who break alcohol and drug rules to attend counseling or educational programs to reduce their alcohol intake and binge-drinking episodes. Colleges and communities offer a variety of educational and treatment strategies for individuals with alcohol dependency.

262 **PART 2** Energy-Yielding Nutrients and Alcohol

Thirty-two percent of all motor vehicle fatalities are alcohol-related.

Table 8-5 Impact of Binge Drinking on College Campuses
Death: 1825 college students between the ages of 18 and 24 die each year from alcohol-related unintentional injuries, including motor vehicle crashes.
Injury: 599,000 students between the ages of 18 and 24 are unintentionally injured each year under the influence of alcohol.
Assault: more than 696,000 students between the ages of 18 and 24 are assaulted each year by another student who has been drinking.
Sexual abuse: more than 97,000 students between the ages of 18 and 24 are victims of alcohol-related sexual assault or date rape each year.
Unsafe sex: each year, about 400,000 students between the ages of 18 and 24 have unprotected sex, and more than 100,000 students between the ages of 18 and 24 have been too intoxicated to know if they consented to having sex.
Academic problems: about 25% of college students report academic consequences of their drinking, including missing class, falling behind, doing poorly on exams or papers, and receiving lower grades overall.
Health problems/suicide attempts: more than 150,000 students develop an alcohol-related health problem, and between 1.2 and 1.5% of students indicate that they tried to commit suicide within the past year because of drinking or drug use.
Drunk driving: 3.4 million students between the ages of 18 and 24 drive under the influence of alcohol each year.
Vandalism: about 11% of college student drinkers report that they have damaged property while under the influence of alcohol.
Property damage: more than 25% of administrators from schools with relatively low drinking levels and more than 50% from schools with high drinking levels say their campuses have a "moderate" or "major" problem with alcohol-related property damage.
Police involvement: about 5% of 4-year college students are involved with the police or campus security as a result of their drinking, and an estimated 110,000 students between the ages of 18 and 24 are arrested for an alcohol-related violation, such as public drunkenness or driving under the influence.
Alcohol abuse and dependence: 31% of college students met the criteria for a diagnosis of alcohol abuse and 6% for a diagnosis of alcohol dependence in the past 12 months, according to questionnaire-based self-reports about their drinking.
The consequences of excessive and underage drinking affect virtually all college campuses, college communities, and college students, whether they choose to drink or not.
Source: www.collegedrinkingprevention.gov/facts/snapshot.aspx.

▶ *Healthy People 2020* goals[7] regarding alcohol use include

- Increase the proportion of at-risk adolescents aged 12 to 17 years who, in the past year, refrained from using alcohol for the first time.

- Reduce the proportion of persons engaging in binge drinking of alcoholic beverages.

- Reduce the proportion of adults who drank excessively in the previous 30 days.

As noted in Table 8-5, binge drinking has serious consequences, which affect virtually all college campuses, college communities, and college students, even those who choose not to drink alcohol. Thus, it is important that binge drinkers be aware that these behaviors can cause lifelong problems, especially when drinking becomes habitual.

According to the National Institute on Alcohol Abuse and Alcoholism, nearly 4% of the adult U.S. population is dependent on alcohol.[11] In young adults, ages 18 to 29 years, these rates jump to 9%. Underage drinking also is a significant public health and safety issue. By age 14 to 15, approximately half of all adolescents have consumed alcohol and approximately 20% have been drunk at least once.[12] Underage drinkers are particularly vulnerable to alcohol's damaging effects and are at much greater risk of alcoholism in adulthood.[13]

Take Action

Alcohol and Driving

Laura, Diane, Marc, and Jade attended an off-campus college graduation party over the weekend. The friends agreed to stay for 3 hours because Laura and Jade had to work the next day. When it came time to leave, Laura and Diane noticed that Marc and Jade seemed loud and boisterous and were slurring words. Marc also lost his balance and tripped several times as they walked to the car. Laura and Diane wondered if they should still ride home with their friends or if they should call a cab or take the bus instead. What would you do in their situation? Based on Marc's and Jade's behavior and symptoms, what do you think their blood alcohol concentration (BAC) was? Was their BAC within a legally safe limit to drive?

 ## 8.4 Health Effects of Alcohol

Low to moderate use of alcohol has been associated with several social and health-related benefits. However, despite the possible benefits of regular, moderate alcohol use, excessive alcohol intake has serious effects on health and nutritional status.

Guidance for Using Alcohol Safely

The U.S. Surgeon General's office, National Academy of Science, U.S. Department of Agriculture, and U.S. Department of Health and Human Services do not recommend that a nondrinker start consuming alcohol because risks often outweigh possible benefits. However, they do not specifically discourage moderate alcohol use. The following are suggestions for individuals who choose to drink alcohol.

- Drinking alcohol should be done sensibly and in moderation—defined as the consumption of up to 1 drink per day for women and up to 2 drinks per day for men.
- Alcoholic beverages should not be consumed by some individuals, including those who cannot restrict their alcohol intake to moderate levels, women who are or may be pregnant, anyone younger than the legal drinking age, individuals taking medications that can interact with alcohol, and those with specific medical conditions.
- Alcoholic beverages should be avoided by individuals engaging in activities that require attention, skill, or coordination, such as driving or operating machinery.

Potential Benefits of Alcohol Intake

Many people enjoy meeting a friend for a beer or having a glass of wine in the evening with dinner. Others report a reduced feeling of anxiety and stress after having a drink at the end of their workday. In elderly individuals, moderate alcohol use can stimulate appetite and increase dietary intake. These behaviors are not considered harmful as long as they are practiced by individuals of a legal drinking age, continue in moderation, and cause no obvious harm.[14]

In middle-aged and older adults, moderate alcohol use has been shown to lower the risk of cardiovascular disease and overall mortality in comparison with nondrinkers.[14-16] Alcohol can lower serum low-density lipoprotein (LDL) levels, increase protective high-density lipoprotein (HDL) levels, and decrease platelet aggregation (blood cell accumulation)—all of which may help reduce the risk of heart disease. Some studies suggest that the heart disease prevention benefits are predominantly associated with red wine consumption and may be

Of all the alcohol sources, red wine is often singled out as the best choice because of the added bonus of the many phytochemicals (e.g., resveratrol) present. These leach out of the grape skins when red wine is made. Dark beer also contains some phytochemicals, but in lower amounts.

264   **PART 2**   Energy-Yielding Nutrients and Alcohol

Figure 8-2 Alcohol affects virtually every organ.

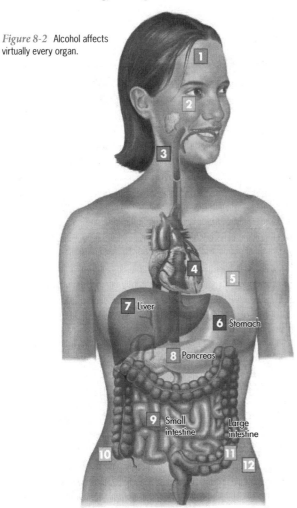

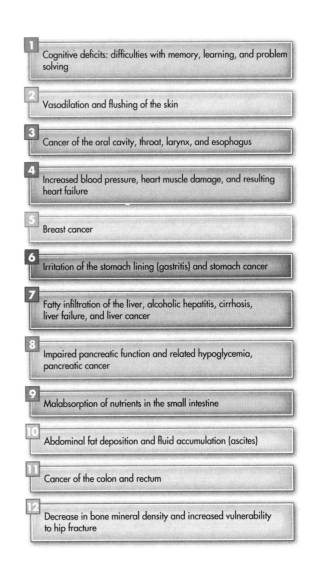

1	Cognitive deficits: difficulties with memory, learning, and problem solving
2	Vasodilation and flushing of the skin
3	Cancer of the oral cavity, throat, larynx, and esophagus
4	Increased blood pressure, heart muscle damage, and resulting heart failure
5	Breast cancer
6	Irritation of the stomach lining (gastritis) and stomach cancer
7	Fatty infiltration of the liver, alcoholic hepatitis, cirrhosis, liver failure, and liver cancer
8	Impaired pancreatic function and related hypoglycemia, pancreatic cancer
9	Malabsorption of nutrients in the small intestine
10	Abdominal fat deposition and fluid accumulation (ascites)
11	Cancer of the colon and rectum
12	Decrease in bone mineral density and increased vulnerability to hip fracture

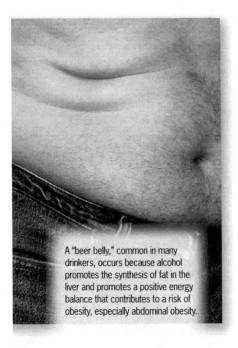

A "beer belly," common in many drinkers, occurs because alcohol promotes the synthesis of fat in the liver and promotes a positive energy balance that contributes to a risk of obesity, especially abdominal obesity.

attributed to a phytochemical in red wine called resveratrol.[17] However, other compounds and types of alcohol may produce similar benefits.

Although the heart health benefits of alcohol have received the most attention, a few studies have shown an association between moderate alcohol use and reduced risk of type 2 diabetes and dementia.[18, 19] These associations are more controversial and require additional research.

Risks of Excessive Alcohol Intake

The excessive consumption of alcohol contributes significantly to 5 of the 10 leading causes of death in North America—heart failure, certain forms of cancer, cirrhosis of the liver, motor vehicle and other accidents, and suicides. Alcohol-related conditions lead to 100,000 deaths in the U.S. each year.

As shown in Figure 8-2, excessive alcohol intake affects many organs and systems in the body. Heavy drinkers may develop heart damage that causes arrhythmias (abnormal heartbeats) and fluid retention in the lungs. Excess alcohol intake also can contribute to high blood pressure and the risk of stroke. Limiting alcohol intake to no more than 2 drinks per day (men) and 1 drink per day (women) may help prevent or improve these conditions. Cancer also is related to alcohol consumption—acetaldehyde, a compound formed in the metabolism of ethanol, is a known carcinogen. Cancers of the oral cavity, throat, larynx, and esophagus are the most strongly related to alcohol consumption, with heavy drinking

(5 to 6 drinks per day) increasing the risk 50-fold.[20-22] Tobacco, often used simultaneously with alcohol, interacts with alcohol to further increase the risk of these cancers. Alcohol ingestion also elevates the risk for colorectal and breast cancers, although to a much lesser extent.

Prolonged, excessive alcohol intake can cause significant liver damage and lead to the development of cirrhosis of the liver. Alcohol-related liver damage also can increase the risk of liver cancer. Other adverse effects of excessive alcohol intake are osteoporosis, brain damage, inflammation of the stomach lining, intestinal bleeding, pancreatitis,[23] suppression of the immune system (with an increased risk of infections), sleep disturbances, impotence, hypoglycemia (an effect of acute excessive alcohol intake), hyperglycemia (an effect of chronic excessive alcohol intake on pancreatic function), abdominal obesity, high blood triglyceride levels, and nutrient deficiencies.

Cirrhosis of the Liver

The liver is one of the largest organs in the body. It has many functions, including nutrient storage, protein and enzyme synthesis, and the metabolism of protein, fats, and carbohydrates. It also is vital for removing toxins from the body and for metabolizing drugs. Because the liver is the main organ for alcohol metabolism, long-term alcohol abuse damages the liver.

The first change seen in the liver is fat accumulation, known as **fatty liver**, or steatosis. Fatty liver occurs in response to the increased synthesis of fat and trapping of fat in the liver. More than 90% of heavy drinkers develop fatty liver. This condition is reversible, but only if the person abstains from drinking alcohol.

If alcohol consumption persists, inflammation of the liver cells, known as alcoholic hepatitis, develops. Alcoholic hepatitis produces symptoms of nausea, poor appetite, vomiting, fever, pain, and **jaundice** (yellow-orange coloration of the skin and whites of the eyes; Fig. 8-3), resulting from the liver's inability to excrete bile pigments, which instead spill from damaged hepatocytes (liver cells) into the blood. Alcoholic hepatitis is a serious condition, which frequently progresses to the chronic, irreversible liver disease known as cirrhosis.

Cirrhosis is characterized by the loss of functioning hepatocytes (Fig. 8-4). As cirrhosis progresses, the synthesis of proteins, such as those required for normal blood clotting and

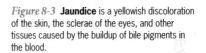

Figure 8-3 **Jaundice** is a yellowish discoloration of the skin, the sclerae of the eyes, and other tissues caused by the buildup of bile pigments in the blood.

fatty liver Accumulation of triglycerides and other lipids inside liver cells; most often caused by excessive alcohol intake. Other causes include malnutrition and obesity.

cirrhosis Chronic degenerative disease, caused by poisons (e.g., alcohol) that damage liver cells, that results in a reduced ability to synthesize proteins and metabolize nutrients, drugs, and poisons.

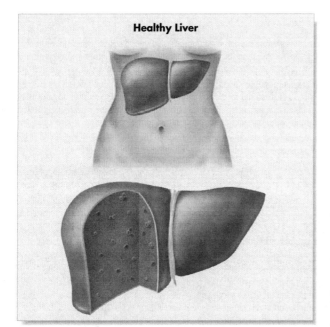

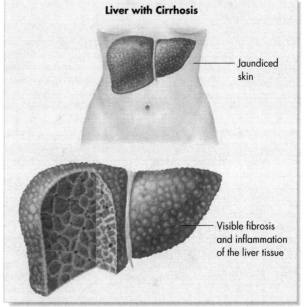

Jaundiced skin

Visible fibrosis and inflammation of the liver tissue

Figure 8-4 Notice the difference between the healthy liver on the left and the liver with cirrhosis on the right.

nutrient transport, decreases dramatically. Ascites, abnormal fluid retention in the abdomen, amounting to as much as 4 gallons (15 liters), is another common complication of cirrhosis. Nutritional status also is often poor.[24]

Whereas the early stages of alcoholic liver injury (fatty liver and alcoholic hepatitis) are reversible, cirrhosis is not; thus, liver failure develops. The overt signs of liver failure associated with cirrhosis are jaundice, ascites, and loss of liver functions. Once a person has cirrhosis, there is a 50% chance of death within 4 years. Approximately 28,000 people die from cirrhosis each year in the U.S.—most are between the ages of 40 and 65 years. A liver transplant is necessary for long-term survival, and successful liver transplantation requires that patients abstain from consuming any alcohol.

Cirrhosis develops in about 10 to 15% of cases of alcoholism and affects about 2 million people in the U.S. Although cirrhosis can be caused by any substance that poisons liver cells, in North America most cases are caused by excess alcohol consumption. Cirrhosis is commonly associated with a 10-year or longer consumption of approximately 80 g of alcohol (the equivalent of 6 to 7 standard-size drinks) per day. Some evidence suggests that damage is caused by chronic intakes as low as 40 g/day for men (about 3 beers) and 20 g/day for women. In addition to the amount and duration of alcohol consumption, genetic factors and individual factors, such as obesity, diabetes, exposure to hepatotoxins (e.g., acetaminophen [Tylenol']), iron overload disorders, and infections causing hepatitis, determine one's risk of the disease. (About 4 million people in the U.S. are infected with the virus that causes hepatitis C.)

A number of possible mechanisms are thought to cause the liver damage that results from alcohol abuse. In chronic alcoholism, the increased concentration of acetaldehyde in the liver is thought to damage this organ. The accumulation of fat in liver cells causes inflammation and cell damage. Scientists also believe that the production of free radicals from alcohol metabolism contributes to liver damage. The highly reactive free radical molecules destroy cell membranes and lead to chronic inflammation.[3]

A nutritious diet may help delay some of the complications associated with alcoholism and alcoholic liver disease. However, alcoholism usually brings about the serious destruction of vital tissues regardless of the quality of one's diet. In fact, studies in laboratory animals show that, even when a nutritious diet is consumed, alcohol abuse leads to cirrhosis. However, a poor diet often results in nutrient deficiencies that compound the problem of cirrhosis by making the liver more vulnerable to toxic substances produced by alcohol metabolism and by causing additional health concerns related to malnutrition.[3]

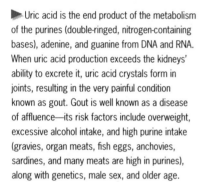

► Uric acid is the end product of the metabolism of the purines (double-ringed, nitrogen-containing bases), adenine, and guanine from DNA and RNA. When uric acid production exceeds the kidneys' ability to excrete it, uric acid crystals form in joints, resulting in the very painful condition known as gout. Gout is well known as a disease of affluence—its risk factors include overweight, excessive alcohol intake, and high purine intake (gravies, organ meats, fish eggs, anchovies, sardines, and many meats are high in purines), along with genetics, male sex, and older age.

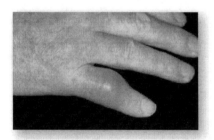

Effects of Alcohol Abuse on Nutritional Status

Individuals who abuse alcohol often have poor nutritional status and are at risk of developing many nutrient deficiencies because they tend to replace much of the food in their diets with alcohol, a poor source of nutrients. For instance, if a person were to use beer as a nutrient source, he or she would need to consume daily 40 to 55 bottles (12 oz each) to meet protein needs and 65 bottles for thiamin needs.

When an individual relies on alcohol for the majority of his or her energy needs, protein-energy malnutrition develops. The symptoms of protein-energy malnutrition with alcoholism are similar to those seen in individuals with kwashiorkor (see Chapter 7). In addition to protein deficiencies, deficiencies of vitamins and minerals are likely and can result in further complications. These deficiencies are usually the result of decreased intake, impaired absorption, altered metabolism, and alcohol-related tissue damage.

It is important for medical personnel to be aware of the severe consequences of alcohol abuse on nutritional health. Early intervention, guided by a dietitian and physician, is an essential part of the treatment for alcoholism to correct nutrient deficiencies, minimize tissue damage, and restore overall health.

Water-Soluble Vitamins

Excessive alcohol intake can lead to deficiencies of the water-soluble vitamins thiamin, niacin, vitamin B-6, vitamin B-12, and folate (see Chapter 13). For example, chronic alcohol abuse often leads to a severe form of thiamin deficiency called **Wernicke-Korsakoff syndrome.** This causes significant changes in brain and nervous system function, which, if untreated, result in irreversible paralysis of the eye muscles, loss of sensation in the lower extremities, loss of balance with abnormal gait, and memory loss.[3]

Alcoholics are at increased risk of developing niacin deficiency because alcohol metabolism requires large quantities of this vitamin. The metabolism of alcohol can increase the excretion of vitamin B-6 in the urine, which, if not offset with increased dietary intake, increases the risk of developing anemia and peripheral neuropathy (weakness or numbness in the arms and legs). Excessive alcohol intake also can impair the absorption of vitamin B-12, which also increases the risk of anemia and neuropathy.

Fat-Soluble Vitamins

Excessive alcohol intake can result in deficiencies of the fat-soluble vitamins A, D, E, and K (see Chapters 14 and 15). Chronic alcohol abuse damages the liver and pancreas, which impairs the liver's ability to secrete bile and the pancreas's ability to secrete enzymes that digest fats. Decreased bile and pancreatic lipase secretions, in turn, lead to poor absorption of fat and fat-soluble vitamins.[24]

Alcohol abusers are at increased risk of protein, vitamin, and mineral deficiencies.

The risk of vitamin A deficiency is compounded by the liver's increased rate of breakdown and excretion of this vitamin, as well as the liver's inability to produce the protein needed to deliver vitamin A to all parts of the body. Alcohol also can decrease the amount of beta-carotene (a precursor of vitamin A) that the liver converts to vitamin A. Because of these changes in liver function, vitamin A stores in individuals with alcoholism are diminished, regardless of whether dietary vitamin A intake is low, adequate, or high. This alcohol-induced vitamin A deficiency often causes alcoholics to have trouble seeing in the dark (a condition called night blindness).

Individuals with alcoholic liver disease are less able to synthesize vitamin K–containing compounds that are needed to help blood clot, in turn increasing the risk of bleeding. Additionally, damage to the liver can lead to a vitamin D deficiency because the liver plays a key role in converting vitamin D to its biologically active form. Vitamin D is required for calcium absorption and bone health; thus, a deficiency can cause bone loss and increase the risk of osteoporosis.

Minerals

Individuals who abuse alcohol are at increased risk of developing mineral deficiencies as well. Deficiencies of calcium, magnesium, zinc, and iron are most common (see Chapters 14 and 15). Poor absorption of calcium (because of low vitamin D status) contributes to a deficiency of this mineral. Increased urinary excretion of magnesium contributes to low blood concentrations of magnesium and deficiency symptoms. One of the classic symptoms of magnesium deficiency is tetany, a condition characterized by muscle twitches, cramps, spasms, and seizures. Decreased absorption and increased urinary excretion contribute to zinc deficiency, which leads to changes in taste and smell, loss of appetite, and impaired wound healing.

Iron deficiency commonly occurs in alcoholics. Excessive alcohol consumption can damage gastrointestinal tissues, causing bleeding, malabsorption, and the eventual development of iron deficiency.

Wernicke-Korsakoff syndrome Thiamin deficiency disease caused by excessive alcohol consumption. Symptoms include eye problems, difficulty walking, and deranged mental function.

Alcohol Consumption during Pregnancy and Breastfeeding

More than half of all women in the U.S. of childbearing age drink alcohol. If a woman chooses to drink during pregnancy, she may cause serious harm to her developing offspring. Alcohol slows nutrient and oxygen delivery to the fetus, thereby retarding growth and development. Alcohol also may displace nutrient-dense foods in the mother's diet. Although the most severe damage occurs during the first 12 to 16 weeks of pregnancy, when organs are undergoing major developmental steps, consuming alcohol at any time during pregnancy can cause lifelong damage.

Of every 1000 babies born in the U.S. each year, as many as 30 have alcohol-related health consequences. About one-tenth of these babies suffer the greatest damage and are classified as having an irreversible condition called **fetal alcohol syndrome**.[25] The main characteristics of fetal alcohol syndrome are facial malformations (Fig. 8-5), growth retardation, and central nervous system defects, including a small brain size and profound mental retardation. Children with fetal alcohol syndrome are among the smallest in height, weight, and head circumference for their age. They often face many challenges throughout life.

Prenatal exposure to alcohol also may cause somewhat lesser effects known as **fetal alcohol spectrum disorder**. These children may experience behavioral, learning, or nervous system abnormalities caused by alcohol exposure. They may have lifelong learning difficulties, short attention spans, and hyperactivity. Some also have physical birth defects similar to those associated with fetal alcohol syndrome.

It is not clear how alcohol causes physical malformations and disabilities. They may be the result of alcohol itself or compounds produced during alcohol metabolism. Within minutes after consumption, the alcohol travels through the mother's blood to the developing offspring. The effects of alcohol are intensified by the offspring's small size and are prolonged because the fetus is unable to metabolize the alcohol and must wait for maternal blood to carry it away.

Drinking alcohol during pregnancy poses grave danger for the developing offspring.

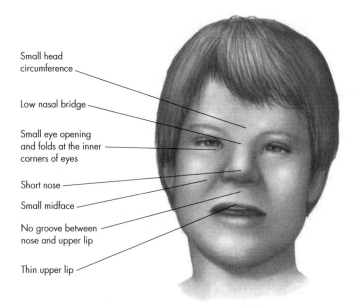

Small head circumference

Low nasal bridge

Small eye opening and folds at the inner corners of eyes

Short nose

Small midface

No groove between nose and upper lip

Thin upper lip

Figure 8-5 The facial features shown are typical of children with fetal alcohol syndrome. Additional abnormalities in the brain and other internal organs accompany fetal alcohol syndrome but are not immediately apparent from simply looking at the child. Milder forms of alcohol-induced changes from a lower alcohol exposure to the fetus are known as fetal alcohol spectrum disorder.

GLBAL PERSPECTIVE

Alcohol Intake around the World

International alcohol intake patterns vary tremendously. According to World Health Organization data, residents of Russia and Europe drink the most alcohol, whereas those in the eastern Mediterranean region and parts of Africa drink the least. Worldwide, nearly half of men and two-thirds of women do not drink. In the U.S., only 36% abstain from alcohol consumption.[26]

Alcohol intake around the world is increasing, perhaps in response to Westernization and aggressive marketing by the alcohol industry. One extreme example is in certain areas of Russia, where some consume as much as a bottle of vodka daily. Worldwide, about 4% of deaths are attributed to alcohol intake, yet in areas of Russia, more than half of the deaths of men aged 15 to 54 years are due to alcohol.[26, 27] These deaths are caused by accidents and violence, acute heart disease, tuberculosis, pneumonia, liver and pancreatic disease, and cancers of the mouth, esophagus, and liver. Many are from alcohol poisoning, which kills more than 40,000 Russians each year.

Alcohol, typically wine, consumed with meals is a tradition enjoyed in many cultures. As you know, this type of moderate alcohol intake may offer some health benefits for those who choose to drink alcohol. Moderation is key to reaping benefits—risks rise quickly when women consume more than 1 drink per day and men consume more than 2 drinks daily. Risks are particularly high when many alcoholic beverages are consumed in rapid succession—this practice can result in alcohol poisoning and death.

No one is sure how much alcohol it takes to cause developmental problems. However, consuming as little as 1 ounce per day has resulted in mental and physical defects. The more alcohol consumed during pregnancy, the worse the effects are likely to be. Thus, health experts agree that women should abstain from drinking alcohol during pregnancy. Because of the potentially deleterious effect during the early part of pregnancy, experts also recommend that women planning a pregnancy avoid alcohol, in case they do become pregnant, and that women who drink alcohol take precautions to avoid becoming pregnant. For more information about fetal alcohol syndrome, visit the website www.cdc.gov/ncbddd/fasd/index.html.

For centuries, health-care providers advised new mothers to drink a little wine or beer before breastfeeding to relax and allow babies to suckle longer. However, alcohol actually reduces the mother's ability to produce milk and causes babies to drink less and have disrupted sleep patterns. In addition, infants are not efficient at breaking down alcohol, so its detrimental effects are much more pronounced than in adults. The safest plan for mothers who are breastfeeding is to avoid alcohol altogether.[28] However, breastfeeding women who want to drink alcohol are advised to limit their intake to no more than 1 drink and then wait 3 to 4 hours before breastfeeding. The amount of alcohol in breast milk peaks about 30 to 60 minutes after the mother ingests it, then declines.[29]

Knowledge Check

1. What are the guidelines for using alcohol safely?
2. What are possible benefits of moderate alcohol intake by middle-aged and older adults?
3. What levels of alcohol intake are associated with the development of cirrhosis?
4. How does alcohol abuse impair nutritional status?
5. What are the dangers of consuming alcohol during pregnancy?

8.5 Alcohol Use Disorders:
Alcohol Abuse and Alcoholism

Alcohol abuse and alcoholism (also known as alcohol dependency) pose serious risks for many individuals.[30] Alcohol abuse is characterized by a pattern of drinking accompanied by at least one of these problems:

- Failing to fulfill major responsibilities at work, school, or home because of drinking
- Drinking when it is physically dangerous, such as while driving a car
- Having recurring alcohol-related legal problems, such as physically hurting someone while drunk
- Having social or relationship problems that are worsened by alcohol intake

Alcoholism, or alcohol dependency, is a chronic disease with the following symptoms:

- Craving—a strong need to drink
- Loss of control—not being able to stop drinking once started
- Withdrawal symptoms—such as nausea, sweating, anxiety, or shakiness after stopping drinking
- Tolerance—the need to drink larger amounts of alcohol in order to feel its effects
- Unsuccessful attempts to cut down on use

Nearly 1 in 3 Americans abuses or becomes dependent on alcohol over a lifetime.[31] At any given time, about 8.5% of people in the U.S. (1 in 12) meet the criteria for either alcohol abuse or alcohol dependency.[11] About 30% of people in the U.S. can be considered at high risk of alcohol-related problems because of excessive intakes.[31] The factors linked to developing alcohol-related problems include genetics, gender, age of drinking onset, and ethnicity. Parental and peer attitudes favoring excessive drinking and the presence of mental health disorders, such as depression and anxiety disorder, are other significant risk factors.[11]

Genetic Influences

Genetic factors account for approximately 40 to 50% of a person's risk of alcoholism.[30] Twins and first-degree relatives (parents, siblings, and offspring) share a tendency toward alcohol addiction. Children of alcoholics have a 4 times greater risk of developing alcoholism, even when adopted by a family with no history of alcoholism.

Scientists are actively studying the genetic basis for alcohol dependency. The genes regulating alcohol metabolism enzymes—alcohol dehydrogenase and aldehyde dehydrogenase—have been of particular interest to researchers.[4, 32] These genes have several possible variants (polymorphisms) that can occur. Scientists are trying to understand how polymorphisms alter alcohol metabolism and increase the risk of developing alcohol dependency or alcoholic liver disease. For example, as discussed earlier, the inability to completely metabolize alcohol quickly may cause a person to feel ill, causing him or her to be unlikely to drink large amounts of alcohol.[4] Other genes, such as those that make antioxidant enzymes, neurotransmitters, and immune factors, are also under study.

Individuals with a family history of alcoholism need to be especially alert for evidence of the early signs of alcohol dependency. However, it is important to recognize that genetic risk is not destiny—not all children of alcoholic parents go on to develop alcohol use problems. Some alcoholics have no family history of alcohol problems at all, so genetic factors do not fully explain why some individuals develop alcohol-related problems but others do not.

Effect of Gender

Gender plays a key role in alcohol dependency and metabolism. The male:female ratio of alcohol dependency is 4:1. However, women are more susceptible to the adverse effects of alcohol—liver disease, heart muscle damage, cancer, and brain injury. As previously

Women cannot metabolize alcohol as efficiently as men.

noted, the recommended limit for alcohol use is lower for women than for men because an equivalent amount of alcohol is more concentrated in women—they are smaller and have more fat and less body water than men. Additionally, women cannot metabolize alcohol as quickly as men, due to lower activity of the alcohol dehydrogenase in the stomach, so blood alcohol concentrations remain elevated for longer periods.

Age of Onset of Drinking

Not only does alcohol consumption in underage youths contribute to approximately 4500 deaths in the U.S. each year (mainly from homicides, motor vehicle accidents, and suicides),[33] but drinking at a young age also is an important risk factor for later alcohol dependency. Researchers have found that drinking before age 14 is especially problematic. In fact, 45% of these adolescents go on to develop alcohol dependency, compared with 10% of those who wait until age 21 years or later to begin drinking.[13] This is particularly worrisome, considering that about 40% of high school students report that they currently consume alcohol.[12, 13]

Drinking alcohol at a young age increases the risk of alcohol addiction.

Ethnicity and Alcohol Abuse

Patterns of alcohol use vary among ethnic groups. In North America, Native American Indians, Alaska Natives, and Native Hawaiians have the highest alcohol use, whereas Asian Americans have the lowest use. The major causes of death among Native Americans are motor vehicle accidents and unintentional injuries related to alcohol use. Native American populations also have a higher rate of alcohol-related suicide, homicide, domestic abuse, and fetal alcohol syndrome than other ethnic groups. Differences in alcohol use may result from social factors, such as the availability of alcohol in communities, and biological factors that affect vulnerability to alcohol. As discussed previously, many Asian Americans experience uncomfortable effects after drinking alcohol, which likely accounts for low alcohol use in this population.

Mental Health and Alcohol Abuse

Mental health disorders, such as depression and generalized anxiety disorder, often go hand in hand with alcohol use disorders.[34] Alcohol dependency and abuse may aggravate or even cause mental health disorders. Conversely, individuals with depression or other disorders may use alcohol to self-medicate their conditions. It's important that both mental health disorders and alcohol abuse be identified and treated.

The majority of suicides and interfamily homicides are alcohol-related. Alcohol consumption appears to increase the risk of youth suicide—the younger the drinker, the more likely he or she is to commit suicide.

Each year in the U.S., the cost of alcohol abuse is about $185 billion in lost productivity, premature deaths, direct treatment expenses, and legal fees. A liver transplant costs about $300,000 and is needed in cases of excessive alcohol use. In contrast, a typical counseling program to treat a person who is abusing alcohol costs only about $5000.

CASE STUDY FOLLOW-UP

Charles is consuming 13 to 16 beers per week. Using the average of 14.5 beers per week, his beer consumption provides an additional 2175 calories each week and 26,100 calories in the 12-week period. Dividing 26,100 calories by 3500 calories per pound of fat yields an estimated weight gain of 7.5 pounds. It is very likely that Charles's weight gain is due to his new beer drinking habit.

Knowledge Check

1. What are 3 factors that predispose a person to alcohol dependency?
2. Why is the age at which a person started drinking alcohol of concern?
3. Why might women suffer more ill effects from alcohol consumption than men?
4. Which ethnic groups are at increased risk of alcohol-related problems?

MEDICAL PERSPECTIVE

Diagnosis and Treatment of Alcoholism

Alcohol abuse and dependency often begin during young adulthood.

▶ Swiss chemist Paracelsus (1493–1541) made the observation that "the dose determines the poison." This is true for alcohol because, the greater the dose of alcohol, the greater the risk of alcohol poisoning and death.

▶ There are several other screening tools for alcohol abuse. Visit www.alcoholscreening.org.

CRITICAL THINKING

José is a well-liked 17-year-old. It always seems as if everything is going his way—an A on a test, a scholarship to college, you name it. Lately, however, José has experienced some disappointments. His grandfather has just passed away and he and his girlfriend have broken up. When he arrived home late with the smell of alcohol on his breath, his parents started to worry. What signs and symptoms should they be aware of that indicate a problem with alcohol?

Alcoholism is often considered a 2-phase problem. Initially, it begins as problem drinking. This includes the repetitive use of alcohol, often to alleviate anxiety or solve other emotional problems. Alcohol addiction, the second phase of alcoholism, then follows. In addition to the symptoms listed at the beginning of Section 8.5, other signs of alcoholism include frequent alcohol odor on the breath, flushed face, and nervous system disorders, such as tremors. Unexplained work absences, frequent accidents, and falls or injuries of vague origin may be other signs. Laboratory tests also are helpful. These tests include measures of impaired liver function and high triglyceride and uric acid concentrations in the blood.

Determining Whether a Problem with Alcohol Intake Exists

Asking a person about the quantity and frequency of his or her alcohol consumption is an important means of detecting abuse and dependence. The CAGE questionnaire is commonly used in routine health care:[35]

C: Have you ever felt you ought to *cut* down on drinking?

A: Have people *annoyed* you by criticizing your drinking?

G: Have you ever felt bad or *guilty* about your drinking?

E: Have you ever had a drink first thing in the morning (an *eye-opener*) to steady your nerves or get rid of a hangover?

More than a single positive response in the CAGE questionnaire suggests an alcohol problem.

Other questions to ask along with the CAGE questionnaire are the following:

1. Does it take more to make you inebriated than it did in the past? That is, do you have an increased tolerance for alcohol?
2. Have you had memory lapses or blackouts due to drinking?
3. Do you continue to drink, even though you have health problems caused by alcohol?
4. Do you get withdrawal symptoms, such as headaches, chills, shakes, and a strong craving

for alcohol, and, as a result, drink more to get rid of these symptoms?
5. Do you take part in high-risk behaviors, such as having unsafe sex or driving a car or boat when under the influence of alcohol?
6. Has drinking caused trouble at school, at home, at work, or in relationships with others?
7. Do you have to drink alcohol for any of the following reasons?
    a. To get through the day or unwind at the end of the day
    b. To cope with stressful life events
    c. To escape from ongoing problems

An affirmative answer to any of these questions indicates that an individual should seek help from a physician or certified counselor. Unfortunately, about 75% of people with alcohol problems do not seek treatment.[11]

Recovery from Alcoholism

The treatment of alcoholism or alcohol abuse typically involves behavioral therapy, along with medication.[36] Behavioral therapy is usually facilitated by a psychologist, social worker, or counselor. An important goal of counseling is to identify ways to compensate for the loss of pleasure from drinking. This helps the drinker confront the immediate problem of how to stop drinking. Total abstinence must be the ultimate objective because, for most alcoholics, there is no such thing as controlled drinking. Most problem drinkers cannot return safely to social drinking.[6] Because other mental health disorders, such as depression, bipolar disorder, and mood and anxiety disorders, often go hand in hand with alcoholism or alcohol abuse, these conditions must be treated as well for successful outcomes.

Three medications are approved in the U.S. to treat alcoholism:[37]

- Naltrexone (ReVia®) blocks the craving for alcohol and the pleasure of intoxication (Fig. 8-6).[38]

- Acamprosate (Campral®) is thought to act on neurotransmitter pathways in the brain to decrease the desire to drink.
- Disulfiram (Antabuse®) causes physical reactions, such as vomiting, when drinking alcohol. It does so by blocking the complete breakdown of alcohol in the liver in a way similar to that experienced naturally by some individuals of Asian decent (as described earlier in the chapter).

Self-help programs also facilitate the recovery from alcohol dependency. Alcoholics Anonymous® (AA),[39] a 12-step program, is one of the most well-known programs. At AA meetings, men and women share their experiences, strengths, challenges, and hopes with each other as they try to solve their common problems and help each other recover from alcoholism. As an informal society chartered in 1935, AA includes more than 2 million recovered alcoholics. The only requirement for membership is the desire to stop drinking. There are no rules, regulations, dues, or fees. In addition, the group is not a political or formal organization. Further information about AA is available at www.aa.org. Another organization, Al-Anon, helps family members and friends recover from the effects of living with an alcohol-dependent person; visit www.al-anon.alateen.org for more information.

Current research does not support the generally negative public opinion about the prognosis for recovery from alcoholism. In most job-related alcoholism treatment programs, where workers are socially stable and well motivated (because of the risk of job and pension loss), recovery rates reach 60% or more.[6] This remarkably high cure rate is probably accounted for by early detection. Once a person moves from problem drinking to an advanced stage of alcoholism, treatment success seldom exceeds 50%. Early identification and intervention remain the most important steps in the treatment of alcoholism.

▶ Alcoholics who stop drinking may substitute caffeine, nicotine, and/or sweets for alcohol. Because alcoholics usually have poor nutritional status, these substitutions often have a significant negative impact on their overall nutritional status. However, these substitutions are not as harmful as alcohol abuse.

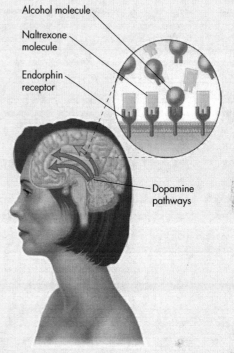

Figure 8-6 The euphoria that arises from alcohol use involves alcohol binding to endorphin receptors in the brain. Endorphins are chemical compounds produced in the brain that act as natural painkillers and elicit feelings of well-being. It is likely that this binding, in turn, causes a release of the neurotransmitter dopamine, which is thought to cause the characteristic high associated with alcohol use. Naltrexone (ReVia®) works by blocking alcohol's ability to bind to brain receptors. This, then, reduces dopamine release and blocks the pleasant feelings elicited by alcohol use.

Knowledge Check

1. Why is tolerance to alcohol considered a risk factor for alcohol dependence?
2. How might the CAGE questionnaire be used to identify those with alcohol problems?
3. How do medications currently approved to treat alcoholism limit alcohol intake?
4. In addition to medications, what programs are available to help individuals with alcohol use problems?

Take Action

Might You or Someone You Know Have a Problem with Alcoholism?

Problem drinking often has its seeds in the teen years. Significant health consequences of this practice typically occur in adulthood. Alcohol abuse is a prominent contributor to 5 of the 10 leading causes of death in North America. The social consequences of alcohol dependency include divorce, unemployment, and poverty. The following questionnaire was developed by the National Countil on Alcoholism and Drug Dependence, Inc. (NCADD) www.ncadd.org. With this assessment, you can determine whether you or someone you know might need help.

Yes No 1. Do you occasionally drink heavily after disappointment, after a quarrel, or when someone gives you a hard time?

Yes No 2. When you have trouble or feel under pressure, do you drink more heavily than usual?

Yes No 3. Have you ever noticed that you're able to handle liquor better than you did when you first started drinking?

Yes No 4. Do you ever wake up the morning after you've been drinking and discover that you can't remember part of the evening before, even though your friends tell you that you didn't pass out?

Yes No 5. When drinking with other people, do you try to have a few extra drinks when others won't know it?

Yes No 6. Are there certain occasions when you feel uncomfortable if alcohol isn't available?

Yes No 7. Have you recently noticed that, when you begin drinking, you're in more of a hurry to get the first drink than you used to be?

Yes No 8. Do you sometimes feel a little guilty about your drinking?

Yes No 9. Are you secretly irritated when your family or friends discuss your drinking?

Yes No 10. Have you recently noticed an increase in the frequency of memory blackouts?

Yes No 11. Do you often find that you wish to continue drinking after your friends say they've had enough?

Yes No 12. Do you usually have a reason for the occasions when you drink heavily?

Yes No 13. When you're sober, do you often regret things you have done or said while drinking?

Yes No 14. Have you tried switching brands or following different plans to control your drinking?

Yes No 15. Have you often failed to keep promises you've made to yourself about controlling or stopping your drinking?

Yes No 16. Have you ever tried to control your drinking by changing jobs or moving to a new location?

Yes No 17. Do you try to avoid family or close friends while you're drinking?

Yes No 18. Are you having an increasing number of financial and work problems?

Yes No 19. Do more people seem to be treating you unfairly without good reason?

Yes No 20. Do you eat very little or irregularly when you're drinking?

Yes No 21. Do you sometimes have the "shakes" in the morning and find that it helps to have a little drink?

Yes No 22. Have you recently noticed that you can drink more than you once did?

Yes No 23. Do you sometimes stay drunk for several days at a time?

Yes No 24. Do you sometimes feel very depressed and wonder whether life is worth living?

Yes No 25. Sometimes after periods of drinking do you see or hear things that aren't there?

Yes No 26. Do you get terribly frightened after you have been drinking heavily?

Interpretation

These are all symptoms that may indicate alcoholism. "Yes" answers to several of the questions indicate the following stages of alcoholism.

Questions 1 to 8: Potential drinking problem

Questions 9 to 21: Drinking problem likely

Questions 22 to 26: Definite drinking problem

It is vital to assess yourself honestly. If you or someone you know demonstrates some of these symptoms, it is important to seek help. If there is even a question in your mind, talk to a professional about it.

Reprinted with permission from the National Council on Alcoholism and Drug Dependence, Inc. (NCADD) www.ncadd.org. About NCADD: National Council on Alcoholism and Drug Dependence, Inc. (NCADD) and its Affiliate Network is a voluntary health organization dedicated to fighting the Nation's #1 health problem—alcoholism, drug addiction and the devastating consequences of alcohol and other drugs on individuals, families and communities.

Summary

8.1 Alcohol, chemically known as ethanol, is found in beer, wine, distilled spirits (hard liquor, such as vodka and rum), liqueurs, cordials, and hard cider. These beverages range from 5% alcohol to more than 40% alcohol. A standard drink is defined as 15 g of alcohol, and that equates to 12 oz of beer, 5 oz of wine, and 1.5 oz of distilled spirits. Ethanol is produced by the chemical process known as fermentation. Grains, cereals, fruits, honey, milk, potatoes, and other carbohydrate-rich foods are used to make alcoholic beverages.

8.2 Alcohol is readily absorbed in the GI tract because it does not require digestion. The rate of absorption is affected by gender, ethnicity, body size and composition, and alcohol and food intake. Alcohol is primarily metabolized in the liver, although small amounts also are metabolized in the stomach. The body uses the alcohol dehydrogenase (ADH) pathway to metabolize small amounts of alcohol and the microsomal ethanol oxidizing system (MEOS) to metabolize moderate to large amounts of alcohol. Blood alcohol levels can be determined by measuring the amount of alcohol excreted through the lungs with a breathalyzer test. A blood alcohol content of 0.08% is the legal definition of intoxication and is associated with impaired judgment and coordination. Alcohol poisoning, a very dangerous condition, occurs when blood alcohol content continues to rise, causing vomiting, irregular breathing and heartbeat, low blood sugar, severe dehydration, seizures, confusion, coma, and death.

8.3 About 62% of North American adults consume alcohol; most are light or moderate drinkers, but 5% consume excessive amounts. College students are frequent drinkers and many engage in binge drinking. Binge drinking is a dangerous practice associated with a variety of accidents, crimes, health risks, and even death.

8.4 If alcohol is consumed, it should be consumed in moderation with meals. Women are advised to drink no more than 1 drink per day, men, no more than 2 drinks a day. The benefits of alcohol use are associated with low to moderate alcohol consumption. These benefits include the pleasurable and social aspects of alcohol use and possibly a reduced risk of cardiovascular disease. Excessive consumption of alcohol contributes significantly to 5 of the 10 leading causes of death in North America. Alcohol increases the risk of developing heart damage, inflammation of the pancreas, GI tract damage, certain forms of cancer, and hypertension. The liver is particularly vulnerable to the toxic effects of alcohol. Liver damage occurs as fatty liver, alcoholic hepatitis, and cirrhosis. Fatty liver can be relieved by abstention from alcohol, but cirrhosis cannot. Cirrhosis results in the impaired synthesis of vital proteins and abnormal fluid retention. Most people with cirrhosis are malnourished. Liver failure is the typical outcome of cirrhosis. Nutritional problems are common among alcoholics. Alcohol abuse can impair nutrient intake and absorption, alter nutrient metabolism, and increase nutrient excretion. Deficiencies of protein, fat- and water-soluble vitamins, and the minerals calcium, magnesium, iron, and zinc are most common.

8.5 Alcoholism and alcohol abuse affect 8.5% of the adult population in the U.S. Many personal, social, and employment problems result from excessive alcohol use. Genetic factors account for 40 to 50% of a person's risk of alcoholism. Differences in the alcohol-metabolizing genes may account for some of these genetic risks. Males have higher rates of alcoholism, but women are at higher risk of alcohol-related damage throughout the body. Drinking at a young age puts one at risk of alcohol problems later in life. Some ethnic groups, particularly Native American Indians, have higher rates of alcohol use and abuse. Mental health and alcohol use disorders often occur together. The CAGE questionnaire is one of several that can help a person determine whether he or she has an alcohol problem. The treatment of alcoholism or alcohol abuse includes behavioral and pharmacologic therapy. Three medications are approved to treat alcoholism. Alcoholics Anonymous* is another avenue for help. Recovery rates from alcoholism and alcohol abuse can be high, especially with early intervention.

Study Questions

1. An 80-proof alcohol is approximately 80% alcohol.

   a. true   **b.** false

2. A standard drink is defined as the amount that provides approximately 15 g of alcohol. Which of the following is considered a standard-size drink?

   a. 16-ounce beer
   b. 20-ounce wine cooler
   c. 5-ounce glass of wine
   d. 4-ounce pour of hard liquor

3. Alcohol requires no digestion and can enter cells without specific transport mechanisms.

   a. true   **b.** false

4. Which of the following is the primary pathway used in the metabolism of small amounts of alcohol?

   a. alcohol dehydrogenase pathway
   b. microsomal ethanol oxidizing system
   c. catalase pathway
   d. none of the above

276 **PART 2** Energy-Yielding Nutrients and Alcohol

5. Which of the following affects the metabolism of alcohol?

    a. gender   **c.** ethnicity
    b. diet composition   **d.** all of the above

6. What blood alcohol concentration denotes legal intoxication in the U.S. and Canada?

    a. 1.0%   **c.** 0.05%
    b. 0.08%   **d.** 0.10%

7. Compared with individuals who begin drinking alcohol at a legal age, those who begin drinking as teenagers have higher rates of alcohol dependency and alcohol abuse in adulthood.

    a. true   **b.** false

8. Which of the following would be considered moderate drinking?

    a. 1 drink per day for women and 2 drinks per day for men
    b. 2 drinks per day for both men and women
    c. 2 drinks per day for women and 3 drinks per day for men
    d. 4 drinks on any single occasion for men and women

9. In moderation, alcohol may help raise HDL-cholesterol.

    a. true   **b.** false

10. Risk of cancer of the _____ increases greatly with high alcohol consumption.

    a. esophagus   **c.** bone
    b. lung   **d.** all of the above

11. The first stage of alcoholic liver disease is _____.

    a. cirrhosis   **c.** steatosis
    b. alcoholic hepatitis **d.** inflammation of the liver

12. The symptoms of cirrhosis include _____.

    a. abnormal fluid retention **c.** poor nutritional status
    b. jaundice   **d.** all of the above

13. Alcohol intake should be avoided during pregnancy.

    a. true   **b.** false

14. Which of the following is *not* a common nutritional concern in alcoholics?

    a. vitamin B-12 deficiency   **c.** vitamin A toxicity
    b. protein-energy malnutrition **d.** iron deficiency

15. Medications used to treat alcohol dependency act on _____.

    a. the brain to reduce alcohol cravings
    b. the liver to block complete metabolism of alcohol
    c. the stomach to prevent alcohol absorption
    d. both a and b

16. What is a standard-size serving of alcohol? How many servings are considered moderate for men and women?

17. Describe how alcohol is metabolized. What is a by-product of alcohol metabolism?

18. Define binge drinking and list 4 problems associated with this practice.

19. Describe the health benefits and risks of alcohol use.

20. What criteria may indicate that someone is dependent on alcohol?

Answer Key: 1-b; 2-c; 3-a; 4-a; 5-d; 6-b; 7-a; 8-a; 9-a; 10-a; 11-c; 12-d; 13-a; 14-c; 15-d; 16-refer to Section 8.1; 17-refer to Section 8.2; 18-refer to Section 8.3; 19-refer to Section 8.4; 20-refer to Section 8.5

Websites

To learn more about the topics covered in this chapter, visit these websites.

www.niaaa.nih.gov

www.asam.org

www.mentalhelp.net/selfhelp

www.nlm.nih.gov/medlineplus

www.findtreatment.samhsa.gov

www.nacoa.org

www.aa.org

www.al-anon.alateen.org

www.cdc.gov/ncbddd/fasd

References

1. National Institute on Alcohol Abuse and Alcoholism. Database resources/statistical tables. 2011; www.niaaa.nih.gov.

2. Kerr W and others. Alcohol content variation of bar and restaurant drinks in northern California. *Alcohol Clin Exp Res.* 2008;32:1623.

3. Lieber C. Nutrition in liver disorders and the role of alcohol. In: Shils ME and others, eds. *Modern nutrition in health and disease.* Philadelphia: Lippincott Williams & Wilkins; 2006.

4. National Institute on Alcohol Abuse and Alcoholism. Alcohol alert 72. Alcohol metabolism: An update. 2007; pubs.niaaa.nih.

5. Agrawal A and others. Measuring alcohol consumption for genomic meta-analysis of alcohol intake: opportunities and challenges. *Am J Clin Nitr* 2012;95:539.

6. Schukit M. Alcohol and alcoholism. In: Longo D and others, eds. *Harrison's principles of internal medicine.* New York: McGraw-Hill, 2011.

7. U.S. Department of Health and Human Services. *Healthy People 2020.* 2010; www.healthypeople.gov.

8. O'Brien MC and others. Caffeinated cocktails: Energy drink consumption, high-risk drinking, and alcohol-related consequences among college students. *Acad Emerg Med.* 2008;15:453.

9. Brewer R, Swahn M. Binge drinking and violence. *JAMA.* 2005;294:6165.

10. American Academy of Pediatrics, Committee on Substance Abuse. Alcohol use by youth and adolescents: A pediatric concern. *Pediatrics.* 2010;125:1078.

11. National Institute on Alcohol Abuse and Alcoholism. Alcohol alert 70. National epidemiologic survey on alcohol and related conditions. 2006; pubs.niaaa.nih.gov/publications/AA70/AA70.htm.

12. Moritsugu K. Underage drinking: A call to action. *J Am Diet Assoc.* 2007;107:1464.

13. Hingson RW and others. Age at drinking onset and alcohol dependence: Age at onset, duration, and severity. *Arch Pediatr Adolesc Med.* 2006;160:739.

14. Ferreira M, Weems S. Alcohol consumption by aging adults in the United States: Health benefits and detriments. *J Am Diet Assoc.* 2008;108:1668.

15. Ronksley PE and others. Association of alcohol consumption with selected cardiovascular disease outcomes: a systematic review and meta-analysis. *BMJ* 2011; 342: d 671.

16. Di Castelnuovo A and others. Alcohol dosing and total mortality in men and women: An updated meta-analysis of 34 prospective studies. *Arch Intern Med.* 2006;166:2437.

17. Penumathsa S, Maulik N. Resveratrol: A promising agent in promoting cardioprotection against coronary heart disease. *Can J Physiol Pharmcol.* 2009;87:275.

18. Crandall J and others. Alcohol consumption and diabetes risk in the Diabetes Prevention Program. *Am J Clin Nutr.* 2009;90:595.

19. Mehlig K and others. Alcoholic beverages and the incidence of dementia: 34-year follow-up of the prospective population study of women in Goteborg. *Am J Epidemiol.* 2008;167:684.

20. Harris SL and others. Never-smokers, never-drinkers: Unique clinical subgroup of young patients with head and neck squamous cell cancers. *Head & Neck.* 2010;32:499.

21. Warnakulasuriya S and others. Demonstration of ethanol-induced protein adducts in oral leukoplakia (pre-cancer) and cancer. *J Oral Pathol Med.* 2008;37:157.

22. World Cancer Research Fund/American Institute for Cancer Research. Food, nutrition, physical activity and the prevention of cancer: A global perspective. Washington, DC: AICR; 2007.

23. Clemens DL, Mahan KJ. Alcoholic pancreatitis: Lessons from the liver. *World J Gastroenterol.* 2010;16:1314.

24. Everitt H and others. Nutrition and alcoholic liver disease. *Br Nutr Foundation.* 2007;32:138.

25. Jones KL. The effects of alcohol on fetal development. *Birth Defects Res C Embryo Today.* 2011; 93:3.

26. Rehm J and others. Global burden of disease and injury and economic cost attributable to alcohol use and alcohol-use disorders. *Lancet.* 2009;373:2223.

27. Zaridze D and others. Alcohol and cause-specific mortality in Russia: A retrospective case-control study of 48,557 adult deaths. *Lancet.* 2009;373:2201.

28. American Academy of Pediatrics. Breastfeeding and the use of human milk. *Pediatrics.* 2005;115:496.

29. Mennella J, Gerrish C. Effects of exposure to alcohol in mother's milk on infant sleep. *Pediatrics.* 1998;101:e2.

30. Schuckit M. Alcohol-use disorders. *Lancet.* 2009;373:492.

31. Hasin DS and others. Prevalence, correlates, disability, and comorbidity of DSM-IV alcohol abuse and dependence in the United States: Results from the National Epidemiologic Survey on Alcohol and Related Conditions. *Arch Gen Psychiatry.* 2007;64:830.

32. Edenberg HJ and others. Association of alcohol dehydrogenase genes with alcohol dependence: A comprehensive analysis. *Hum Mol Genet.* 2006;15:1539.

33. Centers for Disease Control and Prevention. Alcohol-related disease impact. 2010; www.cdc.gov/alcohol/ardi.htm.

34. Grant B and others. Prevalence and co-occurrence of substance use disorders and independent mood and anxiety disorders. Results from the National Epidemiologic Survey on Alcohol and Related Conditions. *Arch Gen Psychiatry.* 2004;61:807.

35. U.S. Preventive Services Task Force. Screening and behavioral counseling interventions in primary care to reduce alcohol misuse: Recommendation statement. *Am Fam Physician.* 2004;70:353.

36. Anton RF and others. Combined pharmacotherapies and behavioral interventions for alcohol dependence: The COMBINE Study: A randomized controlled trial. *JAMA.* 2006;295:2003.

37. Laaksonen E and others. A randomized, multicentre, open-label, comparative trial of disulfiram, naltrexone and acamprosate in the treatment of alcohol dependence. *Alcohol Alcohol.* 2008;43:53.

38. Ray LA and others. Naltrexone for the treatment of alcoholism: Clinical findings, mechanisms of action, and pharmacogenetics. *CNS Neurolog Dis Drug Targets.* 2010;9:13.

39. Gossop M and others. Attendance at Narcotics Anonymous and Alcoholics Anonymous meetings, frequency of attendance and substance use outcomes after residential treatment for drug dependence: A 5-year follow-up study. *Addiction.* 2008;103:119.

Metabolism and Energy Balance

Life depends on energy from the sun. During photosynthesis, plants transform solar energy into chemical energy in the form of carbohydrates. During energy metabolism, we transform this chemical energy into ATP. Learn more at **health.nih.gov.**

PART 3 Metabolism and Energy Balance

9   Energy Metabolism

Student Learning Outcomes

After studying this chapter, you will be able to

1. Explain the differences among metabolism, catabolism, and anabolism.

2. Describe aerobic and anaerobic metabolism of glucose.

3. Illustrate how energy is extracted from glucose, fatty acids, amino acids, and alcohol using metabolic pathways, such as glycolysis, beta-oxidation, the citric acid cycle, and the electron transport chain.

4. Describe the role that acetyl-CoA plays in cell metabolism.

5. Identify the conditions that lead to ketogenesis and its importance in survival during fasting.

6. Describe the process of gluconeogenesis.

7. Discuss how the body metabolizes alcohol.

8. Compare the fate of energy from macronutrients during the fed and fasted states.

9. Describe common inborn errors of metabolism.

THE MACRONUTRIENTS AND ALCOHOL ARE rich sources of energy; however, the energy they provide is neither in the form that cells can use nor in the amount needed to carry out the thousands of chemical reactions that occur every day in the human body. Thus, the body must have a process for breaking down energy-yielding compounds to release and convert their chemical energy to a form the body can use.[1] That process is energy metabolism—an elaborate, multistep series of energy-transforming chemical reactions. Energy metabolism occurs in all cells every moment of every day for our entire lifetime; it is slowest when we are resting and fastest when we are physically active.

Understanding energy metabolism clarifies how carbohydrates, proteins, fats, and alcohol are interrelated and how they serve as fuel for body cells. In this chapter, you will see how the macronutrients and alcohol are metabolized and discover why proteins can be converted to glucose but most fatty acids cannot. Studying energy metabolism pathways in the cell also sets the stage for examining the roles of vitamins and minerals. As you'll see in this and subsequent chapters, many micronutrients contribute to the enzyme activity that supports metabolic reactions in the cell.[2] Thus, both macronutrients and micronutrients are required for basic metabolic processes.

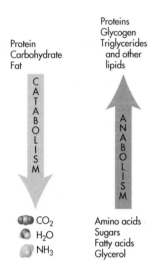

Figure 9-1 Anabolism and catabolism are opposite processes that together make up metabolism. Anabolism (the process of building compounds) relies on catabolism (the process of breaking down compounds) to provide the energy (ATP) required to build compounds.

metabolic pathway Series of chemical reactions occurring in a cell.

intermediate Compound formed in a metabolic pathway.

9.1 Metabolism: Chemical Reactions in the Body

Metabolism refers to the entire network of chemical processes involved in maintaining life. It encompasses all the sequences of chemical reactions that occur in the body. Some of these biochemical reactions enable us to release and use energy from carbohydrate, fat, protein, and alcohol. They also permit us to synthesize one substance from another and prepare waste products for excretion.[1] A group of biochemical reactions that occur in a progression from beginning to end is called a **metabolic pathway.** Compounds formed in one of the many steps in a metabolic pathway are called **intermediates.**

All of the pathways that take place within the body can be categorized as either anabolic or catabolic. **Anabolic** pathways use small, simpler compounds to build larger, more complex compounds (Fig. 9-1). The human body uses compounds, such as glucose, fatty acids, cholesterol, and amino acids, as building blocks to synthesize new compounds, such as glycogen, hormones, enzymes, and other proteins, to keep the body functioning and to support normal growth and development. For example, to make glycogen (a storage form of carbohydrate), we link many units of the simple sugar glucose. Energy must be expended for anabolic pathways to take place.

Conversely, **catabolic** pathways break down compounds into small units. The glycogen molecule discussed in the anabolism example is broken down into many glucose molecules when blood levels of glucose drop. Later, the complete catabolism of this glucose results in the release of carbon dioxide (CO_2) and water (H_2O). Energy is released during catabolism: some is trapped for cell use and the rest is lost as heat.

The body strives for a balance between anabolic and catabolic processes. However, there are times when one is more prominent than the other. For example, during growth there is a net anabolic state because more tissue is being synthesized than broken down. However, during weight loss or a wasting disease, such as cancer, more tissue is being broken down than synthesized.

Energy for the Cell

Cells use energy for the following purposes: building compounds, contracting muscles, conducting nerve impulses, and pumping ions (e.g., across cell membranes).[1] This energy comes from catabolic reactions that break the chemical bonds between the atoms in carbohydrate, fat, protein, and alcohol. These energy-containing compounds are produced during photosynthesis, when plants convert solar energy and carbon dioxide into glucose and other organic (carbon-containing) compounds (see Chapter 5). Virtually all organisms use the sun—either indirectly, as we do, or directly—as their source of energy.[1]

As shown in Figure 9-2, the series of catabolic reactions that produce energy for body cells begins with digestion and continues when monosaccharides, amino acids, fatty acids, glycerol, and alcohol are sent through a series of metabolic pathways, which finally trap a portion of the energy they contain into a compound called **adenosine triphosphate (ATP)**—the main form of energy the body uses. Heat, carbon dioxide, and water also result from

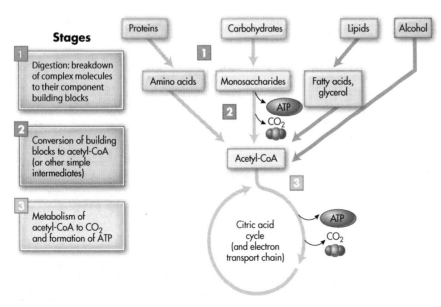

Figure 9-2 Three stages of catabolism.

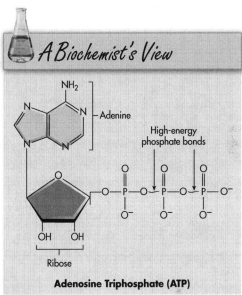

Figure 9-3 ATP is a storage form of energy for cell use because it contains high-energy bonds. P_i is the abbreviation for an inorganic phosphate group.

these catabolic pathways. The heat produced helps maintain body temperature. Plants can use the carbon dioxide and water to produce glucose and oxygen via photosynthesis.

Adenosine Triphosphate (ATP)

Only the energy in ATP and related compounds can be used directly by the cell.[3] A molecule of ATP consists of the organic compound adenosine (comprised of the nucleotide adenine and the sugar ribose) bound to 3 phosphate groups (Fig. 9-3). The bonds between the phosphate groups contain energy and are called high-energy phosphate bonds. Hydrolysis of the high-energy bonds releases this energy. To release the energy in ATP, cells break a high-energy phosphate bond, which creates **adenosine diphosphate (ADP)** plus P_i, a free (inorganic) phosphate group (Fig. 9-4). Hydrolysis of ADP results in the compound **adenosine monophosphate (AMP)** in a reaction muscles are capable of performing during intense exercise when ATP is in short supply (ADP + ADP → ATP + AMP). ATP can be regenerated by adding the phosphates back to AMP and ADP.

Every cell requires energy from ATP to synthesize new compounds (anabolic pathways), contract muscles, conduct nerve impulses, and pump ions across membranes. Catabolic pathways in cells release energy, which allows ADP to combine with P_i and form ATP. Every cell has pathways to break down and resynthesize ATP. A cell is constantly breaking down ATP in one site while rebuilding it in another. This recycling of ATP is an important strategy because the body contains only about 0.22 lb (100 g) of ATP at any given time, but a sedentary adult uses about 88 lb (40 kg) of ATP each day. The requirement increases even more during exercise—during 1 hour of strenuous exercise, an additional 66 lb (30 kg) of ATP are used. In fact, the runner who currently holds the American record for the men's marathon was estimated to use 132 lb (65 kg) to run the race.[24]

Oxidation-Reduction Reactions: Key Processes in Energy Metabolism

The synthesis of ATP from ADP and P_i involves the transfer of energy from energy-yielding compounds (carbohydrate, fat, protein, and alcohol). This process uses oxidation-reduction reactions, in which electrons (along with hydrogen ions) are transferred in a series of reactions from energy-yielding compounds eventually to oxygen. These reactions form water and release much energy, which can be used to produce ATP.

A substance is *oxidized* when it loses 1 or more electrons. For example, copper is oxidized when it loses an electron:

$$Cu^+ \rightleftharpoons Cu^{2+} + e^-$$

A substance is *reduced* when it gains 1 or more electrons. For example, iron is reduced when it gains an electron:

$$Fe^{3+} + e^- \rightleftharpoons Fe^{2+}$$

A Biochemist's View

Adenosine Triphosphate (ATP)

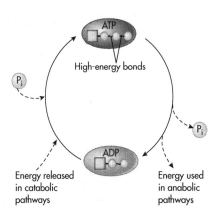

Figure 9-4 ATP stores and yields energy. ATP is the high-energy state; ADP is the lower-energy state. When ATP is broken down to ADP plus P_i, energy is released for cell use. When energy is trapped by ADP plus P_i, ATP can be formed.

282   **PART 3**   Metabolism and Energy Balance

▶ The mnemonic "LEO [loss of electrons is oxidation] the lion says GER [gain of electrons is reduction]" can help you differentiate between oxidation and reduction.

A Biochemist's View

CH₂OH
Glucose

Pyruvate

The movement of electrons governs oxidation-reduction processes. If one substance loses electrons (is oxidized), another substance must gain electrons (is reduced). These processes go together; one cannot occur without the other.[2] In the previous examples, the electron lost by copper can be gained by the iron, resulting in this overall reaction:

$$Cu^+ + Fe^{3+} \rightarrow Cu^{2+} + Fe^{2+}$$

Oxidation-reduction reactions involving organic (carbon-containing) compounds are somewhat more difficult to visualize. Two simple rules help identify whether these compounds are oxidized or reduced:

If the compound gains oxygen or loses hydrogen, it has been *oxidized*.

If it loses oxygen or gains hydrogen, the compound has been *reduced*.

Enzymes control oxidation-reduction reactions in the body. Dehydrogenases, one class of these enzymes, remove hydrogens from energy-yielding compounds or their breakdown products. These hydrogens are eventually donated to oxygen to form water. In the process, large amounts of energy are converted to ATP.[1]

Two B-vitamins, niacin and riboflavin, assist dehydrogenase enzymes and, in turn, play a role in transferring the hydrogens from energy-yielding compounds to oxygen in the metabolic pathways of the cell.[2] In the following reaction, niacin functions as the **coenzyme** nicotinamide adenine dinucleotide (NAD). NAD is found in cells in both its oxidized form (NAD) and its reduced form (NADH). During intense (anaerobic) exercise, the enzyme lactate dehydrogenase helps reduce pyruvate (made from glucose) to form lactate. During reduction, 2 hydrogens, derived from NADH + H⁺, are gained. Lactate is oxidized back to pyruvate by losing 2 hydrogens. NAD⁺ is the hydrogen acceptor. That is, the oxidized form of niacin (NAD⁺) can accept 1 hydrogen ion and 2 electrons to become the reduced form NADH + H⁺. (The plus [+] on NAD⁺ indicates it has 1 less electron than in its reduced form. The extra hydrogen ion [H⁺] remains free in the cell.) By accepting 2 electrons and 1 hydrogen ion, NAD⁺ becomes NADH + H⁺, with no net charge on the coenzyme.

▶ The term *antioxidant* is typically used to describe a compound that can donate electrons to oxidized compounds, putting them into a more reduced (stable) state. Oxidized compounds tend to be highly reactive; they seek electrons from other compounds to stabilize their chemical configuration. Dietary antioxidants, such as vitamin E, donate electrons to these highly reactive compounds, in turn, putting these oxidized compounds into a less reactive state (see Chapter 15).

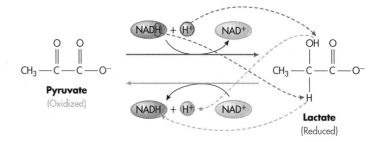

Pyruvate
(Oxidized)

Lactate
(Reduced)

Riboflavin plays a similar role. In its oxidized form, the coenzyme form is known as flavin adenine dinucleotide (FAD). When it is reduced (gains 2 hydrogens, equivalent to 2 hydrogen ions and 2 electrons), it is known as FADH₂.

The reduction of oxygen (O) to form water (H₂O) is the ultimate driving force for life because it is vital to the way cells synthesize ATP. Thus, oxidation-reduction reactions are a key to life.

coenzyme Compound that combines with an inactive protein, called an apoenzyme, to form a catalytically active protein, called a holoenzyme. In this manner, coenzymes aid in enzyme function.

Knowledge Check

1. What is the main form of energy used by the body?
2. What are catabolic and anabolic reactions?
3. What is the difference between oxidation and reduction reactions?
4. How do niacin and riboflavin play a role in metabolism?

9.2 ATP Production from Carbohydrates

Cells release energy stored in food and then traps as much of this energy as possible in the form of ATP. The body cannot afford to lose all energy immediately as heat, even though some heat is necessary for the maintenance of body temperature. This section examines how ATP is produced from carbohydrates. Subsequent sections will explore how ATP is produced using the energy stored in fats, proteins, and alcohol. Along the way, you will see how these energy-yielding processes are interconnected.

ATP is generated through cellular respiration. The process of **cellular respiration** oxidizes (removes electrons) food molecules to obtain energy (ATP). Oxygen is the final electron acceptor. As you know, humans inhale oxygen and exhale carbon dioxide. When oxygen is readily available, cellular respiration may be **aerobic.** When oxygen is not present, **anaerobic** pathways are used. Aerobic respiration is far more efficient than anaerobic metabolism at producing ATP. As an example, the aerobic respiration of a single molecule of glucose will result in a net gain of 30 to 32 ATP. In contrast, the anaerobic metabolism of a single molecule of glucose is limited to a net gain of 2 ATP.

The 4 stages of aerobic cellular respiration of glucose are as follows (Fig. 9-5).[1,4]

Stage 1: Glycolysis. In this pathway, glucose (a 6-carbon compound) is oxidized and forms 2 molecules of the 3-carbon compound pyruvate, produces $NADH + H^+$, and generates a net of 2 molecules of ATP. Glycolysis occurs in the **cytosol** of cells.

▶ A new tool for understanding how individuals differ in the metabolic response to nutrients may lie in the ability to track the actual metabolic intermediates made during metabolism, such as how we respond to exposure to different fatty acids. This approach, called *metabolomics*, should be more accurate than looking for differences in DNA between individuals to predict dietary responses.

---

cellular respiration Oxidation (electron removal) of food molecules resulting in the eventual release of energy, CO_2, and water.

aerobic Requiring oxygen.

anaerobic Not requiring oxygen.

cytosol Water-based phase of a cell's cytoplasm; excludes organelles, such as mitochondria.

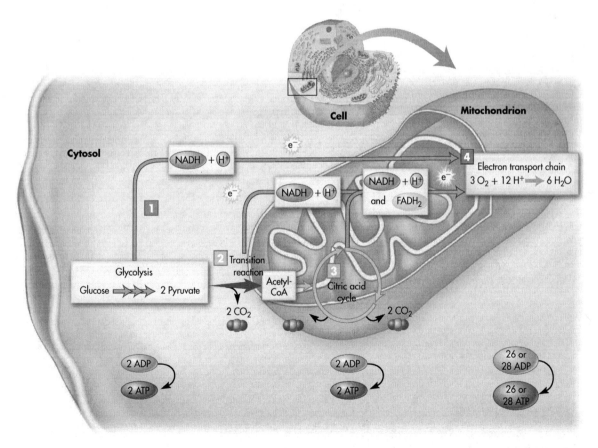

Figure 9-5 The 4 stages of aerobic carbohydrate metabolism. Glycolysis in the cytoplasm produces pyruvate (stage **1**), which enters mitochondria if oxygen is available. The transition reaction (stage **2**), citric acid cycle (stage **3**), and electron transport chain (stage **4**) occur inside the mitochondria. The electron transport chain receives the electrons that were removed from glucose breakdown products during stages 1 through 3. The result of glucose breakdown is 30 to 32 ATP, depending on the particular cell.

► A number of defects are related to the metabolic processes that take place in mitochondria. A variety of medical interventions, some of which use specific nutrients and related metabolic intermediates, can be used to treat the muscle weakness and muscle destruction typically arising from these disorders.

Acetyl-CoA

► CoA is short for *coenzyme A*. The *A* stands for *acetylation* because CoA provides the 2-carbon acetyl group to start the citric acid cycle.

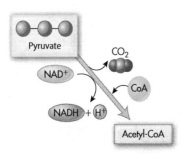

Figure 9-6 During the transition reaction, pyruvate is metabolized to acetyl-CoA, which then enters the citric acid cycle. In the process, NADH + H⁺ is produced and CO_2 is lost. The pyruvate dehydrogenase enzyme assists in the transition reaction of pyruvate to acetyl-CoA.

mitochondria Main sites of energy production in a cell. They also contain the pathway for oxidizing fat for fuel, among other metabolic pathways.

Stage 2: Transition reaction. In this stage, pyruvate is further oxidized and joined with coenzyme A (CoA) to form acetyl-CoA (Fig. 9-6). The transition reaction also produces NADH + H⁺ and releases carbon dioxide (CO_2) as a waste product. The transition reaction takes place in the **mitochondria** of cells.

Stage 3: Citric acid cycle. In this pathway, acetyl-CoA enters the citric acid cycle, resulting in the production of NADH + H⁺, $FADH_2$, and ATP. Carbon dioxide is released as a waste product. Like the transition reaction, the citric acid cycle takes place within the mitochondria of cells.

Stage 4: Electron transport chain. The NADH + H⁺ produced by stages 1 through 3 of cellular respiration and $FADH_2$ produced in stage 3 enter the electron transport chain, where NADH + H⁺ is oxidized to NAD⁺, and $FADH_2$ is oxidized to FAD. At the end of the electron transport chain, oxygen is combined with hydrogen ions (H⁺) and electrons to form water. The electron transport chain takes place within the mitochondria of cells. Most ATP is produced in the electron transport chain; thus, the mitochondria are the cell's major energy-producing organelles.

Glycolysis

Because glucose is the main carbohydrate involved in cell metabolism, we will track its step-by-step metabolism as an example of carbohydrate metabolism. Glucose metabolism begins with **glycolysis,** which means "breaking down glucose." Glycolysis has 2 roles: to break down carbohydrates to generate energy and to provide building blocks for synthesizing other needed compounds. During glycolysis, glucose passes through several steps, which convert it to 2 units of a 3-carbon compound called pyruvate. The details of glycolysis can be found in Figure 9-7.

Transition Reaction: Synthesis of Acetyl-CoA

Pyruvate passes from the cytosol into the mitochondria, where the pyruvate dehydrogenase enzyme complex converts pyruvate into the compound acetyl-CoA in a process called a transition reaction[5] (see Fig. 9-6). This overall reaction is irreversible, which has important metabolic consequences. Whereas glycolysis requires only the B-vitamin niacin as NAD, the conversion of pyruvate to acetyl-CoA requires coenzymes from 4 B-vitamins—thiamin, riboflavin, niacin, and pantothenic acid. In fact, CoA is made from the B-vitamin pantothenic acid. For this reason, carbohydrate metabolism depends on an ample supply of these vitamins (see Chapter 13).[2]

The transition reaction oxidizes pyruvate and reduces NAD⁺. Each glucose yields 2 acetyl-CoA. As with the NADH + H⁺ produced by glycolysis, the 2 NADH + 2 H⁺ produced by the transition reaction will eventually enter the electron transport chain. Carbon dioxide is a waste product of the transition reaction and is eventually eliminated by way of the lungs.

Knowledge Check

1. What is the goal of glycolysis?
2. How many 3-carbon compounds are made from a 6-carbon glucose molecule?
3. What is the end product of glycolysis?
4. What vitamins are involved in the transition reaction?

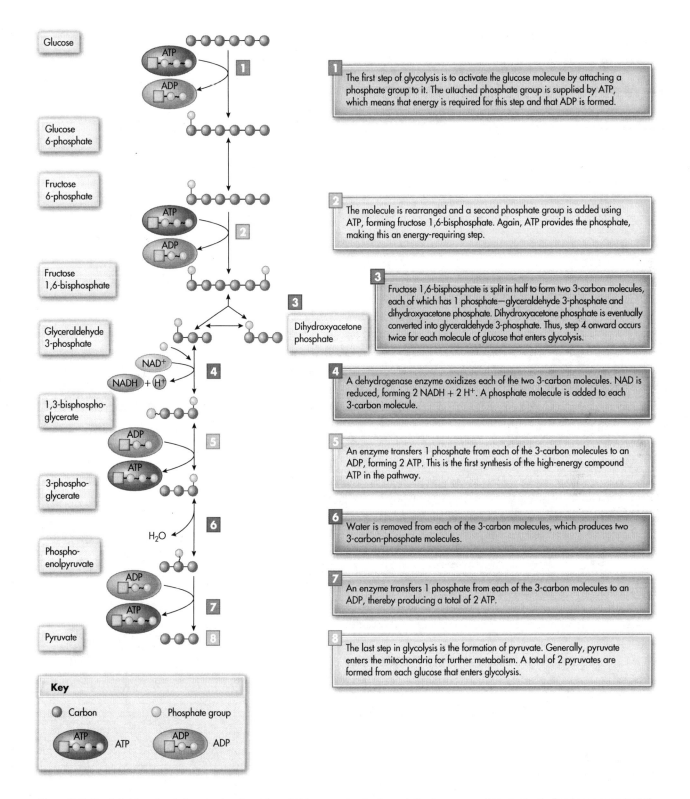

1 The first step of glycolysis is to activate the glucose molecule by attaching a phosphate group to it. The attached phosphate group is supplied by ATP, which means that energy is required for this step and that ADP is formed.

2 The molecule is rearranged and a second phosphate group is added using ATP, forming fructose 1,6-bisphosphate. Again, ATP provides the phosphate, making this an energy-requiring step.

3 Fructose 1,6-bisphosphate is split in half to form two 3-carbon molecules, each of which has 1 phosphate—glyceraldehyde 3-phosphate and dihydroxyacetone phosphate. Dihydroxyacetone phosphate is eventually converted into glyceraldehyde 3-phosphate. Thus, step 4 onward occurs twice for each molecule of glucose that enters glycolysis.

4 A dehydrogenase enzyme oxidizes each of the two 3-carbon molecules. NAD is reduced, forming 2 NADH + 2 H$^+$. A phosphate molecule is added to each 3-carbon molecule.

5 An enzyme transfers 1 phosphate from each of the 3-carbon molecules to an ADP, forming 2 ATP. This is the first synthesis of the high-energy compound ATP in the pathway.

6 Water is removed from each of the 3-carbon molecules, which produces two 3-carbon-phosphate molecules.

7 An enzyme transfers 1 phosphate from each of the 3-carbon molecules to an ADP, thereby producing a total of 2 ATP.

8 The last step in glycolysis is the formation of pyruvate. Generally, pyruvate enters the mitochondria for further metabolism. A total of 2 pyruvates are formed from each glucose that enters glycolysis.

Key

● Carbon   ○ Phosphate group

ATP   ADP

Figure 9-7 Glycolysis takes place in the cytosol portion of the cell. This process breaks glucose (a 6-carbon compound) into 2 units of a 3-carbon compound called pyruvate. More details can be found in Appendix C.

Citric Acid Cycle

The acetyl-CoA molecules produced by the transition reaction enter the citric acid cycle, which also is known as the tricarboxylic acid cycle (TCA cycle) and the Krebs cycle. The citric acid cycle is a series of chemical reactions that cells use to convert the carbons of an acetyl group to carbon dioxide while harvesting energy to produce ATP.[3]

It takes 2 turns of the citric acid cycle to process 1 glucose molecule because glycolysis and the transition reaction yield 2 acetyl-CoA. Each complete turn of the citric

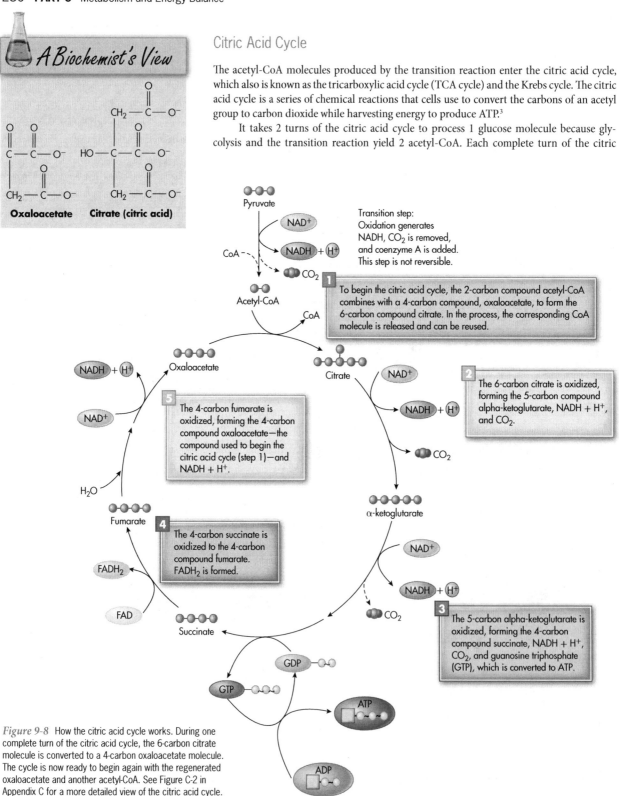

A Biochemist's View

Oxaloacetate   **Citrate (citric acid)**

Transition step:
Oxidation generates NADH, CO_2 is removed, and coenzyme A is added. This step is not reversible.

1 To begin the citric acid cycle, the 2-carbon compound acetyl-CoA combines with a 4-carbon compound, oxaloacetate, to form the 6-carbon compound citrate. In the process, the corresponding CoA molecule is released and can be reused.

2 The 6-carbon citrate is oxidized, forming the 5-carbon compound alpha-ketoglutarate, NADH + H^+, and CO_2.

3 The 5-carbon alpha-ketoglutarate is oxidized, forming the 4-carbon compound succinate, NADH + H^+, CO_2, and guanosine triphosphate (GTP), which is converted to ATP.

4 The 4-carbon succinate is oxidized to the 4-carbon compound fumarate. $FADH_2$ is formed.

5 The 4-carbon fumarate is oxidized, forming the 4-carbon compound oxaloacetate—the compound used to begin the citric acid cycle (step 1)—and NADH + H^+.

Figure 9-8 How the citric acid cycle works. During one complete turn of the citric acid cycle, the 6-carbon citrate molecule is converted to a 4-carbon oxaloacetate molecule. The cycle is now ready to begin again with the regenerated oxaloacetate and another acetyl-CoA. See Figure C-2 in Appendix C for a more detailed view of the citric acid cycle.

acid cycle produces 2 molecules of CO_2 and 1 potential ATP in the form of 1 molecule of guanosine triphosphate (GTP), as well as 3 molecules of NADH + H$^+$ and 1 molecule of FADH$_2$. Oxygen does not participate in any of the steps in the citric acid cycle; however, it does participate in the electron transport chain. The details of the citric acid cycle can be found in Figure 9-8; further details are in Appendix C.

Electron Transport Chain

The final pathway of aerobic respiration is the electron transport chain located in the mitochondria. The electron transport chain functions in most cells in the body. Cells that need a lot of ATP, such as muscle cells, have thousands of mitochondria, whereas cells that need very little ATP, such as adipose cells, have fewer mitochondria. Almost 90% of the ATP produced from the catabolism of glucose is produced by the electron transport chain.

The electron transport chain involves the passage of electrons along a series of electron carriers. As electrons are passed from one carrier to the next, small amounts of energy are released. NADH + H$^+$ and FADH$_2$, produced by glycolysis, the transition reaction, and the citric acid cycle, supply both hydrogen ions and electrons to the electron transport chain. The metabolic process, called **oxidative phosphorylation**, is the way in which energy derived from the NADH + H$^+$ and FADH$_2$ is transferred to ADP + P$_i$ to form ATP (Fig. 9-9). Oxidative phosphorylation requires the minerals copper and iron. Copper is a component of an enzyme, whereas iron is a component of **cytochromes** (electron-transfer compound) in

▶ Intermediates of the citric acid cycle, such as oxaloacetate, can leave the cycle and go on to form other compounds, such as glucose. Thus, the citric acid cycle should be viewed as a traffic circle, rather than as a closed circle.

▶ How many ATP are produced by 1 molecule of glucose? The metabolism of 1 glucose molecule will yield

Glycolysis	2 NADH
	2 ATP
Transition reaction	2 NADH
Citric acid cycle	6 NADH
	2 FADH$_2$
	2 GTP
Total	**10 NADH**
	2 FADH$_2$
	2 GTP
	2 ATP

The NADH, FADH$_2$, and GTP generated undergo oxidative phosphorylation in the electron transport chain to yield

2.5 ATP molecules per NADH

1.5 ATP molecules per FADH$_2$

1.0 ATP molecule per GTP

Thus, 28 ATP molecules are synthesized in the electron transport chain.

Net Production of ATP from Each Glucose Molecule

Glycolysis	2 ATP
Citric acid cycle	2 ATP
Electron transport chain ATP	28 ATP
Total	**32 ATP**

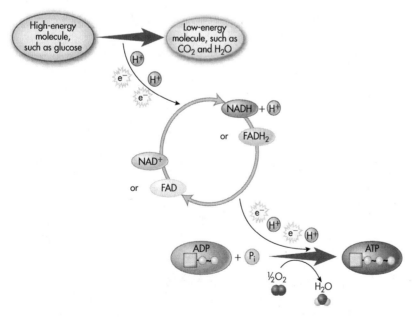

Figure 9-9 Simplified depiction of electron transfer in energy metabolism. High-energy compounds, such as glucose, give up electrons and hydrogen ions to NAD$^+$ and FAD. The NADH + H$^+$ and FADH$_2$ that are formed transfer these electrons and hydrogen ions, using specialized electron carriers, to oxygen to form water (H_2O). The energy yielded by the entire process is used to generate ATP from ADP and P$_i$.

288   **PART 3**   Metabolism and Energy Balance

the electron transport chain. In addition to ATP production, hydrogen ions, electrons, and oxygen combine to form water. The details of the electron transport chain are presented in Figure 9-10.

The Importance of Oxygen

NADH + H$^+$ and FADH$_2$ produced during the citric acid cycle can be regenerated into NAD$^+$ and FAD only by the eventual transfer of their electrons and hydrogen ions to oxygen, as occurs in the electron transport chain. The citric acid cycle has no ability to oxidize NADH + H$^+$ and FADH$_2$ back to NAD$^+$ and FAD. This is ultimately why oxygen is essential to many life forms—it is a final acceptor of the electrons and hydrogen ions generated from the breakdown of energy-yielding nutrients. Without oxygen, most of our cells are unable to extract enough energy from energy-yielding nutrients to sustain life.[1]

▶ In Figure 9-10, step 1, NADH + H$^+$ donates its chemical energy to an FAD-related compound called flavin mononucleotide (FMN). In contrast, FADH$_2$ donates its chemical energy at a later point in the electron transport chain. This different placement of FAD and NAD$^+$ in the electron transport chain results in a difference in ATP production. Each NADH + H$^+$ in a mitochondrion releases enough energy to form the equivalent of 2.5 ATP, whereas each FADH$_2$ releases enough energy to form the equivalent of 1.5 ATP.[1]

Figure 9-10   The electron transport chain.

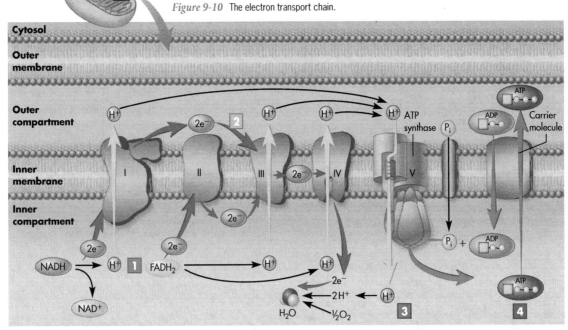

1 NADH + H$^+$ and FADH$_2$ transfer their hydrogen ions and electrons to the electron carriers located on the inner mitochondrial membrane. Although NADH + H$^+$ and FADH$_2$ transfer their hydrogens to the electron transport chain, the hydrogen ions (H$^+$), having been separated from their electron (H→H$^+$ + e$^-$), are not carried down the chain with the electrons. Instead, the hydrogen ions are pumped into the outer compartment (located between the inner and outer membrane of a mitochondrion). The NAD$^+$ and FAD regenerated from the oxidation of the NADH + H$^+$ and FADH$_2$ are now ready to function in glycolysis, the transition reaction, and the citric acid cycle.

2 Pairs of electrons are then separated by coenzyme Q (CoQ) and each electron is then passed along a group of iron-containing cytochromes. At each transfer from one cytochrome to the next, energy is released. Some of this energy is used to pump hydrogen ions into the outer compartment. A portion of the energy is eventually used to generate ATP from ADP and P$_i$, but much is simply released as heat.

3 As hydrogen ions diffuse back into the inner compartment through special channels, ATP is produced by the enzyme ATP synthase. At the end of the chain of cytochromes, the electrons, hydrogen ions, and oxygen combine to form water. Oxygen is the final electron acceptor and is reduced to form water.

4 One carrier molecule moves ADP into the inner compartment and a different carrier molecule moves phosphate (P$_i$) into the inner compartment. In the inner compartment, the energy generated by the electron transport chain unites ADP to P$_i$ to form ATP. ATP is transported out of the inner compartment by a carrier protein molecule that exchanges ATP for ADP.

Anaerobic Metabolism

Some cells lack mitochondria and, so, are not capable of aerobic respiration. Other cells are capable of turning to anaerobic metabolism when oxygen is lacking. When oxygen is absent, pyruvate that is produced through glycolysis is converted into lactate, or lactic acid. Anaerobic metabolism is not nearly as efficient as aerobic respiration because it converts only about 5% of the energy in a molecule of glucose to energy stored in the high-energy phosphate bonds of ATP.[1]

The anaerobic glycolysis pathway encompasses glycolysis and the conversion of pyruvate to lactate (Fig. 9-11). The one-step reaction, catalyzed by the enzyme pyruvate dehydrogenase, involves a simple transfer of a hydrogen from NADH + H[+] to pyruvate to form lactate and NAD[+]. The synthesis of lactate regenerates the NAD[+] required for the continued function of glycolysis. The reaction can be summarized as

$$\text{Pyruvate} + \text{NADH} + \text{H}^+ \rightarrow \text{Lactate} + \text{NAD}^+$$

For cells that lack mitochondria, such as red blood cells, anaerobic glycolysis is the only method for making ATP because they lack the electron transport chain and oxidative phosphorylation. Therefore, when red blood cells convert glucose to pyruvate, NADH + H[+] builds up in the cell. Eventually, the NAD[+] concentration falls too low to permit glycolysis to continue.[5] The anaerobic glycolysis pathway produces lactate to regenerate NAD[+]. The lactate produced by the red blood cell is then released into the bloodstream, picked up primarily by the liver, and used to synthesize pyruvate, glucose, or some other intermediate in aerobic respiration.

Even though muscles cells contain mitochondria, during intensive exercise they also produce lactate when NAD[+] is depleted. By regenerating NAD[+], the production of lactate allows anaerobic glycolysis to continue. Muscle cells can then make the ATP required for muscle contraction even if little oxygen is present. However, as you will find out in Chapter 11, it becomes more difficult to contract those muscles as the lactate concentration builds up.

Knowledge Check

1. How is citric acid in the citric acid cycle formed?
2. How many NADH + H[+] are formed in the citric acid cycle?
3. Why is the citric acid cycle called a cycle?
4. What is the purpose of the electron transport chain?
5. What are the end products of the electron transport chain?

▶ Coenzyme Q-10 is sold as a nutrient supplement in health-food stores (*10* signifies that it is the form found in humans). However, when the mitochondria need coenzyme Q, they make it. Thus, to maintain overall health, coenzyme Q is not needed in the diet or as a supplement. (Such use may be helpful, however, in people with heart failure.)[12]

▶ In anaerobic environments, some microorganisms, such as yeast, produce ethanol, a type of alcohol, instead of lactate from glucose. Other microorganisms produce various forms of short-chain fatty acids. All this anaerobic metabolism is referred to as fermentation.

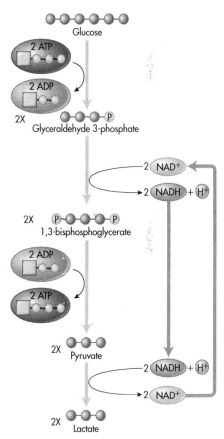

Figure 9-11 Anaerobic glycolysis "frees" NAD[+] and it returns to the glycolysis pathway to pick up more hydrogen ions and electrons.

Quick bursts of activity rely on the production of lactate to help meet the ATP energy demand.

CASE STUDY

Melissa is a 45-year-old woman who is obese. At her last physical, her doctor told her that she needs to lose weight. Melissa decided to follow a low-carbohydrate, high-protein diet. She knows it will be difficult to follow because many of the foods Melissa likes are rich in carbohydrates, and the diet eliminates almost all carbohydrates during the first 2 weeks. Although she is ready to try the diet, she is confused about certain phases of the program, especially the part where the author talks about ketones. In the book, the author states that anyone going on this diet should purchase ketone strips to dip in his or her urine for the detection of ketones. The author strongly suggests these tests, especially during the extremely low-carbohydrate part of the diet. Melissa wonders if she should be considering this diet if the author is telling her to check something and she wonders what ketones are.

What are ketones and why does a very-low-carbohydrate diet produce an increase in ketones in both the blood and the urine? Can you speculate at this time why low carbohydrates cause ketones? Why do some fad diets produce ketones?

9.3 ATP Production from Fats

Just as cells release the energy in carbohydrates and trap it as ATP, they also release and trap energy in triglyceride molecules. This process begins with **lipolysis,** the breaking down of triglycerides into free fatty acids and glycerol. The further breakdown of fatty acids for energy production is called **fatty acid oxidation** because the donation of electrons from fatty acids to oxygen is the net reaction in the ATP-yielding process. This process takes place in the mitochondria.

Fatty acids for oxidation can come from either dietary fat or fat stored in the body as adipose tissue. Following high-fat meals, the body stores excess fat in adipose tissue. However, during periods of low calorie intake or fasting, triglycerides from fat cells are broken down into fatty acids by an enzyme called hormone-sensitive lipase and released in the blood. The activity of this enzyme is increased by hormones such as glucagon, growth hormone, and epinephrine and is decreased by the hormone insulin. The fatty acids are taken up from the bloodstream by cells throughout the body and are shuttled from the cell cytosol into the mitochondria using a carrier called **carnitine** (Fig. 9-12).[6]

▶How many ATP are produced by a 16-carbon fatty acid? The metabolism of a 16-carbon fatty acid will yield

Beta-oxidation	7 FADH₂
	7 NADH
Citric acid cycle (8 turns; once for each 2-carbon fragment)	8 FADH₂
	24 NADH
	8 GTP
Total	**15 FADH₂**
	31 NADH
	8 GTP

The NADH, FADH₂, and GTP undergo oxidative phosphorylation in the electron transport chain to yield

  2.5 ATP molecules per NADH

  1.5 ATP molecules per FADH₂

  1.0 ATP molecule per GTP

Thus, 108 ATP molecules are synthesized in the electron transport chain.

Net ATP Production from a 16-Carbon Fatty Acid*	
Beta-oxidation	0 ATP
Citric acid cycle	8 ATP
Electron transport chain	100 ATP
Total	**108 ATP**
ATP Used for Activation	**· 2 ATP**
Net ATP	**106 ATP**

*Note: Only NADH and FADH₂ are formed during beta-oxidation, which are subsequently converted to ATP in the electron transport chain.

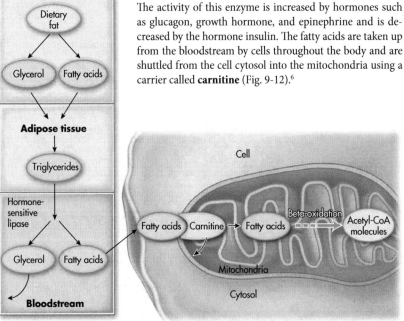

Figure 9-12 Lipolysis is the breakdown of triglycerides into free fatty acids and glycerol. Because of the action of hormone-sensitive lipase, fatty acids are released from triglycerides in adipose cells and enter the bloodstream. The fatty acids are taken up from the bloodstream by various cells and shuttled by carnitine into the inner portion of the cell mitochondria. The fatty acid then undergoes beta-oxidation, which yields acetate molecules equal in number to half of the carbons in the fatty acid.

ATP Production from Fatty Acids

Almost all fatty acids in nature are composed of an even number of carbons, ranging from 2 to 26. The first step in transferring the energy in such a fatty acid to ATP is to cleave the carbons, 2 at a time, and convert the 2-carbon fragments to acetyl-CoA. Fatty acid oxidation is also called beta-oxidation because the process of converting a free fatty acid to multiple acetyl-CoA molecules begins with the beta carbon, the 2nd carbon on a fatty acid (counting after the carboxyl [acid] end).[1] (See Chapter 6.) During beta-oxidation, $NADH + H^+$ and $FADH_2$ are produced (Fig. 9-13). Thus, as with glucose, a fatty acid is eventually degraded into a number of the 2-carbon compound acetyl-CoA (the exact number produced depends on the number of carbons in the fatty acid). Some of the chemical energy contained in the fatty acid is transferred to $NADH + H^+$ and $FADH_2$.

The acetyl-CoA enters the citric acid cycle, and 2 carbon dioxides are released, just as with the acetyl-CoA produced from glucose. Thus, the breakdown product of both glucose and fatty acids—acetyl-CoA—enter the citric acid cycle. One big difference, however, is that a 16-carbon fatty acid yields 106 ATP, whereas the 6-carbon glucose yields only 30 to 32 ATP. The difference in ATP production occurs because each 2-carbon segment in the fatty acid goes around the citric acid cycle; thus, a 16-carbon fatty acid goes around the citric acid cycle 8 times. Additionally, each fatty acid carbon results in about 7 ATP, whereas about 5 ATP per carbon result from glucose oxidation. This is because fatty acids have

▶ Carnitine helps shuttle free fatty acids in the cytosol into mitochondria. Carnitine is a popular nutritional supplement. In healthy people, cells produce the carnitine needed, and carnitine supplements provide no benefit. In patients hospitalized with acute illnesses, however, carnitine synthesis may be inadequate. These patients may need to have carnitine added to their intravenous feeding (total parenteral nutrition) solutions.

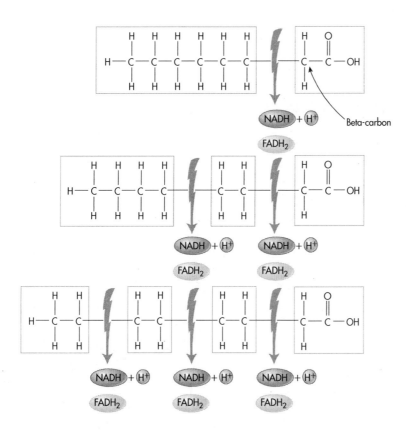

Figure 9-13 In beta-oxidation, each 2-carbon fragment cleaved from a fatty acid (acetyl group) yields electrons and hydrogen ions to form $NADH + H^+$ and $FADH_2$ as the fragments are split off the parent fatty acid. The 2-carbon acetyl molecule then typically enters the citric acid cycle (as acetyl-CoA); see Fig. 9-14.

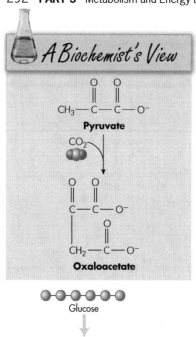

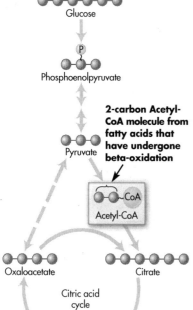

Figure 9-14 As acetyl-CoA concentrations increase due to beta-oxidation, oxaloacetate levels are maintained by pyruvate from carbohydrate metabolism. In this way, carbohydrates help oxidize fatty acids.

ketone bodies Incomplete breakdown products of fat, containing 3 or 4 carbons. Most contain a chemical group called a ketone. An example is acetoacetic acid.

ketosis Condition of having a high concentration of ketone bodies and related breakdown products in the bloodstream and tissues.

more carbon-hydrogen bonds and fewer carbon-oxygen atoms than glucose. The carbons of glucose exist in a more oxidized state than fat; as a result, fats yield more energy than carbohydrates (9 kcal/g versus 4 kcal/g).[1]

Occasionally, a fatty acid has an odd number of carbons, so the cell forms a 3-carbon compound (propionyl-CoA) in addition to the acetyl-CoA. The propionyl-CoA enters the citric acid cycle directly, bypassing acetyl-CoA. It can then go on to yield NADH + H$^+$ and FADH$_2$, CO$_2$, and even other products, such as glucose (see Section 9.4).

Carbohydrate Aids Fat Metabolism

In addition to its role in energy production, the citric acid cycle provides compounds that leave the cycle and enter biosynthetic pathways. This results in a slowing of the cycle, as eventually not enough oxaloacetate is formed to combine with the acetyl-CoA entering the cycle. Cells are able to compensate for this by synthesizing additional oxaloacetate. One potential source of this additional oxaloacetate is pyruvate (Fig. 9-14). Thus, as fatty acids create acetyl-CoA, carbohydrates (e.g., glucose) are needed to keep the concentration of pyruvate high enough to resupply oxaloacetate to the citric acid cycle. Overall, the entire pathway for fatty acid oxidation works better when carbohydrate is available.

Ketogenesis

Ketone bodies are products of incomplete fatty acid oxidation.[7] This occurs mainly with hormonal imbalances—chiefly, inadequate insulin production to balance glucagon action in the body. These imbalances lead to a significant production of ketone bodies and a condition called **ketosis.** The key steps in the development of ketosis are shown in Figure 9-15.

Most ketone bodies are subsequently converted back into acetyl-CoA in other body cells, where they then enter the citric acid cycle and can be used for fuel. One of the ketone bodies formed (acetone) leaves the body via the lungs, giving the breath of a person in ketosis a characteristic, fruity smell.

Ketosis in Diabetes

In type 1 diabetes, little to no insulin is produced. This lack of insulin does not allow for normal carbohydrate and fat metabolism. Without sufficient insulin, cells cannot readily utilize glucose, resulting in rapid lipolysis and the excess production of ketone bodies.[8] If the concentration of ketone bodies rises too high in the blood, they spill into the urine, pulling the electrolytes sodium and potassium with them. Eventually, severe ion imbalances occur in the body. The blood also becomes more acidic because 2 of the 3 forms of ketone bodies contain acid groups. The resulting condition, known as **diabetic ketoacidosis,** can induce coma or death if not treated immediately, such as with insulin, electrolytes, and fluids (see Chapter 5). Ketoacidosis usually occurs only in ketosis caused by uncontrolled type 1 diabetes; in fasting, blood concentrations of ketone bodies typically do not rise high enough to cause the problem.

Ketosis in Semistarvation or Fasting

When a person is in a state of semistarvation or fasting, the amount of glucose in the body falls, so insulin production falls. This fall in blood insulin then causes fatty acids to flood into the bloodstream and eventually form ketone bodies in the liver. The heart, muscles, and some

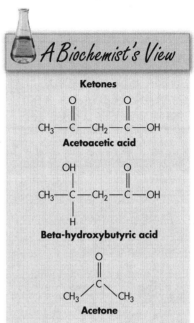

Stages

1 Blood insulin drops, usually as a result of type 1 diabetes or low carbohydrate intake.

2 A fall in blood insulin promotes lipolysis, which causes fatty acids stored in adipose cells to be released rapidly into the bloodstream.

3 Most of the fatty acids in the blood are taken up by the liver.

4 As the liver oxidizes the fatty acids to acetyl-CoA, the capacity of the citric acid cycle to process the acetyl-CoA molecules decreases. This is mostly because the metabolism of fatty acids to acetyl-CoA yields many ATP. When the cells have plenty of ATP, there is no need to use the citric acid cycle to produce more.

5 These metabolic changes encourage liver cells to combine 2 acetyl-CoA molecules to form a 4-carbon compound. This compound is further metabolized and eventually secreted into the bloodstream as ketone bodies (acetoacetic acid and the related compounds, beta-hydroxybutyric acid and acetone).

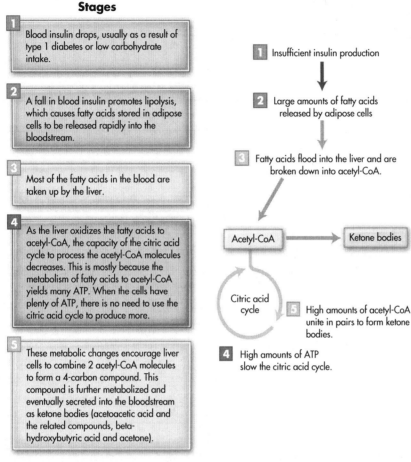

1 Insufficient insulin production

2 Large amounts of fatty acids released by adipose cells

3 Fatty acids flood into the liver and are broken down into acetyl-CoA.

Acetyl-CoA → Ketone bodies

Citric acid cycle

5 High amounts of acetyl-CoA unite in pairs to form ketone bodies.

4 High amounts of ATP slow the citric acid cycle.

Figure 9-15 Key steps in ketosis. Any condition that limits insulin or glucose availability to cells results in some ketone body production.

CRITICAL THINKING

The use of a very-low-carbohydrate diet to induce ketosis for weight loss is covered in Chapter 10. Why is careful physician monitoring needed if this type of diet is followed?

parts of the kidneys then use ketone bodies for fuel. After a few days of ketosis, the brain also begins to metabolize ketone bodies for energy.

This adaptive response is important to semistarvation or fasting. As more body cells begin to use ketone bodies for fuel, the need for glucose as a body fuel diminishes. This then reduces the need for the liver and kidneys to produce glucose from amino acids (and from the glycerol released from lipolysis), sparing much body protein from being used as a fuel source (see Section 9.4). The maintenance of body protein mass is a key to survival in semistarvation or fasting—death occurs when about half of the body protein is depleted, usually after about 50 to 70 days of total fasting.[9]

Metabolism is part of everyday life; metabolic activity increases when we increase physical activity and slows during fasting and semistarvation.

Knowledge Check

1. How are fatty acids shuttled into the mitochondria for energy production?
2. What is the end product of beta oxidation?
3. How do fatty acids enter the citric acid cycle?
4. What conditions must exist in the body to promote the formation of ketones?

9.4 Protein Metabolism

▶ Branched-chain amino acids are added to some liquid meal replacement supplements given to hospitalized patients. Some fluid replacement formulas marketed to athletes also contain branched-chain amino acids (see Chapter 11).

The metabolism of protein (i.e., amino acids) takes place primarily in the liver. Only branched-chain amino acids—leucine, isoleucine, and valine—are metabolized mostly at other sites—in this case, the muscles.[2]

Protein metabolism begins after proteins are degraded into amino acids. To use an amino acid for fuel, cells must first deaminate them (remove the amino group) (see Chapter 7). These pathways often require vitamin B-6 to function. Removal of the amino group produces carbon skeletons, most of which enter the citric acid cycle. Some carbon skeletons also yield acetyl-CoA or pyruvate.[5]

Some carbon skeletons enter the citric acid cycle as acetyl-CoA, whereas others form intermediates of the citric acid cycle or glycolysis (Fig. 9-16). Any part of the carbon skeleton that can form pyruvate (i.e., alanine, glycine, cysteine, serine, and threonine) or bypass acetyl-CoA and enter the citric acid cycle directly (such amino acids include asparagine, arginine, aspartic acid, histidine, glutamic acid, glutamine, isoleucine, methionine, proline, valine, and phenylalanine) are called **glucogenic amino acids** because these carbons can become

Figure 9-16 Gluconeogenesis. Amino acids that can yield glucose can be converted to pyruvate ▣, directly enter the citric acid cycle ▣, or be converted directly to oxaloacetate ▣. Amino acids that cannot yield glucose are converted to acetyl-CoA and are metabolized in the citric acid cycle ▣. The glycerol portion of triglycerides ▣ can be converted to glucose. The glycerol portion of amino acids ▣ can be used to make glucose. Fatty acids with an even number of carbons ▣ and ketogenic amino acids ▣ cannot become glucose.

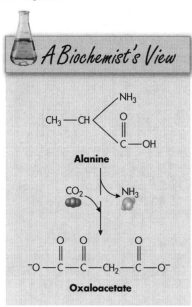

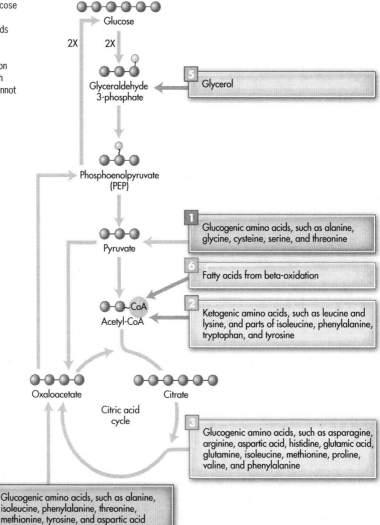

the carbons of glucose. Any parts of carbon skeletons that become acetyl-CoA (leucine and lysine, as well as parts of isoleucine, phenylalanine, tryptophan, and tyrosine) are called **ketogenic amino acids** because these carbons cannot become parts of glucose molecules. The factor that determines whether an amino acid is glucogenic or ketogenic is whether part or all of the carbon skeleton of the amino acid can yield a "new" oxaloacetate molecule during metabolism, 2 of which are needed to form glucose.

Gluconeogenesis: Producing Glucose from Glucogenic Amino Acids and Other Compounds

The pathway to produce glucose from certain amino acids—**gluconeogenesis**—is present only in liver cells and certain kidney cells. The liver is the primary gluconeogenic organ. A typical starting material for this process is oxaloacetate, which is derived primarily from the carbon skeletons of some amino acids, usually the amino acid alanine. Pyruvate also can be converted to oxaloacetate (see Fig. 9-14).

Gluconeogenesis begins in the mitochondria with the production of oxaloacetate. The 4-carbon oxaloacetate eventually returns to the cytosol, where it loses 1 carbon dioxide, forming the 3-carbon compound phosphoenolpyruvate, which then reverses the path back through glycolysis to glucose. It takes 2 of these 3-carbon compounds to produce the 6-carbon glucose. This entire process requires ATP, as well as coenzyme forms of the B-vitamins biotin, riboflavin, niacin, and B-6.[5]

To learn more about gluconeogenesis, examine Figure 9-16 and trace the pathway that converts the amino acid glutamine to glucose. Glutamine first loses its amino group to form its carbon skeleton, which enters the citric acid cycle directly and is converted by stages to oxaloacetate. Oxaloacetate loses 1 carbon as carbon dioxide, and the 3-carbon phosphoenolpyruvate produced then moves through the gluconeogenic pathway to form glucose. Eventually, 2 glutamine molecules are needed to form 1 glucose molecule.

Gluconeogenesis from Typical Fatty Acids Is Not Possible

Typical fatty acids cannot be turned into glucose because those with an even number of carbons—the typical form in the body—break down into acetyl-CoA molecules. Acetyl-CoA can never re-form into pyruvate; the step between pyruvate and acetyl-CoA is irreversible. The options for acetyl-CoA are forming ketones and/or combining with oxaloacetate in the citric acid cycle. However, 2 carbons of acetyl-CoA are added to oxaloacetate at the beginning of the citric acid cycle, and 2 carbons are subsequently lost as carbon dioxide when citrate converts back to the starting material, oxaloacetate. Thus, at the end of one cycle, no carbons from acetyl-CoA are left to turn into glucose; it is impossible to convert typical fatty acids into glucose.[5]

The glycerol portion of a triglyceride is the part that can become glucose. Glycerol enters the glycolysis pathway and can follow the gluconeogenesis pathway from glyceraldehyde 3-phosphate to glucose. Glucose yield from glycerol is insignificant.[1]

Disposal of Excess Amino Groups from Amino Acid Metabolism

The catabolism of amino acids yields amino groups (–NH$_2$), which then are converted to ammonia (NH$_3$). The ammonia must be excreted because its buildup is toxic to cells. The liver prepares the amino groups for excretion in the urine with the urea cycle. Some stages of the urea cycle occur in the cytosol and some in the mitochondria. During the urea cycle, 2 nitrogen groups—1 ammonia group and 1 amino group—react through a series of steps with carbon dioxide molecules to form urea and water. Eventually, urea is excreted in the urine (Fig. 9-17).[5]

gluconeogenesis Generation (*genesis*) of new (*neo*) glucose from certain (glucogenic) amino acids.

Ammonia (NH$_3$) + Amino group (–NH$_2$) + CO$_2$

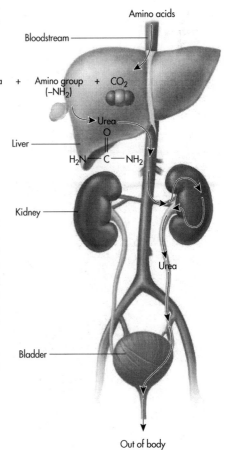

Figure 9-17 Disposal of excess amino groups. The nitrogen groups, one as ammonia and the other as an amino group, form part of urea, which is excreted in urine. The nitrogen groups originally came from amino acids that went through transamination reactions and ultimately deamination to yield the free nitrogen groups.

GL⬤BAL PERSPECTIVE

Cancer Cell Metabolism

Cancer is characterized by abnormal, uncontrolled cell growth (see Medical Perspective in Chapter 12 for more information). As you can see in Figure 9-18, this disease affects many people in nations around the world.[27] Scientists have been working for years to find successful treatments for cancer. One area of investigation focuses on preventing cancer cell growth by disrupting the metabolism of these cells.[28]

Recall that, in normal metabolism, ATP is generated through glycolysis, the citric acid cycle, and the electron transport chain. During glycolysis, glucose is converted to pyruvate. When oxygen levels are low, pyruvate is converted to lactate and only the 2 ATP from glycolysis are generated. When oxygen is sufficient, pyruvate is routed to the citric acid cycle and electron transport chain, generating a total of 30 to 32 ATP. Things are different, however, in cancer cells.

Even when oxygen is plentiful, cancer cells use glycolysis and produce lactate. This alteration in metabolism during cancer, known as the Warburg effect, was first observed by Nobel Prize winner Otto Warburg over 80 years ago. Researchers believe that this altered glucose metabolism ensures that cancer cells have the energy needed to support their rapid growth. Because cancer cells are burning glucose in this wasteful manner, they starve healthy cells of energy and nutrients. As the starving healthy cells weaken and die, cancer cells gain the space they need to proliferate. This wasteful use of glucose also may promote cancer cell growth—that's because their excessive nutrient use produces free radicals, which may increase DNA mutations and promote cancer (see Chapter 15).

Cancer cells also use protein and fats wastefully. In both healthy and cancer cells, the nitrogen component (amino group) of the amino acid glutamine is used to synthesize nonessential amino acids (via transamination), which are then used to build body proteins (see Chapter 7). Cancer cells grow rapidly and need a large supply of glutamine to support cell synthesis—the high rate of glutamine use by cancer cells impairs normal protein synthesis in the body. Cancer cells also burn glutamine for energy in the citric acid cycle (see Figure 9-16). Cancer cells also can use fat for energy, but they use fat mostly to make the new lipids and phospholipids they need for their cell membranes (see Chapter 6).

Many cancer cells die when glucose is withdrawn; however, blocking glycolysis has not been shown to be a useful cancer treatment. One potential treatment involves blocking the enzymes needed to convert pyruvate to lactate or lactate back to pyruvate. Another possibility is blocking the enzyme needed to convert glutamine to glutamate, the form required to enter the citric acid cycle and generate energy. Still another possibility involves blocking the enzymes needed to build new lipids from fatty acids. Drugs that alter the enzymes cancer cells use during metabolism may prove to be effective cancer treatments.

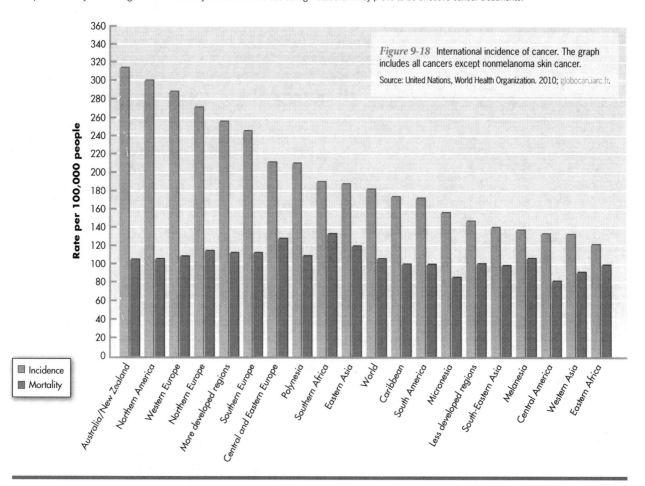

Figure 9-18 International incidence of cancer. The graph includes all cancers except nonmelanoma skin cancer.

Source: United Nations, World Health Organization. 2010; globocan.iarc.fr.

In liver disease, ammonia can build up to toxic concentrations in the blood, whereas in kidney disease the toxic agent is urea. The form of nitrogen in the blood—ammonia or urea—is a diagnostic tool for detecting liver or kidney disease.

Knowledge Check

1. In order to use amino acids as a fuel, what must happen to the nitrogen attached to the amino acid?
2. Where does the nitrogen attached to an amino acid used as fuel end up?
3. What part of the amino acid is used in the metabolic pathways?
4. What is the name of the pathway that converts amino acids to glucose?
5. Can fat be used to synthesize glucose? Why or why not?

 9.5 Alcohol Metabolism

The alcohol dehydrogenase (ADH) pathway is the main pathway for alcohol metabolism. In the first step of this pathway, alcohol is converted in the cytosol to acetaldehyde by the action of the enzyme alcohol dehydrogenase and the coenzyme NAD^+. NAD^+ picks up 2 hydrogen ions and 2 electrons from the alcohol to form $NADH + H^+$ and produces the intermediate acetaldehyde (Fig. 9-19). In the next step of the ADH pathway, the acetaldehyde formed is converted to acetyl-CoA, again yielding $NADH + H^+$ with the aid of the enzyme aldehyde dehydrogenase and coenzyme A.

Alcohol, carbohydrate, protein, and fat all contribute chemical energy to the body.

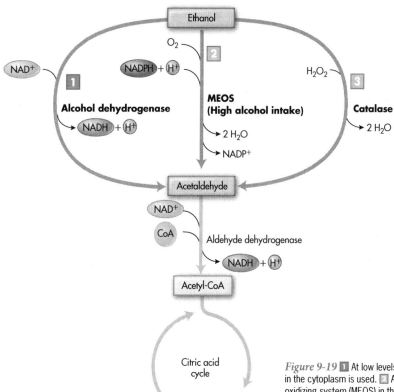

Figure 9-19 **1** At low levels of alcohol intake, the alcohol dehydrogenase pathway in the cytoplasm is used. **2** At high levels of alcohol intake, the microsomal ethanol oxidizing system (MEOS) in the cytoplasm is used. The MEOS uses rather than yields energy and accounts in general for about 10% of alcohol metabolism. **3** Catalase occurs in the peroxisomes of cells and is a minor pathway.

CRITICAL THINKING

Your roommate heard that the more alcohol you drink the more you can metabolize, so, if you gradually increase your alcohol intake, you can drink all you want with no harmful effects. What advice would you give your roommate about alcohol and the body's ability to metabolize it?

The metabolism of alcohol occurs predominantly in the liver, although approximately 10 to 30% of alcohol is metabolized in the stomach. Different forms (known as polymorphisms) of alcohol dehydrogenase and aldehyde dehydrogenase are found in the stomach and the liver.

The acetyl-CoA formed through the ADH pathway has several metabolic fates. Small amounts can enter the citric acid cycle to produce energy. However, the breakdown of alcohol in the ADH pathway utilizes NAD^+ and converts it to NADH. As NAD^+ supplies become limited and NADH levels build, the citric acid cycle slows and blocks the entry of acetyl-CoA. Because of the toxic effects of alcohol and acetaldehyde, the metabolism of alcohol takes priority over continuation of the citric acid cycle. Thus, most of the acetyl-CoA is directed toward fatty acid and triglyceride synthesis, resulting in the accumulation of fat in the liver (called steatosis). Clinicians are often alerted to this condition by high levels of triglycerides in the blood.

When a person drinks moderate to excessive amounts of alcohol, the ADH pathway cannot keep up with the demand to metabolize all the alcohol and acetaldehyde. To prevent the toxic effects of alcohol and acetaldehyde, the body utilizes a second pathway, called the microsomal ethanol oxidizing system (MEOS), to metabolize the excess alcohol. As shown in Figure 9-19, this system uses oxygen and a different niacin-containing coenzyme (NADP) and produces water and acetaldehyde. When excessive amounts of alcohol are consumed at one time, the ability of these enzyme systems to metabolize alcohol completely is exceeded, and the result is alcohol poisoning (see Chapter 8).

The MEOS differs in several ways from the ADH pathway. First, the MEOS uses potential energy (in the form of $NADPH + H^+$, another niacin coenzyme), rather than yielding potential energy (as $NADH + H^+$ in the ADH pathway) in the conversion of ethanol to acetaldehyde. This use of energy may, in part, explain why individuals who consume large amounts of alcohol do not gain as much weight as might be expected from the amount of alcohol-derived energy they consume.

The body has an additional pathway, called the catalase pathway, for metabolizing alcohol. However, this is a relatively minor pathway in comparison with the ADH and MEOS pathways.

Knowledge Check

1. Where does the alcohol dehydrogenase pathway function?
2. Which intermediate in the alcohol dehydrogenase pathway is toxic?
3. In addition to the ADH pathway, what other pathways allow the metabolism of alcohol?

9.6 Regulation of Energy Metabolism

As shown in Figure 9-20, energy metabolism can take many forms in the body. Carbohydrates can be used for fat synthesis—the acetyl-CoA from the breakdown of carbohydrate is the building block for fatty acid synthesis. By stringing together glycolysis and the citric acid cycle, cells can convert carbohydrates into carbon skeletons for the synthesis of certain amino acids and can use the energy in carbohydrates to form ATP. These pathways also can turn the carbon skeletons of some amino acids into the carbon skeletons of others. In addition, they can convert carbon skeletons from some amino acids to glucose or have them drive ATP synthesis by serving as substrates (precursors) for intermediates in the citric acid cycle. Finally, fatty acids can provide energy for ATP synthesis or produce ketone bodies; however,

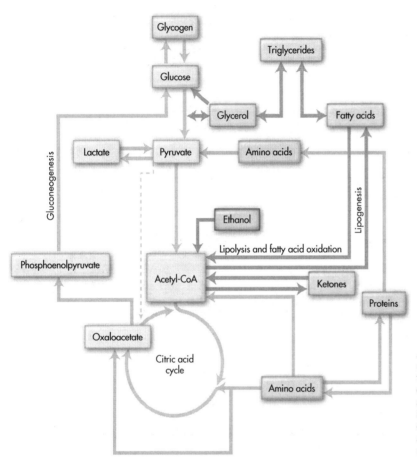

Figure 9-20 Overview of cell metabolism. Note that acetyl-CoA forms a crossroads for many pathways and that the citric acid cycle also can be used to help build compounds. Anabolic and catabolic processes may appear to share the same pathways, but generally this is true for only a few steps. Because a specific set of enzymes must be activated to promote anabolism and a different set to activate catabolism, the cell has significant control over metabolism.

they cannot become glucose. The glycerol part of the triglyceride either can be converted into glucose and be used for fuel or can contribute to ATP synthesis via participation in glycolysis, the citric acid cycle, and electron transport chain metabolism (Table 9-1).

Table 9-1 **What Happens Where: A Review**	
Pathway	**Location**
Glycolysis (glucose → pyruvate)	Cytosol
Transition reaction (pyruvate → acetyl-CoA)	Mitochondria
Citric acid cycle (acetyl-CoA → CO_2)	Mitochondria
Gluconeogenesis	Begins in mitochondria, then moves to cytosol
Beta oxidation (fatty acid → acetyl-CoA)	Mitochondria
Glucogenic amino acid oxidation (amino acids → pyruvate)	Cytosol
Non-glucogenic amino acid oxidation (amino acids → acetyl-CoA)	Mitochondria
Alcohol oxidation (ethanol → acetaldehyde) (acetaldehyde → acetyl-CoA)	Cytosol Mitochondria

300   **PART 3**   Metabolism and Energy Balance

When it comes to regulating these metabolic pathways, the liver plays the major role—it responds to hormones and makes use of vitamins. Additional means of regulating metabolism involve ATP concentrations, enzymes, hormones, vitamins, and minerals.[1]

The Liver

The liver is the location of many nutrient interconversions (Fig. 9-21). Most nutrients must pass first through the liver after absorption into the body. What leaves the liver is often different from what entered. The key metabolic functions of the liver are conversions between various forms of simple sugars, fat synthesis, the production of ketone bodies, amino acid metabolism, urea production, and alcohol metabolism. Nutrient storage is an additional liver function.[2]

ATP Concentrations

ATP concentration in a cell helps regulate metabolism. High ATP concentrations decrease energy-yielding reactions, such as glycolysis, and promote anabolic reactions, such as protein synthesis, that use ATP. High ADP concentrations, on the other hand, stimulate energy-yielding pathways.[10]

Enzymes, Hormones, Vitamins, and Minerals

Enzymes are key regulators of metabolic pathways; both their presence and their rate of activity are critical to chemical reactions in the body. Enzyme synthesis and rates of activity are controlled by cells and by the products of the reactions in which the enzymes participate. For example, a high-protein diet leads to increased synthesis of enzymes associated with amino acid catabolism and gluconeogenesis. Within hours of a shift to a low-protein diet, the synthesis of enzymes associated with amino acid metabolism slows.[5]

Hormones, including insulin, regulate metabolic processes. Low levels of insulin in the blood promote gluconeogenesis, protein breakdown, and lipolysis. Increased blood insulin levels promote the synthesis of glycogen, fat, and protein.

Figure 9-21 Most nutrients must pass first through the liver after absorption into the body. What leaves the liver is often different from what entered.

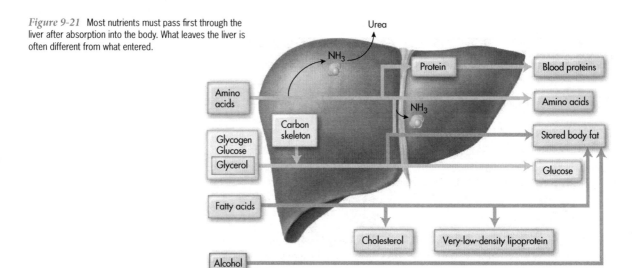

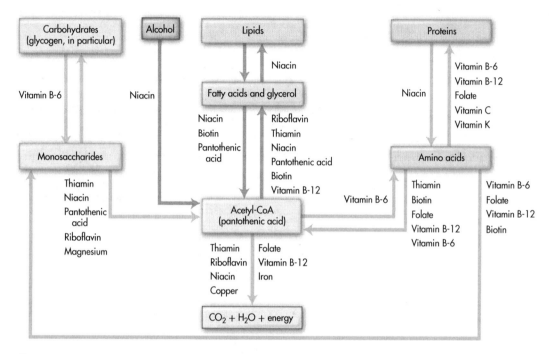

Figure 9-22 Many vitamins and minerals participate in the metabolic pathways.

Many vitamins and minerals are needed for metabolic pathways to operate (Fig. 9-22). Most notable are the B-vitamins, thiamin, riboflavin, niacin, pantothenic acid, biotin, vitamin B-6, folate, and vitamin B-12, as well as the minerals iron and copper. Because so many metabolic pathways depend on nutrient input, health problems can develop from nutrient deficiencies.[2] (The roles that vitamins and minerals play in metabolism are discussed in greater detail in Chapters 12 through 15.)

Knowledge Check

1. Where does glycolysis take place in a cell?
2. What factors determine the regulation of glycolysis and citric acid cycle pathways?
3. What factors regulate energy metabolism?

9.7 Fasting and Feasting

Both fasting and feasting affect metabolism. The form of each macronutrient and the rate at which it is used vary when the calorie supplies are insufficient or exceed needs.

Fasting

In the first few hours of a fast, the body fuels itself with stored liver glycogen and fatty acids from adipose tissue. As the fast progresses, body fat continues to be broken down and liver glycogen becomes exhausted. Although most cells can use fatty acids for energy,

302 **PART 3** Metabolism and Energy Balance

Postprandial fasting (0 to 6 hours after eating)

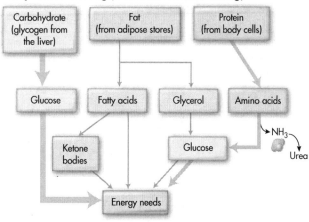

Short-term fasting (3 to 5 days)

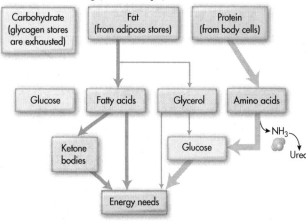

Long-term fasting (5 to 7 days and beyond)

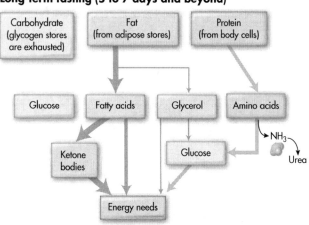

the nervous system and red blood cells use only glucose for energy. To provide the needed glucose, the body begins breaking down lean body tissue and converts glucogenic amino acids, via gluconeogenesis, to glucose (Fig. 9-23).[6, 7] During the first few days of a fast, body protein is broken down rapidly—in fact, it supplies about 90% of needed glucose, with the remaining 10% coming from glycerol. At this rate of breakdown, body protein would be quickly depleted and death would occur within 2 to 3 weeks. (Death would occur regardless of the amount of body fat a person has because fatty acids cannot be used for gluconeogenesis.) Sodium and potassium depletion also can result during fasting because these elements are drawn into the urine along with ketone bodies. Finally, blood urea levels increase because of the breakdown of protein.

Fortunately, the body undergoes a series of adaptations that prolong survival. One of these adaptations is the slowing of metabolic rate and a reduction in energy requirements. This helps slow the breakdown of lean tissue to supply amino acids for gluconeogenesis. Another adaptation allows the nervous system to use less glucose (and, hence, less body protein) and more ketone bodies. After several weeks of fasting, half or more of the nervous system's energy needs are met by ketone bodies; nonetheless, some glucose must still be supplied via the catabolism of lean body mass. When lean body mass declines by about 50% (usually within 7 to 10 weeks of total fasting), death occurs.

Feasting

The most obvious result of feasting is the accumulation of body fat. In addition, feasting increases insulin production by the pancreas, which in turn encourages the burning of glucose for energy, as well as the synthesis of glycogen and, to a lesser extent, protein and fat (Fig. 9-24).[6, 11]

Fat consumed in excess of need goes immediately into storage in adipose cells.[2] Compared with the conversion of carbohydrate and protein, relatively little energy is required to convert dietary fat into body fat. Therefore, high-fat, high-energy diets promote the accumulation of body fat.

Protein consumed in excess of need—contrary to popular belief—does not promote muscle development. Some of the excess protein can reside in amino acid pools in the body,

Figure 9-23 Postprandial fasting encourages the use of mostly glucose, as well as some fatty acids and amino acids for energy needs. As the fast progresses, glycogen stores are depleted, which causes the rapid use of carbon skeletons of certain amino acids from body protein to produce glucose. This supplies glucose to glucose-dependent cells, such as red blood cells. Long-term fasting leads to reduced breakdown of body protein and increased use of adipose stores, which are used to produce ketones. Ketones can provide a significant proportion of the fuel required by glucose-dependent cells, thereby sparing body protein and prolonging life. Note that the thickness of the arrows in the figures conveys the relative use of each energy source during the stages of fasting.

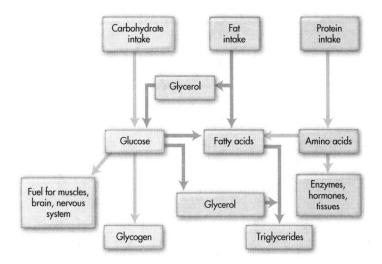

Figure 9-24 Feasting encourages glycogen and triglyceride synthesis and storage and allows amino acids to participate in the synthesis of body proteins. Minimal synthesis of fatty acids using glucose or carbon skeletons of amino acids occurs unless intake is quite excessive in comparison with overall energy needs.

but the amount is not significant. Amino acids left over in the body after a large meal can be used to synthesize fatty acids, but this is typically of minor importance in humans.[11] The process of storing amino acids as fat requires ATP and the B-vitamins biotin, niacin, and pantothenic acid.[2] The energy cost of converting dietary protein to body fat is higher than it is for the conversion of dietary fat to body fat.

Carbohydrate consumed in excess of need is used first to maximize glycogen stores. Once glycogen stores are filled, carbohydrate consumption stimulates the use of carbohydrate as fuel and the storage of excess amounts as body fat. This then lessens the need for any fat catabolism. However, the pathway for storing carbohydrate as body fat is not very active in humans.[11] In addition, it requires the B-vitamins biotin, niacin, and pantothenic acid, and it is energetically expensive to convert carbohydrate to body fat (Table 9-2). Anyone who consumes more calories from any of the energy-yielding nutrients than what the body can expend will gain weight.

The pathways for the synthesis of fat from excess carbohydrate or protein intake, called lipogenesis, are found primarily in the cytosol of liver

Feasting especially encourages the synthesis of glycogen and the storage of fat.

▶ Fasting encourages the following:

Glycogen breakdown

Fat breakdown

Gluconeogenesis

Synthesis of ketone bodies

▶ Feasting encourages the following:

Glycogen synthesis

Fat synthesis

Protein synthesis

Urea synthesis

Table 9-2 Metabolism of ATP-Yielding Compounds

Nutrient	Yields Glucose?	Yields Amino Acids for Body Proteins?	Yields Fat for Adipose Tissue Stores?	Energy Cost of Conversion to Adipose Tissue Stores
Glucose	Yes	No	Yes, but is inefficient	High
Fatty acids	No	No	Yes	Minimal
Glycerol	Yes, but not a major pathway	No	Yes	High
Amino Acids	Yes	Yes	Yes, but is inefficient	High
Alcohol	No	No	Yes	High

304   **PART 3**   Metabolism and Energy Balance

Take Action

Weight Loss and Metabolism

A friend is very overweight and describes to you his method of weight loss. He fasted completely for 1 week and is now on a strict diet of 400 to 600 kcal/day under a physician's supervision. The food energy comes from a liquid formula, which he drinks for breakfast. He skips lunch and eats a small dinner of 3 ounces of protein, ½ cup of vegetables, 1 cup of fruit, and 2 starch items (a small potato, a piece of bread). He has lost approximately 25 lb in 12 weeks.

Based on your knowledge of energy metabolism, answer the following questions he poses.

1. During the fasting stage, what were the likely sources of energy for the body's cells? What metabolic adaptations occurred to provide glucose for the nervous system?

2. When he began eating 400 to 600 kcal/day, how did the metabolic processes in his body most likely change from the fasting state?

cells. Synthesis involves a series of steps that link the acetyl-CoA formed from either glucose or amino acids into a 16-carbon saturated fatty acid, palmitic acid. Insulin increases the activity of a key enzyme—fatty acid synthase—used in the pathway. Palmitic acid can later be lengthened to an 18- or 20-carbon chain either in the cytosol or in the mitochondria.[1] Ultimately, the fatty acids and glycerol (produced during glycolysis from glyceraldehyde 3-phosphate) are used to synthesize triglycerides, which are subsequently delivered by very-low-density lipoproteins (see Chapter 6) via the bloodstream to adipose tissues for storage.

CASE STUDY FOLLOW-UP

A very-low-carbohydrate diet that produces ketones is not the best way to lose body fat. Although body weight may decline, the large production of ketones means that the body is not capable of oxidizing fatty acids and therefore excretes them in the urine. The body is using protein (amino acids) as a fuel source for the brain and nervous system. This loss of amino acids, especially from muscle, is part of the loss of body mass. A better weight-loss program would be to reduce total calories to create a calorie deficit and maintain an exercise or fitness program.

Knowledge Check

1. In the first few hours of a fast, what is the primary fuel for the body?
2. What adaptations occur that help slow the breakdown of lean body mass during prolonged fasting?
3. What happens to excess amounts of ingested fat, protein, and carbohydrate?

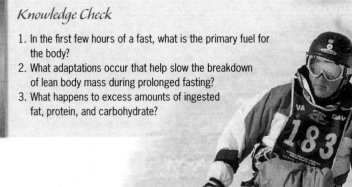

The energy used to perform physical activity is in the form of ATP, which can be supplied by carbohydrate, fat, or protein. The proportion supplied by each macronutrient depends on length of time after eating and type and intensity of exercise.

MEDICAL PERSPECTIVE

Inborn Errors of Metabolism

Some people lack a specific enzyme to perform normal metabolic functions—they are said to have an inborn error of metabolism. The metabolic pathway in which the enzyme is supposed to participate does not function normally. Typically, this causes alternative metabolic products to be formed, some of which are toxic to the body.

Inborn errors of metabolism occur when a person inherits a defective gene coding for a specific enzyme from both parents. Both parents are likely to be carriers of the defective gene—that is, they have 1 healthy gene and 1 defective gene for the enzyme in their chromosomes. When each parent donates the defective form of the gene to the offspring, the offspring has 2 defective copies of the gene and therefore little or no activity of the enzyme that the gene normally would produce. If a person has a defective gene, he or she produces a defective protein based on the instructions contained in that defective gene. It also is possible that one or both parents have the disease and are not simply carriers. Generally, however, individuals who have an inborn error of metabolism are advised to see a genetic counselor to assess the risk of passing on the inborn error of metabolism to their offspring (see Chapter 1).

The following are some characteristics of inborn errors of metabolism.[13]

- They appear soon after birth. Such a disorder is suspected when otherwise physically well children develop a loss of appetite, vomiting, dehydration, physical weakness, or developmental delays soon after birth. For some of these conditions, infants are screened for the potential to have a specific inborn error of metabolism.
- They are very specific, involving only 1 or a few enzymes. These enzymes usually participate in catabolic pathways (in which compounds are degraded).
- No cure is possible, but typically the disorders can be controlled. The type of control depends on the inborn error—control might include reducing intake of the substance they are unable to metabolize normally, taking pharmacological doses of vitamins, and replacing a compound that cannot be synthesized.

Some of the most common inborn errors of metabolism are phenylketonuria (PKU), galactosemia, and glycogen storage disease. A number of other, very rare inborn errors of metabolism involve various amino acids, fatty acids, and the sugars fructose and sucrose. Typically, in large hospitals and in state health departments, physicians, nurses, and registered dietitians can help affected persons and their families cope with these and other inborn errors of metabolism.[13]

Newborn Screening

Newborn screening is the process of testing newborn babies for treatable genetic errors of metabolism.[14] Newborn screening is a public health program that provides early identification and follow-up for the treatment of infants with genetic and metabolic disorders. There are no national mandates to test newborns. Currently, each state determines which newborn screening tests are required—as a result, required tests vary widely among states. In 2004, the American College of Medical Genetics recommended that all states test for 29 conditions—only some states require all of these tests. To learn more, visit www.marchofdimes.com/298_834.asp.

Phenylketonuria (PKU)

PKU is estimated to occur in about 1 per 13,500 to 1 in 19,000 births.[14] Most carriers can be detected with a simple blood test. People of Irish descent are especially affected.[15] Today, most infants in the U.S. are diagnosed within a few days of life because all states require them to be tested for this inborn error of metabolism.[16]

The majority of PKU cases occur because the enzyme phenylalanine hydroxylase does not function efficiently in the liver. Normally, phenylalanine hydroxylase converts the amino acid phenylalanine into the amino acid tyrosine. If this reaction does not take place, phenylalanine

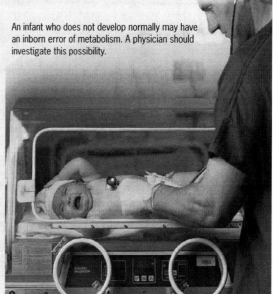

An infant who does not develop normally may have an inborn error of metabolism. A physician should investigate this possibility.

accumulates in the blood and tyrosine is deficient. If not corrected within 30 days of birth, this phenylalanine buildup leads to the production of toxic phenylalanine by-products, such as phenylpyruvic acid, which then can lead to severe, irreversible mental retardation.[17]

Sufficient phenylalanine
hydroxylase activity

Normal: Phenylalanine ⟶ Tyrosine

Reduced phenylalanine
hydroxylase activity

PKU: Phenylalanine ⟶ Phenylpyruvic acid

Phenyllactic acid

Other related
products

As soon as they are diagnosed, infants are started on a phenylalanine-restricted diet.[18] Recall that phenylalanine is an essential amino acid, which means that even someone with PKU has to obtain phenylalanine from his or her diet; however, the amount of phenylalanine consumed needs to be controlled carefully to prevent toxic amounts from building up.[17, 19] During infancy, nutritional needs can

(continued)

continued

change frequently, so these infants are monitored continually through blood phenylalanine testing.

Starting in infancy, special formulas are used to provide nutrients for individuals with PKU. Because infants have high protein needs, satisfying protein requirements—without also having high intakes of phenylalanine—is impossible without these specially prepared formulas. For infants, formulas are designed to provide about 90% of protein needs and 80% of energy needs. Human milk or regular infant formula then can be used to make up the difference and supply small amounts of phenylalanine.[12]

Later in life, foods can be used to make up the difference, especially foods low in phenylalanine. Fruits and vegetables are naturally low in phenylalanine, and breads and cereals have a moderate amount. Dairy products, eggs, meats, and nuts are very high in amino acids, including phenylalanine, so they are not allowed in the diet. Foods and beverages that contain the alternative sweetener aspartame also are not allowed because aspartame contains phenylalanine (see Chapter 5). Older children and adults can use a formula (such as Phenyl-Free®) that is very low in phenylalanine, which allows the person to consume more foods but limits phenylalanine intake. Overall, the majority of the person's nutrient intake throughout life will come from a special formula.

Ideally, the low-phenylalanine diet is followed for life.[20] At one time, health-care professionals thought it was appropriate to end the diet after age 6 years because brain development was complete. However, it is now known that discontinuing this diet leads to decreased intelligence and behavior problems, such as aggressiveness, hyperactivity, and decreased attention span.[12]

If a woman with PKU has abandoned the diet, she needs to return to it at least 6 months before becoming pregnant.[21] Otherwise, the fetus—even though it does not have PKU—will be exposed to a high blood phenylalanine level and related toxic products from the mother. This can result in miscarriage or birth defects. All pregnancies for women with PKU are high risk and require close medical supervision.

Galactosemia

Galactosemia is a rare genetic disease—the most common form occurs in 1 in 47,000 births.[14, 22] It is more common in those of Italian and Irish descent.[23] In galactosemia, 2 specific enzyme defects lead to a reduction in the metabolism of the monosaccharide galactose to glucose (a third defect is very rare). Galactose then builds up in the bloodstream, which can lead to very serious bacterial infections, mental retardation, and cataracts in the eyes.

An infant with galactosemia typically develops vomiting after a few days of consuming infant formula or breast milk. Both contain much galactose as part of the milk sugar lactose. The child is then switched to a soy formula. In addition, all dairy products and other lactose-containing products (e.g., butter, milk solids), organ meats, and some fruits and vegetables must be avoided. Strict label reading also is important for controlling the disease because lactose can be found in a variety of products. Even in well-controlled cases, slight mental retardation (e.g., speech delays) and cataracts occur.

Glycogen Storage Disease

Glycogen storage disease is a group of diseases that occurs in 1 in 60,000 births. In glycogen storage disease, the liver is unable to convert glycogen to glucose. There are a number of possible enzyme defects along the pathway from glycogen to glucose. The most common forms cause poor physical growth, low blood glucose, and liver enlargement. Low blood glucose results because liver glycogen breakdown is typically used to maintain blood glucose between meals (see Chapter 5). People with glycogen storage

Children with PKU must restrict their intake of high-protein foods, such as milk and meat.

▶ A new drug, sapropterin dihydrochloride, 6-R-L-erythro-5,6,7,8-tetrahydrobiopterin (BH4), which has been used in Europe to treat mild forms of PKU, has been approved for use in the U.S. Although the drug cannot cure PKU, it appears to lower blood levels of phenylalanine.[25, 26]

disease typically have to consume frequent meals in order to regulate blood glucose. They also consume raw cornstarch between meals because it is slowly digested and helps maintain steady blood glucose. Careful monitoring of blood glucose is very important for these people, so that low blood glucose levels can be detected and treated quickly.[12]

Knowledge Check

1. What are the characteristics of inborn errors of metabolism?
2. What is the cause of PKU?
3. What dietary restrictions must those with galactosemia observe?

Take Action

Newborn Screening in Your State

There are no mandatory national newborn screening standards in the U.S., even though dozens of metabolic diseases are detectable by newborn screening tests. Each state has developed its own newborn screening program for infants born there. To learn which metabolism disorder tests are required for newborns in your state, visit this website: genes-r-us.uthscsa.edu. Why don't all states require the same tests? Once a newborn has tested positive, what resources and professionals can help the family manage the disorder?

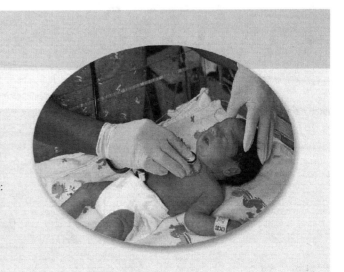

Summary

9.1 Metabolism refers to the entire network of chemical processes involved in maintaining life. It encompasses all the sequences of chemical reactions that occur in the body. Some of these biochemical reactions enable us to release and use energy from carbohydrate, fat, protein, and alcohol. Metabolism is the sum total of all anabolic and catabolic reactions. A molecule of ATP consists of the organic compound adenosine (comprised of the nucleotide adenine and the sugar ribose) bound to 3 phosphate groups. ATP is the energy currency for the body. As ATP is broken down to ADP plus P_i, energy is released from the broken bond. Every cell contains catabolic pathways, which release energy to allow ADP to combine with P_i to form ATP. The synthesis of ATP from ADP and P_i involves the transfer of energy from energy-yielding compounds (carbohydrate, fat, protein, and alcohol). This process uses oxidation-reduction reactions, in which electrons (along with hydrogen ions) are transferred in a series of reactions from energy-yielding compounds eventually to oxygen. The process of cellular respiration oxidizes (removes electrons) to obtain energy (ATP). Oxygen is the final electron acceptor. When oxygen is readily available, cellular respiration may be aerobic. When oxygen is not present, anaerobic pathways are used.

9.2 Glucose metabolism begins with glycolysis, which literally means "breaking down glucose." Glycolysis has 2 roles: to break down carbohydrates to generate energy and to provide building blocks for synthesizing other needed compounds. During glycolysis, glucose passes through several steps, which convert it to 2 units of a 3-carbon compound called pyruvate. Glycolysis nets 2 ATP. Pyruvate passes from the cytosol into the mitochondria, where the enzyme pyruvate dehydrogenase converts pyruvate into the compound acetyl-CoA in a process called a transition reaction. Acetyl-CoA molecules enter the citric acid cycle, which is a series of chemical reactions that convert carbons in the acetyl group to carbon dioxide while harvesting energy to produce ATP. In the citric acid cycle, acetyl-CoA undergoes many metabolic conversions, which result in the production of GTP, ATP, NADH, and $FADH_2$. NADH and $FADH_2$ enter the electron transport chain, which passes electrons along a series of electron carriers. As electrons pass from one carrier to the next, small amounts of energy are released. This metabolic process is called oxidative phosphorylation, and it is the pathway in which energy derived from glycolysis, the transition reaction, and the citric acid cycle is transferred to ADP + P_i to form ATP and water.

9.3 The first step in generating energy from a fatty acid is to cleave the carbons, 2 at a time, and convert the 2-carbon fragments to acetyl-CoA. The process of converting a free fatty acid to multiple acetyl-CoA molecules is called beta-oxidation, because it begins with the beta carbon, which is the second carbon on a fatty acid chain. Fatty acids can be oxidized for energy but cannot be converted into glucose. During low carbohydrate intakes and uncontrolled diabetes, more acetyl-CoA is produced in the liver than can be metabolized. This excess acetyl-CoA is synthesized into ketone bodies, which can be used as an energy source by other tissues or excreted in the urine and breath.

9.4 Protein metabolism begins after proteins are degraded into amino acids. To use an amino acid for fuel, cells must first deaminate them (remove the amino group, $-NH_2$). Resulting carbon skeletons mostly enter the citric acid cycle. Some carbon skeletons also yield acetyl-CoA or pyruvate. The process of generating glucose from amino acids is called gluconeogenesis. Acetyl-CoA molecules cannot participate in gluconeogenesis; thus, ketogenic amino acids cannot participate in gluconeogenesis. Cancer cells use glycolysis for energy even when oxygen is abundant. Altered glucose, glutamine, and fat metabolism are hallmarks of cancer cells.

9.5 The alcohol dehydrogenase (ADH) pathway is the main pathway for alcohol metabolism. Alcohol is converted in the cytosol to acetaldehyde by the action of the enzyme alcohol dehydrogenase and the coenzyme NAD^+. NAD^+ picks up 2 hydrogen ions and 2 electrons from the alcohol to form $NADH + H^+$ and produces the intermediate acetaldehyde. Acetaldehyde is converted to acetyl-CoA, again yielding $NADH + H^+$ with the aid of the enzyme aldehyde dehydrogenase and coenzyme A. Most of the acetyl-CoA is used to synthesize fatty acids and triglycerides, resulting in the accumulation of fat in the liver. When an individual consumes too much alcohol, a second pathway—called the microsomal ethanol oxidizing system (MEOS)—is activated to help metabolize the excess alcohol.

9.6 The liver plays the major role in regulating metabolism. Additional means of regulating metabolism involve enzymes, ATP concentrations, and minerals. Many micronutrients (thiamin, niacin, riboflavin, biotin, pantothenic acid, vitamin B-6, magnesium, iron, and copper) play important roles in the metabolic pathway.

9.7 During fasting, the body breaks down both amino acids and fats for energy. The body undergoes a series of adaptations that prolong survival. One of these adaptations is the slowing of metabolic rate and the reduction in energy requirements. This helps slow the breakdown of lean tissue to supply amino acids for gluconeogenesis. Another adaptation allows the nervous system to use less glucose and more ketone bodies. Fat consumed in excess of need goes into storage in adipose cells. Compared with the conversion of carbohydrate and protein, relatively little energy is required to convert dietary fat into body fat. Therefore, high-fat diets promote the accumulation of body fat. Inborn errors of metabolism occur when a person inherits a defective gene coding for a specific enzyme from one or both parents. Some of the most common inborn errors of metabolism are phenylketonuria (PKU), galactosemia, and glycogen storage disease. Strict diets can help those with these inborn errors of metabolism minimize many of the serious effects of these diseases.

Study Questions

1. The energy currency in the body is _____.

   a. NAD
   b. FAD
   c. TCA
   d. ATP

2. Glycolysis is a biochemical pathway that _____.

   a. breaks down glucose
   b. generates energy
   c. takes place in the cytosol
   d. all of the above

3. Glycolysis begins with_____ and ends with_____.

   a. pyruvate; water
   b. pyruvate; glucose
   c. glucose; pyruvate
   d. pyruvate; acetyl-CoA

4. When muscle tissue is exercising under anaerobic conditions, the production of _____ is important because it assures a continuous supply of NAD.

   a. glucose-6-phosphate
   b. pyruvate
   c. lactate
   d. glycogen

5. The net energy production of ATP via glycolysis is _____.

   a. 1 ADP
   b. 2 ATP
   c. 4 FADH
   d. 2 GTP
   e. none of the above

6. The common pathway for the oxidation of glucose and fatty acid is _____.

   a. glycolysis
   b. the urea cycle
   c. the citric acid cycle
   d. ketosis

7. The oxidation of fatty acids occurs in the _____.

   a. cell membrane
   b. mitochondria
   c. nucleus
   d. cytosol

Match the definitions on the right with the terms on the left.

8. beta-oxidation   a. breakdown of glucose to pyruvate

9. ketosis   b. breakdown of fat to 2-carbon units called acetyl-CoA

10. electron transport chain   c. synthesis of glucose from noncarbohydrate sources

11. gluconeogenesis   d. formation of excess ketone bodies

12. glycolysis   e. electrons transferred back and forth to make ATP

13. Metabolism is regulated by _____.

   a. hormones
   b. enzymes
   c. the energy status of the body
   d. all of the above

14. During periods of starvation, the body uses protein as a fuel source for the brain and central nervous system in a pathway called gluconeogenesis.

   a. true
   b. false

15. Insulin is _____.

   a. a coenzyme in the glycolytic pathway
   b. a cofactor needed for gluconeogenesis
   c. an anabolic hormone
   d. a catabolic hormone

310 **PART 3** Metabolism and Energy Balance

16. What is the "common denominator" compound of many pathways of energy metabolism (citric acid cycle, glycolysis, beta-oxidation)? Why is it considered important in the body's metabolism?

17. Describe the process of glycolysis.

18. Explain why most fatty acids cannot become glucose.

19. Trace the steps of gluconeogenesis from body protein to the formation of glucose.

20. Describe the metabolism of alcohol.

21. Identify the vitamins and minerals used in ATP synthesis.

22. Describe how the fuels used by the body change as a fast progresses from a few hours to a week.

Answer Key: 1-d; 2-d; 3-c; 4-c; 5-b; 6-c; 7-b; 8-b; 9-d; 10-e; 11-c; 12-a; 13-d; 14-a; 15-c; 16-refer to Sections 9.1 to 9.4; 17-refer to Section 9.2; 18-refer to Section 9.3; 19-refer to Section 9.4; 20-refer to Section 9.5; 21-refer to Section 9.6; 22-refer to Section 9.7

Websites

To learn more about the topics covered in this chapter, visit these websites.

Metabolic Pathways

www.johnkyrk.com/glycolysis.html

metacyc.org

Cancer Cell Metabolism

www.cancer.org

www.cancer.gov

Inborn Errors of Metabolism

www.marchofdimes.com

genes-r-us.uthscsa.edu

www.nlm.nih.gov/medlineplus

www.aafp.org

References

1. Berg J and others. *Biochemistry.* 7th ed. New York: WH Freeman; 2012.

2. Gropper SS and others. *Advanced nutrition and human metabolism.* 5th ed. Belmont, CA: Thomson/Wadsworth; 2009.

3. Mayes P, Bender D. The citric acid cycle: The catabolism of acetyl-CoA. In: Murray R and others, eds. *Harper's illustrated biochemistry.* 28th ed. New York: Appleton & Lange Medical Books/McGraw-Hill; 2009.

4. Mayes P, Bender D. Overview of metabolism. In: Murray R and others, eds. *Harper's illustrated biochemistry.* 28th ed. New York: Appleton & Lange Medical Books/McGraw-Hill; 2009.

5. Harvey RA and others. *Biochemistry.* 5th ed. Philadelphia: Lippincott Williams & Wilkins; 2010.

6. Acetyl-L-carnitine monograph. *Altern Med Rev.* 2010;15:76.

7. Botham K, Mayes P. Oxidation of fatty acids: Ketogenesis. In: Murray R and others, eds. *Harper's illustrated biochemistry.* 28th ed. New York: Appleton & Lange Medical Books/McGraw-Hill; 2009.

8. Gebel E. Passing the acid test. What you need to know about diabetic ketoacidosis. *Diabetes Forecast.* 2010;63:31.

9. VanItallie T, Nufert T. Ketones: Metabolism's ugly duckling. *Nutr Rev.* 2003;61:327.

10. Botham K, Mayes P. Bioenergetics. In: Murray R and others, eds. *Harper's illustrated biochemistry.* 28th ed. New York: Appleton & Lange Medical Books/McGraw-Hill; 2009.

11. Timlin M, Parks E. Temporal pattern of denovo lipogenesis in the postprandial state in healthy men. *Am J Clin Nutr.* 2005;81:35.

12. Bentinger M and others. Coenzyme Q—Biosynthesis and functions. *Biochem Biophys Res Comm.* 2010;396:74.

13. Trahms C. Medical Nutrition Therapy for Genetic Metabolic Disorders. IN: Mahan L, Escott-Stump S and Raymond J. Krause's *Food and the Nutrition Care Process.* 13th ed. St. Louis: Elsevier/Saunders; 2012.

14. Resta R. 2012. Generation n + 1: Projected numbers of babies born to women with PKU compared to babies with PKU in the United States in 2009. *Am J Med Genet Part A,* 2012;158A:1.

15. O'Donnell KA and others. The mutation spectrum of hyperphenylalaninaemia in the Republic of Ireland: The population history of the Irish revisited. *Eur J Human Genet.* 2002;10:530.

16. Champion MP. An approach to the diagnosis of inherited metabolic disease. *Arch Dis Child Educ Pract Ed.* 2010;95:40.

17. de Groot MJ and others. Pathogenesis of cognitive dysfunction in phenylketonuria: Review of hypotheses. *Mol Genet Metab.* 2010;99:S86.

18. Poustie VJ, Wildgoose J. Dietary interventions for phenylketonuria. *Cochrane Database Syst Rev.* 2010;CD001304.

19. van Spronsen FJ, Enns GM. Future treatment strategies in phenylketonuria. *Mol Genet Metab.* 2010;99:S90.

20. Ney DM and others. Dietary glycomacropeptide supports growth and reduces the concentrations of phenylalanine in plasma and brain in a murine model of phenylketonuria. *J Nutr.* 2008;138:316.

21. Koch R and others. Psychosocial issues and outcomes in maternal PKU. *Mol Genet Metab.* 2010;99:S68.

22. Coman DJ and others. Galactosemia, a single gene disorder with epigenetic consequences. *Pediatr Res.* 2010;67:286.

23. Murphy M and others. Genetic basis of transferase-deficient galactosemia in Ireland and the population history of the Irish Travellers. *Eur J Hum Genet.* 1999;7:549.

24. Buono MJ, Kolkhorst FW. Estimating ATP synthesis during a marathon run: A method to introduce metabolism. *Adv Physiol Educ.* 2001;25:70.

25. Vernon HJ and others. Introduction of sapropterin dihydrochloride as standard of care in patients with phenylketonuria. *Mol Genet Metab.* 2010;100:229.

26. Somaraju UR, Merrin M. Sapropterin dihydrochloride for phenylketonuria. *Cochrane Database Syst Rev.* 2010:CD008005.

27. World Health Organization, International Agency for Research on Cancer. *Globocan.* 2010; globocan.iarc.fr.

28. Kaelin WG, Thompson CB. Clues from cell metabolism. *Nature.* 2010;465:562.

Increasing portion sizes have been implicated in the obesity epidemic. Researchers have investigated how portion sizes changed over the years using a variety of methods, such as comparing the size of fast food sandwiches, fries, and soft drinks from the 1950s with those sold today. Other researchers turned to paintings of one of the most famous meals in history, the Last Supper. According to a study published in the International Journal of Obesity (2010;34:943), portions have been increasing for at least a millennium. Compare the size of the food, bread, and plates in Duccio's (early 1300s; left) and Crespi's (late 1620s; right) paintings with the heads of the people. Learn more about portion distortion at **mindlesseating.org** and **hp2010.nhlbihin.net/portion.**

10 Energy Balance, Weight Control, and Eating Disorders

Chapter Outline

Student Learning Outcomes

After studying this chapter, you will be able to

1. Describe energy balance and uses of energy by the body.

2. Compare methods used to measure energy expenditure by the body.

3. Explain internal and external regulation of hunger, appetite, and satiety.

4. Discuss methods for assessing body composition and determining whether body weight and composition are healthy.

5. Describe the impact of genetics and environment on body weight and composition.

6. Outline the key components of programs designed to treat overweight and obesity.

7. Discuss the characteristics of fad diets.

8. Evaluate weight-loss programs to determine whether they are safe and likely to result in long-term weight loss.

9. Describe treatments for severe obesity.

10. Outline recommendations for treating underweight individuals.

11. Describe the causes of, effects of, typical persons affected by, and treatment for anorexia nervosa, bulimia nervosa, and binge-eating disorder.

12. Explain methods for reducing the development of eating disorders, including the use of warning signs to identify early cases.

THIS CHAPTER BEGINS WITH SOME good news and some bad news. The good news is that, if you stay at a healthy body weight, you increase your chances of living a long and healthy life. The bad news is that, in the last 20 years, there has been a dramatic increase in the percentage of individuals who are obese. This problem is occurring not only in the U.S. but around the world, especially in developing countries where Westernized dietary patterns (high-fat, high-calorie) are increasing in popularity. In 1990, no state in the U.S. had an obesity prevalence rate exceeding 15%. By 2010, no state had an obesity prevalence rate less than 20%, and 36 states had a rate of 25% or higher.[1] Currently in North America, 2 out of 3 adults weigh more than is healthy. The current trend is not likely to be reversed without a national commitment to weight maintenance and approaches that make our social environment more favorable to maintaining a healthy weight. Despite new data suggesting the increase in obesity rate may be slowing, there is a good chance that many of us will have significant weight gain in adulthood.[2, 3] There is no quick cure for overweight, despite what advertisements claim. Any success comes from hard work and commitment.

314   **PART 3**   Metabolism and Energy Balance

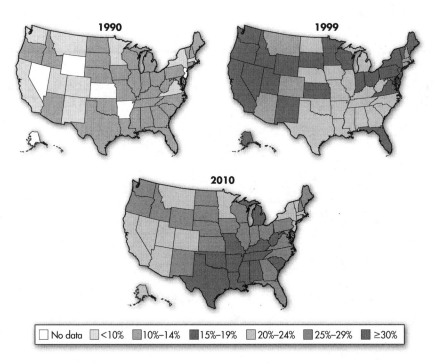

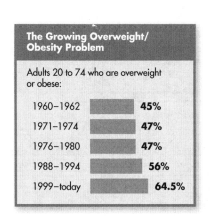

The Growing Overweight/Obesity Problem

Adults 20 to 74 who are overweight or obese:

1960–1962	**45%**
1971–1974	**47%**
1976–1980	**47%**
1988–1994	**56%**
1999–today	**64.5%**

No data   <10%   10%–14%   15%–19%   20%–24%   25%–29%   ≥30%

Figure 10-1   Obesity trends among U.S. adults: 1990, 1999, 2010 (BMI ≥30, or about 30 lb overweight for a 5′4″ person). To see other years, visit www.cdc.gov/obesity/data/trends.html.

Source: CDC Behavioral Risk Factor Surveillance System.

Unfortunately, for most people, weight-reduction efforts fizzle before they achieve a healthy weight range (Fig. 10-1).

Popular ("fad") diets are generally monotonous, ineffective, and confusing; they may even be dangerous for some population groups and individuals with health disorders. The relentless pursuit of thinness may drive some to develop eating disorders, which involve severe distortions of the eating process. The safest and most logical approach to maintaining a healthy weight is to watch calorie intake, exercise regularly, and get problem eating behaviors under control.[4] Preventing excess weight gain in the first place is the most successful approach of all.[5]

10.1 Energy Balance

Energy balance is the relationship between energy intake and energy expenditure. When the calories consumed from food and beverages (energy intake) match the amount of energy expended, **energy equilibrium** occurs. If energy intake exceeds energy expended, the result is a **positive energy balance.** The excess energy consumed is stored, resulting in weight gain (Fig. 10-2). There are some situations in which positive energy balance is desired, such as during the growth stages of the life cycle (pregnancy, infancy, childhood, adolescence) and to restore body weight to healthy levels after losses caused by starvation, disease, or injury. However, during other times, such as adulthood, positive energy balance over time can cause body weight to climb to unhealthy levels. The process of aging itself does not cause weight gain; rather, weight gain stems from a pattern of excess food intake coupled with limited physical activity and slower metabolism.[4]

CRITICAL THINKING

A 20-year-old classmate of yours has been watching her parents and grandparents gain weight over the years. How should she explain energy balance to them?

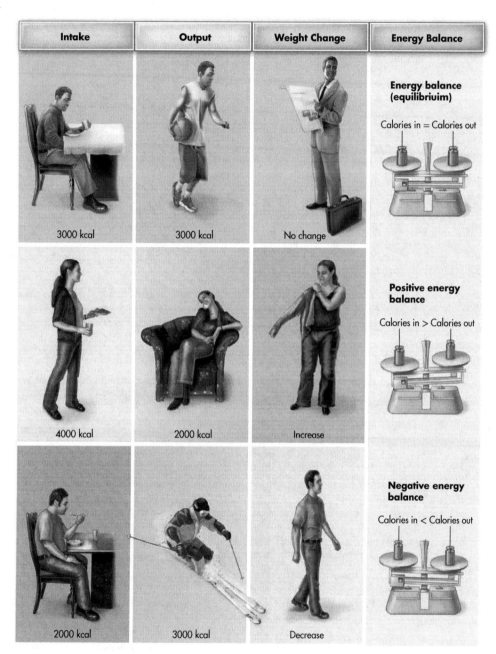

Intake	Output	Weight Change	Energy Balance
3000 kcal	3000 kcal	No change	**Energy balance (equilibriuim)** Calories in = Calories out
4000 kcal	2000 kcal	Increase	**Positive energy balance** Calories in > Calories out
2000 kcal	3000 kcal	Decrease	**Negative energy balance** Calories in < Calories out

Figure 10-2 States of energy balance.
- Energy equilibrium occurs when calories consumed equal calories expended.
- Positive energy balance is when intake of calories exceeds calories burned.
- Negative energy balance results when fewer calories are eaten than used.

Negative energy balance results when energy intake is less than energy expenditure. Weight loss occurs because energy stored in the body—fat and muscle—is used to make up for the shortfall in energy intake. Negative energy balance is desired in adults when body fatness exceeds healthy levels. Negative energy balance during growth stages of the life cycle generally is not recommended because it can impair normal growth.

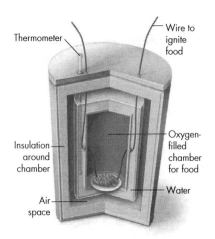

Figure 10-3 Bomb calorimeters measure calorie content by igniting and burning a dried portion of food. The burning food raises the temperature of the water surrounding the chamber holding the food. The increase in water temperature indicates the number of kilocalories in the food because 1 kilocalorie equals the amount of heat needed to raise the temperature of 1 kg of water by 1°C.

▶ When a person is resting, the following are the approximate percentages of total energy used by the body's organs.

Liver	27%	380 kcal/day
Brain	19%	265 kcal/day
Skeletal muscle	18%	250 kcal/day
Kidney	10%	140 kcal/day
Heart	7%	100 kcal/day
Other	19%	265 kcal/day

Classwork leads to mental activity but little physical activity. Hence, energy is burned at a rate of only about 1.5 kcal per minute.

Energy Intake

The amount of energy in a food or beverage can be estimated using nutrient databases or nutrient analysis software. Calorie values in these tables and programs can be derived by directly measuring calorie content using a device called a **bomb calorimeter** (Fig. 10-3). Calorie content is most commonly calculated by determining the grams of carbohydrate, protein, and fat (and possibly alcohol) in a food and multiplying these compounds by their physiological fuel values. (Recall from Chapter 1 that the physiological fuel values are 4 kcal/g for carbohydrates and proteins, 9 kcal/g for fat, and 7 kcal/g for alcohol.)

Energy Expenditure

The body uses energy for 3 main purposes: basal metabolism; physical activity; and the digestion, absorption, and processing of ingested nutrients. A fourth, minor form of energy output, known as thermogenesis, is the energy expended during fidgeting or shivering in response to cold (Fig.10-4).[4]

Basal Metabolism

Basal metabolism (expressed as **basal metabolic rate [BMR]**) represents the minimum amount of energy expended in a fasting state (12 hours or more) to keep a resting, awake body alive in a warm, quiet environment. For a sedentary person, basal metabolism accounts for about 60 to 70% of total energy expenditure. Some of the processes involved include the beating of the heart, respiration by the lungs, and the activity of other organs, such as the liver, brain, and kidneys.[4] It does not include energy expended for physical activity or the digestion, absorption, and processing of nutrients recently consumed. If the person is not fasting or completely rested, the term **resting metabolism** is used (expressed as **resting metabolic rate [RMR]**). RMR is typically 6% higher than BMR.

Both BMR and RMR are expressed as the number of calories burned per unit of time. A rough estimate of basal metabolic rate for women is 0.9 kcal/kg per hour and 1.0 kcal/kg per hour for men. To see how basal metabolism contributes to energy needs, consider a 130 lb woman. First, knowing that there are 2.2 lb for every kg, convert her weight into metric units:

$$130 / 2.2 = 59 \text{ kg}$$

Then, using a rough estimate of the basal metabolic rate of 0.9 kcal/kg per hour for an average female, calculate her basal metabolic rate:

$$59 \times 0.9 = 53 \text{ kcal/hour}$$

Finally, use this hourly basal metabolic rate to find her basal metabolic rate for an entire day:

$$53 \times 24 = 1272 \text{ kcal/day}$$

These calculations are only an estimate of actual basal metabolism—it can vary 25 to 30% among individuals. The following factors increase basal metabolism.

- Greater muscle mass
- Larger body surface area
- Male gender (males typically have more body surface area and muscle mass than females)
- Body temperature (fever or cold environmental conditions)
- Higher than normal secretions of thyroid hormones (a key regulator of basal metabolism)
- Aspects of nervous system activity (e.g., the release of stress hormones)
- Growth stages of the life cycle
- Caffeine and tobacco use (using tobacco to control body weight is not recommended because too many health risks are increased)
- Recent exercise

Of these factors, the amount of muscle mass a person has is the most important.

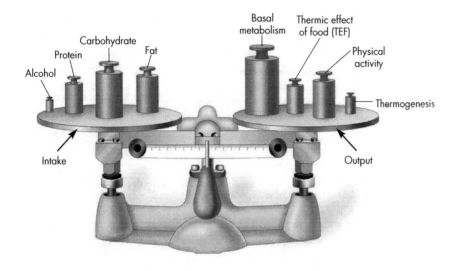

Figure 10-4 Major components of energy intake and expenditure. The size of each component shows the relative contribution of that component to energy balance. Alcohol is an additional source of energy only for those who consume it.

These factors decrease basal metabolism.

- Lower than normal secretions of thyroid hormones (hypothyroidism)
- Restricted calorie intake
- Less body surface area and muscle mass
- Aging after age 30 years

Basal metabolism decreases by about 10 to 20% (about 150 to 300 kcal/day) when calorie intake declines and the body shifts into a conservation mode. This shift helps us survive during periods of famine and starvation, but it also is a barrier to sustained weight loss during dieting that involves extremely low calorie intake.[5] Basal metabolism drops 1 to 2% for each decade past the age of 30 years as a result of the lean body mass loss that typically occurs with advancing age. However, physical activity helps maintain lean body mass and helps preserve BMR throughout adulthood.[6]

Energy for Physical Activity

Physical activity increases energy expenditure above and beyond basal energy needs by as much as 25 to 40%. In choosing to be active or inactive, we determine much of our total energy expenditure for a day. Climbing stairs rather than riding the elevator, walking rather than driving to the store, and standing in a bus rather than sitting increase physical activity and, hence, energy expenditure. The increased rate of obesity in North America is caused, in part, by our inactivity.[6]

Thermic Effect of Food

The **thermic effect of food (TEF)** is the energy the body uses to digest, absorb, transport, store, and metabolize the nutrients consumed in the diet. The TEF accounts for about 5 to 10% of the energy consumed each day. If daily energy intake were 3000 calories, TEF would account for 150 to 300 calories. As with other components of energy output, the total amount varies somewhat among individuals.[4] In addition, food composition influences TEF. For example, the TEF value for a protein-rich meal (20 to 30% of the energy consumed) is higher than that of a carbohydrate-rich (5 to 10%) or fat-rich (0 to 3%) meal because it takes more energy to metabolize amino acids into fat than to convert glucose into glycogen or transfer absorbed fat into adipose stores. In addition, large meals result in higher TEF values than the same amount of food eaten over many hours.[4]

Adaptive Thermogenesis

Thermogenesis, the process of heat production by humans and other organisms, makes a fairly small contribution to overall energy expenditure. Thermogenesis goes by other names, such as thermoregulation and non-exercise activity thermogenesis (NEAT). Adaptive

▶ The TEF of alcohol is 20%. About 90% of the energy in food can be used by the body as an energy source, whereas only 80% of the energy in alcohol can be used by the body to make energy.[53]

basal metabolism   Minimum amount of energy the body uses to support itself when fasting, resting, and awake in a warm, quiet environment.

thermic effect of food   Energy the body uses to digest, absorb, transport, store, and metabolize nutrients.

thermogenesis   Heat production by humans.

Expert Perspective from the Field

High-Fructose Corn Syrup and Your Waistline

High-fructose corn syrup (HFCS) is a common sweetener in the U.S. food supply. Although it is called fructose, HFCS really is a combination of glucose and fructose. One of the main types is HFCS-42, which is 42% fructose, 53% glucose, and 5% other saccharides. It is used to sweeten baked goods, canned fruit, condiments, jams, jellies, and some dairy products, such as yogurt. HFCS-55, used to sweeten beverages, ice cream, and frozen desserts, is 55% fructose, 42% glucose, and 3% other saccharides. The very sweet HFCS-90 contains 90% fructose and is used in tiny amounts to sweeten some low-sugar foods.[7]

HFCS is made by milling corn to produce cornstarch. Then, in a series of steps, enzymes are used to break the long polysaccharide chain in the cornstarch into glucose. Finally, other enzymes are used to convert some of the glucose into fructose.

Food manufacturers use HFCS instead of table sugar (sucrose) because it costs less to produce—corn is more abundant in the U.S., and this crop is subsidized by the U.S. government. Another reason manufacturers favor HFCS is that it is easier to use because it is a liquid and dissolves easily. HFCS first entered the U.S. food supply in 1966 and, by 2005, the per capita availability of the sweetener was about 59 lb per year.[8] During the same time period, the per capita availability of table sugar (made from sugarcane and sugar beets) dropped to 63 lb, down from a peak of 102 lb per capita in 1972.[8]

In 2004, some respected nutrition scientists noted that the rate of HFCS use paralleled the rising rates of obesity.[9] They hypothesized that the high intakes of HFCS may be linked to excess weight gain. According to Maureen Storey, Ph.D.,* several theories have been proposed to explain how HFCS might be related to weight gain. One theory suggests that HFCS triggers a desire to eat sweet foods and beverages, which leads to excessive energy consumption. However, as Storey explains, HFCS-42 is less sweet than sucrose, and HFCS-55 has the same sweetness as sucrose. Another theory speculates that, as intake of HFCS increases and that of sucrose decreases, this change in the fructose:glucose ratio in our diets leads to adverse metabolic consequences, such as greater fat synthesis in the liver and diminished release of satiety hormones. However, the fructose:glucose ratio in the food supply has not changed.[7] Storey also notes that there is no scientific evidence that the body metabolizes HFCS and sucrose differently. A recent study found that the impacts of HFCS and sucrose on fasting plasma glucose, insulin, and the appetite-regulating hormones ghrelin and leptin were the same.[10]

Currently, scientific evidence does not support the theory that HFCS promotes weight gain to a greater extent than sucrose or any other caloric sweetener. However, since 1970 the consumption of all caloric sweeteners has increased nearly 20%, likely contributing to excessive energy intake and weight gain in many individuals.

Maureen Storey is President and Chief Executive Officer of the Alliance for Potato Research and Education. Formerly, she was Senior Vice President, Science Policy, American Beverage Association and Affiliate Research Professor, Department of Nutrition and Food Science, University of Maryland.

thermogenesis heat is produced when the body expends energy for nonvoluntary physical activity triggered by cold conditions or overeating. Examples of nonvoluntary activities include fidgeting, shivering when cold, maintaining muscle tone, and holding the body up when not lying down. Some studies show that certain people are able to resist weight gain from overeating by inducing thermogenesis, whereas others experience little thermogenesis.

Brown adipose tissue is a specialized form of fat tissue that participates in thermogenesis. The brown appearance results from the large number of capillaries it contains. It is found in small amounts in infants and hibernating animals. Brown fat contributes to thermogenesis because it releases much of the energy from energy-yielding nutrients as heat. Brown fat has a protein (uncoupling protein) that uses the food we consume to generate heat for the body instead of creating energy in the form of ATP. Adults have very little brown fat, and its role in adulthood is not known. It is thought to be important mostly for thermoregulation during infancy, when brown fat accounts for as much as 5% of body weight. Hibernating animals use brown fat to generate heat during cold winter months.

Knowledge Check

1. What percentage of total energy expenditure is spent on basal metabolism?
2. What factors increase basal metabolism?
3. How much energy is expended via the thermic effect of food?
4. What is adaptive thermogenesis?
5. What is brown fat and what function does it play in an infant?

 10.2 Measuring Energy Expenditure

The amount of energy a body uses can be measured by both direct and indirect calorimetry or can be estimated based on height, weight, degree of physical activity, and age.

Direct calorimetry estimates energy expenditure by measuring the amount of body heat released by a person. Direct calorimetry works because almost all the energy the body uses eventually leaves as heat. Heat release is measured by placing a person in an insulated chamber, often the size of a small bedroom, that is surrounded by a layer of water. The change in water temperature before and after the body releases heat is used to determine the amount of energy the person has expended. Recall that a calorie is related to the amount of heat required to raise the temperature of water. Few studies use direct calorimetry, mostly because it is expensive and complex to use.

Indirect calorimetry, the most commonly used method to determine energy use by the body, involves collecting expired air from an individual during a specified amount of time (Fig. 10-5). This method works because a predictable relationship exists between the body's use of energy and the amount of oxygen consumed and carbon dioxide produced. The procedure to collect the air can be done in a laboratory or with a handheld device that allows the individual to be mobile and not restricted to the lab. Data tables showing energy costs of different exercises are based on information from indirect calorimetry studies.

In another approach to indirect calorimetry, a person drinks doubly labeled water (^2H_2O and $H_2{}^{18}O$); then, his or her urine and blood samples are analyzed to examine ^2H and ^{18}O excretion. The labeled oxygen is eliminated from the body as water and carbon dioxide, whereas the labeled hydrogen is eliminated only as water. Subtracting hydrogen losses from oxygen losses provides a measure of carbon dioxide output. This method is quite accurate but also very expensive. It is the basis for determining Estimated Energy Requirements for humans.

Estimated Energy Requirements (EERs) are measurements based on formulas, developed by the Food and Nutrition Board, that can estimate energy needs using a person's weight, height, gender, age, and physical activity level. The following are the formulas for adults (remember to do the multiplication and division before the addition and subtraction).

Men 19 Years and Older

$$EER = 662 - (9.53 \times AGE) + PA \times ([15.91 \times WT] + [539.6 \times HT])$$

Women 19 Years and Older

$$EER = 354 - (6.91 \times AGE) + PA \times ([9.36 \times WT] + [726 \times HT])$$

The variables in the formulas correspond to the following:

EER = Estimated Energy Requirement
AGE = Age in years
 PA = Physical Activity Estimate (see the accompanying table on page 320)
WT = Weight in kg (lb ÷ 2.2)
HT = Height in meters (inches ÷ 39.4)

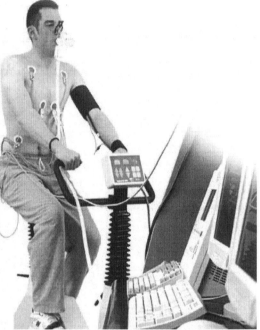

Figure 10-5 Indirect calorimetry measures oxygen intake and carbon dioxide output to determine energy expended during daily activities. Handheld indirect calorimeters also are available.

	Calorie Guidelines		
Children	**Sedentary** →		**Active**
2–3 years	1000	⟶	1400
Females	**Sedentary** →		**Active**
4–8 years	1200	⟶	1800
9–13	1600	⟶	2200
14–18	1800	⟶	2400
19–30	2000	⟶	2400
31–50	1800	⟶	2200
51+	1600	⟶	2200
Males	**Sedentary** →		**Active**
4–8 years	1200	⟶	2000
9–13	1800	⟶	2600
14–18	2200	⟶	3200
19–30	2400	⟶	3000
31–50	2200	⟶	3000
51+	2000	⟶	2800

Energy expenditure estimates by age and activity.

▶ Resting Energy Expenditure (REE) is the amount of calories needed during a nonactive period. It is used to estimate calorie needs in clinical situations. The Harris-Benedict equation can be used to estimate resting energy expenditure:

Men
REE = 66.5 + (13.8 × WT) + (5 × HT) − (6.8 × AGE)

Women
REE = 655.1 + (9.6 × WT) + (1.9 × HT) − (4.7 × AGE)

The variables in the formulas correspond to the following:
 REE = Resting Energy Expenditure
 WT = Weight in kg (lb ÷ 2.2)
 HT = Height in cm (inches × 2.54)
 AGE = Age in years

Physical Activity (PA) Estimates[55]

Activity Level	PA (Men)	PA (Women)
Sedentary (e.g., no exercise)	1.00	1.00
Low activity (e.g., walks the equivalent of 2 miles per day at 3 to 4 mph)	1.11	1.12
Active (e.g., walks the equivalent of 7 miles per day at 3 to 4 mph)	1.25	1.27
Very active (e.g., walks the equivalent of 17 miles per day at 3 to 4 mph)	1.48	1.45

Consider a man who is 25 years old, is 5 feet 9 inches (1.75 meters) tall and 154 lb (70 kg), and has an active lifestyle. His EER is

$$EER = 662 − (9.53 × 25) + 1.25 × ([15.91 × 70] + [539.6 × 1.75]) = 2997$$

Remember, EERs are only estimates—many other factors, such as genetics and hormones, can affect actual energy needs.

A simple method of tracking energy expenditure, and thus energy needs, is to use the forms in Appendix M. Begin listing all the activities performed (including sleep) in a 24-hour period and recording the number of minutes spent in each activity; the total should be 1440 minutes (24 hours). Next, record the energy cost for each activity in kcal per minute, following the directions in Appendix M. Multiply the energy cost by the minutes to determine the energy expended for each activity. Finally, total all the kcal values to calculate your estimated energy expenditure for the day.

Knowledge Check

1. How do direct and indirect calorimetry differ?
2. Why is it possible to use direct calorimetry and indirect calorimetry to measure energy expenditure?
3. What is your Estimated Energy Requirement?

CASE STUDY

Christy is a college freshman. She is excited about college and has good support from her family and friends to help her succeed. Her greatest concerns this first semester are to establish good study habits and time management, to get along with her new roommate, and to avoid the "Freshman 15." For the last 3 months, all she has heard about is the amount of weight that she will gain in her freshman year. She has never had a weight problem, but in high school she was on the track team and played basketball. She is not quite sure what she should be eating, so for now she has a salad for lunch and dinner and skips breakfast because she has an 8 A.M. class. She gets very hungry at around 10 P.M. and her roommate has been having pizza delivered to the dorm—she cannot resist having several slices. What advice would you give Christy? With these eating habits, is the Freshman 15 likely to happen to Christy? Why can't she resist eating pizza?

10.3 Eating Behavior Regulation

Two factors drive our desire to eat: hunger and appetite (Fig. 10-6). **Hunger,** the physiological drive to find and eat food, is controlled primarily by internal body mechanisms, such as organs, hormones, hormonelike factors, and the nervous system.[11] **Appetite,** the psychological drive to eat, is affected mostly by external factors that encourage us to eat, such as social custom, time of day, mood (e.g., feeling sad or happy), memories of pleasant tastes, and the sight of a tempting dessert.

Internal and external signals that drive hunger and appetite generally operate simultaneously and lead us to decide whether to reject or eat a food. For example, external signals can cause cephalic phase responses by the body—that is, saliva flows and digestive hormones and insulin are released in response to seeing, smelling, and initially tasting food. These physiological responses encourage eating and prepare the body for the meal.[11] Although hunger and appetite are closely intertwined, they don't always coincide. Almost everyone has encountered a mouthwatering dessert and devoured it, even on a full stomach. Alternately, there are times when we are hungry but have no appetite for the food being served. Where food is ample, appetite—not hunger—mostly triggers eating.

Fulfilling either or both drives by eating sufficient food normally brings a state of **satiety,** in which we feel satisfaction and no

We have an innate taste for sweet and acquire a taste for fat.

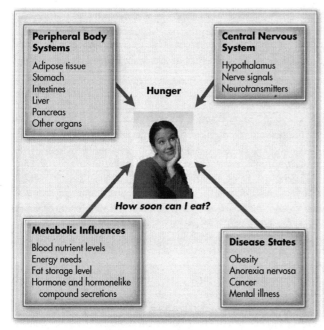

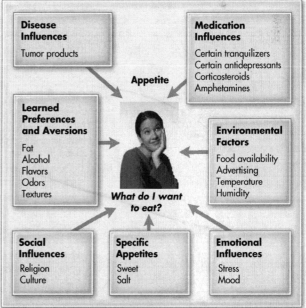

Figure 10-6 Although some factors have an impact on both hunger and appetite, internal factors are mainly responsible for the physiological drive to eat (hunger), whereas external factors primarily influence the psychological drive to eat (appetite). These factors combine to play a role in the complex and interrelated processes that help determine when, what, and how much we eat.

322   **PART 3**   Metabolism and Energy Balance

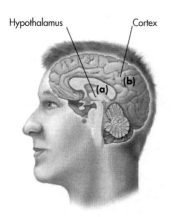

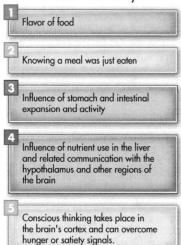

Process of Satiety

1 Flavor of food

2 Knowing a meal was just eaten

3 Influence of stomach and intestinal expansion and activity

4 Influence of nutrient use in the liver and related communication with the hypothalamus and other regions of the brain

5 Conscious thinking takes place in the brain's cortex and can overcome hunger or satiety signals.

Figure 10-7 The hypothalamus and satiety. (a) The hypothalamus is the region in the brain that does most of the processing of signals regarding food intake. (b) The process of satiety starts with eating food and concludes with actions in the hypothalamus and other regions of the brain, such as the cortex.

sympathetic nervous system Part of the nervous system that regulates involuntary vital functions, including the activity of the heart muscle, smooth muscle, and adrenal glands.

ghrelin Hormone made by the stomach that increases food intake.

leptin Hormone made by adipose tissue that influences long-term regulation of fat mass.

longer have the drive to eat. The hypothalamus, a portion of the brain, is the key integration site for the regulation of satiety (Fig. 10-7). The hypothalamus communicates with the endocrine and nervous systems and integrates many internal cues, including blood glucose levels, hormone secretions, and **sympathetic nervous system** activity, that both inhibit and encourage food intake.[11] If these internal signals stimulate the satiety centers of the hypothalamus, we stop eating. If they stimulate the feeding centers in the hypothalamus, we eat more.[11] Surgery and some cancers and chemicals can harm the hypothalamus. Damage to the satiety center causes humans to become obese, whereas damage to the feeding center inhibits eating and eventually leads to weight loss.[11]

Feelings of satiety are elicited first by the sensory aspects of food (e.g., food flavor and smell, the size and shape of the portion served, and dietary variety) and the knowledge that a meal has been eaten (see Fig. 10-6). Chewing also seems to contribute to satiety, in part linked to the release of the neurotransmitter histamine, which affects the satiety center in the brain. Next, the stomach and intestines expand (called gastrointestinal distension) as they fill with digesting food and drink, which further contributes to satiety. Low-energy-dense foods (those high in water and/or fiber) promote satiety because they expand the stomach and intestines to a greater extent than lighter-weight foods (e.g., oils and snack foods).

Finally, the effects of digestion, absorption, and metabolism promote satiety. For example, the secretion of hormones, such as cholecystokinin, glucagon-like peptide-1 (GLP-1), and peptide YY_{3-36}, during digestion helps shut off hunger. Nutrient receptors in the small intestines also are thought to help promote satiety. (Infusing fats or carbohydrates directly into the small intestine causes feelings of satiety, whereas infusing these nutrients directly into the blood does not cause this effect.) Studies suggest that an apolipoprotein on chylomicrons absorbed into the blood after a meal also signals satiety to the brain. The metabolism of certain nutrients, especially carbohydrates, is linked to an increased production of serotonin (a brain neurotransmitter), which causes us to feel calm and may reduce our food intake.[11] The metabolism of protein may promote short-term satiety by decreasing the secretion of hormones, such as **ghrelin** (made by the stomach), that stimulate eating.[12] Nutrient use in the liver also signals satiety.

Several hours after eating, concentrations of macronutrients in the blood begin to fall and the body starts using energy from body stores. This change causes feelings of satiety to diminish, and feeding signals begin to dominate again.[11] Endorphins, the body's natural painkillers, and hormones, such as cortisol and ghrelin, stimulate appetite and increase food intake.

In addition to the short-term control of satiety depicted in Figure 10-7, food intake also is affected by body composition—specifically, the amount of body fat. **Leptin** is a protein made by adipose tissue that influences the long-term regulation of fat mass. Leptin was isolated from the obesity gene (ob gene) and acts as a hormone. When the ob gene is functioning normally, leptin is made. When there is a mutation in the ob gene, leptin is not made in sufficient quantities. Theoretically, when adipose tissue stores are increasing, leptin signals satiety. Conversely, when adipose tissue stores are decreasing, leptin production drops and the desire to eat is enhanced. Because treating people with leptin doesn't cause significant weight loss, experts suggest that, instead of protecting against obesity, leptin may be more important for signaling low body fat stores and setting in motion adaptations that promote energy conservation, delaying the effects of starvation.[11]

As you can see, the regulation of food intake and satiety is complex and involves body cells (brain, adipose tissue, stomach, intestines, liver, and other organs), hormones (e.g., cholecystokinin and ghrelin), neurotransmitters (e.g., serotonin), dietary components, and social customs. This system is not perfect, however; your body weight can increase (or decrease) over time if you are not careful to balance your energy intake with your energy output.

Knowledge Check

1. What factors affect hunger?
2. What factors affect appetite?
3. What factors affect satiety?
4. How do body fat stores affect food intake?

CRITICAL THINKING

Why do you eat what you do? Keep track of what triggers your eating for a few days. Is it primarily hunger or appetite?

10.4 Estimating Body Weight and Composition

Over the last 50 years, the use of the weight-for-height tables issued by the Metropolitan Life Insurance Company has been the typical method for determining if a person's weight is healthy. These tables consider gender and frame size, predicting the weight range at a specific height that is associated with the greatest longevity. The latest table (issued in 1983) and methods for determining frame size can be found in Appendix G.

Most of the weight-for-height tables came from studies of large populations. When applied to the population, they provide a good estimate of weights associated with health and longevity (Fig. 10-8). However, these tables do not necessarily refer directly to an individual's health status. As a result, in recent years the focus has shifted from using weight-for-height tables to considering the components of body weight (e.g., body fat and fat-free mass [muscle, bone, water]) and their relative proportions because of the increased health risks associated with excess body fatness. Instead of just assessing body weight, experts now recommend evaluating total amount of body fat, the location of body fat, and the presence or absence of weight-related medical problems.[5]

Weight in pounds

Height	100	110	120	130	140	150	160	170	180	190	200	210	220	230	240	250
4'6"	24	27	29	31	34	36	39	41	43	46	48	51	53	56	58	60
4'8"	22	25	27	29	31	34	36	38	40	43	45	47	49	52	51	56
4'10"	21	23	25	27	29	31	34	36	38	40	42	44	46	48	50	52
5'0"	20	22	23	25	27	29	31	33	35	37	39	41	43	45	47	49
5'2"	18	20	22	24	26	27	29	31	33	35	37	38	40	42	44	46
5'4"	17	19	21	22	24	26	28	29	31	33	34	36	38	40	41	43
5'6"	16	18	19	21	23	24	26	27	29	31	32	34	36	37	39	40
5'8"	15	17	18	20	21	23	24	26	27	29	30	32	34	35	37	38
5'10"	14	16	17	19	20	22	23	24	26	27	29	30	32	33	35	36
6'0"	13	15	16	18	19	20	22	23	24	26	27	28	30	31	33	34
6'2"	13	14	15	17	18	19	21	22	23	24	26	27	28	30	31	32
6'4"	12	13	15	16	17	18	20	21	22	23	24	26	27	28	29	30
6'6"	12	13	14	15	16	17	19	20	21	22	23	24	25	27	28	29
6'8"	11	12	13	14	15	17	18	19	20	21	22	23	24	26	26	28

Height in feet and inches

☐ Underweight   ▨ Healthy weight   ▨ Overweight   ▨ Obese

Developed by the National Center for Health Statistics in collaboration with the National Center for Chronic Disease Prevention and Health Promotion

Figure 10-8 Weight-for-height table based on BMI. A healthy weight for height generally falls within a BMI range of 19.5 to 24.9 kilograms/meters^2.

324   **PART 3**   Metabolism and Energy Balance

Figure 10-9 Examples of body shapes associated with different BMI values.

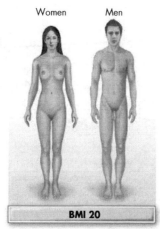
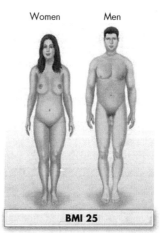
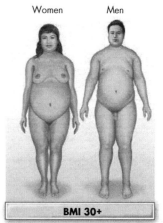

Body Mass Index

Currently, body mass index (BMI) is the preferred weight-for-height standard because it is more closely related to body fat content (Fig. 10-9).[4] BMI is convenient to use because it is easier to measure height and weight than body fat and because BMI values apply to both men and women. Table 10-1 lists the BMI for various heights and weights. Either of the following equations can be used to calculate BMI.

$$\frac{\text{Body weight (in kg)}}{\text{Height}^2 \text{ (in meters)}} \quad \text{or} \quad \frac{\text{Body weight (in lb)} \times 703}{\text{Height}^2 \text{ (in inches)}}$$

Table 10-1 Body Weight in Pounds According to Height and Body Mass Index (BMI)

	Healthy BMI							Overweight BMI				Obese BMI		
	19	20	21	22	23	24	25	26	27	28	29	30	35	40
Height (Inches)	Body Weight (Pounds)													
58	91	96	100	105	110	115	119	124	129	134	138	143	167	191
59	94	99	104	109	114	119	124	128	133	138	143	148	173	198
60	97	102	107	112	118	123	128	133	138	143	148	153	179	204
61	100	106	111	116	122	127	132	137	143	148	153	158	185	211
62	104	109	115	120	126	131	136	142	147	153	158	164	191	218
63	107	113	118	124	130	135	141	146	152	158	163	169	197	225
64	110	116	122	128	134	140	145	151	157	163	169	174	204	232
65	114	120	126	132	138	144	150	156	162	168	174	180	210	240
66	118	124	130	136	142	148	155	161	167	173	179	186	216	247
67	121	127	134	140	146	153	159	166	172	178	185	191	223	255
68	125	131	138	144	151	158	164	171	177	184	190	197	230	262
69	128	135	142	149	155	162	169	176	182	189	196	203	236	270
70	132	139	146	153	160	167	174	181	188	195	202	207	243	278
71	136	143	150	157	165	172	179	186	193	200	208	215	250	286
72	140	147	154	162	169	177	184	191	199	206	213	221	258	294
73	144	151	159	166	174	182	189	197	204	212	219	227	265	302
74	148	155	163	171	179	186	194	202	210	218	225	233	272	311
75	152	160	168	176	184	192	200	208	216	224	232	240	279	319
76	156	164	172	180	189	197	205	213	221	230	238	246	287	328

Each entry gives the body weight in pounds for a person of a given height and BMI (kg/m²). Pounds have been rounded off. To use the table, find the appropriate height in the far left column. Move across the row to a weight. The number at the top of the column is the BMI for the height and weight.

Table 10-2 **Obesity-Related Health Conditions**
Surgical risk
Pulmonary disease and sleep disorders
Type 2 diabetes
Hypertension
Cardiovascular disease (e.g., coronary heart disease and stroke)
Bone and joint disorders (including gout)
Gallstones
Skin disorders
Various cancers, such as kidney, gallbladder, colon and rectum, and uterus (women) and prostate gland (men)
Shorter stature (in some cases of obesity)
Pregnancy risks*
Reduced physical agility and increased risk of accidents and falls
Menstrual irregularities and infertility*
Vision problems
Premature death
Infections[54]
Liver damage and eventual failure
Erectile dysfunction in men

*Estrogen, the primary "female" hormone, is synthesized mainly by the ovaries but also by adipose tissue. Greater than normal amounts of body fat increase estrogen levels in obese women. Higher than normal estrogen levels can adversely affect pregnancy, menstruation, and fertility.

The greater the degree of obesity, the more likely and the more serious these health problems generally become. They are much more likely to appear among people who have excess upper-body fat distribution and/or are greater than twice healthy body weight.

▶ One BMI unit equals about 6 to 7 lb.

▶ *Healthy weight* is currently the preferred term to use for weight recommendations. Older terms, such as *ideal weight* and *desirable weight,* are no longer used in medical literature, although you still may hear them used in clinical practice.

Pounds per Inch Shortcut for Estimating Healthy Body Weight

Women: Start with 100 lb; then add 5 lb for each inch of height above 5 feet.

Men: Start with 106 lb; then add 6 lb for each inch of height above 5 feet.

The weight estimate is given a ±10% range.

Example: A 6-foot-tall man's healthy weight is 178 lb (106 + [12 × 6] = 178).

The 10% range is about 18 lb (178 × 10%).

His healthy weight range = 160 to 196 (178 ±18).

Obese: BMI ≥ 30
Overweight: BMI 25–29.9
Healthy weight: BMI 18.5–24.9
Underweight: BMI < 18.5

A healthy weight-for-height is a BMI ranging from 18.5 to <25. Health risks from excess weight may begin when BMI is 25 or more. When interpreting BMI, it is important to remember that any weight-for-height standard is a crude estimate of body fatness—a BMI of 25 to <30 is a marker of overweight, not necessarily a marker of overfat. Even agreed-upon standards for BMI are not appropriate for everyone; they do not apply to children, teens, older adults, and pregnant and lactating women.[13] Many men (especially athletes) have a BMI greater than 25 because of extra muscle tissue. Adults less than 5 feet tall may have a high BMI but are not overweight or overfat. For this reason, BMI alone should not be used to diagnose overweight or obesity. Still, overfat and overweight conditions generally appear together.

Measuring Body Fat Content

Body fat can range from 2 to 70% of body weight. Desirable amounts of body fat are about 8 to 24% of body weight for men and 21 to 35% for women. Men with over 24% body fat and women with over about 35% body fat are considered obese. Women need more body fat because some "sex-specific" fat is associated with reproductive functions. This fat is normal and factored into calculations. The farther body fatness rises above desirable levels, the greater the health risks are likely to be (Table 10-2).

To measure body fat content accurately using typical methods, both body weight and body volume must be measured. Body weight is easy to measure. Of the typical methods used to estimate body volume, **underwater weighing** is one of the most accurate (2 to 3% error margin).[14] This technique determines body volume by measuring body weight when under water and body weight in air and entering these values into a mathematical formula that accounts for the differences in the relative densities of fat tissue and lean tissue (Fig. 10-10).

Figure 10-10 During underwater weighing, the person exhales as much air as possible and then holds his or her breath and bends over at the waist. When the person is totally submerged, underwater weight is recorded. Body volume is calculated by entering this value and weight in air into a formula.

326   **PART 3**   Metabolism and Energy Balance

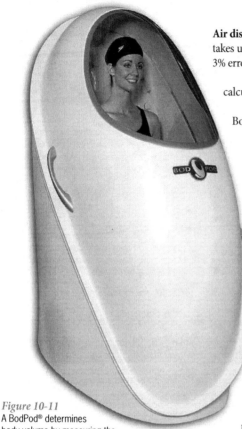

Figure 10-11
A BodPod® determines body volume by measuring the volume of air displaced when a person sits in a sealed chamber for a few minutes.

Air displacement, another method for determining body volume, measures the space a person takes up inside a small chamber, such as the BodPod® (Fig. 10-11). This method also has a 2 to 3% error margin and is an accurate alternative to underwater weighing.[15]

Once body weight and body volume are known, body density and body fat can be calculated:

$$\text{Body density} = \frac{\text{Body weight}}{\text{Body volume}} \qquad \text{\% body fat} = (495 \, / \, \text{Body density}) - 450$$

For example, if the person in the underwater weighing tank in Figure 10-10 has a body density of 1.06 g/cm³, he has 17% body fat ([495 / 1.06] − 450 = 17).

Skinfold thickness is a common anthropometric method to estimate total body fat content. Technicians use calipers to measure the fat layer directly under the skin at multiple sites and then enter those values into a mathematical formula (Fig. 10-12). The accuracy of this method is good (3 to 4% error margin) when performed by a trained technician.[14]

Bioelectrical impedance estimates body fat content by sending a painless, low-energy electrical current through the body. Researchers surmise that adipose tissue resists electrical flow more than lean tissue does because adipose tissue contains less electrolytes and water than lean tissue. Thus, greater electrical resistance is associated with more adipose tissue. Electrical resistance measurements can be used to estimate total body fat (3 to 4% error margin) if the individual has prepared by having normal body hydration, resting for 12 hours, fasting for 4 hours, and not drinking alcohol for 48 hours before the test (Fig. 10-13).

Dual energy X-ray absorptiometry (DEXA) is considered the most accurate way to determine body fat (1 to 4% error margin), but the equipment is very expensive and not widely available. The usual whole-body scan requires about 5 to 20 minutes and the dose of radiation is less than a chest X-ray. This method can estimate body fat, fat-free soft tissue, and bone minerals. Thus, obesity, osteoporosis, and other health conditions can be investigated using DEXA (Fig. 10-14).

▶ Another method to assess body fat is to measure total-body electrical conductance (TOBEC) when placed in an electromagnetic field. Still another method exposes the bicep muscle to a beam of near-infrared light and assesses interactions of the light beam with fat and lean tissues. This inexpensive, flashlight-size device can quickly estimate body composition; however, this method is not very accurate.

▶ To determine if body weight is healthy, consider these factors:

- Weight
- Body composition
- Body fat distribution
- Age and physical development
- Health status
- Family history of obesity and weight-related diseases
- Personal feelings about one's body weight

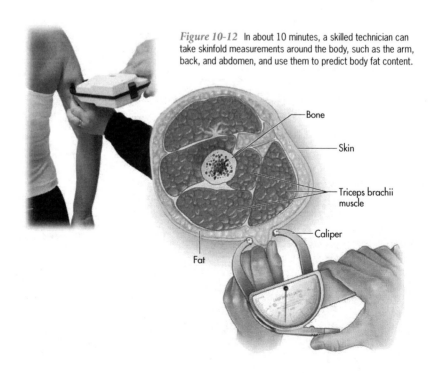

Figure 10-12 In about 10 minutes, a skilled technician can take skinfold measurements around the body, such as the arm, back, and abdomen, and use them to predict body fat content.

Bone

Skin

Triceps brachii muscle

Caliper

Fat

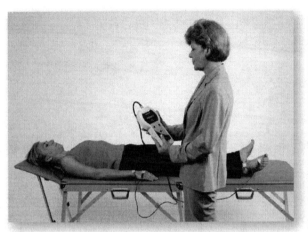

Figure 10-13 Bioelectrical impedance estimates total body fat in less than 5 minutes and is based on the principle that body fat resists the flow of electricity because it is low in water and electrolytes. The degree of resistance to electrical flow is used to estimate body fatness.

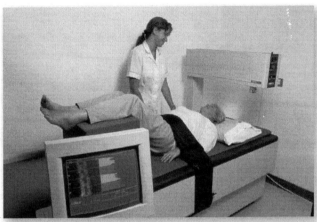

Figure 10-14 Dual energy X-ray absorptiometry (DEXA) measures body fat by releasing small doses of radiation through the body to assess body fat and bone density. DEXA is considered the most accurate method for determining body fat.

Assessing Body Fat Distribution

Some people store fat in upper-body areas. Others accumulate fat lower on the body. Excess fat in either place generally presents health risks, but each storage space also has its unique risks. Upper-body (android) obesity is more often related to cardiovascular disease, hypertension, and type 2 diabetes.[16] Instead of emptying fat directly into general circulation like other adipose cells, abdominal adipose cells release fat directly to the liver by way of the portal vein. This direct delivery to the liver likely interferes with the liver's ability to clear insulin and alters the liver's lipoprotein metabolism. Abdominal adipose cells also make substances that increase inflammation, insulin resistance, blood clotting, and blood vessel constriction. All these changes can lead to long-term health problems.

High blood testosterone (primarily a male hormone) levels apparently encourage upper-body fat storage, as does a diet with a high glycemic load, alcohol intake, and smoking. This characteristic male pattern of fat storage appears in an apple shape (large abdomen [potbelly] and thinner buttocks and thighs). Upper-body obesity is assessed by simply measuring the waist at the narrowest point just above the navel when relaxed. A waist circumference more than 40 inches (102 cm) in men and more than 35 inches (88 cm) in women indicates upper-body obesity (Fig. 10-15).[4]

Estrogen and progesterone (primarily female hormones) encourage the storage of fat in the lower body. The small abdomen and much larger buttocks and thighs give a pearlike appearance. After menopause, blood estrogen levels fall, encouraging abdominal fat distribution in women.

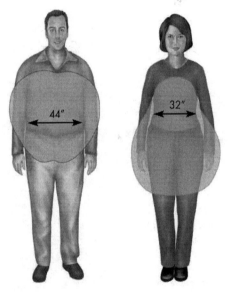

Upper-body fat distribution   Lower-body fat distribution
(android: apple shape)   (gynoid: pear shape)

Figure 10-15 Body fat stored primarily in the upper-body (android) form brings higher risks of ill health associated with obesity than does lower-body (gynoid) fat. The woman's waist circumference of 32 inches and the man's waist circumference of 44 inches indicate that the man has upper-body fat distribution but the woman does not, based on a cutoff of 35 inches for women and 40 inches for men.

Knowledge Check

1. What is body mass index and how is it calculated?
2. When determining if a person's weight is healthy, what factors should be considered?
3. What are 3 techniques used to assess body fat?
4. How is body fat distribution used to assess health risks?
5. Which body shape is at the greatest risk of health problems?

10.5 Factors Affecting Body Weight and Composition

Observations indicate that a child with no obese parent has only a 10% chance of becoming obese. When a child has 1 obese parent, that risk rises to 40%; when both parents are obese, it soars to 80%. This section explores whether this increasing risk is due to nature or nurture.

Role of Genetics

Studies of **identical twins** provide some insight into the contribution of nature (genetics) to body weight. Even when identical twins are raised apart, they tend to show similar weight-gain patterns, both in overall weight and in body fat distribution. Nurture—eating habits and nutrition, which vary between twins who are raised apart—seems to have less to do with weight-gain patterns than nature does.[4]

Research suggests that genes account for up to 40 to 70% of weight differences between people. The genes may be those that determine body type, metabolic rate, and the factors that affect hunger and satiety. For example, basal metabolism increases as body surface increases, and therefore those who inherited genes that cause them to grow tall use more energy than shorter people, even at rest. As a result, tall people appear to have an inherently easier time maintaining healthy body weight. Some individuals are thought to have a genetic predisposition to obesity because they inherit a "thrifty metabolism"—one that uses energy frugally. This metabolism enables them to store fat readily and use less energy to perform tasks than a typical individual. In earlier times when food supplies were scarce, a thrifty metabolism would have been a safeguard against starvation. Now, with the abundant food supply available in Westernized countries, people with a thrifty metabolism need to engage in physical activity and make wise food choices to prevent storing excess amounts of fat. If you think you are prone to weight gain, you may have inherited a thrifty metabolism.

identical twins Two offspring that develop from a single ovum and sperm and, consequently, have the same genetic makeup.

Does the difference in body fat between grandfathers and grandsons arise from nature, from nurture, or both?

The **set-point theory** proposes that humans have a genetically predetermined body weight or body fat content, which the body closely regulates. It is not known what cells control this set point or how it actually functions in weight regulation. There is evidence, however, that mechanisms exist that help regulate weight. For example, some research suggests that the hypothalamus monitors the amount of body fat and tries to keep that amount constant over time. Recall from earlier in the chapter that the hormone leptin forms a communication link between adipose cells and the brain, which allows for some weight regulation.[11]

Evidence that supports the set-point theory includes numerous studies indicating that the body tries to maintain its weight and resist weight loss. For instance, when volunteers who lost weight through starvation had access to food, they tended to eat in such a way as to regain their original weight. Also, after an illness is resolved, a person generally regains lost weight. When energy intake is reduced, secretions of thyroid hormones fall, which slows basal metabolism and conserves body weight. When weight is lost, the body becomes more efficient at storing fat by increasing the activity of the enzyme lipoprotein lipase, which takes fat into cells.

Some evidence also supports the idea that a set point helps prevent weight gain. Studies in the 1960s using prisoners with no history of obesity found it was hard for some men to gain weight, even with high calorie intakes. If a person overeats, basal metabolism and thermogenesis tend to increase in the short run, which causes some resistance to weight gain. However, in the long run, evidence that the set point helps us resist weight gain is weaker than the evidence that the set point helps us resist weight loss. When a person gains weight and stays at that weight for a while, the body tends to establish a new set point.

Opponents of the set-point theory argue that weight does not remain constant throughout adulthood—the average person gains weight slowly, at least until old age. In addition, if an individual is placed in a different social, emotional, or physical environment, weight can be altered and maintained at markedly higher or lower levels. These arguments suggest that humans, rather than having a set point determined by genetics or number of adipose cells, actually settle into a particular stable weight based on their circumstances, often referred to as a "settling point."

Student life is often full of physical activity. This is not necessarily true for a person's later working life; hence, weight gain is a strong possibility.

Role of Environment

Some researchers argue that body weight similarities among family members stem more from learned behaviors than from genetic similarities. Even couples and friends (who generally have no genetic link) may behave similarly toward food and eventually assume similar degrees of leanness or fatness.[17] The effects of environment are supported by the fact that our gene pool has not changed much in the last 50 years, but the ranks of obese people recently have grown in what the U.S. Centers for Disease Control and Prevention describes as epidemic proportions.

Environmental factors have important effects on what we eat. These factors may define when eating is appropriate, what is preferable to eat, and how much food should be eaten. As you recall from Chapter 1 (Fig. 1-6), our food choices are affected by numerous environmental factors, including food availability and preferences, food marketing, social networks, culture, education, lifestyle, health concerns, and income—all of which can affect calorie intake and weight gain. For example, those with limited incomes tend to have a greater risk of obesity. People who experience significant emotional stress, are members of a cultural or

set-point theory Proposes that humans have a genetically predetermined body weight or fat content that is closely regulated.

Table 10-3 **Factors That Encourage Excess Body Fat Storage and Obesity**

Factors	How They Promote Fat Storage
Aging	Adults tend to gain weight as they age due to the slowing of basal metabolism and increasingly sedentary lifestyles.
Female gender	Women naturally have greater fat stores than men. Women may not lose all weight gained in pregnancy. At menopause, abdominal fat deposition is favored.
High-calorie diet	Excess energy intake, binge eating, and preference for high-energy-density foods favor weight gain.
Sedentary lifestyle	A low or decreasing amount of physical activity ("couch potato") favors weight gain.
Weight history	Overweight children and teens have an increased risk of being overweight in adulthood.
Social and behavioral factors	Lower socioeconomic status, overweight friends and family, a cultural/ethnic group that prefers higher body weight, a lifestyle that discourages healthy meals and adequate exercise, easy availability of inexpensive high-calorie food, excessive television viewing, smoking cessation, lack of adequate sleep, emotional stress, and a greater number of meals eaten away from home are linked with increased fat storage.
Certain medications	Certain medications stimulate appetite, causing food intake to increase.
Geographic location	Regional differences, such as high-fat diets and sedentary lifestyles in the Midwest and areas of the South, lead to different rates of obesity in different places.
Genetic characteristics	These affect basal metabolic rate, the thermic effect of food, adaptive thermogenesis, the efficiency of storing body fat, the relative proportion of fat and carbohydrate used by the body, and possibly increased hunger sensations linked to the activity of various brain chemicals.

ethnic group that prefers higher body weight, have a social network of overweight friends, or get insufficient sleep are more likely to carry excess body fat. These patterns suggest the important role of nurture in determining body weight and composition.

Genetic and Environmental Synergy

Even though our genetic backgrounds have a strong influence on body weight and composition, genes are not destiny—both nature and nurture are involved (Table 10-3). Hereditary factors interact with environmental factors to determine actual body weight and composition. Even with a genetic potential for leanness, it is possible for a person who overeats to gain excess fat. Conversely, an individual genetically predisposed to obesity can avoid excess fat storage with a healthy diet and sufficient amounts of regular physical activity.

Diseases and Disorders

Body weight and fatness can be affected by certain diseases, hormonal abnormalities, rare genetic disorders, and psychological disturbances. For instance, cancer, AIDS, hyperthyroidism, **Marfan syndrome,** and anorexia nervosa tend to cause a person to have limited fat stores. A very small percentage of obesity cases are caused by brain tumors, ovarian cysts, hypothyroidism, and congenital syndromes, such as **Prader-Willi syndrome.**

Marfan syndrome Genetic disorder affecting muscles and skeleton, characterized by tallness, long arms, and little subcutaneous fat. Some medical historians speculate that Abraham Lincoln suffered from Marfan syndrome.

Prader-Willi syndrome Genetic disorder characterized by shortness, mental retardation, and uncontrolled appetite, caused by a dysfunction of the nervous system, leading to extreme obesity.

Knowledge Check

1. What evidence supports the role of genetics in determining body weight?
2. What evidence supports the role of the environment in determining body weight?
3. Why is it likely that both genetics and the environment determine body weight?

10.6 Treatment of Overweight and Obesity

The treatment of overweight and obesity should be considered similar to the treatment of any chronic disease: it requires long-term lifestyle changes.[5] Too often, however, people view a "diet" as something they go on temporarily and, once the weight is lost, they revert to their old dietary habits and physical activity routines. It is mostly for this reason that so many people regain lost weight (called weight cycling). Instead, overweight and obese (as well as underweight) people should emphasize healthy, active lifestyles with lifelong dietary modifications (Fig. 10-16)—if started early, these modifications also can help prevent obesity.[18]

▶ Weight-control objectives from *Healthy People 2020* include

- Reduce the proportion of adults who are obese.
- Increase the proportion of adults who are at a healthy weight.
- Reduce the proportion of children and adolescents who are considered obese.
- Prevent inappropriate weight gain in youth and adults.
- Increase the proportion of physician office visits that include counseling or education related to nutrition or weight.

RATE OF LOSS

☐ Encourages slow and steady weight loss, rather than rapid weight loss, to promote lasting weight
☐ Sets goal of 1 to 2 lb of fat loss per week
☐ Includes a period of weight maintenance for a few months after 10% of body weight is lost
☐ Evaluates need for further dieting before more weight loss begins

---

FLEXIBILITY

☐ Supports participation in normal activities (e.g., parties, restaurants)
☐ Adapts to individual habits and tastes

INTAKE

☐ Meets nutrient needs (except for energy needs)
☐ Includes common foods, with no foods being promoted as magical or special
☐ Recommends a fortified ready-to-eat breakfast cereal or balanced multivitamin/mineral supplement, especially when intake is less than 1600 kcal per day
☐ Uses MyPlate as a pattern for food choices

BEHAVIOR MODIFICATION

☐ Focuses on maintenance of healthy lifestyle (and weight) for a lifetime
☐ Promotes reasonable changes that can be maintained
☐ Encourages social support
☐ Includes plans for relapse, so that one does not quit after a setback
☐ Promotes changes that control problem eating behaviors

OVERALL HEALTH

☐ Requires screening by a physician for people with existing health problems, those over 40 (men) to 50 (women) years of age who plan to increase physical activity substantially, and those who plan to lose weight rapidly
☐ Encourages regular physical activity, sufficient sleep, stress reduction, and other healthy changes in lifestyle
☐ Addresses underlying psychological weight issues, such as depression or marital stress

---

Figure 10-16 Characteristics of a sound weight-loss diet. If you are considering a weight-loss diet, compare it to this checklist. The healthiest weight-loss diets have all of these characteristics. Keep in mind that, during times of underfeeding or overfeeding, the body makes numerous physiological adjustments that resist weight change. This compensation is most pronounced during times of underfeeding and is why slow, steady weight loss is advocated.

332 **PART 3** Metabolism and Energy Balance

Figure 10-17 The key to weight loss and maintenance can be thought of as a triangle, in which the 3 corners consist of ▧ controlling energy intake, ▧ performing regular physical activity, and ▧ controlling problem behaviors. The 3 corners of the triangle support each other—without 1 corner, the triangle becomes incomplete.

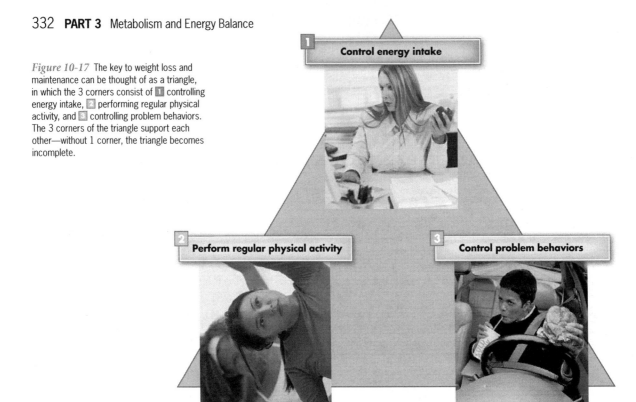

A sound weight-loss program should include 3 key components:[6, 18]

1. Control of energy intake
2. Regular physical activity
3. Control of problem behaviors

A one-sided approach that focuses only on restricting energy intake is a difficult plan of action. Instead, adding physical activity and the control of problem behaviors will contribute to success in weight loss. Accepting that these changes must be maintained for a lifetime improves the likelihood that lost weight will not be regained (Fig. 10-17).

A weight-loss program should be considered successful only when the subjects involved in the process remain at or close to their lower weights. Only about 5% of people who follow commercial diet programs actually lose weight and then remain close to that weight. Typically, one-third of the weight lost during dieting is regained within a year after the diet ends, and almost all weight lost is regained within 3 to 5 years. Some programs have success rates higher than 5%, as do some people who simply lose weight on their own without enrolling in a supervised plan. Overall, however, the statistics are grim. Currently, only the surgical approaches to obesity treatment routinely show success in maintaining the weight loss in most people (see Medical Perspective).

Because lost weight is frequently regained, many dieters try a variety of weight-loss diets. The negative health consequences associated with this weight cycling are an increased risk of upper-body fat deposition, discouragement, diminished self-esteem, and possibly a decline in high-density lipoprotein (HDL) cholesterol and immune system function. Nevertheless, experts still encourage obese people to attempt weight loss, with a strong focus on maintaining that lower weight.

Control of Energy Intake

Foods, such as fruit, that are nutrient dense and have low energy density help weight-control efforts.

Adipose tissue, which is mostly fat, contains about 3500 kcal/lb. Therefore, to lose 1 pound of adipose tissue per week, energy intake must be decreased by approximately 500 kcal/day or physical activity must be increased by 500 kcal per day. Alternately, a combination of both strategies can be used.[4] A goal of losing 1 lb or so of stored fat per week may require limiting energy intake to 1200 kcal/day for women and 1500 kcal/day for men. The energy allowance could be higher for very active people. Keep in mind that, in our very sedentary society, decreasing energy intake is a vital component of weight loss.

To reduce energy intake, some experts suggest consuming less fat (especially saturated fat and *trans* fat), whereas others suggest consuming less carbohydrate, especially from refined (high glycemic load) carbohydrate sources. Protein intakes in excess of what is typically needed by adults are also sometimes used as a weight-loss strategy (especially plant protein sources).[20] All these approaches can be used simultaneously. It currently appears that low-energy-density (low-fat, high-fiber) approaches are the most successful in long-term studies. There is no long-term evidence for the effectiveness of the other approaches.[21]

The success of low-energy-density diets may be because foods low in energy density provide bigger portions for a given number of calories. Water is the dietary component that has the biggest impact on the energy density of foods; water adds weight but no calories and therefore decreases energy density. Increasing the water content of recipes (e.g., by adding vegetables) helps reduce energy intake and enhance satiety. A surprising finding in recent years is that people tend to eat a consistent weight or volume of food over a day or two. Thus, when foods contain fewer calories per gram, people consume less energy but still report feeling just as full and satisfied. Using energy density as a guide to food selection helps individuals consume foods that health professionals recommend—fruits, vegetables, legumes, low-fat dairy products, and whole grains.[22]

Overall, it is best to consider healthy eating a lifestyle change, rather than simply a weight-loss plan. Healthy eating choices that bring calories under control start with eating smaller portions and using MyPlate as a pattern for daily intake. Many people often underestimate portion size, so measuring cups and a food-weighing scale can help them learn appropriate portion sizes. Reading Nutrition Facts panels also can help individuals find low-energy-density foods. Learning to identify lower-calorie versions of favorites also is helpful (Table 10-4). Note that liquids do not stimulate satiety mechanisms as strongly as solid foods;

Slow, steady weight loss is one of the characteristics of a sound weight-loss program.

▶ As you read brochures, articles, or research reports about specific diet plans, look beyond the weight loss promoted by the diet's advocate to see if the reported weight loss was maintained. If the weight maintenance aspect is missing, then the program is not successful.

▶ Meal replacement formulas to replace a meal or snack are appropriate to use once or twice a day, if one desires. These are not a magic bullet for weight loss, but they have been shown to help some people control calorie intake.

▶ Learn how portion sizes have changed over the years. Visit hp2010.nhlbihin.net/portion.

Table 10-4 Saving Calories: Ideas for Getting Started

Save	140 kcal	by choosing	3 oz lean beef	instead of	3 oz well-marbled beef
Save	175 kcal	by choosing	½ broiled chicken	instead of	½ batter-fried chicken
Save	210 kcal	by choosing	3 oz lean roast beef	instead of	½ cup beef stroganoff
Save	65 kcal	by choosing	½ cup boiled potatoes	instead of	½ cup fried potatoes
Save	140 kcal	by choosing	1 cup raw vegetables	instead of	½ cup potato salad
Save	150 kcal	by choosing	2 tbsp low-kcal salad dressing	instead of	2 tbsp regular salad dressing
Save	310 kcal	by choosing	1 apple	instead of	1 slice apple pie
Save	150 kcal	by choosing	1 English muffin	instead of	1 Danish pastry
Save	60 kcal	by choosing	1 cup cornflakes	instead of	1 cup sugar-coated cornflakes
Save	45 kcal	by choosing	1 cup 1% milk	instead of	1 cup whole milk
Save	150 kcal	by choosing	6 oz wine cooler made with sparkling water	instead of	6 oz gin and tonic
Save	150 kcal	by choosing	1 cup plain popcorn	instead of	1 oz potato chips
Save	185 kcal	by choosing	1 slice angel food cake	instead of	1 slice white iced cake
Save	150 kcal	by choosing	12 oz sugar-free soft drink	instead of	12 oz regular soft drink
Save	140 kcal	by choosing	12 oz light beer	instead of	12 oz regular beer

thus, experts advise choosing beverages that have few or no calories. Another method is to become aware of calorie and nutrient intake by writing down food intake for 24 hours, calculating energy intake by using nutrient analysis software, and then adjusting future food choices as needed.

Regular Physical Activity

Regular physical activity is very important for everyone, especially people who are trying to lose weight or maintain a lower body weight.[6] Obviously, more energy is burned during physical activity than at rest. Even expending only 100 to 300 extra kcal/day above and beyond normal daily activity, while controlling energy intake, can lead to a steady weight loss. Physical activity also has so many other benefits, including a boost for overall self-esteem and maintenance of bone mass.

Adding any of the activities in Table 10-5 to one's lifestyle can increase energy expenditure. Duration and regular performance, rather than intensity, are the keys to success with this weight-loss approach. Another key is finding activities that are enjoyable and can be continued throughout life. There is no one activity that is better than another—for example, walking vigorously

▶ Spot-reducing by using diet and physical activity is not possible. "Problem" local fat deposits can be reduced in size, however, using lipectomy (surgical removal of fat). This procedure carries some risks and is designed to help a person lose about 4 to 8 lb per treatment.

▶ A pedometer is a low-cost device that monitors the number of steps taken. An often-stated goal for activity is to take 10,000 steps/day—typically, we take half that many or less.

Physical activity complements any diet plan.

Table 10-5 Approximate Energy Costs of Various Activities

Activity	kcal/kg per Hour	Activity	kcal/kg per Hour	Activity	kcal/kg per Hour
Aerobics—heavy	8.0	Dressing/showering	1.6	Running or jogging (10 mph)	13.2
Aerobics—medium	5.0	Driving	1.7	Downhill skiing (10 mph)	8.8
Aerobics—light	3.0	Eating (sitting)	1.4	Sleeping	1.2
Backpacking	9.0	Food shopping	3.6	Swimming (.25 mph)	4.4
Basketball—vigorous	10.0	Football—touch	7.0	Tennis	6.1
Cycling (5.5 mph)	3.0	Golf	3.6	Volleyball	5.1
Bowling	3.9	Horseback riding	5.1	Walking (2.5 mph)	3.0
Calisthenics—heavy	8.0	Jogging—medium	9.0	Walking (3.75 mph)	4.4
Calisthenics—light	4.0	Jogging—slow	7.0	Water skiing	7.0
Canoeing (2.5 mph)	3.3	Ice skating (10 mph)	5.8	Weight lifting—heavy	9.0
Cleaning	3.6	Lying—at ease	1.3	Weight lifting—light	4.0
Cooking	2.8	Racquetball—social	8.0	Window cleaning	3.5
Cycling (13 mph)	9.7	Roller skating	5.1	Writing (sitting)	1.7

The values refer to total energy expenditure, including that needed to perform the physical activity plus that needed for basal metabolism, the thermic effect of food, and thermogenesis.
Example: For a 150 lb person who played tennis for 1.5 hours,
    150 lb/2.2 = 68 kg
    68 kg × 6.1 kcal/hr × 1.5 hr = 622 kcal expenditure

3 miles daily can be as helpful as aerobic dancing or jogging. Activities of lighter intensity are less likely to lead to injuries, as well. Some resistance exercises, such as weight training, also should be added to increase lean body mass and, in turn, fat use (see Chapter 11). As lean muscle mass increases, so does overall metabolic rate.

Unfortunately, opportunities to expend energy in our daily lives continue to diminish as technology eliminates almost every reason to move our muscles.[2] The easiest way to increase physical activity is to make it an enjoyable part of a daily routine. To start, one might wear walking shoes and walk between classes and to and from the parking lot. Some people find wearing a pedometer helps motivate them to walk. There are also plenty of other simple ways to increase the activity of daily living, such as parking the car farther away from the shopping mall entrance or getting up to change the channels on the television.

Control of Problem Behaviors

Controlling energy intake and increasing physical activity also means modifying problem behaviors.[6, 19] Only the dieter can decide which behaviors derail weight-loss efforts. What events start (or stop) the action of eating or exercising? Becoming aware of these events can help dieters change their behaviors and improve their habits. The following key behavior modification techniques help organize intervention strategies into manageable steps and bring problem behaviors under control.

- **Chain-breaking** separates the link between behaviors that tend to occur together—for example, snacking on chips while watching television (Fig. 10-18).

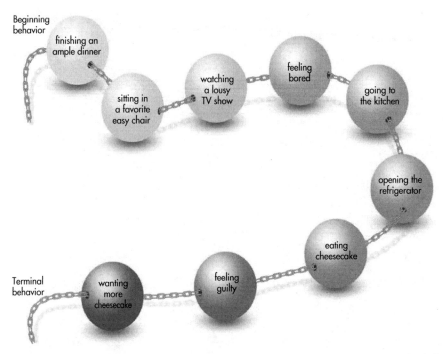

Figure 10-18 Analyzing behavior chains is a good way to understand more about your behaviors and to pinpoint how to change unwanted habits. The earlier in the chain that you substitute a nonfood link, the easier it is to stop a chain reaction. Behaviors that can be substituted to break a behavior chain include:
1. Fun activities (taking a walk, calling a friend).
2. Necessary activities (writing a paper, cleaning a room, taking a shower).
3. Urge-delaying activity (set a kitchen timer and wait 30 minutes before eating).
Using activities to interrupt behavior patterns that lead to inappropriate eating (or inactivity) can be a powerful means of changing behaviors.

Table 10-6 Behavior Modification Principles for Weight Loss and Control

Shopping

1. Shop for food after eating—buy nutrient-dense foods.
2. Shop from a list; limit purchases of irresistible "problem" foods. It helps to shop first for fresh foods around the perimeter of the store. Shopping online also can help control purchases of problem foods.
3. Avoid ready-to-eat foods.

Plans

1. Plan to limit food intake as needed.
2. Plan meals, snacks, and physical activity.
3. Eat meals and snacks at scheduled times; don't skip meals.
4. Exercise with a partner and schedule a time together.
5. Plan to take an exercise class at the YMCA or local recreation center.

Activities

1. Store food out of sight, preferably in the freezer, to discourage impulsive eating.
2. Eat food only in a "dining" area.
3. Keep serving dishes off the table, especially dishes of sauces and gravies.
4. Use smaller dishes, glasses, and utensils.
5. Keep exercise equipment handy and visible.

Holidays and Parties

1. Drink fewer alcoholic beverages.
2. Plan eating behavior before parties.
3. Eat a low-calorie snack before parties.
4. Practice polite ways to decline food.
5. Take opportunities to dance, swim, or engage in other physical activities at parties.

Eating Behavior

1. Put your fork down between mouthfuls and chew thoroughly before taking the next bite.
2. Leave some food on the plate.
3. Concentrate on eating; do nothing else while eating (e.g., do not watch TV).
4. Don't label certain foods "off limits"; this sets up an internal struggle that can keep you feeling deprived and defeated. Control problem foods by buying small amounts and eating a little at a time, such as 1 snack-size candy bar.
5. Limit eating out to once or twice a week.

Portion Control

1. Make substitutions, such as a regular hamburger instead of a "quarter pounder" or cucumbers instead of croutons in salads.
2. Think small. Share an entrée with another person. Order a cup of soup instead of a bowl or an appetizer in place of an entrée.
3. Use a to-go container (doggie bag). Ask your server to put half the entrée in a to-go container before bringing it to the table.
4. Become aware of portion sizes and use guides (see Chapter 2, Fig. 2-9) to judge portions.
5. Learn to recognize feelings of satiety and stop eating.

Reward and Social Support

1. Plan specific nonfood rewards for specific behavior (behavioral contracts).
2. Solicit help from family and friends and suggest how they can help you. Encourage family and friends to provide this help in the form of praise and nonfood rewards.
3. Use self-monitoring records as a basis for rewards.

Self-Monitoring

1. Keep a diet diary (note the time and place of eating, the type and amount of food eaten, who is present, and how you feel) and use it to identify problem areas.
2. Keep a physical activity diary (note which exercise is done, when, and how long) and use it to identify when more physical activity can be included.
3. Check body weight regularly.

Cognitive Restructuring

1. Avoid setting unreasonable goals.
2. Think about progress, not shortcomings.
3. Avoid imperatives, such as *always* and *never*.
4. Counter negative thoughts with positive restatements.
5. Don't get discouraged by an occasional setback. Take charge immediately—think about how progress got disrupted and make a plan for avoiding it next time.
6. Eating a particular food doesn't make a person "bad" and shouldn't lead to feelings of guilt. Change responses such as "I ate a cookie, so I'm a failure" to "I ate a cookie and enjoyed it. Next time, I'll have a piece of fruit."
7. Seek professional help before weight, dietary intake, and/or sedentary behavior get out of control.

- **Stimulus control** alters the environment to minimize the stimuli for eating—for example, storing foods out of sight and avoiding the path by the vending machines. Positive stimulus control includes keeping low-fat snacks on hand to satisfy hunger/appetite or placing walking shoes in a convenient, visible location.
- **Cognitive restructuring** changes one's frame of mind regarding eating—for example, instead of using a difficult day as an excuse to overeat, substitute another pleasure or reward, such as a relaxing walk with a friend.
- **Contingency management** prepares one for situations that may trigger overeating (e.g., when snacks are within arm's reach at a party) or hinder physical activity (e.g., rain).
- **Self-monitoring** tracks which foods are eaten, when, why, how one feels (usually using a diary), which physical activities are completed, and body weight. Self-monitoring helps people understand more about their habits and reveals patterns—such as unconscious overeating—that may explain problem behaviors that lead to weight gain.

Controlling energy intake and boosting energy expenditure are critical for losing and maintaining lost weight. Many times, we know what we should do, but some eating and exercise behaviors keep us from reaching our goals. Table 10-6 lists steps for modifying behaviors that promote weight loss and maintenance.

We are faced with many opportunities to overeat. It takes much perseverance to control dietary intake.

Weight-Loss Maintenance

Losing excess weight might be easier than keeping it off. Several studies from the National Weight Registry have identified 4 behaviors for successful maintainers.[6, 23]

1. Eat a low-fat, high-carbohydrate diet. Individuals who have been successful at losing weight and keeping it off appear to eat about 25% of their total intake as fat and about 56% of their calories as carbohydrates, mainly in the form of fruits, vegetables, and whole grains.
2. Eat breakfast. About 90% of the participants in the National Weight Registry eat breakfast at least 4 days a week. By eating breakfast, the body burns more fat throughout the day and there is less tendency to overeat due to hunger.[24, 25] Most of the participants in the studies eat whole-grain cereal, skim milk, and fruit for breakfast.
3. Self-monitor by regularly weighing oneself and keeping a food journal. Self-monitoring helps individuals know when weight is creeping up and signals them to pay more attention to their diets and exercise.
4. Have a physical activity plan. Participants in the National Weight Registry program exercise about 1 hour a day. A regular exercise program helps individuals maintain lost weight and feel better.

Knowledge Check

1. What are the 3 components of a sound weight-loss program?
2. What are key behavior modification techniques that can help bring problem behaviors under control?
3. What are 4 behaviors that help keep weight off?

338 **PART 3** Metabolism and Energy Balance

Expert Perspective from the Field

Tailoring a Healthy Eating Plan to Fit Your Lifestyle

According to Dr. Judith Rodriguez,* finding a weight loss diet that suits your lifestyle is the key to controlling weight and eating a healthy diet. In her book, *The Diet Selector*, Dr. Rodriguez grouped diets based on common principles to help consumers match their lifestyles with popular diets. Find what you like to eat or the concerns you have about your diet in the first column and consider the descriptions/characteristics of the diet program in the center column. Finally, take a look at the diet resources listed in the last column to help you achieve the diet changes that are important to you.

Eating Pattern/Lifestyle	Characteristics/Descriptions	Resources
Enjoy eating a variety of foods from different food groups in a reasonable balance	These diets develop and manage healthy eating patterns	• *The New Sonoma Diet* by Connie Guttersen, PhD, RD • *Cinch* by Cynthia Sass, MPH, RD • *Intuitive Eating* by Evelyn Tribole, RD • *Change One* by John Hastings, Peter Jaret, Mindy Hermann, RD
Would like to manage lifestyle diseases through diet	These diets have specific eating patterns and foods to consume based on certain diseases or risk of disease	• *Healthy Eating for Lower Blood Pressure* by Paul Gayler • *Prevent a Second Heart Attack* by Janet Bond Brill, PhD, RD, LD • *The Cancer Fighting Kitchen* by Rebecca Katz • *DASH Diet for Hypertension* by Thomas J. Moore, Mark Jenkins • *Better Digestion* by The American Dietetic Association, Leslie Bonci, RD
Would like to manage weight and healthy food choices in college	These diets teach students who either live on their own or in dorms how to make better food choices for health and weight management	• *The College Student's Guide to Eating Well on Campus* by Ann Litt, MS, RD
Enjoy eating ethnic foods and making them a part of a normal diet	These plans and diets help focus on International foods and eating patterns	• Mediterranean Diet & Pyramid • Latino Diet & Pyramid • African Diet & Pyramid • Asian Diet & Pyramid All at http://www.oldwayspt.org/
Enjoy eating more vegetables and whole grains compared to animal products	These diets encourage consumers to consume more fruits, vegetables and whole grains to help with weight loss and prevention of lifestyle disease	• *Volumetrics Weight-Control Plan* by Barbara Rolls PhD, RD • *The Whole Grain Diet Miracle* by Lisa Hark, PhD, RD • *The Flexitarian Diet* by Dawn Jackson Blatner, RD • *Food Matters: A Guide to Conscious Eating* by Mark Bittman
Enjoy eating more animal products instead of cereals, breads and pasta	These diets focus on a low-carbohydrate diet and higher protein diet that include lean meats and healthy fats	• *South Beach Diet* by Arthur Agatston, MD • *The New Atkins for a New You* by Eric C. Westman, Stephen D. Phinney, Jeff S. Volek
Enjoy preparing quick meals and want nutrition tips for busy families with kids	These resources provide tips for teaching children healthy eating and making family food fun.	• *Quick Meals for Healthy Kids and Busy Parents: Wholesome Family Recipes in 30 Minutes or Less From Three Leading Child Nutrition Experts* by Sandra Nissenberg RD, Margaret L. Bogle, Audrey C. Wright. • www.kidseatright.org website

Judith Rodriguez, PhD, RD FADA, LDN is Chairperson and professor of Nutrition in the Brooks College of Health, Department of Nutrition & Dietetics at the University of North Florida. She is author of The Diet Selector: From Atkins to The Zone, More than 50 Ways to Help You Find the Best Diet For You, and Contemporary Nutrition for Latinos: Latino Lifestyle Guide to Nutrition and Health. Dr. Rodriguez has served as President of the American Dietetic Association, has received the Distinguished Dietitian Award from Florida Dietetic Association, and was named an Outstanding Dietetics Educator by the American Dietetic Association (now called The Academy of Nutrition and Dietetics).

10.7 Fad Diets

Fad diets claim miraculous weight loss or improved health—often by unhealthy or unrealistic eating plans and, perhaps, touting "miracle" foods, specific rituals (e.g., eating only fruit for breakfast or cabbage soup every day), or certain foods that people would not normally eat in large amounts. Some are so monotonous that they are hard to follow for more than a short time. Fad diets may lead to some immediate weight loss simply because daily energy intake is monitored and food choices are monotonous. Fad diets rarely lead to lasting weight loss or help retrain eating and exercise habits. Plus, some can actually cause harm (Table 10-7).

Table 10-7 A Summary of Popular Diet Approaches to Weight Control

Approach	Examples		Characteristics	Outcomes

Moderate energy restriction	Set-Point Diet
	Slim Chance in a Fat World
	Weight Watcher's Diet
	Mary Ellen's Help Yourself
	  Diet Plan
	Biggest Loser Diet
	Staying Thin
	Joy Bauer's Food Cures
	Master Your Metabolism
	Volumetrics
		Lose the Last 10 Pounds
		You on a Diet
		Dieting for Dummies
		Wedding Dress Diet
		Flat Belly Diet
		How the Rich Get Thin
		French Women Don't Get Fat
		No Fad Diet: A Personal Plan
		  for Healthy Weight
		Sonoma Diet
			Generally, 1200 to 1800
			  kcal/day, with moderate
			  fat intake
			Reasonable balance of
			  macronutrients
			Encourage exercise
			May use behavioral approach
				Acceptable if a balanced
				multivitamin and mineral
				supplement is used and if
				physician approval is
				obtained

Restricted carbohydrate	Dr. Atkins' New Diet
	  Revolution
	All New Atkins Advantage
	The Duke Diet
	Calories Don't Count
	Woman Doctor's Diet for
	  Women
	Doctor's Quick Weight
	  Loss Diet
	Complete Scarsdale Diet
	Good Calories Bad Calories
		4-Day Wonder Diet
		Endocrine Control Diet
		Enter the Zone
		Protein Power
		Five-Day Miracle Diet
		Healthy for Life
		Carbohydrate Addict's Diet
		Sugar Shack
		South Beach Diet Supercharged
		No Crave Diet
			Generally, less than 100 g of
			  carbohydrate per day
				Ketosis; reduced exercise
				capacity due to poor
				glycogen stores in the
				muscles; excessive animal
				fat and cholesterol intake;
				constipation, headaches,
				halitosis (bad breath), and
				muscle cramps

Low fat	Rice Diet Report
	Macrobiotic Diet (some
	  versions)
	Pritikin Diet
	Eat More, Weigh Less
	35+ Diet
	20/30 Fat and Fiber
	Fat to Muscle Diet
	T-Factor Diet
	Your Big Fat Boyfriend
	Two-Day Diet
	Turn Off the Fat Genes
		Maximum Metabolism Diet
		Pasta Diet
		McDougall Plan
		Ultrafit Diet
		Stop the Insanity
		G-Index Diet
		Outsmarting the Female
		  Fat Cell
		Foods That Cause You to
		  Lose Weight
		Lean Bodies
			Generally, less than 20% of
			  energy intake from fat
			Limited (or elimination of)
			  animal protein sources; also
			  limited fats, nuts, and seeds
				Flatulence; possibly poor
				mineral absorption from
				excess fiber; limited food
				choices sometimes lead
				to deprivation
				Not necessarily to be
				avoided, but certain
				aspects of many of the
				plans possibly
				unacceptable

Novelty diets	Dr. Abravenel's Body Type
	  and Lifetime Nutrition Plan
	Slim for Life
	Dr. Berger's Immune Power
	Blood Type Diet
	Fit for Life
	Belly Fat Cure
	Dorm Room Diet
	Beverly Hills Diet
	Cortisol Connection Diet
	Sun Sign Diet
	F-Plan Diet
	Fat Attack Plan
	Autohypnosis Diet
	Princeton Diet
	Diet Bible
		Eat to Succeed
		Underburner's Diet
		Thin Is the New Happy
		Paris Diet
		Cabbage-Soup Diet
		Eat Great, Lose Weight
		Eat Smart, Think Smart
		Scent-sational Weight Loss
		Eat Right 4 Your Type
		Greenwich Diet
		3 Season Diet
		Eat Clean Diet Recharged
		God's Diet
		Hot Latin Diet
		Paleo Diet
		21 Pounds in 21 Days
			Promote certain nutrients,
			  foods, or combinations of
			  foods as having unique,
			  magical, or previously
			  undiscovered qualities
			Promote gimmicks that
			  have no effect on weight
			  loss
				Malnutrition; no change in
				habits, which leads to
				relapse; unrealistic food
				choices lead to possible
				bingeing

340   **PART 3**   Metabolism and Energy Balance

People on diets often have a healthy BMI—rather than worrying about weight loss, these individuals should focus on a healthy lifestyle that promotes weight maintenance and acceptance of one's body characteristics. For those at a healthy weight, the desire to lose weight may stem from unrealistic weight expectations (especially for women) and lack of appreciation for the natural variety in body shape and weight. Not everyone can look like a movie star, but all of us can strive for good health and a healthy lifestyle.

▶ Some believe fasting is an effective weight loss method. However, many misconceptions are associated with fasting.

• Does fasting cause weight loss? Yes, in the form of water loss—with one trip to the water fountain, a faster's prunelike, dried-out body plumps up to juicy plum-size again.

• Does fasting rid the body of accumulated toxins? Toxins are poisons—a "buildup" would cause illness and death quickly. The liver and kidneys work continuously to filter out toxins we ingest or produce (e.g., ammonia), detoxify them, and rapidly excrete them. In reality, fasting may produce more toxins than normal in the form of ammonia and ketones that need to be detoxified and excreted immediately.

Instead of adding to the $33 billion a year Americans already spend on fad diets,[26] a better choice for losing weight and keeping it off is to follow an eating and exercise plan that you can live with every day for the rest of your life. The goal should be lifelong weight control, not immediate weight loss. How can you tell if a program or diet plan is a fad diet? The Academy of Nutrition and Dietetics published 10 red flags to help consumers determine if the diet or nutrition information they are receiving is credible:[26]

1 ▶ Recommendations that promise a quick fix

2 ▶ Dire warnings of danger from a single product or regimen

3 ▶ Claims that sound too good to be true

4 ▶ Simplistic conclusions drawn from a complex study

5 ▶ Recommendations based on a single study

6 ▶ Dramatic statements that are refuted by reputable scientific organizations

7 ▶ Lists of "good" and "bad" foods

8 ▶ Recommendations made to help sell a product; often, testimonials are used

9 ▶ Recommendations based on studies published without peer review

10 ▶ Recommendations from studies that ignore differences among individuals or groups

Fad diets often promise rapid weight loss. Unfortunately, quick weight loss cannot consist primarily of fat because a high energy deficit is needed to lose a large amount of adipose tissue. Diets that promise a weekly weight loss of 10 to 15 lb cannot ensure that the weight loss is from adipose tissue stores alone. Subtracting enough energy from one's daily intake to lose that amount of adipose tissue simply is not possible. Lean tissue and water, rather than adipose tissue, account for the major part of the weight lost when weight loss exceeds a few pounds weekly.

Probably the cruelest characteristic of these diets is that they essentially guarantee failure for the dieter. The diets are not designed for permanent weight loss. Habits are not changed, and the food selection is so limited that the person cannot follow the diet for long. Although dieters assume they have lost fat, they have actually lost mostly muscle and other lean tissue mass. As soon as they begin eating normally again, much of the lost weight returns in a matter of weeks. The dieter appears to have failed, when actually the diet has failed. The gain and loss cycle (or "yo-yo" dieting) can cause blame, guilt, and negative health effects.

Health professionals can help dieters design and follow a healthy weight-loss plan—unfortunately, current trends suggest that people are spending more time and money on fad diets and quick fixes than on professional help.[3, 5]

Low-carbohydrate diets lead to reduced glycogen synthesis and therefore reduced amounts of water in the body (about 3 g of water are stored per gram of glycogen). As discussed in Chapter 9, a very low carbohydrate intake forces the liver to produce glucose via gluconeogenesis. The source of carbons for this glucose is mostly body proteins. (Recall also from Chapter 9 that typical fatty acids cannot form glucose.) Thus, a low-carbohydrate diet results in the loss of lean body tissue, which is about 72% water, as well as the loss of ions, such as potassium, in the urine. Because lean tissue is mostly water, dieters lose weight very rapidly, but, when a normal diet is resumed, protein tissue is rebuilt and the weight is regained.

Low-carbohydrate diets work primarily in the short run because they limit total food intake. In long-term studies, these diets have not shown an advantage over diets that simply limit energy intake in general. In addition, low carbohydate diets increase LDL-cholesterol.[27]

When you see a new diet advertisement, look first to see how much carbohydrate it contains. If breads, cereals, fruits, and vegetables are extremely limited, you are probably looking at a low-carbohydrate diet (see Table 10-7). Diet plans that use a low-carbohydrate approach are the Dr. Atkins' New Diet Revolution, the Scarsdale Diet, and the 4-Day Wonder Diet. More moderate approaches are found in the South Beach (especially initial phases), Zone, and Sugar Busters Diets.

Low-fat diets, especially those that are very low in fat, turn out to be very-high-carbohydrate diets. These diets contain approximately 5 to 10% of energy intake as fat. The most notable are the Pritikin Diet and Dr. Dean Ornish's Eat More, Weigh Less plans. Low-fat diets are not harmful for healthy adults, but they are difficult to follow. These diets contain mostly grains, fruits, and vegetables. Eventually, many people get bored with this type of diet because they cannot eat favorite foods—they want some foods higher in fat or protein. Low-fat diets are very different from the typical North American diet, which makes it hard for many adults to follow them consistently.

Novelty diets are built on gimmicks. Some emphasize one food or food group and exclude almost all others. They might include only grapefruit, rice, or eggs. The rationale behind these diets is that you can eat only these foods for just so long before becoming bored and, in theory, reduce your energy intake. However, chances are that you will abandon the diet entirely before losing much weight.

The most questionable of the novelty diets propose that "food gets stuck in your body." Examples are Fit for Life, Beverly Hills Diet, and Eat Great, Lose Weight. The supposition is that food gets stuck in the intestine, putrefies, and creates toxins that cause disease. In response, these diets recommend not consuming certain foods or eating them only at certain times of the day. These recommendations make no physiological sense, however—as you know from Chapter 4, the digestive tract is efficient at digesting foods and eliminating waste.

Quack fad diets usually involve a costly product or service that doesn't lead to weight loss. Often, those offering the gimmick don't realize that they are promoting quackery because they have been victims themselves. For example, they tried the product and by pure coincidence lost weight, and they erroneously believe it worked for them, so they wish to sell it to others. Numerous weight-loss gimmicks have come and gone and are likely to resurface again.[28] If you hear that an important aid for weight loss is discovered, you can feel confident that, if it is legitimate, major peer-reviewed journals and authorities, such as the Surgeon General's Office or the National Institutes of Health, will make North Americans aware of it. Information in diet books, websites, infomercials, and advertisements needs to be viewed with a scientist's skeptical, questioning eye.

In time, very-low-carbohydrate, high-protein diets typically leave a person wanting more variety in meals, so the diets are abandoned. Dropout rates are very high on these diets.

▶ Operation Waistline is a program designed by the U.S. Federal Trade Commission to stop fraudulent claims made by weight-loss charlatans. The program hopes to put an end to the billions of dollars spent annually in the U.S. on counterfeit products.

Knowledge Check

1. What are the 10 red flags that can help you determine if nutrition information is credible?
2. Why can't rapid weight loss consist mainly of fat?
3. What are the characteristics of each of the main types of fad diets?

MEDICAL PERSPECTIVE

Professional Help for Weight Control

The first professional to see for weight-control advice is one's family physician. Doctors are best equipped to assess overall health and the appropriateness of weight loss and weight gain. The physician may then recommend a registered dietitian for a specific eating plan and answers to diet-related questions. Registered dietitians are uniquely qualified to help design eating plans for weight control because they understand both food composition and the psychological importance of food. Exercise physiologists also can provide advice about physical activity. The expense for professional interventions is tax deductible in the U.S. in some cases (see a tax advisor) and often covered by health insurance if prescribed by a physician.

Drug Treatment for Weight Loss

In skilled hands, prescription medications can aid weight loss in some instances. However, drug therapy alone has not been found to be successful. Success with medications has been shown only in those who also modify their behavior, decrease their energy intake, and increase their physical activity.[5, 29]

People who are candidates for medications for obesity include those with a BMI of 30 or more or a BMI of 27 to 29.9 with weight-related (i.e., comorbid) conditions, such as type 2 diabetes, cardiovascular disease, hypertension, or excess waist circumference; those with no contraindications to the use of the medication; and those ready to undertake lifestyle changes that support weight loss. The following are the general classes of medications used. Significant research is underway to develop additional medications.[30]

- Medications that enhance norepinephrine and serotonin activity in the brain by reducing the re-uptake of these neurotransmitters by nerve cells. This effect causes the neurotransmitters to remain active in the brain longer, which prolongs a sense of reduced hunger. These medications appear to be effective in helping some people who eat healthy diets but who simply eat too much.[5]
- Amphetamine-like medication (phenteramine [Fastin® or Ionamin®]), which prolongs epinephrine and norepinephrine activity in the brain. This therapy is effective for some people

in the short run but has not yet been proven effective in the long run.

- Medications that inhibit lipase enzyme action in the small intestine, thereby reducing fat digestion by about 30% (orlistat [Xenical®, Alli®]). Malabsorbed fat is deposited in the feces. Fat intake has to be controlled, however, because large amounts of fat in the feces can cause gas, bloating, and oily discharge. The malabsorbed fat also carries fat-soluble vitamins into the feces, so a multivitamin and mineral supplement is recommended.
- Medications that are not approved for weight loss, per se, can have weight loss as a side effect. For example, certain antidepressants (e.g., bupropion [Wellbutrin®]) have this effect.[29] Using a medication in this way is termed off-label because the product label does not include weight loss as an FDA-approved use.

Treatment of Severe Obesity

Severe (morbid) obesity—weighing at least 100 lb over healthy body weight (or twice one's healthy body weight)—requires professional treatment. Because of the serious health implications of severe obesity, drastic measures may be necessary. Such treatments are recommended only when traditional diets fail because these treatments have serious physical and psychological side effects that require careful monitoring by a physician. These practices include very-low-calorie diets and gastroplasty.

Very-low-calorie diets (VLCDs), or modified fasts, are used to treat severe obesity if more traditional dietary changes have failed. Optifast® is one such commercial program. VLCDs provide 400 to 800 calories daily, often in liquid form, and tend to be used if a person has obesity-related diseases that are not well controlled (e.g., hypertension, type 2 diabetes).[5] About half the calories in these diets are carbohydrate, and the rest is high-quality protein. This low-carbohydrate intake often causes ketosis, which may help decrease hunger. However, the main reasons for weight loss are minimal calorie intake and absence of food choice. About 3 to 4 lb can be lost per week; men tend to lose at a faster rate than women. Careful monitoring by a physician is crucial throughout this very restrictive form of weight

loss. Major health risks include heart problems and gallstones. If behavioral therapy and physical activity supplement a long-term support program, maintenance of the weight loss is more likely but still difficult. Medications for obesity also may be included in the maintenance phase of a VLCD.

Gastroplasty (gastric bypass surgery, also called stomach stapling) may be recommended for those who are morbidly obese (BMI ≥40), have been obese for at least 5 years with several nonsurgical attempts to lose weight, and have no history of alcoholism or major psychiatric disorders. Gastroplasty works by reducing the stomach capacity to about 30 ml (the volume of 1 egg or shot glass) and bypassing a short segment of the upper small intestine (Fig. 10-19). Another surgical approach is banded gastroplasty. In vertical-banded gastroplasty, a vertical staple line is made down the length of the stomach to create a small stomach pouch. At the pouch outlet, a band is placed to keep the opening from stretching. With gastric banding, a band is placed around the upper portion of the stomach to create a small stomach pouch. A salt solution can be injected into the band through a port to adjust the size of the pouch over time.

With gastroplasty, weight loss is achieved because most of the food bypasses the stomach and small intestine, which results in less digestion and absorption of nutrients. Gastroplasty requires major lifestyle changes, such as the need for frequent, small meals and the elimination of sugars from the diet, to avoid **dumping syndrome** (severe diarrhea that begins almost immediately after eating concentrated sugar, such as regular soft drinks, candy, and cookies).

The surgery is costly and may not be covered by health insurance. In addition, the patient faces months of difficult adjustments. However, with gastroplasty, about 75% of people with severe obesity eventually lose half or more of their excess body weight. In addition, the surgery's success at long-term maintenance often leads to dramatic health improvements, such as reduced blood pressure and the elimination of type 2 diabetes. The risks of this very serious surgery include bleeding, blood clots, hernias, and severe infections. About 2% die from the surgery itself. In the long run, nutrient deficiencies can develop if the person is not adequately treated in the years

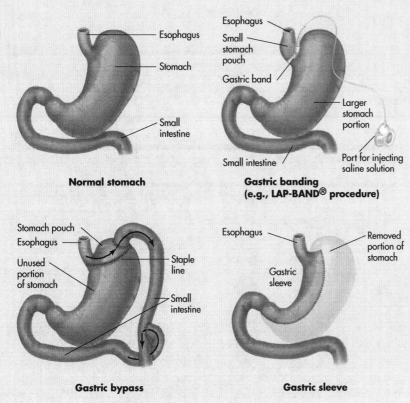

Normal stomach

Gastric banding (e.g., LAP-BAND® procedure)

Esophagus

Small stomach pouch

Gastric band

Larger stomach portion

Port for injecting saline solution

Small intestine

Esophagus

Stomach

Small intestine

Gastric bypass

Stomach pouch

Esophagus

Unused portion of stomach

Staple line

Small intestine

Gastric sleeve

Esophagus

Gastric sleeve

Removed portion of stomach

Figure 10-19 The most common forms of gastroplasty for treating severe obesity. The gastric bypass is the most effective method. In banded gastroplasty, the band prevents expansion of the outlet for the stomach pouch.

of energy from thermogenesis. One approach for treating underweight individuals is to replace less-energy-dense foods with higher-energy-dense foods. For example, a cup of granola instead of bran flakes can add an extra 300 to 500 calories. Choosing bean soup over vegetable soup adds 50 calories or more. Portion sizes may need to be increased gradually. Having a regular meal and snack schedule also aids in weight gain and maintenance. Making time to eat regular meals can help underweight individuals attain an appropriate weight and help with digestive disorders, such as constipation, that are sometimes associated with irregular eating schedules. Excessively physically active people can reduce their activity. If their weight remains low, they can add muscle mass through resistance training (weight lifting), but to gain weight they must increase energy intake to support that physical activity. If these changes do not lead to weight gain within a few weeks, the underweight person should seek medical intervention to identify the cause of this condition and get appropriate treatment.

following the surgery (chewable multivitamin and mineral supplements are often used). Follow-up surgery frequently is needed after weight loss to remove excess skin that was previously padded with fat.

Treatment of Underweight

Being underweight (BMI below 18.5) also carries health risks, including loss of menstrual function, low bone mass, complications with pregnancy and surgery, and slow recovery after illness. In growing children and teens, underweight can interfere with normal growth and development. Significant underweight also is associated with increased death rates, especially when combined with cigarette smoking.

Underweight can be caused by excess physical activity, severely restricted calorie intake, and health conditions such as cancer, infectious disease (e.g., tuberculosis), digestive tract disorders (e.g., chronic inflammatory bowel disease), eating disorders, and mental stress or depression. Active children and teens who do not take the time to consume enough energy to support their needs may become underweight. Genetic background may confer characteristics that promote low body weight, such as a higher metabolic rate, a lean or petite body frame, or both.

Gaining weight can be a formidable task for an underweight person. An extra 500 calories per day may be required to gain weight, even at a slow pace, in part because of the increased expenditure

Although the media and the fashion world promote a very thin physique, being underweight carries severe risks.

Knowledge Check

1. Which weight-loss medications may be used to treat obesity?
2. Who should use a modified fast for weight loss?
3. What is gastroplasty?
4. What health risks are associated with being underweight?

344 **PART 3** Metabolism and Energy Balance

Take Action

Changing for the Better

Even if you are satisfied with your current weight, many people see their weight climb as they get older, so it is a good idea to be aware of how to keep weight under control. This behavioral change method can help you do just that. It also can be applied to changing exercise habits, self-esteem, and many other behaviors (Fig. 10-20).

1. **Become aware of the problem.** Calculate your current weight status to determine if you have a weight problem. First, measure your height and weight. Then, using Table 10-1, record your BMI: _____. When BMI exceeds 25, health risks from overweight may start. It is especially advisable to consider weight loss if your BMI exceeds 30.

   Now, use a tape measure to measure the circumference of your waist (at the narrowest point just above the navel with stomach muscles relaxed). Record the circumference: _____ inches.

   When BMI exceeds 25 and a waist circumference is more than 40 inches (102 cm) in men or 35 inches (88 cm) in women, health risks rise. Does your waist circumference exceed the standard for your gender? _____

   Whether you feel the need to pursue a program of weight loss now or in the future, it is important to find out more about how to make changes.

2. **Gather baseline data.** Look back at the food diary you completed in Chapter 1. What factors most influence your eating habits? Do you eat out of stress, boredom, or depression? Is eating too much food your problem or do you mainly eat a poor diet? Next, think about whether it is worth changing these practices—a cost:benefit analysis can help you decide (Fig. 10-21).

3. **Set goals.** Setting realistic, achievable goals and allowing a reasonable amount of time to pursue them increase the likelihood of success. What final goal would you like to achieve? Why do you want to pursue this goal (e.g., improve health, lose weight, boost self-esteem)?

Figure 10-21 Benefits and costs analysis applied to changing eating habits. This process helps put behavioral change into the context of total lifestyle.

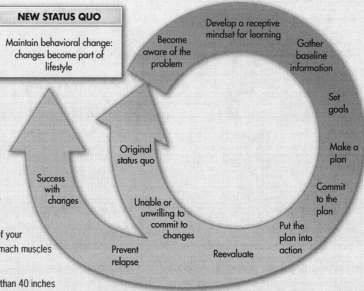

Figure 10-20 A model for behavioral change. It starts with awareness of the problem and ends with the incorporation of new behaviors intended to address the problem.

Benefits of changing eating habits

What do you expect to get, now or later, that you want?
What may you avoid that would be unpleasant?

feel better physically and psychologically
look better

Costs involved in changing eating habits

What do you have to do that you don't want to do?
What do you have to stop doing that you would rather continue doing?

take time to plan meals and shop
must give up some food volume

Benefits of not changing eating habits

What do you get to do that you enjoy doing?
What do you avoid having to do?

no need for planning
can eat without feeling guilty

Costs of not changing eating habits

What unpleasant or undesirable effects are you likely to experience now or in the future?
What are you likely to lose?

creeping weight gain
low self-esteem and poor health

CHAPTER 10 Energy Balance, Weight Control, and Eating Disorders 345

4. **Make a plan.** List several steps that will be necessary to achieve your goal. Changing only a few behaviors at a time increases the chances of success. You might choose to walk 60 minutes daily, eat less fat, eat more whole grains, or not eat after 8 P.M. What steps will you take to achieve the goal? If you are having trouble listing the steps, you may want to consult a health professional for assistance.

5. **Commit to the plan.** Next, ask yourself, "Can I do this?" Be honest with yourself. Commitment is an essential component in the success of behavioral change. Permanent change is not quick or easy. Drawing up a behavioral contract often adds incentive to follow through with a plan (Fig. 10-22). The contract can list goal behaviors and objectives, milestones for measuring progress, and regular rewards for meeting the terms of the contract. After finishing a contract, you should sign it in the presence of some friends. This formality encourages commitment.

6. **Put the plan into action.** Thinking of a lifetime commitment can be overwhelming, so start with a trial of 6 or 8 weeks. Aim for a total duration of 6 months of new activities before giving up. Keep your plan on track:

   - Focus on reducing, but not necessarily extinguishing, undesirable behaviors. For example, it's usually unrealistic to say that you will never eat a certain food again. It's better to say, "I won't eat that problem food as often as before."

   - Monitor progress. Note your progress in a diary and reward positive behaviors. While conquering some habits and seeing improvement, you may find yourself quite encouraged about your plan of action—that can motivate you to move ahead with the plan.

   - Control environments. In the early phases of behavioral change, try to avoid problem situations, such as parties, favorite restaurants, and people who try to derail your plans. Once new habits are firmly established, you can probably more successfully resist the temptations of these environments.

7. **Reevaluate and prevent relapse.** After practicing a program for several weeks to months, take a close and critical look at your original

---

Name *Alan Young*

Goal
I agree to *ride my exercise bike*
(specify behavior)
under the following circumstances *for 30 minutes, 4 times per week in the evening.*
(specify where, when, how much, etc.)

Substitute behavior and/or reinforcement schedule *I will reinforce myself if I've achieved my goal after a month with a weekend off campus.*

Charting progress
To keep track of my progress, *I will mark the days I exercise on a calendar.*

Environmental planning
To help me do this, I am going to (1) arrange my physical and social environment by *buying a new portable DVD player*

and (2) control my internal environment (thoughts, images) by *coordinating riding the bike with the first T.V. watching I do in the evening.*

Reinforcements
Reinforcements provided by me daily or weekly (if contract is kept):
I will buy myself a new piece of clothing for off-campus trip.

Reinforcements provided by others daily or weekly (if contract is kept):
at the end of a month, if I've completed my goal, my parents will buy me a fitness club membership for winter.

Social support
Behavioral change is more likely to take place when other people support you. During the quarter/semester, please meet with the other person at least 3 times to discuss your progress. The name of my "significant helper" is *Mr. and Mrs. Young*

Figure 10-22 Completing such a contract can help generate commitment to behavioral change. What would your contract look like?

---

plan. Does it actually lead to the goals you set? Are there any new steps toward your goal that you want to add? Do you need new reinforcements? Have you experienced relapses? What triggered these relapses? How can you avoid future relapses? You may have noticed a behavior chain in some of your relapses (see Fig. 10-18)—how can you break the chain?

8. **Maintain behavioral change.** If you have used the activities in this section, you are well on your way to permanent behavioral change. Change isn't easy, but the results can be worth the effort.

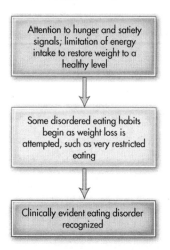

 10.8 Eating Disorders

Disordered eating can be defined as mild and short-term changes in eating patterns that occur in response to a stressful event, an illness, or a desire to modify the diet for health and/or personal appearance reasons. The problem may be no more than a bad habit, a style of eating adapted from friends or family members, or an aspect of preparing for athletic competition. Although disordered eating can lead to changes in body weight and certain nutritional problems, it rarely requires in-depth professional attention. However, in today's world, given the common practice of dieting, skipping meals, eating at odd times, and having hectic jobs and schedules, it may not be obvious when disordered eating stops and an eating disorder begins (Fig. 10-23).

Although obesity is the most common eating disorder in our society, the eating disorders explored in this section involve much more severe distortions of the eating process that can develop into life-threatening conditions if left untreated.[31] What is most alarming about these disorders is the increasing number of cases reported each year.[32] Some people are more susceptible to these disorders for genetic, psychological, and physical reasons. Until recently, most researchers reported that eating disorders primarily affect middle- and upper-class white women. Although some non-White cultures may be more accepting of larger body shapes, studies show greater similarities in the rates of body dissatisfaction and disordered-eating behaviors across ethnic and cultural groups. Eating disorders are not restricted to any socioeconomic class, ethnicity, age group, or gender.

Many **eating disorders** start with a simple diet. Stress and a lack of appropriate coping mechanisms, dysfunctional family relationships, and drug abuse may cause dieting to get out of control.[33] Stress may be caused by physical changes associated with entering puberty, having to maintain a certain weight to look attractive or competent on a job, having to maintain a lean profile for a sport, leaving home for college, or losing a friend. Disordered eating can escalate into physiological changes associated with sustained food restriction, binge eating, purging, and fluctuations in weight that interfere with everyday activities. It also involves emotional and cognitive changes that affect how people perceive and experience their bodies, such as feelings of distress or extreme concern about body shape or weight.[31]

Eating disorders are not due to a failure of will power or behavior; rather, they are real, treatable medical illnesses that require complex professional intervention that must go beyond nutritional therapy.[34] Without treatment, eating disorders can cause serious physical health complications, including heart conditions and kidney failure, which may even lead to death. Self-help groups for those with eating disorders, as well as their families and friends, represent nonthreatening first steps into treatment. People also can attend self-help group meetings to get a sense of whether they really do have an eating disorder.

The main types of eating disorders are anorexia nervosa, bulimia nervosa, and Eating Disorder Not Otherwise Specified (EDNOS).[35] Another type, binge-eating disorder, has been recognized by the psychiatric community since 1994. Recently, health professions have recommended that binge-eating disorder be formally included as a diagnosable disease.[48] More than 5 million people in North America have one of these disorders; eating disorders are 6 to 10 times more common in females than males. Eating disorders develop 85% of the time during adolescence or early adulthood, but some reports indicate that their onset can occur during childhood or later in adulthood. Currently, up to 5% of women in North America will

Figure 10-23 Progression from ordered to disordered eating.

Even well-intentioned parents may place expectations on their children that compound the anxiety felt during turbulent periods of childhood and adolescence. As a result, children and teens may find comfort in exerting control over their environment through the restrictive behaviors associated with eating disorders.

For people with eating disorders, the difference among real, perceived, and desired body images may be too difficult to accept.

disordered eating Mild and short-term changes in eating patterns that occur in relation to a stressful event, an illness, or a desire to modify one's diet for a variety of health and personal appearance reasons.

eating disorder Severe alterations in eating patterns linked to physiological changes; the alterations include food restricting, binge eating, purging, weight fluctuations, and emotional and cognitive changes in perceptions of one's body.

anorexia nervosa Eating disorder involving a psychological loss or denial of appetite followed by self-starvation; it is related, in part, to a distorted body image and to social pressures.

bulimia nervosa Eating disorder in which large quantities of food are eaten at one time (binge eating) and counteracted by purging food from the body, fasting, and/or excessive exercise.

binge-eating disorder Eating disorder characterized by recurrent binge eating and feelings of loss of control over eating.

Concern over self-image begins early in life—we develop images of "acceptable" and "unacceptable" body types. Of all the attributes that constitute attractiveness, many people view body weight as the most important. Fatness is the most dreaded deviation from our cultural ideals of body image, the one most derided and shunned, even among schoolchildren.

develop some form of anorexia nervosa or bulimia nervosa in their lifetimes.[35] Eating disorders frequently co-occur with other psychological disorders, such as depression, substance abuse, and anxiety disorders.[31]

Anorexia Nervosa

The term *anorexia* implies a loss of appetite; however, a denial of appetite more accurately describes the behavior of people with anorexia nervosa. The term *nervosa* refers to disgust with one's body. **Anorexia nervosa** is characterized by extreme weight loss, a distorted body image, and an irrational, almost morbid fear of obesity and weight gain. These individuals believe they are fat, even though they are not and others tell them so. Some realize they are thin but continue to be haunted by certain areas of their bodies that they believe to be fat (e.g., thighs, buttocks, and stomach). The discrepancy between actual and perceived body shape is an important gauge of the severity of the disease.

Estimating the prevalence of this eating disorder is difficult because of underreporting, but approximately 1 in 200 (0.5%)[31] adolescent girls in North America eventually develops anorexia nervosa. This relatively high number may be due to girls' tendency to blame themselves for weight gain associated with puberty. It happens less commonly among adult women and African-American women. Men account for approximately 10% of cases of anorexia nervosa, partly because the ideal image conveyed for men is big and muscular. Among men, athletes are most prone to develop anorexia nervosa, especially those who participate in sports that require weight classes, such as boxers, wrestlers, and jockeys. Other activities that may foster eating disorders in men include cycling, swimming, dancing, and modeling.[35, 49]

348   **PART 3**   Metabolism and Energy Balance

Eating disorders are commonly seen in people who must maintain low body weight, such as ballet dancers.

The *Diagnostic and Statistical Manual of Mental Disorders* lists these criteria for diagnosing anorexia nervosa:[35]

- Refusal to maintain body weight at or above a minimally normal weight for age and height
- Intense fear of gaining weight or becoming fat, even though underweight
- Disturbance in the way in which one's body weight or shape is experienced, undue influence of body weight or shape on self-evaluation, or denial of the seriousness of the current low body weight
- Amenorrhea (absence of at least 3 consecutive menstrual cycles) in females who have passed puberty

Although food is entwined in this disease, it stems more from psychological conflict. A common thread underlying many—but not all—cases of anorexia nervosa is conflict within the family structure, typically manifested by an overbearing mother and an emotionally absent father. When family expectations are too high, including those regarding body weight, frustration leads to fighting. Overinvolvement, rigidity, overprotection, and denial are typical daily transactions of such families.

Issues of control are central to the development of anorexia nervosa. The eating disorder can allow an anorexic person to exercise control over an otherwise powerless existence.[34] Losing weight may be the first independent success the person has had. People with anorexia evaluate their self-worth almost entirely in terms of self-control. Some sexually abused children develop anorexia nervosa, believing that, if they control their appetite for food, they can control and thereby eliminate their shameful feelings. Moreover, food restriction, which arrests development and shuts down sexual impulses, may be a strategy to prevent future victimization and guilt feelings. Often, anorexic persons feel hopeless about human relationships and socially isolated because of their dysfunctional families. They focus on food, eating, and weight instead of human relationships.

Some characteristics of those with anorexia nervosa are listed in Table 10-8. Keep in mind that only a health professional can correctly evaluate the criteria required to make a

---

Table 10-8 Typical Characteristics of Those with Eating Disorders

Anorexia Nervosa	Bulimia Nervosa
• Rigid dieting, causing dramatic weight loss, generally to less than 85% of what would be expected for one's age (or BMI of 17.5 or less)	• Secretive binge eating; generally not overeating in front of others
• False body perception—thinking "I'm too fat," even when extremely underweight; relentless pursuit of control	• Eating when depressed or under stress
• Rituals involving food, excessive exercise, and other aspects of life	• Bingeing on a large amount of food, followed by fasting, laxative or diuretic abuse, self-induced vomiting, or excessive exercise (at least twice a week for 3 months)
• Maintenance of rigid control in lifestyle; security found in control and order	• Shame, embarrassment, deceit, and depression; low self-esteem and guilt (especially after a binge)
• Feeling of panic after a small weight gain; intense fear of gaining weight	• Fluctuating weight (±10 lb or 5 kg) resulting from alternate bingeing and fasting
• Feelings of purity, power, and superiority through maintenance of strict discipline and self-denial	• Loss of control; fear of not being able to stop eating
• Preoccupation with food, its preparation, and observing another person eat	• Perfectionism, "people pleaser"; food as the only comfort/escape in an otherwise carefully controlled and regulated life
• Helplessness in the presence of food	• Erosion of teeth; swollen glands
• Lack of menstrual periods after what should be the age of puberty for at least 3 months	• Purchase of syrup of ipecac, a compound sold in pharmacies that induces vomiting
• Possible presence of bingeing and purging practices	

People who exhibit only one or a few of these characteristics may be at risk but probably do not have either disorder. They should, however, reflect on their eating habits and related concerns and take appropriate action, such as seeking a careful evaluation by a physician.

diagnosis of eating disorders and exclude other possible diseases. If you think you know someone who is at risk for this or other eating disorders, suggest that the person seek professional evaluation because, the sooner treatment begins, the better the chances are for recovery.[36]

Physical Effects of Anorexia Nervosa

Rooted in the emotional state of the victim, anorexia nervosa produces profound physical effects.[37] The anorexic person often appears to be skin and bones. Body weight less than 85% of that expected is a clinical indicator of anorexia nervosa.[38] BMI is a more reliable indicator of the degree of malnourishment; generally, a BMI of 17.5 or less indicates a severe case. For children under age 18, growth charts should be used to assess weight status (see Chapter 17 and Appendix K).

This state of semistarvation forces the body to conserve as much energy as possible and results in most of the physical effects of anorexia nervosa (Fig. 10-24). Thus, many complications can be ended by returning to a healthy weight, provided the duration of anorexia nervosa has not been too long. These are the predictable effects caused by hormonal responses to and nutrient deficiencies from semistarvation:[31, 34, 35, 39]

- Low body weight (15% or more below what is expected for age, height, and activity level)
- Lowered body temperature and cold intolerance caused by loss of an insulating fat layer
- Slower metabolic rate caused by decreased synthesis of thyroid hormones
- Decreased heart rate as metabolism slows, leading to easy fatigue, fainting, and an overwhelming need for sleep. Other changes in heart function also may occur, including loss of heart tissue and poor heart rhythm.
- Iron deficiency anemia, which leads to further weakness
- Rough, dry, scaly, and cold skin from a deficient nutrient intake, which may show multiple bruises because of the loss of protection from the fat layer normally present under the skin

HISTORICAL PERSPECTIVE

The Golden Cage

The earliest criteria for diagnosing anorexia nervosa described in 1870 were the first medical standards to recognize that societal influences can affect health. Through extensive observations and treatment of eating disorder patients starting in the 1930s, the psychoanalyst Hilde Bruch greatly advanced understanding of the interplay of culture and social structure on eating disorders. Her 1973 book, *Eating Disorders: Obesity, Anorexia Nervosa, and the Person Within*, brought the emotional aspects of eating disorders to the forefront of treatment. A later book, *The Golden Cage: the Enigma of Anorexia Nervosa*, helped consumers grasp the serious and complicated nature of eating disorders. Learn more at: mcgovern.library.tmc.edu/data/www/html/collect/manuscript/Bruch/Bruch_intro.htm

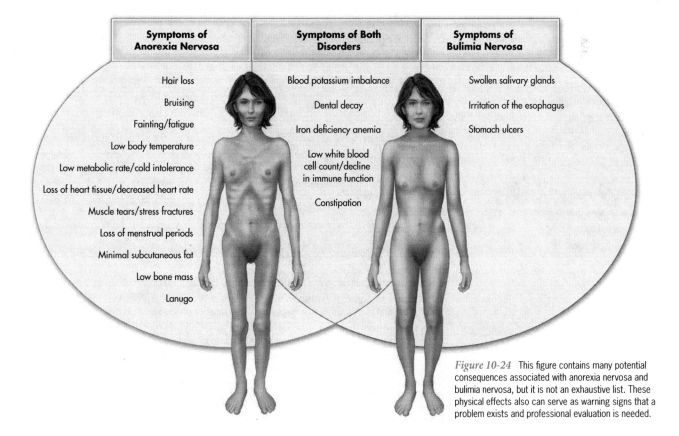

Figure 10-24 This figure contains many potential consequences associated with anorexia nervosa and bulimia nervosa, but it is not an exhaustive list. These physical effects also can serve as warning signs that a problem exists and professional evaluation is needed.

CRITICAL THINKING

Jennifer is an attractive 13-year-old. However, she's very compulsive. Everything has to be perfect—her hair, her clothes, even her room. Since her body started to mature, she's become quite obsessed with having perfect physical features as well. Her parents are worried about her behavior. The school counselor told them to look for certain signs that could indicate an eating disorder. What might those signs be?

- Low white blood cell count, which increases the risk of infection and potentially death
- Abnormal feeling of fullness or bloating, which can last for several hours after eating
- Loss of hair
- Appearance of **lanugo**—downy hairs that appear on the body after a person has lost much body fat through semistarvation—that helps trap air, reducing heat loss that occurs with the loss of fat tissue
- Constipation from semistarvation and laxative abuse
- Low blood potassium caused by a deficient nutrient intake, the use of some types of diuretics, and vomiting. Low blood potassium increases the risk of heart rhythm disturbances, another leading cause of death in anorexic people.
- Loss of menstrual periods because of low body weight, low body fat content, and the stress of the disease. Accompanying hormonal changes cause a loss of bone mass and increase the risk of osteoporosis later in life.
- Changes in neurotransmitter function in the brain, leading to depression
- Eventual loss of teeth caused by acid erosion if frequent vomiting occurs. Loss of teeth (along with low bone mass) can be lasting signs of the disease, even if the other physical and mental problems are resolved.
- In athletes, muscle tears and stress fractures caused by decreased bone and muscle mass

Treatment of Anorexia Nervosa

With prompt, vigorous, and professional help, many people with anorexia nervosa can lead normal lives. Treatment requires a multidisciplinary team of experienced physicians, registered dietitians, psychologists, and other health professionals.[31] An ideal setting is an eating disorders clinic in a medical center. Outpatient therapy, day hospitalization (6–12 hours), or total hospitalization may be used. Hospitalization is necessary once a person falls below 75% of expected weight, experiences acute medical problems, and/or exhibits severe psychological problems or suicidal risk.[31] Still, even in the most skilled hands at the finest facilities, efforts may fail. Thus, the prevention of anorexia nervosa is of utmost importance.

Experienced, professional help is the key. An anorexic patient may be on the verge of suicide and near starvation. In addition, many anorexic people are very clever and resistant. They may try to hide weight loss by wearing many layers of clothes, putting coins in their pockets or underwear, and drinking numerous glasses of water before stepping on a scale. The average time for recovery from anorexia nervosa is 7 years; many insurance companies cover only a fraction of the cost of treatment.

Nutrition therapy The first goal of nutrition therapy is to gain the patient's cooperation and trust in order to increase oral food intake. Ideally, weight gain must be enough to raise the metabolic rate to normal and reverse as many physical signs of the disease as possible. Food intake is designed first to minimize or stop any further weight loss. Then, the focus shifts to restoring appropriate food habits. After this, the expectation can be switched to slow weight gain—2 to 3 lb per week is appropriate. Tube feeding and/or total parenteral nutrition support is used only if immediate renourishment is required because this drastic measure can cause patient distrust.

During the weight-gain phase, an energy intake goal of 1000 to 1600 kcal/day, with a distribution of 50 to 55% carbohydrate, 15 to 20% protein, and 25 to 30% fat, is appropriate. Calories are gradually increased until the patient is gaining an appropriate amount of weight. For females, an appropriate weight is one in which normal menstruation is restored. This nutrition therapy may ultimately require a daily intake of 3000 to 4000 kcal to attain a goal weight because of the increase in body metabolism and anxiety associated with feeding.[40] A multivitamin and mineral supplement is added, as well as enough calcium to raise intake to about 1500 mg/day. As noted previously, nutrient deficiencies are commonly seen in anorexic persons.[31]

Patients need considerable reassurance during the refeeding process because of uncomfortable effects, such as bloating, increase in body heat, and increase in body fat. This

Early treatment of eating disorders improves chances of success. Note that such help is commonly available at student health centers and student guidance/counseling facilities on college campuses.

process is frightening because these changes can lead to the patient feeling out of control. Monitoring for rapid changes in electrolytes and minerals in the blood, especially potassium, phosphorus, and magnesium, is critical as more food is included in the diet.[34]

In addition to helping patients reach and maintain adequate nutritional status, the registered dietitian on the medical team also provides accurate nutrition information, promotes a healthy attitude toward food, and helps the patient learn to eat based on natural hunger and satiety cues. Nutrition therapy with anorexic persons can be frustrating for a dietitian because many anorexic persons are very knowledgeable about the energy and fat content of most food products. The focus should be on helping these patients identify healthy and adequate food choices that promote weight gain to achieve and maintain a clinically estimated goal weight (e.g., BMI of 20 or more).[32] The medical team also should assure patients that they will not be abandoned after gaining weight.

Psychological and related therapy Once the physical problems of anorexic patients are addressed, the treatment focus shifts to the underlying emotional problems of the disorder. To heal, these patients must reject the sense of accomplishment they associate with an emaciated body and begin to accept themselves at a healthy body weight. Establishing a strong relationship with either a therapist or another supportive person is an especially important key to recovery. If therapists can discover reasons for the disorder, they can develop psychological strategies for restoring normal weight and eating habits. A key aspect of psychological treatment is showing affected individuals how to regain control of other facets of their lives and cope with tough situations. As eating evolves into a normal routine, they can return to previously neglected activities.

Family therapy often is important, especially for younger patients who still live at home. Family therapy focuses on the role of the illness among family members, the reactions of individual family members, and the ways in which their subconscious behavior might contribute to the abnormal eating patterns.[31] Frequently, a therapist finds family struggles at the heart of the problem. As the disorder resolves, patients must relate to family members in new ways to gain the attention that was needed and previously tied to the disease. For example, the family may need to help the young person ease into adulthood and accept its responsibilities as well as its advantages.

Medications sometimes are part of the therapy for anorexic patients. However, their use is aimed primarily at preventing relapse in patients who have been treated but have an existing psychiatric disorder, such as depression, anxiety, or obsessive-compulsive disorder.

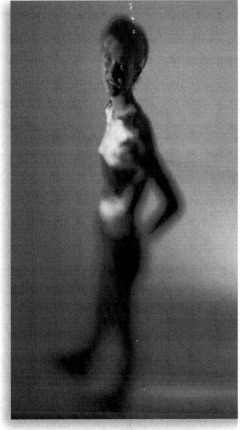

A young woman in a self-help group for those with anorexia nervosa explained her feelings to the other group members: "I have lost a specialness that I thought it gave me. I was different from everyone else. Now I know that I'm somebody who's overcome it, which not everybody does."

Bulimia Nervosa

Bulimia nervosa (*bulimia* means "great [ox] hunger") is characterized by episodes of binge eating followed by attempts to purge the excess energy consumed by vomiting or misusing laxatives, diuretics, or enemas. Some people exercise excessively to try to burn off a binge's high energy intake. Those with bulimia nervosa may think of food constantly. Unlike an anorexic person, who turns away from food when faced with problems, a bulimic person turns toward food in critical situations.[41] Also, unlike those with anorexia nervosa, people with bulimia nervosa recognize their behavior as abnormal.[38] These individuals often have very low self-esteem and are depressed—about 50% have major depression. The lingering effects of child abuse or sexual abuse may be one reason for these feelings. The world sees their competence, but inside they feel out of control, ashamed, and frustrated.

Up to 4% of adolescent and college-age women suffer from bulimia nervosa. About 10% of the cases occur in men.[35] However, many people with bulimic behavior are probably never diagnosed, perhaps because their symptoms are not obvious, and many with bulimia nervosa lead secret lives, hiding their abnormal eating habits. Most diagnoses of bulimia nervosa are based on self-reports; consequently, current estimates of the

Bulimia nervosa can lead to tragic consequences.

352 **PART 3** Metabolism and Energy Balance

▶ Bulimia nervosa is rare in developing countries, which suggests that our culture is an important causal factor.

number of cases are probably low. This disorder, especially in its milder forms, may be much more widespread than commonly thought.

Many susceptible people have genetic factors and lifestyle patterns that predispose them to becoming overweight, and many frequently try weight-reduction diets as teenagers. Like people with anorexia nervosa, those with bulimia nervosa are usually female and successful. Unlike anorexics, however, they are usually at or slightly above a normal weight. Females with bulimia nervosa also are more likely to be sexually active than are those with anorexia nervosa.

The *Diagnostic and Statistical Manual of Mental Disorders* gives these criteria for diagnosing bulimia nervosa:[35]

- Recurrent episodes of **binge eating** (eating during a discrete period of time, such as 2 hours, an amount of food that is larger than most people would eat during a similar time period and under similar circumstances and feeling of lack of control over what or how much one is eating)
- Recurrent inappropriate compensatory behavior to prevent weight gain, such as self-induced vomiting; misuse of laxatives, diuretics, enemas, or other medications; fasting; or excessive exercise
- Binge-eating episodes and inappropriate compensatory behaviors both occurring, on average, at least twice a week for 3 months
- Undue influence of body weight or shape on self-evaluation
- Disturbance does not occur exclusively during episodes of anorexia nervosa.

Over a third of individuals initially diagnosed with anorexia nervosa may cross over to bulimia nervosa, although the crossover from bulimia nervosa to anorexia nervosa is much less likely. Typically, the crossover between eating disorders occurs within the first 5 years of the illness. Anorexic persons who perceive their parents as being highly critical are most likely to cross over to bulimia nervosa. In contrast, bulimic individuals who struggle with alcohol abuse are most likely to cross over to anorexia nervosa.

The typical characteristics of those with bulimia nervosa are described in Table 10-8. In addition to bingeing and purging, those with bulimia nervosa often have elaborate food rules, such as avoiding all sweets. Thus, eating just 1 cookie or doughnut may cause bulimic persons to feel guilty that they have broken a rule and proceed to binge. Usually, this action leads to significant overeating. A binge can be triggered by a combination of hunger from recent dieting, stress, boredom, loneliness, and depression. Bingeing often follows a period of strict dieting and thus can be linked to intense hunger. The binge is not at all like normal eating; once begun, it seems to propel itself. The person not only loses control but generally doesn't even taste or enjoy the food that is eaten during a binge. This separates the practice from simple overeating. Binge-purge cycles may be practiced daily, weekly, or at longer intervals.[42] Often, a special time is set aside. Most binge eating occurs at night, when others are less likely to interrupt them, and usually lasts from 30 minutes to 2 hours.

Most commonly, bulimic people consume sweet, high-carbohydrate convenience foods during binges because these foods can be purged relatively easily and comfortably by vomiting. In a single binge, foods supplying 3000 kcal or more may be eaten.[34] Purging follows, in hopes that no weight will be gained. However, even when vomiting follows the binge, 33 to 75% of the food energy taken in is still absorbed, which causes some weight gain. When laxatives or enemas are used, about 90% of the energy is absorbed because these products act in the large intestine, beyond the point of most nutrient absorption. Clearly, the belief of bulimic persons that purging soon after bingeing will prevent excessive energy absorption and weight gain is a misconception.

Early in the onset of bulimia nervosa, sufferers often induce vomiting by placing their fingers (or other objects) deep into the throat. They may inadvertently bite down on fingers; the resulting bite marks on knuckles are an early sign of this disorder. Once the disease is established, however, a person often can vomit simply by contracting the abdominal muscles. Vomiting also may occur spontaneously.

Another way bulimic people attempt to compensate for a binge is by engaging in excessive exercise to burn the excess calories. Exercise is considered excessive when it is done at inappropriate times or settings or when a person continues to exercise despite injury or medical complications. Some bulimic people try to estimate the amount of energy eaten in a binge and then exercise to counteract this energy intake. This practice, referred to as "debting," represents an effort to control their weight.

After bingeing and purging, those with bulimia nervosa usually feel guilty and depressed.[38] Over time, they experience low self-esteem and feel hopeless about their situation (Fig. 10-25). Sufferers gradually distance themselves from others, spending more and more time preoccupied by and engaging in bingeing and purging.

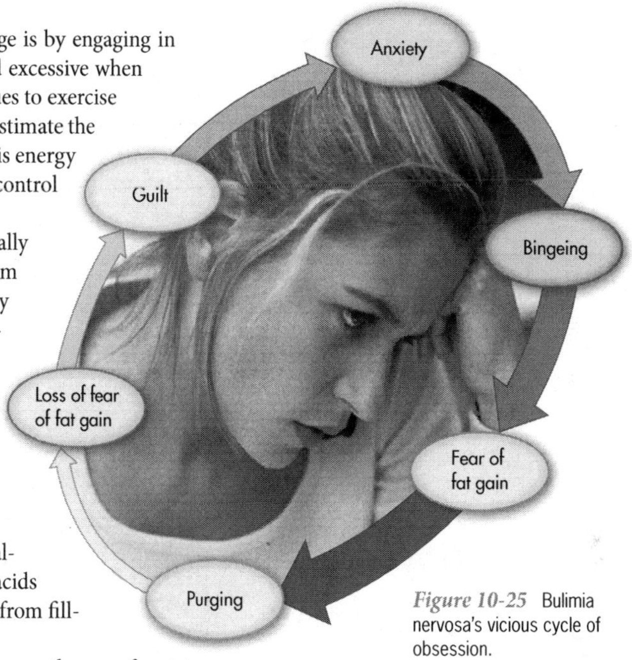

Physical Effects of Bulimia Nervosa

Most of the health problems associated with bulimia nervosa arise from vomiting:[35, 43]

- Repeated exposure of teeth to the acid in vomit causes demineralization, making the teeth painful and sensitive to heat, cold, and acids (Fig. 10-26). Eventually, the teeth may decay severely, erode away from fillings, and finally fall out.
- Blood potassium can drop significantly because of regular vomiting or the use of certain diuretics. This drop can disturb the heart's rhythm and even cause sudden death.
- Salivary glands may swell as a result of infection and irritation from persistent vomiting.
- Stomach ulcers and tears in the esophagus develop, in some cases.
- Constipation may result from frequent laxative use.
- Ipecac syrup, sometimes used to induce vomiting, is toxic to the heart, liver, and kidneys and can cause accidental poisoning when taken repeatedly.
- Overall, bulimia nervosa is a potentially debilitating disorder that can lead to death, usually from suicide, low blood potassium, or overwhelming infections.

Figure 10-25 Bulimia nervosa's vicious cycle of obsession.

Treatment of Bulimia Nervosa

Therapy for bulimia nervosa, as for anorexia nervosa, requires a team of experienced psychotherapists and nutritionists.[42] Bulimic patients are less likely than those with anorexia to enter treatment in a state of semistarvation. However, if a bulimic patient has lost significant weight, this weight loss must be treated before psychological treatment and nutrition counseling begin. Although clinicians have yet to agree on the best therapy for bulimia nervosa, they generally agree that treatment should last at least 16 weeks. Hospitalization may be necessary in cases of extreme laxative abuse, regular vomiting, substance abuse, and depression, especially if physical harm is evident.

The first goal of treatment for bulimia nervosa is to decrease the amount of food consumed in a binge session in order to reduce the risk of esophageal tears from related purging by vomiting. Patients also are taught about bulimia nervosa and its consequences. They must recognize that they are dealing with a serious disorder that can have grave medical complications if not treated. Next follows nutrition counseling and psychotherapy.

Nutrition therapy In general, the focus of nutrition therapy is not on stopping bingeing and purging but, rather, on developing regular eating habits and correcting misconceptions about food. To establish regular eating patterns, some specialists encourage patients to self-monitor by keeping a food diary, in which they record food intake, internal sensations of hunger, environmental factors that trigger binges, and thoughts and feelings that accompany binge-purge cycles. Avoiding binge foods and not constantly stepping on a scale may

Figure 10-26 Excessive tooth decay is common in bulimic patients. Dental professionals are sometimes the first health professionals to notice signs of bulimia nervosa.

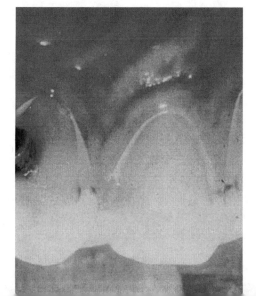

Purging episodes add to the despair felt by people with bulimia nervosa.

Binge eaters usually consume foods that carry the social stigma of so-called junk foods—ice cream, cookies, sweets, potato chips, and similar snack foods.

be recommended early in treatment. Patients also are discouraged from following strict rules about healthy food choices because such rules simply mimic the typical obsessive attitudes associated with bulimia nervosa. Rather, they should be encouraged to adopt a mature perspective on food intake—that is, regularly consume moderate amounts from a variety of foods from each food group.[32] Once the goals of developing regular eating habits and correcting misconceptions about food are achieved, the binge-purge cycle should start to break down.

Psychological and related therapy People with bulimia nervosa need psychological help because they can be very depressed and are at a high risk of suicide. The primary aims of psychotherapy are to improve patients' self-acceptance and to help them be less concerned about body weight. Psychotherapy helps correct the all-or-none thinking typical of bulimic persons: "If I eat 1 cookie, I'm a failure and might as well binge." In addition, the therapist guides the person in using methods other than bingeing and purging to cope with stressful situations. Group therapy often is useful in fostering strong social support. One goal of therapy is to help bulimic persons accept some depression and self-doubt as normal. Certain antidepressants may be used to treat the bulimic patient; however, they should be used in conjunction with other therapies.

Because relapse is likely, therapy should be long-term. About 50% of people with bulimia nervosa recover completely from the disorder. Others continue to struggle with it, to varying degrees, for the rest of their lives. This fact underscores the need for prevention because treatment is difficult.

Eating Disorders Not Otherwise Specified (EDNOS)

EDNOS is a broad category of eating disorders in which individuals have partial syndromes that do not meet the strict criteria for anorexia nervosa or bulimia nervosa.[35] About 50% of people with eating disorders fall into this EDNOS category, especially adolescents. Examples of disordered eating in this category include (1) a woman who meets all the criteria for anorexia nervosa but continues to menstruate; (2) an individual who meets all the criteria for anorexia nervosa but, despite a significant weight loss, has a current weight in the normal range (perhaps a person who was once obese); (3) a person who meets all the criteria for bulimia nervosa but who binges less than twice a week; (4) a person who meets all the criteria for bulimia nervosa but does not binge (this person might eat normal amounts of food but purges regularly out of fear of weight or fat gain); and (5) a person who repeatedly chews and spits out food but does not swallow it.

EDNOS also includes binge-eating disorder, which is likely to be recognized as a separate, diagnosable disease when the next *Diagnostic and Statistical Manual of Mental Disorders* is published. The following are the criteria for binge-eating disorder.

- Recurrent binge-eating episodes.
- During most binge episodes, at least 3 of these occur: eating much more rapidly than usual, eating until feeling uncomfortably full, eating large amounts of food when not feeling physically hungry, eating alone because of being embarrassed by how much one is eating, and/or feeling disgusted with oneself, depressed, or very guilty after overeating.
- Marked feelings of distress regarding binge eating.
- Binge-eating episodes occur, on average, at least 2 days a week for 6 months.
- Binge eating does not occur only during the course of bulimia nervosa or anorexia nervosa.

Although people with anorexia nervosa and bulimia nervosa exhibit a persistent preoccupation with body shape, weight, and thinness, binge eaters do not necessarily share these concerns. Thus, neither purging nor prolonged food restriction is characteristic of binge-eating disorder. Some physicians classify binge-eating disorder as an addiction to food involving psychological dependence. The person becomes attached to the behavior itself and has a drive to continue it, senses only limited control over it, and needs to continue despite negative consequences.

Note that obesity and binge eating are not necessarily linked. Not all obese people are binge eaters, and, although obesity may result, it is not necessarily an outcome of binge eating. Nonetheless, binge-eating disorder is most common among the severely obese and those with a long history of frequent restrictive dieting, although obesity is not a criterion for having binge-eating disorder. Approximately 30 to 50% of subjects in organized weight-control programs have binge-eating disorder, whereas about 1 to 2% of North Americans in general have this disorder. Many more people in the general population have less severe forms of the disease but do not meet the formal criteria for diagnosis. The number of cases of binge-eating disorder is far greater than that of either anorexia nervosa or bulimia nervosa.

For some people, frequent dieting beginning in childhood or adolescence is a precursor to binge-eating disorder. During periods when little food is eaten, they get very hungry and feel driven to eat in a compulsive, uncontrolled way. Many individuals with binge-eating disorder (about 40% of whom are males) perceive themselves as hungry more often than normal. Most started dieting at a young age, began bingeing during adolescence or in their early twenties, and have not succeeded in commercial weight-control programs. Almost half of those with severe binge-eating disorder exhibit clinical depression symptoms and isolate themselves from others.

Stressful events and feelings of depression or anxiety can trigger this binge eating. Giving themselves "permission" to eat a "forbidden" food also can precipitate a binge. Other triggers include loneliness, anxiety, self-pity, depression, anger, rage, alienation, and frustration.[44] In general, people engage in binge eating to induce a sense of well-being and perhaps even emotional numbness, usually in an attempt to avoid feeling and dealing with emotional pain and anxiety.

Binge eaters consume food without regard to biological need and often in a recurrent, ritualized fashion. Some people with this disorder eat food continually over an extended period; others cycle episodes of bingeing with normal eating.[44] For example, someone with a stressful or frustrating job might go home every night and eat until bedtime. Another person might eat normally most of the time but find comfort in consuming large quantities of food when an emotional setback occurs.

People with binge-eating disorder may come from families with alcoholism or may have suffered sexual abuse. Members of such dysfunctional families often do not know how to deal effectively with emotions. They cope by turning to substances. Family members learn to cover up dysfunctional patterns and to nurture the behavior of others at the expense of their own needs.

Overall, people who have binge-eating disorder are usually unsuccessful in controlling it without professional help.[44] Depending on the specific symptoms, these individuals may need treatment as outlined earlier for anorexia nervosa or bulimia nervosa.

The focus of nutrition therapy for people with binge-eating disorder mirrors that of controlling the bingeing associated with bulimia nervosa. Psychological therapy involves helping those with binge-eating disorder identify personal emotional needs and express emotions. Because this problem is a common predisposing factor in binge eating, communication issues should be addressed during treatment. Binge eaters often must be helped to recognize their own buried emotions in anxiety-producing situations, and learning simple but appropriate phrases to say to oneself can help stop bingeing when the desire is strong. Self-help groups, such as Overeaters Anonymous, aim to help recovery from binge-eating disorder. The treatment philosophy attempts to create an environment of encouragement and accountability to overcome this eating disorder. Antidepressants, as well as other medications, may be prescribed to help reduce binge eating in these individuals by decreasing depression.

Night eating syndrome is an eating disorder under study. In this disorder, people eat a lot in the late evening or eat food in order to fall asleep again once awakened in the night. This night eating can contribute to weight gain, so affected persons are urged to seek treatment.

356 **PART 3** Metabolism and Energy Balance

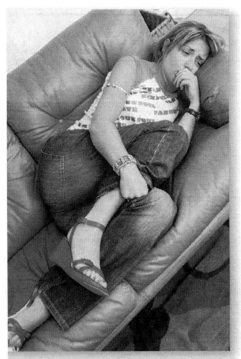

Eating disorders affect many college students. Counselors are aware of this and are available to help.

Other Related Conditions

Although not recognized as diagnosable eating or body image disorders, articles about muscle dysmorphia (bigorexia), orthorexia, and pregorexia are appearing in research journals. Muscle dysmorphia, sometimes called bigorexia, is a condition characterized by an excessive concern that one has underdeveloped muscles.[50] Individuals with muscle dysmorphia, however, tend to have well-developed musculature. This condition appears to be more common among males, especially bodybuilders. Many individuals with muscle dysmorphia devote many hours each day to lifting weights and performing resistance exercises. Most sufferers continue to exercise even when injured and to the point that social relationships and performance at work and school are impaired. Some also use anabolic steroids or other muscle-enhancing drugs, take nutritional supplements, and follow specific dietary patterns they believe will enhance muscle development. Treatment from a sports medicine physician and counselor trained to work with athletes may help individuals overcome this condition.

Orthorexia comes from the Greek word *orthos* (meaning "straight, proper") and *orexia* ("appetite"). Sometimes this condition is called the "health-food eating disorder." Healthy eating is taken to such an extreme that eating the "right" foods dominates a person's life.[51] Individuals with orthorexia spend many hours each day searching for foods that are "pure" (e.g., free of herbicides, pesticides, and artificial ingredients or packaged in a specific manner, such as no plastic packaging). This excessive concern for "righteous eating" can progress to the point that it crowds out other activities, impairs relationships, and even becomes physically dangerous if the diet is severely restricted. Little is known about this condition or how to treat it.

Pregorexia is a term coined by the popular press to describe women who decrease calories and exercise excessively to control weight gain during pregnancy.[52] Whether this problem actually exists or not, eating a diet that is nutrient rich and sufficient in calories is essential for an optimal pregnancy outcome (see Chapter 16). Likely the best treatment for these individuals is similar to that for those with anorexia nervosa.

Prevention of Eating Disorders

A key to developing and maintaining healthful eating behavior is to realize that some concern about diet, health, and weight is normal, as are variations in what we eat, how we feel, and even how much we weigh. For example, most people experience some minimal weight change (up to 2 to 3 lb) throughout the day and even more over the course of a week. A large weight fluctuation or an ongoing weight gain or weight loss is more likely to indicate that a problem is present. If you notice a large change in your eating habits, how you feel, or your body weight, it is a good idea to consult your physician. Treating physical and emotional problems early helps prevent eating disorders and promotes good health.

Not only is the treatment of eating disorders far more difficult than prevention, but these disorders also have devastating effects on the entire family. For this reason, parents, friends, and professionals working with children and teens must emphasize the importance of an overall healthful diet that focuses on moderation, as opposed to restriction and perfection. These caregivers also can help children and teens form positive habits and appropriate expectations, especially regarding body image.[45] The following are some ways that these caregivers and health professionals can help growing children and adolescents avoid eating disorders:

- Discourage restrictive dieting, meal skipping, and fasting (except for religious reasons).
- Encourage children to eat only when hungry.
- Promote good nutrition and regular physical activity in school and at home.
- Promote regularly eating meals as a family unit.[46]
- Provide information about normal changes that occur during puberty.

Take Action

Assessing Risk of Developing an Eating Disorder

British investigators have developed a 5-question screening tool, called the **SCOFF** Questionnaire, for recognizing eating disorders:[47]

1. Do you make yourself **S**ick because you feel full?
2. Do you lose **C**ontrol over how much you eat?
3. Have you lost more than **O**ne stone (about 13 lb) recently?
4. Do you believe yourself to be **F**at when others say you are thin?
5. Does **F**ood dominate your life?

Two or more positive responses suggest an eating disorder.

1. After completing this questionnaire, do you feel that you might have an eating disorder or the potential to develop one?
2. Do you think any of your friends might have an eating disorder?
3. What counseling and educational resources exist in your area or on your campus to help with a potential eating disorder?
4. If a friend has an eating disorder, what do you think is the best way to assist him or her in getting help?

- Correct misconceptions about nutrition, healthy body weight, and approaches to weight loss.
- Carefully phrase any weight-related recommendations and comments.
- Don't overemphasize numbers on a scale. Instead, primarily promote healthful eating irrespective of body weight.
- Increase self-acceptance and appreciation of the power and pleasure emerging from one's body.
- Encourage coaches to be sensitive to weight and body image issues among athletes.
- Emphasize that thinness is not necessarily associated with better athletic performance.
- Enhance tolerance for diversity in body weight and shape.
- Encourage normal expression of emotions.
- Build respectful environments and supportive relationships.
- Provide adolescents with an appropriate, but not unlimited, degree of independence, choice, responsibility, and self-accountability for their actions.

Knowledge Check

1. What is the difference between eating disorders and disordered eating?
2. What are the characteristics of anorexia nervosa, bulimia nervosa, and binge-eating disorder?
3. What kinds of therapy are appropriate for eating disorders?
4. What type of advice should be given to growing children and adolescents to help them avoid eating disorders?

CASE STUDY FOLLOW-UP

There is a good chance that, if Christy keeps eating as she is, she will gain weight in her freshman year of college. Christy skips breakfast, eats a light lunch and dinner, and then becomes hungry late at night and cannot resist the high-calorie, high-fat pizza that is delivered to the dorm. Recent data show that women who skip breakfast are more likely to weigh more than those who eat breakfast.[24] This pattern of eating leads to weight gain. Christy needs to wake up and eat a simple breakfast, such as a bowl of cereal with fat-free milk and a banana. In addition, she needs to eat a balanced lunch and dinner and find ways to add exercise to her daily routine to avoid the Freshman 15.

Summary

10.1 Energy balance considers energy intake and energy output. Negative energy balance occurs when energy output surpasses energy intake, resulting in weight loss. Positive energy balance occurs when energy intake is greater than output, resulting in weight gain. Basal metabolism, the thermic effect of food, physical activity, and thermogenesis account for total energy use by the body. Basal metabolism, which represents the minimum amount of energy used to keep the resting, awake body alive, is primarily affected by lean body mass, body surface area, and thyroid hormone concentrations. Physical activity is energy use above the amount expended when at rest. The thermic effect of food is the increase in metabolism that facilitates the digestion, absorption, and processing of nutrients recently consumed. Thermogenesis is heat production caused by shivering when cold, fidgeting, and other stimuli. In a sedentary person, about 70 to 80% of energy use is accounted for by basal metabolism and the thermic effect of food.

10.2 Direct calorimetry estimates energy expenditure by measuring the amount of body heat released by a person. Indirect calorimetry, the most commonly used method to determine energy use by the body, involves collecting expired air from an individual during a specified amount of time. This method works because a predictable relationship exists between the body's use of energy and the amount of oxygen consumed and carbon dioxide produced. Estimated Energy Requirements (EERs), which are based on formulas developed by the Food and Nutrition Board, can be used to estimate energy needs.

10.3 Groups of cells in the hypothalamus and other regions in the brain affect hunger, the primarily internal desire to find and eat food. These cells monitor macronutrients and other substances in the blood and read low amounts as a signal to promote feeding. A variety of external (appetite-related) forces, such as food availability, affect satiety. Hunger cues combine with appetite cues to promote feeding. Numerous factors elicit satiety, such as flavor, smell, chewing, and the effects of digestion, absorption, and metabolism.

10.4 A person of healthy weight generally shows good health and performs daily activities without weight-related problems. A body mass index (weight in kilograms/height² in meters) of 18.5 to <25 is one measure of healthy weight, although weight in excess of this value may not lead to ill health. A healthy weight is best determined in conjunction with a thorough health evaluation by a health-care provider. A body mass index of 25 to <30 represents overweight. Obesity is defined as a total body fat percentage over 25% (men) or 35% (women), or a body mass index of 30 or more. Fat distribution greatly determines health risks from obesity. Upper-body fat storage, as measured by a waist circumference greater than 40 inches (102 cm) (men) or 35 inches (88 cm) (women), increases the risks of hypertension, cardiovascular disease, and type 2 diabetes more than does lower-body fat storage.

10.5 Research suggests that genes account for up to 40 to 70% of weight differences between people. The genes may be those that determine body type, metabolic rate, and the factors that affect hunger and satiety. Some individuals are thought to have a genetic predisposition to obesity because they inherit a thrifty metabolism. The set-point theory proposes that humans have a genetically predetermined body weight or body fat content, which the body closely regulates. Environmental factors have important effects on what we eat. These factors may define when eating is appropriate, what is preferable to eat, and how much food should be eaten. Even though our genetic backgrounds have a strong influence on body weight and composition, genes are not destiny—both nature and nurture are involved.

10.6 A sound weight-loss program emphasizes a wide variety of low-energy-density foods; adapts to the dieter's habits; consists of readily obtainable foods; strives to change poor eating habits; stresses regular physical activity; and stipulates the participation of a physician if weight is to be lost rapidly or if the person is over the age of 40 (men) or 50 (women) years and plans to perform substantially greater physical activity than usual. A pound of adipose tissue contains about 3500 kcal. Thus, if energy output exceeds intake by about 500 kcal per day, a pound of adipose tissue can be lost per week. Physical activity as part of a weight-loss program should be focused on duration, rather than intensity. Behavior modification is a vital part of a weight-loss program because the dieter may have many habits that discourage weight maintenance.

10.7 Many fad diets promise rapid weight loss; however, these diets are not designed for permanent weight loss. Low-carbohydrate diets work in the short run because they limit total food intake; however, long-term studies have shown that the weight generally returns in about a year. Weight-loss drugs are reserved for those who are obese or have weight-related problems, and they should be administered under close physician supervision. The treatments for severe obesity include surgery to reduce stomach volume to approximately 1 oz (30 ml) and very-low-calorie diets containing 400 to 800 kcal/day. Both of these measures should be reserved for people who have failed at more

CHAPTER 10 Energy Balance, Weight Control, and Eating Disorders   359

conservative approaches to weight loss. They also require close medical supervision. Underweight can be caused by a variety of factors, such as excessive physical activity and genetic background. Sometimes being underweight requires medical attention. A physician should be consulted first to rule out underlying disease. The underweight person may need to increase portion sizes and include energy-dense foods in the diet.

10.8 Anorexia nervosa usually starts with dieting in early puberty and proceeds to the near-total refusal to eat. Early warning signs include intense concern about weight gain and dieting, as well as abnormal food habits. Eventually, anorexia nervosa can lead to numerous negative physical effects. The treatment of anorexia nervosa includes increasing food intake to support gradual weight gain. Psychological counseling attempts to help patients establish regular food habits and find means of coping with the life stresses that led to the disorder. Bulimia nervosa is characterized by secretive bingeing on large amounts of

food within a short time span and then purging by vomiting or misusing laxatives, diuretics, or enemas. Alternately, fasting and excessive exercise may be used to offset calorie intake. Both men and women are at risk. Vomiting as a means of purging is especially destructive to the body. The treatment of bulimia nervosa includes psychological as well as nutritional counseling. During treatment, bulimic persons learn to accept themselves and to cope with problems in ways that do not involve food. Binge-eating disorder is most common among people with a history of frequent, unsuccessful dieting. Binge eaters binge without purging. This condition currently falls under the category Eating Disorders Not Otherwise Specified (EDNOS). Emotional disturbances are often at the root of this disordered form of eating. Treatment addresses deeper emotional issues, discourages food deprivation and restrictive diets, and helps restore normal eating behaviors. The treatment of eating disorders may include certain medications.

Study Questions

1. Positive energy balance occurs when energy output surpasses energy intake.

    a. true   **b.** false

2. What is the approximate basal metabolism of a 175-pound man?

    a. 3840 kcal/day   **c.** 1909 kcal/day
    b. 1227 kcal/day   **d.** 1745 kcal /day

3. All the following raise basal metabolism rate *except* _____.

    a. growing   **c.** fever
    b. muscle mass   **d.** starvation

4. Direct calorimetry estimates energy expenditure by collecting expired air from an individual during a specified amount of time.

    a. true   **b.** false

5. Which protein produced in fat tissue regulates body weight by signaling the brain about changes in body fat stores?

    a. ghrelin   **c.** thyroid hormone
    b. leptin   **d.** cholecystokinin

6. The most accurate method for diagnosing obesity is _____.

    a. underwater weighing
    b. dual energy X-ray absorptiometry (DEXA)
    c. skinfold thickness
    d. body mass index

7. Jane's waist measurement is 35 inches. Which of the following statements about Jane's body fat distribution is correct?

    a. Jane is at an increased risk of developing diabetes, hypertension, and heart disease.
    b. Jane's waist circumference indicates central body fat distribution.
    c. Jane has a "pear" shape.
    d. Both a and c are correct.
    e. Both a and b are correct.

8. The set-point theory proposes that humans have a genetically predetermined body weight or body fat content, which the body closely regulates.

    a. true   **b.** false

9. A sound weight-loss program _____.

    a. includes a wide variety of low-energy-density foods
    b. stresses regular physical activity
    c. includes behavior modification to change problem behaviors
    d. all of the above

360 **PART 3** Metabolism and Energy Balance

10. The danger of low-carbohydrate diets is that they cause fast weight loss in the form of _____.

    a. fat tissue   **d.** a and b
    b. water   **e.** b and c
    c. muscles

11. Surgery to reduce stomach volume should be reserved for people who have failed at more conservative approaches to weight loss.

    a. true   **b.** false

12. Which eating disorder starts with dieting and proceeds to near-total refusal to eat?

    a. bulimia nervosa   **c.** anorexia nervosa
    b. binge eating   **d.** none of the above

13. What is lanugo?

    a. downy, soft hair that develops on people with anorexia nervosa
    b. a sudden drop in blood pressure from excessive dieting
    c. a popular fad diet
    d. a code word for an eating disorder

14. Bulimia nervosa is characterized by all of the following *except* _____.

    a. refusal to eat   **c.** purging
    b. secretive bingeing **d.** misuse of laxatives

15. Binge-eating disorder is more widespread than anorexia or bulimia.

    a. true   **b.** false

16. Create a pie chart showing the relative proportion of the major components of energy expenditure.

17. How does direct calorimetry differ from indirect calorimetry?

18. Contrast the 2 drives that influence our desire to eat.

19. Make a chart that compares the methods for measuring body fat.

20. Why do both genetic and environmental factors affect body weight?

21. What are the characteristics of a sound weight-loss diet?

22. Why is the claim for quick, effortless weight loss by any method always misleading?

23. What are the typical characteristics of individuals with anorexia nervosa and those with bulimia nervosa?

Answer Key: 1-a; 2-c; 3-d; 4-b; 5-b; 6-b; 7-e; 8-a; 9-d; 10-e; 11-a; 12-c; 13-a; 14-a; 15-a; 16-refer to Section 10.1; 17-refer to Section 10.2; 18-refer to Section 10.3; 19-refer to Section 10.4; 20-refer to Section 10.5; 21-refer to Section 10.6; 22-refer to Section 10.7; 23-refer to Section 10.8

Websites

To learn more about the topics covered in this chapter, visit these websites.

Weight Control, Obesity, and Nutrition

win.niddk.nih.gov/index.htm (or call 877-946-4627)

www.caloriecontrol.org

www.weight.com

www.obesity.org

www.cyberdiet.com

Eating Disorders

www.aabainc.org

www.nationaleatingdisorders.org

www.nimh.nih.gov/health/topics/eating-disorders

www.womenshealth.gov/bodyimage

References

1. Centers for Disease Control and Prevention. *U.S. obesity 1985–2010.* Atlanta: CDC; 2011.

2. Flegal K and others. Prevalance and trends in obesity among US adults, 1999–2008. *JAMA.* 2010;303:235.

3. Booth K and others. Obesity and the built environment. *J Am Diet Assoc.* 2005;105:s110.

4. Wadden T and others. Obesity: Management. In: Shils M and others, eds. *Modern nutrition in health and disease.* 10th ed. Philadelphia: Lippincott Williams & Wilkins; 2006.

5. Hill J and others. Obesity: Etiology. In: Shils M and others, eds. *Modern nutrition in health and disease.* 10th ed. Philadelphia: Lippincott Williams & Wilkins; 2006.

6. Jakicic J. The effect of physical activity on body weight. *Obes.* 2009;17:S34.

7. Forshee R and others. A critical examination of the evidence relating high fructose corn syrup and weight gain. *Crit Rev Food Sci Nutr.* 2007;47:561.

8. U.S. Department of Agriculture, Economic Research Service. *Food availability.* 2010; www.ers.usda.gov/Data/FoodConsumption/FoodAvailIndex.htm.

9. Bray G. Soft drink consumption and obesity: It is all about fructose. *Curr Opin Lipidol.* 2010;21:51.

10. Tappy L, Le KA. Metabolic effects of fructose and the worldwide increase in obesity. *Physiol Rev.* 2010;90:23.

CHAPTER 10 Energy Balance, Weight Control, and Eating Disorders   361

11. Smith G. Control of food intake. In: Shils M and others, eds. *Modern nutrition in health and disease.* 10th ed. Philadelphia: Lippincott Williams & Wilkins; 2006.

12. Bowen J and others. Appetite hormones and energy intake in obese men after consumption of fructose, glucose and whey protein beverages. *Int J Obes.* 2007;31:1696.

13. Flicker L and others. Body mass index and survival in men and women aged 70 to 75. *J Am Geriatr Soc.* 2010;58:234.

14. Heyward V, Wagner D. *Applied body composition assessment.* 2nd ed. Champaign, IL: Human Kinetics; 2004.

15. Lee SY, Gallagher D. Assessment methods in human body composition. *Curr Opin Clin Nutr Metab Care.* 2008;11:566.

16. Bajaj HS and others. Clinical utility of waist circumference in predicting all-cause mortality in preventive cardiology clinic population: A PReCIS database study. *Obes.* 2009;17:1615.

17. Christakis N, Fowler J. The spread of obesity in a large social network over 32 years. *New Eng J Med.* 2007;357:370.

18. Grief N and Miranda RL. Weight Loss Maintenance. *Am Fam Physician.* 2010;15:82..

19. Wilson TG. Behavioral treatment of obesity: Introduction. *Behav Res Ther.* 2010;May 23:705.

20. Lepe M and others. Long-term efficacy of high-protein diets: a systematic review. *Nutr Hosp.* 2011;26:1256.

21. Ornish D. Was Dr. Atkins right? *J Am Diet Assoc.* 2004;104:537.

22. Ello-Martin J and others. Dietary energy density in the treatment of obesity: A year-long trial comparing 2 weight-loss diets. *Am J Clin Nutr.* 2007;85:1465.

23. Raynor HA and others. Amount of food group variety consumed in the diet and long-term weight loss maintenance. *Obes Res.* 2005;13:883.

24. Astbury NM and others. Breakfast consumption affects appetite, energy intake, and the metabolic and endocrine responses to foods consumed later in the day in male habitual breakfast eaters. *J Nutr.* 2011;141:1381.

25. Deshmukh-Taskar PR and others. The relationship of breakfast skipping and type of breakfast consumption with nutrient intake and weight status in children and adolescents: The National Health and Nutrition Examination Survey 1999–2006. *J Am Diet Assoc.* 2010:110:869.

26. ADA. Position of the American Dietetic Association: Food and nutrition misinformation. *J Am Diet Assoc.* 2006;106:601.

27. Brinkworth GD and others. Long-term effects of a very low carbohydrate weight loss diet compared with an isocaloric low fat diet after 12 mo. *Am J Clin Nutr.* 2009;90:23.

28. Pittler M, Ernst E. Dietary supplements for body-weight reduction: A systematic review. *Am J Clin Nutr.* 2004;79:529.

29. Moyers S. Medications as adjunct therapy for weight loss: Approved and off-label agents in use. *J Am Diet Assoc.* 2005;105:948.

30. Isidro ML, Cordido F. Approved and off-label uses of obesity medications, and potential new pharmacologic treatment options. *Pharmaceuticals.* 2010;3:125.

31. Treasure J and others. Eating disorders. *Lancet.* 2010;375:583.

32. ADA. Position of the American Dietetic Association: Nutrition intervention in the treatment of eating disorders. *J Am Diet Assoc.* 2011;111:1236.

33. Courbasson C and others. Substance use disorders, anorexia, bulimia, and concurrent disorders. *Can J Public Health.* 2005;96:102.

34. Tchanturia K and others. Cognitive flexibility and clinical severity in eating disorders. *PLoS ONE;* 2011.

35. American Psychiatric Association. *Diagnostic and statistical manual of mental disorders (DSM-IV-TR).* 4th ed. Washington, DC: American Psychiatric Association; 2000.

36. Le Grange D, Eisler I. Family interventions in adolescent anorexia nervosa. *Child Adol Psychiatr Clin N Am.* 2009;18:159.

37. Attia E. Anorexia nervosa: Current status and future directions. *Ann Rev Med.* 2010;61:425.

38. Walsh BT. Eating disorders. In: Fauci AS and others, eds. *Harrison's principles of internal medicine.* New York: McGraw-Hill; 2008.

39. Miller K and others. Medical findings in outpatients with anorexia nervosa. *Arch Intern Med.* 2005;165:561.

40. Van Wymelbeke V and others. Factors associated with the increase in Resting Energy Expenditure during refeeding in malnourished anorexia nervosa patients. *Am J Clin Nutr.* 2004;80:1469.

41. Broussard B. Women's experiences of bulimia nervosa. *J Adv Nurs.* 2005;49:43.

42. Wilson GT, Sysko R. Frequency of binge eating episodes in bulimia nervosa and binge eating disorder: Diagnostic considerations. *Int J Eat Disord.* 2009;42:603.

43. Johannson AK. Eating disorders and oral health: a matched case-control study. *Eur. J Oral Sci.* 2012;120:61.

44. Davis C, Carter JC. Compulsive overeating as an addiction disorder. A review of theory and evidence. *Appetite.* 2009;53:1.

45. Keel PK, Brown TA. Update on course and outcome in eating disorders. *Int J Eat Disord.* 2010;43:195.

46. Neumark-Sztainer D and others. Dieting and disordered eating behaviors from adolescence to young adulthood: findings from a 10-year longitudinal study. *J Am Diet Assoc.* 2011;111:1004.

47. Hill LS and others. SCOFF, the development of an eating disorder screening questionnaire. *Int J Eat Disord.* 2010;43:344.

48. Wonderlich SA and others. The validity and clinical utility of binge eating disorder. *Int J Eat Disord.* 2009;42:687.

49. Riebl SK and others. The prevalence of subclinical eating disorders among male cyclists. *J Am Diet Assoc.* 2007;107:1214.

50. Robert CA and others. The relationship between the drive for muscularity and muscle dysmorphia in male and female weight trainers. *J Strength Cond Res.* 2009;23:1656.

51. Segura-Garcia C. 2012. Orthorexia Nervosa: a frequent eating disordered behavior in athletes. *Eat Weight Disord.* 2012; Feb 21.

52. Mathieu J. What is pregorexia? *J Am Diet Assoc.* 2009;109:977.

53. Suter P and others. Effect of ethanol on energy expenditure. *Am J Physiol Regul Integr Comp Physiol.* 1994;266:4.

54. Karlsson EA and others. Diet-induced obesity impairs the T cell memory response to influenza virus infection. *J Immunol.* 2010;184:3127.

55. Food and Nutrition Board. *Dietary reference intakes for energy, carbohydrate, fiber, fat, fatty acids, cholesterol, protein, and amino acids.* Washington, DC: National Academy Press; 2005.

The best exercise for you is one you want to continue.
Learn more at **www.mayoclinic.com/health/fitness/HQ00171.**

11 # Nutrition, Exercise, and Sports

Chapter Outline

Student Learning Outcomes

After studying this chapter, you will be able to

1. Explain the benefits of physical activity.

2. Design a fitness plan.

3. Discuss the energy sources for muscles and human performance.

4. Describe how the body responds to physical activity.

5. Apply the principles of sports nutrition to create diet plans for athletes.

6. Describe the fluid needs of athletes and how to avoid dehydration and hyponatremia.

7. Describe how the composition of food or fluid consumed before, during, and after exercise training sessions can affect performance.

8. Explain the role of ergogenic aids and describe their effect on athletic performance.

EXERCISE, LIKE HEALTHY EATING, is essential to good health. However, many people get far less exercise than is needed for good health. In fact, the majority of health problems in North America are related to poor diet and insufficient physical activity. Only 18% of adults report engaging in physical activity that lasts 30 minutes or longer on 5 or more days each week. Approximately 40% do not participate in any regular activity. And, when adults do start an exercise program, about half quit within 3 months.

The effects of diet and exercise on health status are closely related to each other. Recall that regular exercise helps chyme move through the intestinal tract, promotes calcium deposition in the bones, and strengthens the heart so that nutrients can be delivered to cells efficiently. Similarly, what you eat and drink affects exercise performance—whether you are a recreational athlete or an elite athlete or you just want to maintain your health.

Athletes invest a lot of time and effort in training; their quest to find a competitive edge has spurred research studies designed to determine how diet affects exercise performance. Good eating habits can't substitute for physical training and genetic endowment, but healthy food and beverage choices are crucial for top-notch performance, contributing to endurance and helping speed the repair of injured tissues.[1] Unfortunately, there is much misinformation regarding the effect of diet and nutrients on exercise performance. A good working knowledge and understanding of sports nutrition can help individuals choose diets that let them perform as close to their potential as possible. In this chapter, you will discover how exercise benefits the entire body and how nutrition relates to fitness and sports performance.

364   **PART 3**   Metabolism and Energy Balance

Figure 11-1 The benefits of regular, moderate physical activity and exercise.

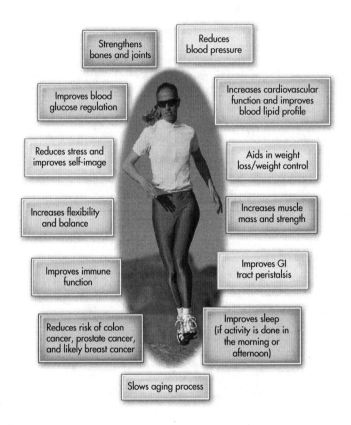

- Strengthens bones and joints
- Reduces blood pressure
- Improves blood glucose regulation
- Increases cardiovascular function and improves blood lipid profile
- Reduces stress and improves self-image
- Aids in weight loss/weight control
- Increases flexibility and balance
- Increases muscle mass and strength
- Improves immune function
- Improves GI tract peristalsis
- Reduces risk of colon cancer, prostate cancer, and likely breast cancer
- Improves sleep (if activity is done in the morning or afternoon)
- Slows aging process

11.1 Benefits of Fitness

▶ Recall how the terms *physical activity* and *exercise* are related. Exercise is physical activity done with the intent to gain health and fitness benefits, whereas physical activity is simply part of day-to-day activities.

The benefits of regular physical activity (and exercise) include enhanced heart function, improved balance, a reduced risk of falling, better sleep habits, healthier body composition (less body fat, more muscle mass), and reduced injury to muscles, tendons, and joints. Physical activity also can reduce stress and positively affect blood pressure, blood cholesterol levels, blood glucose regulation, and immune function. In addition, physical activity aids in weight control, both by raising resting energy expenditure for a short period of time after exercise and by increasing overall energy expenditure (Fig. 11-1).[2-7]

Almost everyone can benefit from regular exercise. *Healthy People 2020* objectives for U.S. adults include the following:

- Reduce the proportion of adults engaging in no leisure-time physical activity.
- Increase the proportion of adults who meet current federal physical activity guidelines for aerobic and muscle-strengthening activity.

The 2008 Physical Activity Guidelines for Americans set 3 goals for physical activity.

- Adults should be physically active.
- For substantial health benefits, each week adults should engage in 150 minutes of moderate-intensity aerobic physical activity, or 75 minutes of vigorous aerobic activity, or an equivalent combination. For more health benefits, each day adults should double these exercise times.
- Adults should perform muscle-strengthening activities 2 or more days each week.

Knowledge Check

1. What are 3 benefits of physical activity?
2. What are the physical activity objectives set by *Healthy People 2020*?
3. What amount of time should be devoted to physical activity to promote weight loss?

 11.2 Characteristics of a Good Fitness Program

A good fitness program is one that meets a person's needs—the ideal program for one individual may not be right for another. The first step in designing a fitness program is to define goals. Some may want a program that trains them for athletic competition; others may want to lose weight or just increase their stamina or improve their balance. Different goals mean different fitness programs. To reach goals, fitness program planning should consider the mode, duration, frequency, intensity, and progression of exercise, as well as consistency and variety. Also, a good fitness program must help individuals achieve and maintain fitness.

Mode

Mode refers to the type of exercise performed. The American College of Sports Medicine (ACSM) defines **aerobic exercise** as "any activity that uses large muscle groups, can be maintained continuously, and is rhythmic in nature." It is a type of exercise that causes the heart and lungs to work harder than at rest. Aerobic exercise usually involves using large muscle groups, for activities such as brisk walking, running, lap swimming, or cycling. **Resistance exercise,** or strength training, is defined as activities that use muscular strength to move a weight or work against a resistant load. A type of exercise that increases the ability of a joint to move through its entire range of motion is called **flexibility exercise.**

Duration

Duration is the amount of time spent in an exercise or physical activity session. Generally, exercise should last at least 30 minutes, not counting time for warm-up and cooldown. Ideally, exercise should be continuous (without stopping), but research has shown that 10-minute bouts of exercise done 3 times throughout the day can lower the risk of cardiovascular disease, cancer, and diabetes.[8]

Frequency

Frequency is the number of times the activity is performed weekly. For the best fitness level, daily aerobic activity is recommended. However, aerobic exercise performed 3 to 5 days a week appears to achieve cardiovascular fitness. To meet desired weight-loss goals, the frequency of exercise may need to be 5 to 6 times per week. To achieve muscular fitness, 2 to 3 days of resistance training are needed weekly. Similarly, 2 to 3 days per week of flexibility exercises are recommended.

▶ To stick with an exercise program, experts recommend the following:

- Start slowly.
- Vary activities; make exercise fun.
- Include friends and others.
- Set specific attainable goals and monitor progress.
- Set aside a specific time each day for exercise; build it into daily routines, but make it convenient.
- Reward yourself for being successful in keeping up with your goals.
- Don't worry about occasional setbacks; focus on long-term benefits to your health.

366 **PART 3** Metabolism and Energy Balance

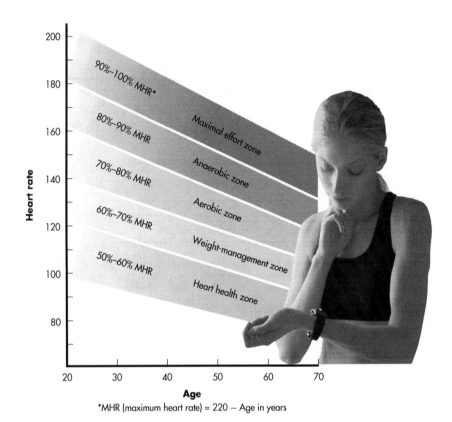

▶ The maximum heart rate for a 20-year-old person is 200 beats per minute:

220 − Age in years = Maximum heart rate

220 − 20 = 200

The target zone for a 20-year-old person is 120 to 180 heartbeats per minute:

Maximum heart rate × 0.6 = Low end of maximum heart rate target zone

200 × 0.6 = 120

Maximum heart rate × 0.9 = High end of maximum heart rate target zone

200 × 0.9 = 180

*MHR (maximum heart rate) = 220 − Age in years

Figure 11-2 Heart rate training chart. This chart shows the number of heartbeats per minute that corresponds to various exercise intensities.

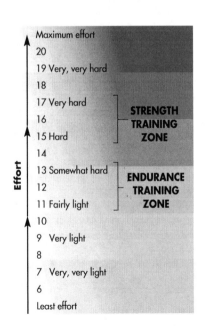

Figure 11-3 Rating of Perceived Exertion (RPE) scale. This scale is used to estimate exercise intensity. A rating between 12 and 15 is recommended to achieve a high physical fitness level.

Intensity

Intensity is the level of effort required, or how hard the exercise is to perform. Intensity can be described as low-intensity (very mild increased heart rate exercise), moderate-intensity (exercise that increases breathing, sweating, and heart rate but permits one to carry on a conversation), or vigorous-intensity (exercise that significantly increases breathing, sweating, and heart rate, which makes it difficult to carry on a conversation).

Traditionally, heart rate has been used to define intensity (Fig. 11-2). This popular and simple method uses a percentage of age-predicted maximum heart rate. To estimate maximum heart rate in beats per minute, subtract a person's age from 220. The range of heart rates between 60 and 90% of maximum is sometimes called the target zone. The lower end of this range is calculated by multiplying maximum heart rate by 0.6; the upper end is computed by multiplying maximum heart rate by 0.9. Medications, such as those for high blood pressure, may affect maximum heart rate. A physician can help those with health conditions personalize their target zone.

Another way to determine exercise intensity is the Borg Scale of Perceived Exertion, which often is called the **Rating of Perceived Exertion (RPE)** scale. The scale ranges from 6 to 20, with numbers corresponding to a subjective feeling of exertion (Fig. 11-3). For example, the number 9 is rated as "very light" exertion and the number 19 is considered close to maximal effort, or "very, very hard," such as would occur in an all-out sprint. To achieve fitness, aim for an intensity of 12 to 15. At this level, you are working at a moderate intensity but can still talk to an exercise partner.

Individuals need to monitor how their bodies feel during exercise. A jogger who wants to engage in moderate-intensity exercise should aim for an RPE scale rating of "somewhat hard" (12 to 14), which is of moderate intensity. If the jogger felt muscle fatigue and breathing was "very light" (9), then he or she could increase the intensity. On the other hand, if the jogger felt the exertion was "extremely hard" (19), he or she should slow down to achieve the moderate-intensity range.

Because this rating is what the exerciser perceives, the actual exertion differs among those with different levels of fitness. That is, a very fit person will have a lower RPE scale rating when jogging than a less fit person engaging in the same activity. Similarly, as a less fit person becomes more fit, his or her RPE will drop over time as the same exercise becomes easier. To continue to increase fitness levels, the exerciser would always aim to exercise at a moderate intensity.

Energy needs dictate the amount of oxygen used by the body's cells (1.5 or 2.5 ATP molecules are produced from each molecule of oxygen). Thus, another way to determine exercise intensity is to measure oxygen consumption during exercise. A treadmill test is commonly used to determine the maximum amount of oxygen a person can consume in a unit of time (ml/min). In this test, oxygen consumption is measured as the treadmill speed and/or grade is gradually increased until the subject can no longer increase oxygen use as workload increases. The oxygen consumption measured at this point is VO_{2max}. Because of individual differences in VO_{2max}, it is generally best to express exercise intensity as a percentage of VO_{2max}.

Exercise intensity also is sometimes expressed in units called metabolic equivalents (METs). One MET is the expenditure of 1 kcal/kg/hour, or on average 3.5 ml O_2/kg/minute. This approximates resting energy expenditure. A brisk walk represents about 4.5 METs of energy expenditure. Exercise prescriptions given to people recovering from a heart attack often are in MET units.[1]

Taking your pulse determines if your exercise output is in the target zone. To measure heart rate (pulse), count the number of heartbeats for 6 seconds and then multiply that number by 10 to determine heart rate per minute. There also are watches that contain heart rate monitors.

Progression

Progression describes how the duration, frequency, and intensity of exercise increase over time. The first 3 to 6 weeks of an exercise program make up the initiation phase. This phase corresponds to the time it takes for the body to adapt to the exercise program. The next 5 to 6 months of training are the improvement stage, during which intensity and duration increase to a point that no further physical gains are achieved. This plateau marks the beginning of the maintenance stage. At this stage, exercisers may want to evaluate their fitness goals. If they have achieved their goals, they can continue their fitness program in the same way to maintain their level of fitness. If they have not reached their goals, they can adjust their exercise duration, frequency, intensity, and/or mode.

Consistency

The easiest way to have consistency in physical activity is to make it part of a daily routine, similar to other regular activities, such as eating. The best time to exercise is whenever it fits best into one's lifestyle—first thing in the morning, at lunchtime, before dinner, or later. Many people find that the best time to exercise is when they need an energy pick-me-up or a break from work or studying. When schedules are tight, exercise can be done in short segments, such as breaks between classes.

Variety

Although some people enjoy doing the same activities day after day, boredom is one reason many people abandon fitness programs. Just as a variety of foods helps ensure a nutritious diet, a varied fitness routine helps exercise different muscles for overall fitness, keeps exercising interesting and fun, and helps individuals stick with their fitness programs.

VO_{2max} Maximum volume of oxygen that can be consumed per unit of time.

Variety can be achieved in a number of ways, such as exercising indoors or outdoors or alternating aerobic exercise with resistance exercise. The Physical Activity Pyramid (Fig. 11-4) shows how to add variety to fitness programs and to increase fitness levels.

Achievement and Maintenance of Fitness

Starting a new fitness program has 2 main activities. The first is to discuss the fitness program goals with a health-care provider. This is especially important for men over 40 and women over 50 years of age who have been inactive for many years or have existing health problems. The second is to assess and record baseline fitness scores—these provide benchmarks against which to measure progress. Benchmarks should be based on fitness program goals. A benchmark for a person wanting to increase muscle strength might be the amount of weight that can be lifted with the arms or the number of push-ups that can be done without stopping. The amount of time it takes to walk a mile and the heart rate after the walk may be appropriate benchmarks for individuals wanting to build stamina. Determining how far a person can bend or stretch can be a benchmark for those wanting to improve flexibility.

Most new exercise programs should start with short intervals of exercise at the lower end of the maximum heart rate target zone and work up to a total of 30 minutes of activity incorporated into each day. If necessary, exercise can be broken into 3 sessions

Figure 11-4 Each week, try to balance your physical activity using this guide.

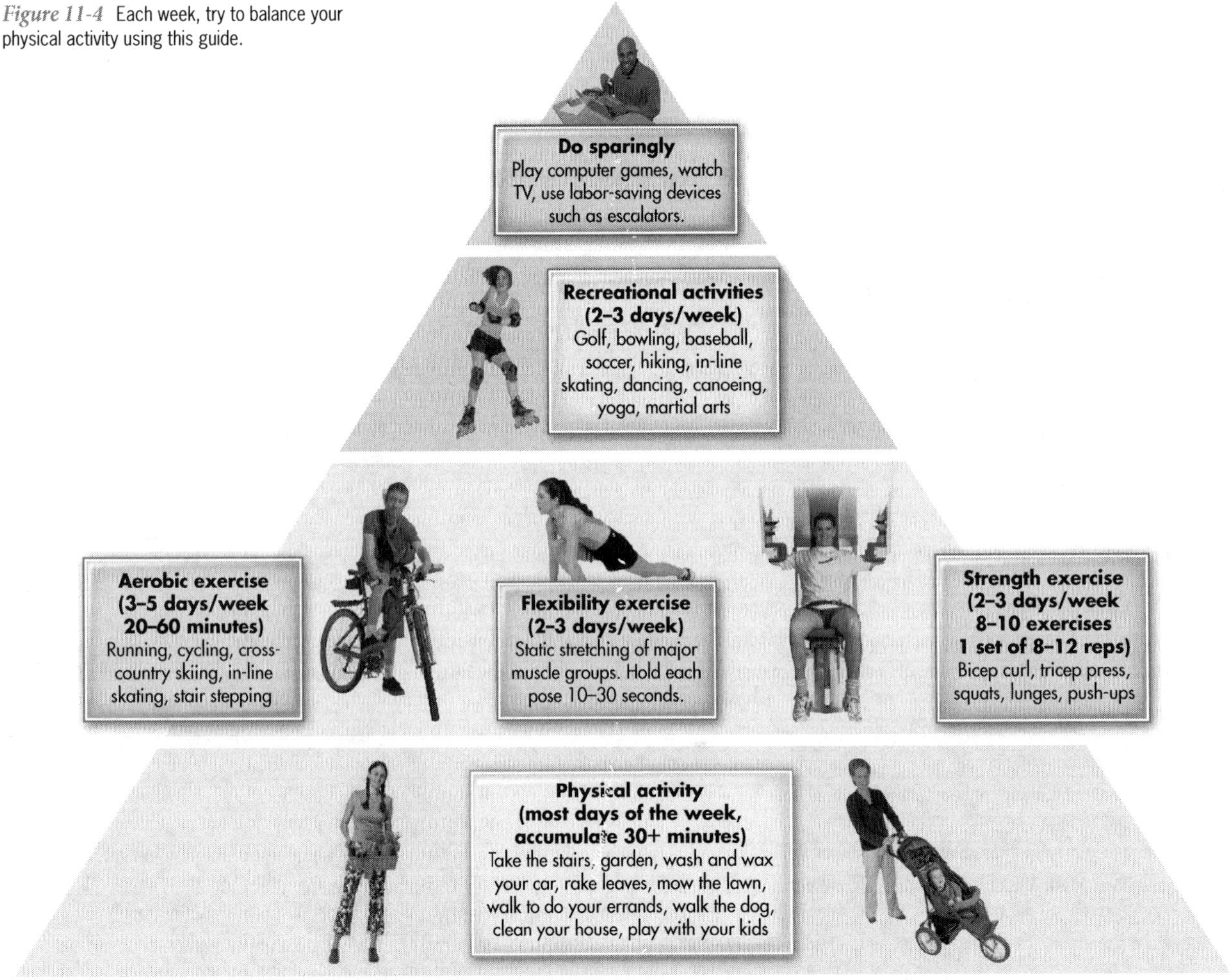

Do sparingly
Play computer games, watch TV, use labor-saving devices such as escalators.

Recreational activities (2–3 days/week)
Golf, bowling, baseball, soccer, hiking, in-line skating, dancing, canoeing, yoga, martial arts

Aerobic exercise (3–5 days/week 20–60 minutes)
Running, cycling, cross-country skiing, in-line skating, stair stepping

Flexibility exercise (2–3 days/week)
Static stretching of major muscle groups. Hold each pose 10–30 seconds.

Strength exercise (2–3 days/week 8–10 exercises 1 set of 8–12 reps)
Bicep curl, tricep press, squats, lunges, push-ups

Physical activity (most days of the week, accumulate 30+ minutes)
Take the stairs, garden, wash and wax your car, rake leaves, mow the lawn, walk to do your errands, walk the dog, clean your house, play with your kids

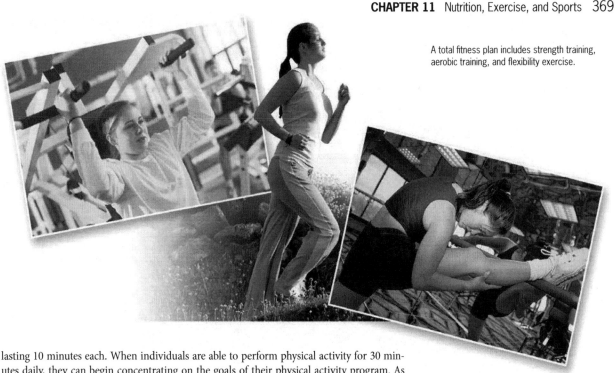

A total fitness plan includes strength training, aerobic training, and flexibility exercise.

lasting 10 minutes each. When individuals are able to perform physical activity for 30 minutes daily, they can begin concentrating on the goals of their physical activity program. As fitness progresses, exercisers can work up to a higher level of their maximum heart rate target zone.

To prepare for and recover safely from an exercise session, warm-up and cooldown periods should be included. Warm-up includes 5 to 10 minutes of low-intensity exercises, such as walking, slow jogging, or stretching, and calisthenics that warm muscles and prepare them for exercise. The warm-up should be gradual and sufficient to increase muscle and body temperature, but it should not cause fatigue or deplete energy stores. Cooldown activities help prevent injury and soreness. These activities are like those performed during the warm-up and should be done gradually to allow the body to recover slowly.

Knowledge Check

1. How do aerobic and resistance exercise differ?
2. What are the components of a comprehensive fitness program?
3. What is perceived exertion and how is it measured?
4. What is your target heart rate zone?

 11.3 Energy Sources for Muscle Use

Recall that cells cannot directly use the energy released from breaking down macronutrients. Rather, to utilize the chemical energy in foods, body cells must first convert the energy in foods to adenosine triphosphate (ATP).

ATP: Immediately Usable Energy

When the body uses energy, 1 of the phosphates in ATP is cleaved off, releasing usable energy for cell functions, including muscle contractions. The product remaining is ADP and inorganic phosphate (P_i). A resting muscle cell contains a small amount of ATP—just enough to keep the muscle working maximally for about 2 to 4 seconds.

370 **PART 3**   Metabolism and Energy Balance

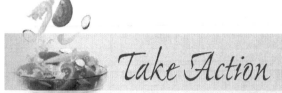

Take Action

How Physically Fit Are You?

The fitness assessments presented here are easy to do and require little equipment. Also included are charts to compare your results with those typical of your peers.

Cardiovascular Fitness: 1-Mile Walk

Measure a mile on a running track or on a little-trafficked neighborhood street. With a stopwatch or watch with a second hand, walk the mile as fast as you can. Note the time it took.

Strength: Push-Ups

Lie facedown on the floor. Get up on your toes and hands. Women can use the same position or can use knees, if necessary, instead of toes. Keep your back straight, with hands flat on the floor directly below your shoulders. Lower your body, bending your elbows, until your chin grazes the floor. Push back up until your arms are straight. Count the number of push-ups you can do (you can rest when in the up position).

Strength: Curl-Ups

Lie on the floor on your back with your knees bent, feet flat. Rest your hands on your thighs. Now, squeeze your stomach muscles, push your back flat, and raise your upper body high enough for your hands to touch the tops of your knees. Don't pull with your neck or head, and keep your lower back on the floor. Count how many curl-ups you can do in 1 minute.

Flexibility: Sit-and-Reach

Place a yardstick on the floor and apply a 2-foot piece of tape on the floor perpendicular to the yardstick, crossing at the 15-inch mark. Sit on the floor with your legs extended and the soles of your feet touching the tape at the 15-inch mark, the 0-inch mark facing you. Your feet should be about 12 inches apart. Put 1 hand on the other, exhale, and very slowly reach forward as far as you can along the yardstick, lowering your head between your arms. Don't bounce! Note the farthest inch mark you reach. Don't hurt yourself by reaching farther than your body wants to. Relax, and then repeat 2 more times.

Now, check your results. If you want to improve,

- Do aerobic exercise that makes you breathe hard for at least half an hour on almost or all days of the week.
- Lift weights that challenge you 2 or 3 times per week.
- Stretch after activity at least a couple of times per week.
- Walk more.

Cardiovascular: 1-Mile Walk (Time, in Minutes)				
	Under 40 Years		**Over 40 Years**	
	Men	**Women**	**Men**	**Women**
Excellent	13:00 or less	13:30 or less	14:00 or less	14:30 or less
Good	13:01–15:30	13:31–16:00	14:01–16:30	14:31–17:00
Average	15:31–18:00	16:01–18:30	16:31–19:00	17:01–19:30
Below average	18:01–19:30	18:31–20:00	19:01–21:30	19:31–22:00
Poor	19:31 or more	20:01 or more	21:31 or more	22:01 or more

Source: Cooper Institute.

Strength: Push-Ups (Number Completed without Rest)

	Ages 17–19		Ages 20–29		Ages 30–39		Ages 40–49		Ages 50–59		Ages 60–65	
	Men	Women	Men	Women	Men	Women	Men	Women	Men	Women	Men	Women
Excellent	>56	>35	>47	>36	>41	>37	>34	>31	>31	>25	>30	>23
Good	47–56	28–35	40–47	30–36	34–41	31–37	28–34	25–31	25–31	21–25	24–30	19–23
Above average	35–46	21–27	30–39	23–29	25–33	22–30	21–28	18–24	18–24	15–20	17–23	13–18
Average	19–34	11–20	17–29	12–22	13–24	10–21	11–20	8–17	9–17	7–14	6–16	5–12
Below average	11–18	6–10	10–16	7–11	8–12	5–9	6–10	4–7	5–8	3–6	3–5	2–4
Poor	4–10	2–5	4–9	2–6	2–7	1–4	1–5	1–3	1–4	1–2	1–2	1
Very poor	<4	<2	<4	<2	<2	0	0	0	0	0	0	0

Source: topendsports.com.

Strength: Curl-Ups (Number Completed in 60 Seconds)

	Ages 18–25		Ages 26–35		Ages 36–45		Ages 46–55		Ages 56–65		Ages 65+	
	Men	Women	Men	Women	Men	Women	Men	Women	Men	Women	Men	Women
Excellent	>49	>43	>45	>39	>41	>33	>35	>27	>31	>24	>28	>23
Good	44–49	37–43	40–45	33–39	35–41	27–33	29–35	22–27	25–31	18–24	22–28	17–23
Above average	39–43	33–36	35–39	29–32	30–34	23–26	25–28	18–21	21–24	13–17	19–21	14–16
Average	35–38	29–32	31–34	25–28	27–29	19–22	22–24	14–17	17–20	10–12	15–18	11–13
Below average	31–34	25–28	29–30	21–24	23–26	15–18	18–21	10–13	13–16	7–9	11–14	5–10
Poor	25–30	18–24	22–28	13–20	17–22	7–14	13–17	5–9	9–12	3–6	7–10	2–4
Very poor	<25	<18	<22	<13	<17	<7	<13	<5	<9	<3	<7	<2

Source: topendsports.com.

Flexibility: Sit-and-Reach (in Inches)

	Men	Women
Super	>10.5	>11.5
Excellent	6.5–10.5	8–11.5
Good	2.5–6.0	4.5–7.5
Average	0–2.0	0.5–4.0
Fair	−3–−0.5	−2.5–0
Poor	−7.5–−3.5	−6.0–−3.0
Very poor	<−7.5	<−6.0

Source: topendsports.com.

These charts are typical of those used by health and fitness experts. For a more thorough assessment of fitness or for development of an exercise plan appropriate for your fitness level, consult a certified personal trainer or another fitness professional.

Table 11-1 Energy Stored in the Human Body

Energy Source*	Major Storage	When Used	Activity
ATP	All tissues	All the time	Sprinting (0–3 sec)
Phosphocreatine (PCr)	All tissues	Short bursts	Shot put, high jump, bench press
Carbohydrate (anaerobic)	Muscles	High intensity lasting 30 seconds to 2 minutes	200-meter sprint
Carbohydrate (aerobic)	Muscles and liver	Exercise lasting 2 minutes to 3 hours or more	Jogging, soccer, basketball, swimming, gardening, car washing
Fat (aerobic)	Muscles and fat cells	Exercise lasting more than a few minutes; greater amounts are used at lower exercise intensities	Long-distance running, marathons, ultra endurance events, cycling, day-long hikes

*All energy sources operate at the same time, however the predominate source depends on the intensity and duration of the exercise.

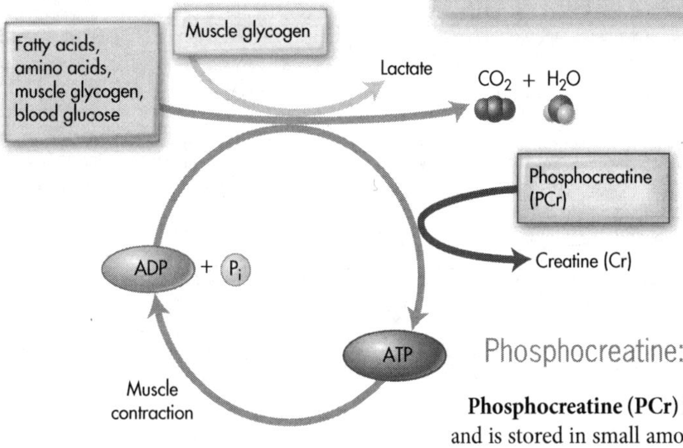

Figure 11-5 Energy sources for muscular activity. Different fuels are used for ATP synthesis. As shown, ATP also can be synthesized rapidly using phosphocreatine.

To produce more ATP for muscle contraction over extended periods, the body uses phosphocreatine. In addition, dietary carbohydrates, fats, and proteins are used as energy sources (Fig. 11-5). The breakdown of all these compounds releases energy to make more ATP (Table 11-1).

Phosphocreatine: Initial Resupply of Muscle ATP

Phosphocreatine (PCr) is a high-energy compound created from ATP and **creatine (Cr)** and is stored in small amounts in muscle cells. Creatine is an organic molecule in muscle cells that is synthesized from 3 amino acids: glycine, arginine, and methionine.[9] It also can be provided by supplements (see Table 11-11). As soon as ADP from the breakdown of ATP begins to accumulate in a contracting muscle, an enzyme is activated, transferring a high-energy P_i from PCr to ADP—this transfer re-forms ATP (Fig. 11-6).

If no other system for resupplying ATP were available, PCr could probably maintain maximal muscle contractions for about 10 seconds.[1] However, because the energy released from the metabolism of glucose and fatty acids also begins to contribute ATP and thus spares some PCr use, PCr can function as the major source of energy for events lasting up to about 1 minute.

The main advantage of PCr is that it can be activated instantly and can replenish ATP quickly enough to meet the energy demands of the fastest and most powerful sports events, such as jumping, lifting, throwing, and sprinting. The disadvantage of PCr is that too little is made and stored in muscles to sustain a high rate of ATP resupply for more than a few minutes.

Carbohydrate: Major Fuel for Short-Term, High-Intensity, and Medium-Term Exercise

As you know, glucose breaks down during glycolysis, producing a 3-carbon compound called pyruvate. Glycolysis does not require oxygen, but it yields only a small amount of ATP. If oxygen is present, pyruvate is metabolized further, yielding much more ATP.

phosphocreatine (PCr) High-energy compound that can be used to re-form ATP from ADP.

creatine (CR) Organic molecule in muscle cells that is a part of the high-energy compound creatine phosphate, or phosphocreatine.

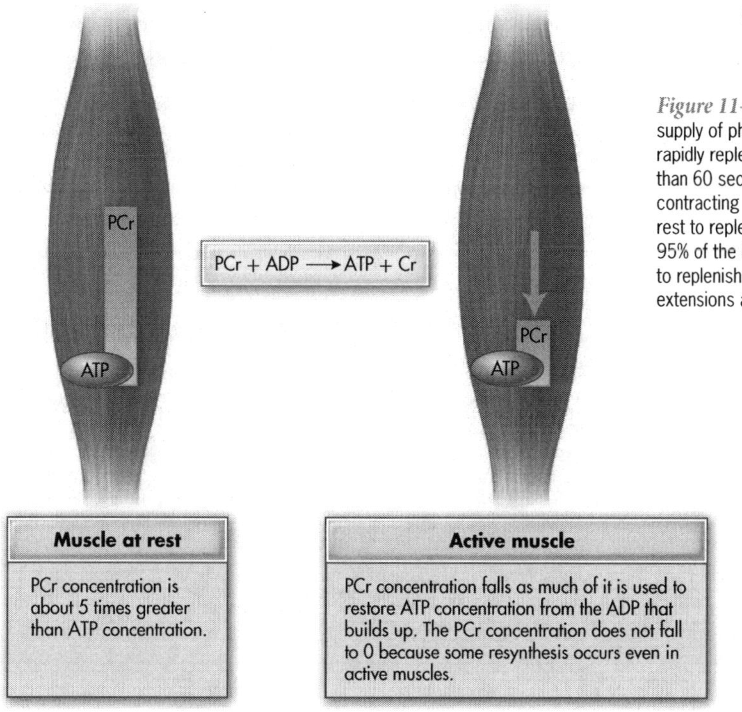

PCr

PCr + ADP ⟶ ATP + Cr

ATP

PCr

ATP

Figure 11-6 Quick energy for muscle use includes a supply of phosphocreatine (PCr). Phosphocreatine can rapidly replenish ATP stores as activity begins, but in less than 60 seconds it can become nearly depleted in maximally contracting human forearm muscles. It takes 4 minutes of rest to replenish half the PCr and 7 minutes to replenish 95% of the PCr. Similarly, it takes about 7 minutes of rest to replenish 95% of the PCr depleted with repeated knee extensions against resistance.

Bursts of muscle activity use a variety of energy sources, including PCr and ATP.

Muscle at rest	Active muscle
PCr concentration is about 5 times greater than ATP concentration.	PCr concentration falls as much of it is used to restore ATP concentration from the ADP that builds up. The PCr concentration does not fall to 0 because some resynthesis occurs even in active muscles.

Anaerobic Pathway

When the oxygen supply in muscle is limited (anaerobic state) or when the physical activity is intense (e.g., running 200 meters or swimming 100 meters), pyruvate from glycolysis accumulates in the muscle and is converted to lactate (Fig. 11-7). Because the breakdown of 1 glucose molecule to 2 pyruvates yields 2 ATP, glycolysis can resupply some ATP depleted in muscle activity.[9] Carbohydrate is the only fuel that can be used for this process.

Glycolysis provides most of the energy for physical activity from about 30 seconds to 2 minutes after it has started. The advantage of the anaerobic pathway is that, other than PCr breakdown, it is the fastest way to resupply ATP in muscle.[1] The anaerobic pathway has 2 major disadvantages:

- It cannot sustain ATP production for long.
- Only about 5% of the energy available from glucose is released during glycolysis.

The rapid accumulation of lactate from anaerobic glycolysis greatly increases the acidity of muscles. This acidity disturbs the normal cell environment and activity of key enzymes in glycolysis, which causes anaerobic ATP production to slow and fatigue to set in. The acidity also leads to a net potassium loss from muscle cells, providing another cause of fatigue.[9] By trial and error, we learn an exercise pace that controls muscle lactate concentrations from anaerobic glycolysis.

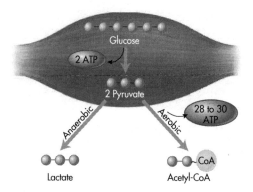

Glucose

2 ATP

2 Pyruvate

Anaerobic

Aerobic

28 to 30 ATP

Lactate

Acetyl-CoA

Figure 11-7 Both anaerobic and aerobic pathways can supply ATP. However, the aerobic pathway can supply more ATP but does it at a slower rate, whereas the anaerobic pathway supplies less ATP at a more rapid rate.

▶ For many years, both scientists and athletes believed that the accumulation of lactate in exercising muscles caused muscle fatigue and soreness. Today, there is little evidence to show that lactate alone causes fatigue and soreness. Depletion of muscle glycogen and blood glucose along with the accumulation of other metabolic by-products in the muscle can contribute to muscle fatigue and soreness.

During anaerobic glycolysis, the lactate that is produced accumulates in the muscles and is eventually released into the bloodstream. The heart can use lactate directly for its energy needs, as can less active muscle cells situated near active ones. The liver (and to some extent the kidneys) takes up some of the lactate from the blood and resynthesizes it into glucose, using an energy-requiring process. This glucose then can reenter the bloodstream and be used by cells for energy.

Aerobic Pathway

If plenty of oxygen is available in muscle tissue (aerobic state) and physical activity is moderate to low intensity (e.g., jogging or distance swimming), most of the pyruvate produced by glycolysis in the cell cytoplasm is shuttled to the mitochondria and metabolized into carbon dioxide and water by a series of oxygen-requiring reactions (see Chapter 9). About 95% of the ATP produced from the complete metabolism of glucose is formed aerobically in the mitochondria (Fig. 11-8).

The aerobic pathway supplies ATP more slowly than the anaerobic pathway, but it releases much more energy. Also, ATP production via the aerobic pathway can be sustained for hours. As a result, this pathway of glucose metabolism makes an important energy contribution to physical activity lasting from about 2 minutes to 3 hours or more (Fig. 11-9).[1]

▶ When acids lose a hydrogen ion, as typically happens at the pH level of the body, they are given the ending -ate. Thus, pyruvic acid is called pyruvate and lactic acid is called lactate when in the context of body metabolism.

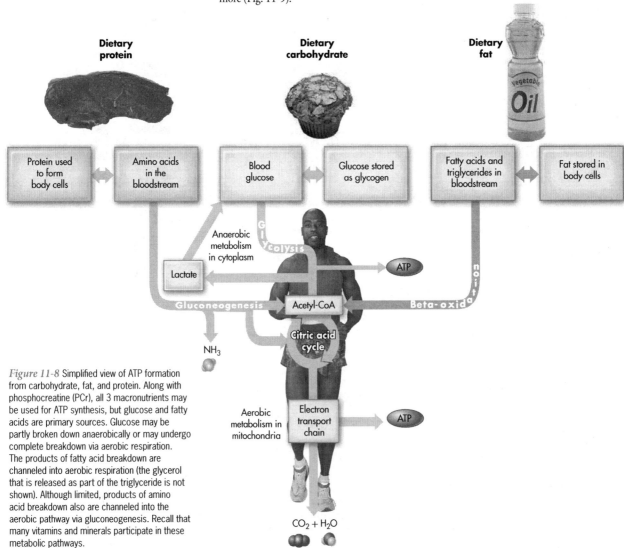

Figure 11-8 Simplified view of ATP formation from carbohydrate, fat, and protein. Along with phosphocreatine (PCr), all 3 macronutrients may be used for ATP synthesis, but glucose and fatty acids are primary sources. Glucose may be partly broken down anaerobically or may undergo complete breakdown via aerobic respiration. The products of fatty acid breakdown are channeled into aerobic respiration (the glycerol that is released as part of the triglyceride is not shown). Although limited, products of amino acid breakdown also are channeled into the aerobic pathway via gluconeogenesis. Recall that many vitamins and minerals participate in these metabolic pathways.

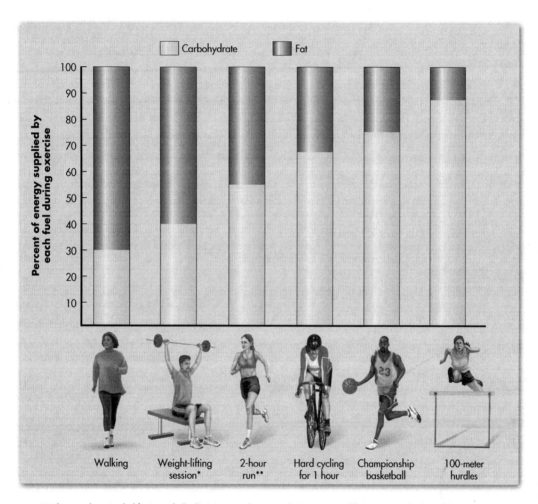

Figure 11-9
Rough estimates of carbohydrate and fat use during various forms of exercise.

*With regard to weight lifting, carbohydrate use can be somewhat greater and fat use somewhat less if the session is intense and fast-paced (e.g., circuit training). Fat use generally is higher because much of the time spent weight lifting is for rest periods.

**With regard to endurance running, the balance of fat and carbohydrate used will vary somewhat depending on whether the athlete is consuming carbohydrate during the run. The values shown are for a runner consuming carbohydrate during the run; more fat and less carbohydrate would be used if carbohydrates were not consumed.

Muscle Glycogen versus Blood Glucose as Muscle Fuel

Recall that glycogen is the temporary storage form of glucose in the liver (about 100 g) and muscles (about 350 g in sedentary people). Glycogen is broken down to glucose, which can be metabolized by both the anaerobic and aerobic pathways. Liver glycogen is used to maintain blood glucose levels, whereas muscle glycogen supplies the glucose to the working muscle. Glycogen is, in fact, the primary source of glucose for ATP production in muscle cells during fairly intense activities that last for less than about 2 hours.

In short events (e.g., less than 30 minutes or so), muscles rely primarily on muscle glycogen stores for carbohydrate fuel. Muscles do not take up much blood glucose during short-term exercise because the action of insulin, which increases glucose uptake by muscles, is blunted by other hormones, such as epinephrine and glucagon, that increase initially during exercise.[1] As exercise time increases, muscle glycogen stores decline and the muscles begin to take up blood glucose to use as an energy source. The depletion of glycogen in the muscles contributes to fatigue, whereas the depletion of glycogen in the liver leads to a fall in blood glucose.[9]

Once glycogen stores are exhausted, a person can continue working at only about 50% of maximal capacity. Athletes call this point of glycogen depletion "hitting the wall," because further exertion is hampered. Thus, for exercise that requires 70% or more of maximal effort for more than an hour or so, athletes (e.g., long-distance runners or cyclists) should consider increasing the amount of carbohydrate stored in their muscles. Diets high in carbohydrate can be used to increase muscle glycogen stores—up to double the typical amounts—in advance of competition, thereby delaying the onset of fatigue and improving endurance. This process is called carbohydrate or glycogen loading (see Section 11.5).

The maintenance of blood glucose becomes an increasingly important consideration as exercise duration increases beyond about 20 to 30 minutes. By maintaining blood glucose levels, the body saves muscle glycogen for muscle use during sudden bursts of effort, such as a sprint to the finish in a marathon race. Without the maintenance of blood glucose, irritability, sweating, anxiety, weakness, headache, and confusion may occur (cyclists call this "bonking"). A carbohydrate intake of 0.7 g/kg/hour (about 30–60 g/hour) during strenuous endurance exercise, such as cycling, that lasts about 1 hour or more, can help maintain adequate blood glucose concentrations, which in turn results in delay of fatigue (see Section 11.5).[10]

Fat: Main Fuel for Prolonged, Low-Intensity Exercise

Fat is the predominant fuel source when at rest and during prolonged exercise, especially when exercise remains at a low or moderate (aerobic) rate (Fig. 11-10). In fact, during very lengthy activities, such as a triathlon, an ultra-marathon, occupations requiring manual labor, or even work at a desk for 8 hours a day, fat supplies about 50 to 90% of the energy required.[1]

The rate at which muscles use fatty acids is affected by training level. The more trained a muscle, the greater its ability to use fat as a fuel. Training increases the size and number of mitochondria and the levels of enzymes involved with the aerobic synthesis of ATP. Training also increases muscle myoglobin, which enhances oxygen availability in muscles, which is needed to metabolize fat (Table 11-2). Overall, training allows an athlete to use fat for fuel more readily, thereby conserving glycogen for when it is really needed—such as for a burst of speed at the end of a race.

As you know, most of the energy stored in the body is in fat, stored as triglycerides. Most of this energy resides in adipose tissue, although some is stored in the muscle itself. That stored in muscles is especially used as activity increases from a low to a moderate pace.

The advantage of fat over other energy sources is that it provides more than twice as much energy (9 kcal/g) and thus can provide more ATP. In addition, there is plenty of fat stored in the body, compared with the very limited carbohydrate stores. However,

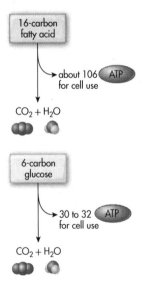

The energy to perform comes from carbohydrate, fat, and protein. The relative mix of fuels depends on the pace and duration of exercise.

ATP Yield from Aerobic Fatty Acid Metabolism and Aerobic Glucose Metabolism

16-carbon fatty acid → about 106 ATP for cell use

$CO_2 + H_2O$

6-carbon glucose → 30 to 32 ATP for cell use

$CO_2 + H_2O$

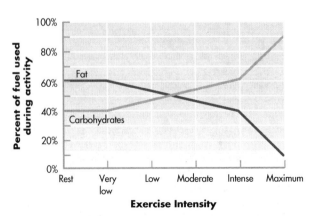

Figure 11-10 As the intensity of exercise increases, the exercising muscles tend to rely more on carbohydrates and less on fat. At lower intensities of exercise, fat is the predominant fuel.

carbohydrate metabolism is more efficient than fat because it produces more ATP per unit of oxygen and it is the only fuel source that can support intense (anaerobic) activity. Fat utilization simply cannot occur fast enough to meet the ATP demands of short-duration, high-intensity physical activity—if fat were the only available fuel, we would be unable to carry out physical activity more intense than a fast walk or jog.[1]

Protein: A Minor Fuel Source during Exercise

Most of the energy supplied from protein comes from metabolism of the branched-chain amino acids—leucine, isoleucine, and valine. These amino acids can be used to make glucose, or they can enter the citric acid cycle as precursors to glucose and provide energy during exercise.

Although amino acids derived from protein can fuel muscles, their contribution is relatively small, compared with that of carbohydrate and fat. As a rough guide, only about 5% of the body's general energy needs, as well as the typical energy needs of exercising muscles, is supplied by amino acid metabolism.[9] However, proteins can contribute to energy needs in endurance exercise, perhaps as much as 15%, especially as glycogen stores in the muscle are exhausted.[9] Endurance exercise is when protein is most likely to make its most significant contribution as a fuel source—but, even then, it provides limited energy, with estimates ranging from 3 to 15%.[9, 11] In contrast, protein is used least in resistance exercise (e.g., weight lifting).

Despite the fact that the primary muscle fuels for weight lifting are phosphocreatine (PCr) and carbohydrate, high-protein supplements are marketed to weight lifters and bodybuilders and sold in nearly every health-food and fitness store. Consuming more protein than the body needs or can use will not lead to greater muscle mass. Eating high-carbohydrate, moderate-protein foods immediately after a weight-training workout can enhance the anabolic effect of the activity. This most likely increases blood concentrations of insulin and growth hormone and contributes to protein synthesis.[1] Remember, it is impossible to increase muscle mass simply by eating protein; putting physical strain on muscle through strength training or other physical activity is needed, as is adequate protein intake to support growth and recovery.

Table 11-2 Adaptations to Endurance Exercise Training in Skeletal Muscle

Change	Advantage
Increased ability of muscle to store glycogen (high-carbohydrate diet increases this even further)	More glycogen fuel available for the final minutes of an event
Increased triglyceride storage in muscle	Conserves glycogen by allowing for increased fat use
Increased mitochondrial size and number	Conserves glycogen by allowing for increased fat use (even at high exercise outputs)
Increased myoglobin content	Increased oxygen delivery to muscles and increased ability to use fat for fuel
Increased cardiac output	Increased blood flow to promote adequate delivery of oxygen and nutrients to muscles

CASE STUDY

Jake, a college junior, is currently 6 feet tall and weighs 175 pounds. He has been lifting weights since he was a college freshman. Although he has gotten significantly stronger over the last 2 years, he decided he wants to have more muscle definition. He read (mainly on the Internet) a lot about nutrition and resistance training, especially about the role of protein and muscle growth, and decided to take a protein supplement to get bigger muscles and more definition. He has been taking the supplement for about 3 weeks. It consists of a whey protein powder, which he mixes with either water or milk. It contains about 60 grams of protein per serving and he has 2 protein drinks per day.

His breakfasts consist of a protein shake and for lunch he has a sandwich with extra meat and a small salad with fat-free dressing. He consumes another shake around 4 P.M. and isn't hungry again until about 7 P.M. Yesterday for dinner, he ate 2 chicken breasts with ½ cup of rice, a small salad with fat-free dressing, and an iced tea.

Unfortunately, this past week he noticed that during his lifting he was tired and could not lift as much weight as the week before. Today while lifting, he started to feel fatigued 20 minutes into the training session. He is not sure why he can't finish his workout and thinks maybe he should eat more protein.

What role does protein have in resistance exercise? What is causing him to be so fatigued that he cannot finish his workout? Should he consume more protein?

378   **PART 3**   Metabolism and Energy Balance

Table 11-3 Fuel Use* Estimate Based on Percent VO$_{2max}$

VO$_{2max}$	Muscle Glycogen	Muscle Triglyceride	Blood Glucose	Free Fatty Acids in the Bloodstream
Low intensity (e.g., fast walk)— 30 to 50% of VO$_{2max}$	5%	20%	5%	70%
Moderate intensity (e.g., fast jog)— 50 to 65% of VO$_{2max}$	30%	30%	10%	30%
High intensity (e.g., 3-hour marathon pace)— 70 to 80% of VO$_{2max}$	55%	15%	15%	15%
Very high intensity (e.g., sprints)— 85 to 150% of VO$_{2max}$	70%	10%	10%	10%

*The total amount of energy is approximate and may vary considerably between individuals.

Fuel Use and VO$_{2max}$

As you can see in Table 11-3, fuel sources for muscle cells can be estimated based on percent of VO$_{2max}$. For example, fat use drops as exercise intensity increases. Carbohydrate use then becomes more important for meeting energy needs. In very-high-intensity activities, the ATP equivalent to the "extra" 50% above 100% of VO$_{2max}$ is produced anaerobically from PCr and glycolysis.

Knowledge Check

1. What is the main form of energy that cells use?
2. What fuels anaerobic exercise?
3. What fuels aerobic exercise?
4. Why is creatine so important for fueling high-intensity, short-duration exercise?
5. How does fitness level affect the fuels burned for exercise?
6. When is protein used as a fuel source during exercise?

11.4 The Body's Response to Physical Activity

Physical activity has many effects on the body. The most pronounced effects are typically seen in the muscular, circulatory, and skeletal systems.

Specialized Functions of Skeletal Muscle Fiber Types

The body contains 3 major types of muscle tissue: skeletal muscle (the type involved in locomotion); smooth muscle (the type found in internal organs, except the heart); and cardiac (heart) muscle. Skeletal muscle is composed of 3 main types of **muscle fibers,** which have distinct characteristics (Table 11-4).[9]

- *Type I (slow-twitch—oxidative).* These muscle fibers contract slowly and have a high capacity for oxidative metabolism. They also are called red fibers because of their high myoglobin content. Type I fibers are fueled by the aerobic respiration of fat.
- *Type IIA (fast-twitch—oxidative, glycolytic).* These muscle fibers have moderate oxidative capacity and are fueled by glycolysis using glucose (anaerobic) plus the aerobic respiration of both fat and glucose.
- *Type IIX (fast-twitch—glycolytic).* These muscle fibers have less oxidative capacity than other muscle fibers. They also are called white fibers (in rodents, type IIX fibers are called type IIB) because they have less mitochondria and myoglobin than other fibers. Type IIX fibers are fueled by glycolysis using glucose (anaerobic).

Prolonged low-intensity exercise, such as a slow jog, mainly uses type I muscle fibers, so the predominant fuel is fat. As exercise intensity increases, type IIA and type IIX fibers are gradually recruited; in turn, the contribution of glucose as a fuel increases. Type IIA and type IIX fibers also are important for rapid movements, such as a jump shot in basketball.

The relative proportions of the 3 fiber types throughout the muscles of the body vary from person to person and are constant throughout each person's life. The individual differences in fiber-type distribution are partially responsible for producing elite marathon runners who could never compete at the same level as sprinters, or elite gymnasts who could never be competitive as long-distance swimmers. Although the proportion of muscle fiber types is largely determined by genetics, appropriate training can develop muscles within limits. For example, aerobic training enhances the capacity of type IIA muscle fibers to produce ATP and may bring about a relative change in size. Overall, great athletes are born, but their genetic potential must be nurtured by training.[9]

Adaptation of Muscles and Body Physiology to Exercise

With training, muscle strength becomes matched to the muscles' work demands. Muscles enlarge after being made to work repeatedly, a response called **hypertrophy.** Certain cells in the muscles gain bulk and improve their ability to work. Conversely, after several days without

Relative Distribution of Muscle Fiber Types

Activity Level	Type I	Type IIA + Type IIX
Nonathlete	45–50%	50–55%
Sprinter	20–35%	65–85%
Marathoner	80%	20%

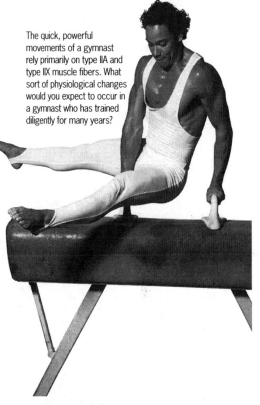

The quick, powerful movements of a gymnast rely primarily on type IIA and type IIX muscle fibers. What sort of physiological changes would you expect to occur in a gymnast who has trained diligently for many years?

muscle fiber Essentially, a single muscle cell; an elongated cell, with contractile properties, that forms the muscles of the body.

Table 11-4 Muscle Fiber Summary

Muscle Fiber	Description	Structure	Primary Fuel Source	Activities When Used
Type I	Slow-twitch; high oxidative metabolism capacity	High density of capillaries, mitochondria, myoglobin	Aerobic respiration of fat	Aerobic activity, such as endurance exercise
Type IIA	Fast-twitch; moderate oxidative metabolism capacity	Rich in capillaries and mitochondria	Anaerobic glycolysis; aerobic respiration of fat and glucose	Aerobic/anaerobic activities, such as middle-distance running, swimming
Type IIX	Fast-twitch; lower oxidative metabolism capacity	Less dense in mitochondria and myoglobin	Anaerobic glycolysis	Anaerobic activity, such as sprinting

Person	Typical VO_{2max} (ml O_2/kg/min)
Sedentary elderly adult	<20
Typical middle-aged adult	35–45
Elite athlete	65–75

activity, muscles diminish in size and lose strength, a response called **atrophy.** Both hypertrophy and atrophy are forms of adaptation to the workload applied. Thus, many marathon runners have well-developed leg muscles but little arm or chest muscle development.

Repeated aerobic exercise produces beneficial changes in the circulatory system. Because the body needs more oxygen during exercise, it responds to training by producing more red blood cells and expanding total blood volume. Training also leads to an increase in the number of capillaries in muscle tissue; as a result, oxygen can be delivered more easily to muscle cells. Finally, training causes the heart, a muscle itself, to strengthen. Then, each contraction empties the heart's chamber more efficiently, so more blood is pumped with each beat. As exercise increases the heart's efficiency, its rate of beating at rest and during submaximal exercise decreases.[1]

The more physically fit a person is, the more work the muscles and body can do and the more oxygen the person can consume. Typical VO_{2max} values range from 20 to 65 ml O_2/kg/min, depending on age, gender, and fitness level. Most people can improve their VO_{2max} by 15 to 20% or more with training.[9]

Another adaptation that occurs with exercise is increased bone density. By placing a mechanical stress on bone, exercise stimulates bone development by promoting the deposition of calcium in bones. Weight-bearing exercise, such as running, gymnastics, basketball, soccer, walking, and volleyball, is essential for the normal development and maintenance of a healthy skeleton.

> *Knowledge Check*
>
> 1. How do the functions of the muscle fiber types differ?
> 2. What is the predominant fuel used by each muscle fiber type?
> 3. How does repeated exercise affect the circulatory system?

  ## 11.5 Power Food: Dietary Advice for Athletes

Athletic training and genetic makeup are very important determinants of athletic performance. A good diet won't substitute for either factor, but making wise food choices will allow an athlete to maximize his or her athletic potential. On the other hand, poor food choices can seriously reduce performance.

Energy Needs

Athletes need varying amounts of food energy, depending on their body size, their body composition, and the type of training or competition. A petite gymnast may need only 1800 kcal/day to sustain normal daily activities without losing body weight; a tall, muscular swimmer may need 4000 kcal/day. If an athlete experiences daily fatigue and/or weight loss, the first consideration should be whether that person is consuming enough food. Up to 6 meals per day may be needed, including 1 before each workout.

Monitoring body weight is an easy way to assess the adequacy of calorie intake. Athletes should strive to maintain weight during competition and training. Generally, if athletes are losing weight, then energy intake is inadequate; however, if athletes are gaining weight, then energy intake is too high. If an athlete needs to lose weight, his or her food intake should be lowered by 200 to 500 kcal per day. This slight reduction will allow the athlete to continue to train and compete yet will create a calorie deficit, so that weight loss can be achieved. Reducing fat intake is the best way to cut calories and not affect performance. On the other hand, if an athlete needs to gain weight, increasing food intake by 500 to 700 kcal/day will eventually achieve that goal. The extra calories should come from a healthy balance of carbohydrate, protein, and fat; exercise needs to be maintained to make sure this gain is mostly in the form of lean muscle mass.

 ► Review Table 10-5 in Chapter 10, which lists the energy costs of typical forms of physical activity.

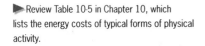 Athletes often expend much energy. An increase in food and beverage intake can easily provide ample carbohydrate, protein, and other nutrients to support activity.

Some athletes compete in sports that require them to maintain a lean profile, whereas others must maintain a certain weight. Gymnasts, swimmers, figure skaters, and dancers are required to maintain a lean profile, whereas wrestlers, boxers, jockeys, judoists, and rowers are often weighed before matches to verify that they meet weight restrictions. Athletes in sports such as these tend to eat and drink less than needed to support training and competition needs—this puts them at risk of eating disorders and the effects of poor nutritional status, including osteoporosis, menstrual dysfunction, kidney failure, heat-related illness, dehydration, and even death.

Carbohydrate Needs

Carbohydrates are the primary energy source for exercising muscles. Anyone who exercises vigorously, especially for more than an hour per day on a regular basis, needs to consume moderate to high amounts of carbohydrates. Numerous servings of whole grains, starchy vegetables, and fruits provide enough carbohydrate to maintain adequate liver and muscle glycogen stores, especially when replacing glycogen losses from workouts on the previous day. Table 11-5 shows some nutritious, carbohydrate-rich foods.

To prevent deaths from unsafe weight-loss practices in wrestlers, the National Collegiate Athletic Association and many states now establish a weight class at the beginning of the season to eliminate the severe weight-loss practices that often happen at the end of the season. Each school must have a physician or an athletic trainer conduct an initial weight assessment during the first week of October using body weight, body composition (body fat), and specific gravity of urine (to determine level of hydration at time of weighing). Minimum wrestling weight is set at the athlete's lean body weight plus 5% body fat. Each wrestler has the option of modifying his weight over an 8-week period under the following guidelines: no more than 1.5% of body weight can be lost per week, and the final weight cannot fall below the calculated minimum wrestling weight. A national certification period is held the first week of December. At that time, the process is repeated and a weight class is set that remains in place for the rest of the wrestling season.

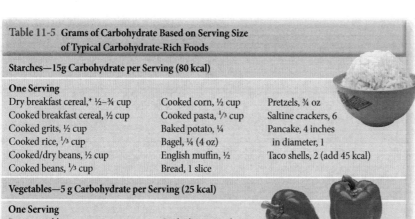

Table 11-5 Grams of Carbohydrate Based on Serving Size of Typical Carbohydrate-Rich Foods

Starches—15g Carbohydrate per Serving (80 kcal)

One Serving

Dry breakfast cereal,* ½–¾ cup	Cooked corn, ½ cup	Pretzels, ¾ oz
Cooked breakfast cereal, ½ cup	Cooked pasta, ⅓ cup	Saltine crackers, 6
Cooked grits, ½ cup	Baked potato, ¼	Pancake, 4 inches
Cooked rice, ⅓ cup	Bagel, ¼ (4 oz)	in diameter, 1
Cooked/dry beans, ½ cup	English muffin, ½	Taco shells, 2 (add 45 kcal)
Cooked beans, ⅓ cup	Bread, 1 slice	

Vegetables—5 g Carbohydrate per Serving (25 kcal)

One Serving

Raw vegetables, 1 cup	Cooked or canned
Vegetable juice, ½ cup	vegetables, ½ cup

Fruits—15 g Carbohydrate per Serving (60 kcal)

One Serving

Canned fruit, ½ cup	Apricots (dried), 8	Grapes, 17
Fruit juice, ½ cup	Grapefruit, ½	Dates, 3
Watermelon cubes, 1¼ cups	Banana, 1 small	Peach, 1
Apple or orange, 1 small	Figs (dried), 1½	

Milk—12 g Carbohydrate per Serving

One Serving

Milk, 1 cup	Soy milk, 1 cup
Plain low-fat yogurt, ⅔ cup	

Sweets—15 g Carbohydrate per Serving (variable kcal)

One Serving

Cake, 2-inch square	Ice cream, ½ cup
Cookies, 2 small	Sherbet, ½ cup

*The carbohydrate content of dry cereal varies widely. Check the labels of those you choose and adjust the serving size accordingly.

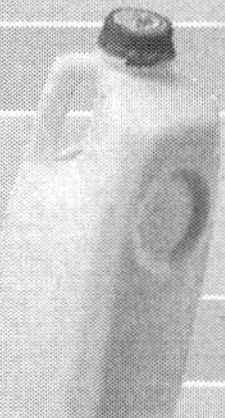

382   **PART 3** Metabolism and Energy Balance

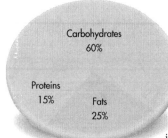

Figure 11-11 Recommended nutrient intakes for athletes.

Carbohydrate intake for nonathletes should range from 5 to 7 g/kg of body weight, whereas athletes engaged in aerobic training and endurance activities (duration 60 minutes or more per day) may need as much as 7 to 9 g/kg of body weight. When exercise duration approaches several hours per day, the carbohydrate recommendation increases up to 10 g/kg of body weight.[12] In other words, triathletes and marathon runners should consider eating close to 500 to 600 grams of carbohydrates daily. Even more may be necessary to prevent chronic fatigue and to load the muscles and liver with glycogen. Attention to carbohydrate intake is especially important when performing multiple training bouts in a day, such as swim practices or track and field events, as well as tournament play, such as volleyball, basketball, or soccer. The depletion of carbohydrate ranks just behind the depletion of fluid and electrolytes as a major cause of fatigue.

Athletes should obtain 55 to 60% of total energy needs from carbohydrates, rather than the 50% typical of most North American diets, especially if exercise duration is expected to exceed 2 hours and total energy intake is about 3000 kcal per day or less (Fig. 11-11). Diets providing 4000 to 5000 kcal/day can have as little as 50% of energy content

Table 11-6 Sample Daily Menus, Based on MyPlate, That Provide Various Total Energy Intakes

1800 kcal	3000 kcal	4000 kcal	5000 kcal
Breakfast	**Breakfast**	**Breakfast**	**Breakfast**
1 cup fat-free milk	1 cup fat-free milk	3 slices French toast	4 slices whole-wheat toast
1 cup Cheerios*	2 cups Cheerios*	2 tbsp syrup	2 tsp margarine
½ whole-wheat bagel	1 whole-wheat bagel	1 tsp margarine	2 poached eggs
1 tsp margarine	1 tsp margarine	1 banana	1 cup low-fat yogurt
	½ cup grapes	1 cup low-fat yogurt	½ cup granola
	1 large muffin		
Lunch	**Lunch**	**Lunch**	**Lunch**
2 oz sliced turkey breast	3 oz sliced turkey breast	4 medium beef and bean	3 chicken enchiladas
2 slices whole-wheat bread	2 slices whole-wheat bread	tacos topped with lettuce	1 oz shredded cheese
1 tsp mayonnaise	1 oz cheese	and shredded cheese	1 cup romaine lettuce with 1 cup
½ cup carrots	1 tsp mayonnaise	1 cup Spanish rice	carrots, celery, and green peppers
1 medium banana	1 banana	1 cup romaine lettuce	2 tbsp salad dressing
1 cup apple juice	½ cup carrots	2 tbsp salad dressing	1 banana
	1 cup yogurt	1½ cups orange juice	1 cup apple juice
	1 cup apple juice		1 fresh orange
			2 oz peanuts
Snack	**Snack**	**Snack**	**Snack**
1 granola bar	1 granola bar	2 slices whole-wheat bread	2 whole-grain bagels
1 cup low-fat yogurt	1 cup applesauce	4 tbsp peanut butter	3 tbsp almond butter
			1 cup grapes
Dinner	**Dinner**	**Dinner**	**Dinner**
3 oz roast beef	1 cup spaghetti with meat sauce	4 oz turkey breast	5 oz grilled salmon (or other fish)
1 medium baked potato	1½ cups pasta	2 cups mashed potatoes	2 cups rice pilaf
1 tsp margarine	1 tbsp Parmesan cheese	½ cup corn	1 cup asparagus
1 cup romaine lettuce	1 cup romaine lettuce	1 roll	1 cup green beans
2 tsp salad dressing	2 tsp salad dressing	1 tsp margarine	2 tsp margarine
1 cup green beans	1 cup green beans	1 cup vanilla pudding	1 cup low-fat yogurt topped with
1 cup fat-free milk	½ cup fat-free milk	½ cup sliced fruit	½ cup melon and ½ cup granola
		1 cup fat-free milk	1½ cups fat-free milk
Nutrient Contribution	**Nutrient Contribution**	**Nutrient Contribution**	**Nutrient Contribution**
57% carbohydrate	64% carbohydrate	50% carbohydrate	48% carbohydrate
20% protein	16% protein	17% protein	18% protein
25% fat	21% fat	33% fat	34% fat

coming from carbohydrate and still provide sufficient carbohydrate (e.g., 500 to 600 g or so per day).[12] Table 11-6 shows sample menus for diets providing food energy ranging from 1800 to 5000 kcal/day. In addition, the Exchange System (see Appendix E) is a useful tool for planning all types of diets, including high-carbohydrate diets for athletes.

Boosting Glycogen Stores

The first source of glucose for the exercising muscle is its own glycogen store. During endurance exercise that exceeds 90 minutes, such as marathon running, muscle glycogen stores progressively decline. When they drop to critically low levels, high-intensity exercise cannot be maintained. In practical terms, the athlete is exhausted and must either stop exercising or drastically reduce the pace.

Glycogen depletion also may be a gradual process, occurring over repeated days of heavy training in which muscle glycogen breakdown exceeds its replacement, as well as during high-intensity exercise that is repeated several times during competition or training. For example, a distance runner who averages 10 miles per day, but does not take the time to consume enough carbohydrates, or a swimmer who completes several interval sets at above maximal oxygen consumption can deplete his or her glycogen stores rapidly.

Because carbohydrates are such an important fuel for exercise and the body has limited capacity to store them, researchers have investigated ways to maximize the body's ability to store carbohydrates. The regimen of getting the body to store more glycogen than typical is called **carbohydrate loading,** or **glycogen loading.** It involves altering both exercise and diet. There are a number of carbohydrate-loading strategies. The classic method of carbohydrate loading depleted muscle glycogen stores with 3 days of heavy training and a very-low-carbohydrate diet. This was followed by 3 days of high carbohydrate intake and rest to promote muscle glycogen synthesis. This classic method often left athletes exhausted and prone to injuries during the first 3 days. A modified method tapers off training intensity and duration on consecutive days after a bout of glycogen-depleting exercise 6 days before competition. During the first 3 days of tapering, the athlete consumes a normal mixed diet, followed by a high-carbohydrate diet 3 days before competition.

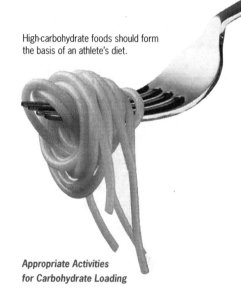

High-carbohydrate foods should form the basis of an athlete's diet.

***Appropriate Activities
for Carbohydrate Loading***

Marathons

Long-distance swimming

Cross-country skiing

30-kilometer runs

Triathlons

Tournament-play basketball

Soccer

Cycling time trials

Long-distance canoe racing

***Inappropriate Activities
for Carbohydrate Loading***

American football

10-kilometer or shorter runs

Walking and hiking

Most swimming events

Single basketball games

Weight lifting

Most track and field events

Carbohydrate-Loading Regimen						
Days before Competition	6	5	4	3	2	1
Exercise Time (Minutes)	60	40	40	20	20	Rest
Carbohydrate Intake (g/kg Body Weight)	5	5	5	10	10	10

The classic and modified carbohydrate-loading regimens usually increase muscle glycogen stores 50 to 85% over typical conditions, when dietary carbohydrate intake is only about 50% of total intake. However, the process is relatively slow. It takes from 2 to 6 days to fully load the muscles with glycogen. These regimens pose problems for athletes who compete on back-to-back days or who do not want to alter their training before a competition. Other carbohydrate-loading strategies, some as short as 1 day in duration, can help athletes increase muscle glycogen levels above typical levels.[13]

Carbohydrate loading is for athletes who compete in continuous, intense aerobic events lasting more than 60 minutes or in shorter events with repeated bouts of exercise occurring more than once in a 24-hour period. Above normal glycogen stores do not allow an athlete to work harder during shorter exercise periods, such as 5 and 10 km races, and may harm performance because of muscle stiffness and heaviness. With each gram of glycogen stored in the muscle, 3 to 4 grams of water also are stored. Although this water aids in maintaining hydration, this additional water weight may make the muscles feel stiff and therefore make carbohydrate loading inappropriate. Athletes who want to try carbohydrate loading should do so during training, and long before an important competition, to experience its effects on performance.

carbohydrate (glycogen) loading Exercise and eating regimen that increases the amount of glycogen stored in muscle to levels higher than normal.

Table 11-7 Current Recommendations for Protein Intake Based on Body Weight (kg)*		
Group	g/kg	Amount for a 70 kg Person (g)
RDA for adults	0.8	56
Strength-trained athletes, muscle mass maintenance phase	1.0–1.2	70–84
Strength-trained athletes, muscle mass gain phase	1.5–1.7	105–119
Moderate-intensity endurance athletes	1.2–1.4	84–98
High-intensity endurance athletes	1.7	112

*Calculate kilograms by dividing pounds by 2.2.
Adapted from Burke L, Deakin V. *Clinical sports nutrition*. Roseville NSW2069, Australia: McGraw-Hill; 2010; and Rodriguez NR and others. Position of the American Dietetic Association, Dietitians of Canada, and the American College of Sports Medicine: Nutrition and athletic performance. *J Am Diet Assoc.* 2009;109:509.

Fat Needs

A fat intake of 15 to 25% of energy is generally recommended for athletes. Rich sources of unsaturated fat, such as canola, soybean, and olive oils, should be emphasized, and saturated fat and *trans* fat intake should be limited.[12]

Protein Needs

Typical recommendations for protein intake for most athletes range from 1.2 to 1.7 g of protein/kg of body weight, which is considerably higher than the RDA of 0.8 g/kg of body weight for adults. As you can see in Table 11-7, recommended protein intake is at the lower end of the range for strength-training maintenance and moderate-intensity endurance activities. The highest recommendations are for high-intensity endurance training and during the muscle mass gain phase of strength training.

Energy needs are not the reason for the higher protein recommendations for athletes (recall that protein is not a major fuel for exercise). The extra protein is needed for the repair of tissue and the synthesis of the new muscle that results from training. The high level set for muscle mass gain during strength training, theoretically, is required for the synthesis of new muscle tissue brought on by the loading effect of this training. Once the desired muscle mass is achieved, protein intake need not exceed 1.2 g/kg of body weight.

Weight-restricted athletes who feel they must significantly limit their energy intake and athletes who are vegetarians should be sure to consume at least 1.2 g of protein per kg of body weight each day, the upper recommendation for most athletes.

Take Action

Meeting the Protein Needs of an Athlete—A Case Study

Mark is a college student who has been lifting weights at the student recreation center. Mark's weight has been stable at 154 lb (70 kg). An analysis of the total energy and protein content of Mark's current diet is 3470 kcal, 125 g of protein (14% of total energy intake supplied by protein). This diet is representative of the food choices and amounts of food that Mark chooses on a regular basis. The trainer at the center recommended a protein drink to help Mark build muscle mass. Answer the following questions and determine whether a protein drink is needed to supplement Mark's diet.

1. Determine Mark's protein needs based on the RDA (0.8 g/kg).

    a. Mark's estimated protein RDA: _____

    b. What are the maximum recommendations for protein intake for athletes? _____

    c. Calculate the maximum protein recommendation for Mark. _____

2. Compare Mark's protein intake with the recommended intake amounts.

    a. What is the difference between Mark's estimated protein needs as an athlete (from question 1) and the amount of protein in his current diet?
    _____

    b. Is his current protein intake inadequate, adequate, or excessive? _____

3. Mark takes his trainer's advice and goes to the supermarket to purchase a protein drink to add to his diet. Four products are available; they contain the following label information.

	Amino Fuel	Sugar-Free 90% Plus Protein	Dynamic Muscle Builder	Super Mega Mass 2000
Serving size	3 tbsp	3 tbsp	3 tbsp	¼ scoop
Kcal	104	110	103	104
Protein (g)	15	24	10	5

The trainer recommends that Mark add the supplement to his diet 2 times a day. Mark chooses Dynamic Muscle Builder.

    a. How much protein would be added to Mark's diet daily from 2 servings of the supplement alone? _____

    b. How much total protein would Mark now consume in 1 day? _____

    c. What is the difference between Mark's estimated protein needs as an athlete and his total protein intake with the supplement? _____

4. What is your conclusion—does Mark need the protein supplement? _____

Answers to Calculations

1a. Mark's estimated protein RDA: 70 kg × 0.8 g/kg = 56 g

1b. Maximum recommendation for protein intake for athletes = 1.7 g/kg

1c. Applied to Mark: 1.7 × 70 = 119 g

2a. Difference between Mark's diet and the maximum amount recommended for athletes: 125 − 119 = 6 g

2b. Mark's current diet is adequate.

3a. Two servings of protein supplement alone = 20 g of protein

3b. Mark's total protein consumption: 125 g + 20 g = 145 g protein

3c. Difference between Mark's estimated maximum protein needs as an athlete and total protein consumption: 145 g − 119 g = 26 g of protein

386   **PART 3**   Metabolism and Energy Balance

High-protein drinks, bars, and other products, which are often marketed to athletes, are unnecessary in most cases.

Although it has long been a popular belief among athletes that additional protein increases strength and enhances performance, sports nutritionists and exercise physiologists generally agree that consuming protein at levels above recommendations does not build bigger or stronger muscles.[14] Protein intakes above recommendations result in an increased use of amino acids for energy needs and has disadvantages, such as insufficient carbohydrate intake and increased urine production, which may interfere with body hydration. No advantages, such as an increase in muscle protein synthesis, are seen. Despite marketing claims, protein supplements are an expensive and unnecessary part of a fitness plan.

Any athlete not specifically on a low-calorie regimen can easily meet protein recommendations simply by eating a variety of foods (see Table 11-6). To illustrate, a 116 lb (53 kg) woman performing endurance activity can meet daily protein needs of 64 g (53 × 1.2) by eating a 3 oz chicken breast, a small hamburger (3 oz), and 2 glasses of milk. Similarly, a 170 lb (77 kg) man wanting to gain muscle mass through strength training needs to consume just 6 oz of chicken, ½ cup of cooked beans, 6 oz of canned tuna, and 3 glasses of milk to achieve an intake of 130 g of protein (77 × 1.7) in a day. Plus, for both athletes, these calculations do not include the protein they will get from the grains they eat. As you can see, simply by meeting their energy needs, many athletes consume much more protein than is required.

Vitamin and Mineral Needs

Vitamin and mineral needs are the same or slightly higher for athletes, compared with those of sedentary adults. Still, because athletes usually have such high energy intakes, they tend to consume plenty of vitamins and minerals. An exception is athletes consuming low-calorie diets (about 1200 kcal or less), such as some female athletes participating in events in which maintaining a low body weight is crucial. These diets may not meet B-vitamin and other micronutrient needs.[15] To meet vitamin and mineral needs, athletes consuming low-calorie diets and vegetarian athletes should consume fortified foods, such as ready-to-eat breakfast cereals, or a balanced multivitamin and mineral supplement.

Iron Deficiency and Impaired Performance

Lean muscle mass builds gradually. The average amount of muscle gained in a week using resistance exercise and recommended protein intakes (see Table 11-7) is about 0.20 to 0.35 lb for women and 0.4 to 0.7 lb for men.[27, 28]

Because iron is involved in red blood cell production, oxygen transport, and energy production, a deficiency of this mineral can noticeably detract from optimal athletic performance.[16] The potential causes for iron deficiency in athletes vary. As in the general population, female athletes are most susceptible to low iron status due to monthly menstrual losses. Special diets followed by athletes, such as low-energy and vegetarian (especially vegan) diets, are likely to be low in iron. Distance runners should pay special attention to iron intake because their intense workouts may lead to gastrointestinal bleeding.

Another concern is sports anemia, which occurs because exercise causes blood plasma volume to expand, particularly at the start of a training regimen before the synthesis of red blood cells increases. This expansion results in dilution of the blood. In sports anemia, even if iron stores are adequate, blood iron tests may appear low. Sports anemia is not detrimental to performance, but it is hard to differentiate between sports anemia and true anemia.

True anemia, noted as a reduced blood hemoglobin and hematocrit levels (see Chapter 15), may affect up to about 15% of male and 30% of female athletes. It is a good idea, especially for women athletes, to have their iron status checked at the beginning of a training season and at least once during midseason, as well as to monitor their dietary iron intake. Once depleted, iron stores can take months to replenish. For this reason, athletes must be especially careful to meet their iron needs.

Any blood test indicating low iron status—sports anemia or not—is cause for follow-up. For some athletes, the use of iron supplements may be advisable. However, the indiscriminate use of iron supplements is not advised because toxic effects are possible. It is important that physicians investigate the cause of the deficiency because iron deficiency can be caused by blood loss. If caught early, serious medical conditions often can be treated or prevented.

Calcium Intake and the Female Athlete Triad

Athletes, especially women trying to maintain a lean profile, can have marginal or low intakes of dietary calcium if they restrict their intake of milk and other dairy products. This practice compromises optimal bone health. Of still greater concern are women athletes who suffer from the female athlete triad, consisting of 3 conditions: menstrual disturbances/amenorrhea, energy deficit/disordered eating, and bone loss/osteoporosis.[17]

Research has clearly documented the importance of regular menstruation to maintain bone mineral density. Disturbing reports show that female athletes who do not menstruate regularly have far less dense spinal bones than both nonathletes and female athletes who menstruate regularly. These female athletes are at increased risk of bone fractures during training and competition. If irregular menstrual cycles persist, severe bone loss, much of which is not reversible, and osteoporosis can result.[18] This combination of risks outweighs the benefits of weight-bearing exercise for bone density.

Women with symptoms of the female athlete triad are best treated by a team that includes a physician, a registered dietitian, a psychologist, and an athletic trainer. The primary goals of treatment are to control and manage the athlete's diet, to restore normal hormone levels and menstruation, and to monitor and treat any injuries or other medical complications. Treatment strategies to reach these goals may include a slight reduction (10 to 20%) in the amount of training and a higher energy intake for a 2 to 5% increase in weight. Some amenorrheic athletes who gain weight either by cutting back on training or by consuming more energy have a better chance of resuming normal menstrual activity. Most amenorrheic athletes fear weight gain and must be counseled that an increase in muscle weight can improve their stamina and performance. Extra calcium in the diet does not necessarily compensate for the effects of menstrual irregularities, but inadequate dietary calcium can make matters worse. Calcium supplementation should be implemented in all athletes presenting with amenorrhea.

► At one time in his career, long-distance runner Alberto Salazar experienced problems sleeping and performed poorly because of low iron intake and related iron deficiency anemia.

► Learn more about the nutrition and health needs of female athletes at www.femaleathletetriad.org.

> ## CRITICAL THINKING
>
> Joe is a wrestler who qualified for the 125 lb weight classification in the annual state high school competition. After a few matches, he began to feel dizzy and faint. He was disqualified because he was unable to continue the match. Later, the coach found out that Joe had spent 2 hours in the sauna before weighing in, which had made him dehydrated. What are the consequences of dehydration? What can you suggest as a safer alternative for weight loss?

> ### Knowledge Check
>
> 1. What is the primary source of energy for an exercising muscle?
> 2. What is glycogen loading?
> 3. How does iron deficiency anemia affect athletic performance?
> 4. What is the female athlete triad?

 ## 11.6 Fluid Needs for Active Individuals

Exercise can raise muscle temperature 15 to 20 times above resting muscle temperature—this heat can be dissipated through the evaporation of sweat from the skin. During prolonged exercise, sweat loss ranges from 3 to 8 cups (750–2000 ml) per hour. Sweat losses tend to be greatest during hot weather and in endurance sports or those that require athletes to wear heavy equipment (e.g., football). As little as a 2% weight loss through sweating puts athletes at risk of dehydration.

Active individuals need more fluids than those who are sedentary to replace fluid lost in sweat and, thereby, maintain blood volume and allow the body to regulate internal temperature normally.[10] Insufficient fluid

Marathon runners can lose 6 to 10% of their body weight during a race.

388   **PART 3**   Metabolism and Energy Balance

Gatorade, a rehydration fluid, was born when a football coach asked Dr. Robert Cade at the University of Florida why players didn't need to urinate during a game. Cade's research discovered that the players lost so much sweat and were so dehydrated that no fluid was left to form urine. Learn more at www.gatorade.com/history.

intake leads to dehydration, which causes a decline in endurance, strength, and overall performance and sets the stage for heat exhaustion, heat cramps, and potentially fatal heatstroke (Fig. 11-12).[19]

Heat exhaustion and heatstroke are on a continuum. **Heat exhaustion** is the first stage of heat-related illness caused by dehydration. Common symptoms of heat exhaustion include profuse sweating, headache, dizziness, nausea, vomiting, muscle weakness, visual disturbances, and flushing of the skin. A person with heat exhaustion should be taken to a cool environment immediately, and excess clothing should be removed. The body should be sponged with cool water. Fluid replacement, as tolerated, should be provided.[19] It is critical that the individual get immediate medical attention to prevent tissue damage and possible death.

Heat cramps are a frequent complication of heat exhaustion, but they may appear without other symptoms of dehydration. Heat cramps occur in skeletal muscles and consist of contractions lasting 1 to 3 minutes at a time. The cramp moves down the muscle and causes excruciating pain. It is important not to confuse heat cramps with other forms of muscle cramps, such as those caused by intestinal tract upset. Heat cramps usually occur in individuals who have experienced significant sweating from exercising for several hours in a hot climate and who have consumed a large volume of water without replacing sodium losses. The best way to prevent heat cramps is to exercise moderately at first, have adequate salt intake before engaging in long and strenuous activity in hot conditions, and avoid becoming dehydrated.[19]

heat exhaustion First stage of heat-related illness that occurs because of depletion of blood volume from fluid loss by the body. This depletion may increase body temperature and can lead to headache, dizziness, muscle weakness, visual disturbances, and other effects.

heat cramps Frequent complication of heat exhaustion. Cramps usually occur in individuals who have experienced large sweat losses from exercising for several hours in a hot climate and have consumed a large volume of water. The cramps occur in skeletal muscles and consist of contractions for 1 to 3 minutes at a time.

heatstroke Condition in which the internal body temperature reaches 104°F or higher. Blood circulation is greatly reduced. Nervous system damage may ensue, and death is likely. Sweating generally ceases, which causes the skin of individuals who suffer heatstroke to feel hot and dry.

Relative humidity (%)	Air temperature (°F)								
	70°	75°	80°	85°	90°	95°	100°	105°	110°
100	72°	80°	91°	108°					
90	71°	79°	88°	102°	122°				
80	71°	78°	86°	97°	113°	136°			
70	70°	77°	85°	93°	106°	124°	144°		
60	69°	76°	82°	90°	100°	114°	132°	149°	
50	70°	75°	81°	88°	96°	107°	120°	135°	150°
40	68°	74°	79°	86°	93°	101°	110°	123°	137°
30	67°	73°	78°	84°	90°	96°	104°	113°	123°
20	66°	72°	77°	82°	87°	93°	99°	105°	112°
10	65°	70°	75°	80°	85°	90°	95°	100°	105°
0	64°	69°	73°	78°	83°	87°	91°	95°	99°

Heat index	Heat disorders possible with prolonged exposure and/or physical activity
80°–89°	Fatigue
90°–104°	Sunstroke, heat cramps, and heat exhaustion
105°–129°	Sunstroke, heat cramps, or heat exhaustion likely and heatstroke possible
130° or higher	Heatstroke/sunstroke highly likely

NOTE: Direct sunshine increases the heat index by up to 15°F.

Figure 11-12 Heat index chart showing associated heat disorders.

Left unchecked, heat exhaustion can rapidly progress to **heatstroke.** Heatstroke can occur when the internal body temperature reaches 104°F or higher. Exertional heatstroke results from high blood flow to exercising muscles, which overloads the body's cooling capacity. Symptoms include nausea, confusion, irritability, poor coordination, seizures, hot and dry skin, rapid heart rate, vomiting, diarrhea, and coma. If heatstroke is left untreated, circulatory collapse, nervous system damage, and death are likely. The death rate from heatstroke is approximately 10%.[19]

For heatstroke victims, cooling the skin with ice packs or cold water is the usually recommended immediate treatment until medical help can be summoned. To decrease the risk of developing heatstroke, athletes should watch for rapid changes in body weight (2% or more), replace lost fluids and sodium, and avoid exercising in extremely hot, humid conditions.

Fluid Intake and Replacement Strategies

Paying attention to fluid intake before exercising can help ensure that athletes begin with optimal fluid levels. During exercise, the recommended fluid status goal is a loss of no more than 2% of body weight, especially in hot weather. Athletes should first calculate 2% of their body weight and then by trial and error determine how much fluid they must drink to avoid losing more than this amount of weight during exercise. This determination is most accurate if an athlete is weighed before and after a typical workout. For every pound (½ kg) lost, 3 cups (about ¾ liter) of fluid should be consumed during or immediately after exercise. If weight change can't be monitored, urine color is another measure of hydration status—it should be no darker than the color of lemonade (Fig. 11-13).[1]

Thirst is a late sign of dehydration and, so, is not a reliable indicator of an athlete's need to replace fluid during exercise. An athlete who drinks only when thirsty is likely to take 48 hours to replenish fluid loss. After several days of training, an athlete relying on thirst as an indicator can build up a fluid debt that will impair performance.

Fluid intake during exercise, when possible, can help minimize fluid loss and a drop in body weight. Drinking fluids during practice is a good idea, even when sweating can go unnoticed, such as when swimming or during the winter.[10] However, fluid replacement mostly has to take place after exercise because it is difficult to consume enough fluid during exercise to prevent weight loss.

The following guidelines can meet most athletes' fluid needs.[12]

Before Exercise
- Freely drink beverages (e.g., sports drinks, water, diluted fruit juice) during the 24-hour period before an event, even if not thirsty.
- Drink 2 to 3 cups of fluid (500 to 750 ml) 2 to 3 hours before exercise. This allows time for both adequate hydration and the excretion of excess fluid.
- Drink 1 to 1.5 cups (250 to 375 ml) of fluid 10 to 15 minutes prior to the exercise or competition, especially if it is a long event.

During Exercise
- Drink 1 to 1.5 cups (250 to 375 ml) of fluid every 10 to 15 minutes.
- Fluids that are flavored and cooler than the environmental temperature promote fluid replacement.[20]
- Drink enough fluids to maintain weight during the exercise bout.
- If exercise lasts more than 1 hour, fluid replacement beverages should contain 4 to 8% carbohydrates to maintain blood glucose levels. Sodium also should be included in the beverage in amounts of 0.5 to 0.7 gram of sodium per liter of water to replace sodium lost in sweat.

After Exercise
- Drink 3 cups of fluid for each pound lost during exercise.
- Restore weight before the next exercise period.

▶ Sufficient fluid intake is important at any age, but it is particularly critical for young children participating in activities such as youth soccer, T-ball, and basketball. That's because, for any given level of dehydration, children's core body temperatures rise faster than those of adults. Children who participate in sports activities must be taught to prevent dehydration by drinking above and beyond thirst and drinking at frequent intervals—for example, every 20 minutes.[21]

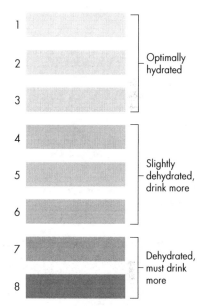

1

2   Optimally
      hydrated

3

4

5   Slightly
      dehydrated,
      drink more

6

7   Dehydrated,
      must drink
8   more

Figure 11-13 Urine color chart.

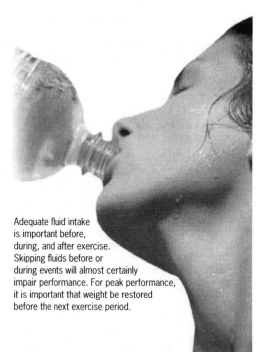

Adequate fluid intake is important before, during, and after exercise. Skipping fluids before or during events will almost certainly impair performance. For peak performance, it is important that weight be restored before the next exercise period.

Water Intoxication

In athletes, water intoxication is most often caused by overdrinking before, during, or after exercise without also replacing sodium losses. To prevent water intoxication, athletes should drink beverages containing sodium and should consume enough fluid during exercise to minimize loss of body weight (i.e., to avoid significant dehydration), but they should avoid overdrinking. Sports drinks containing at least 100 mg of sodium per 8-ounce serving have been shown to help maintain blood sodium level better than plain water.[22]

Sports Drinks

It was once thought that, if physical activity lasted less than an hour, water was the best choice for fluid replacement. However, researchers are finding that using a sports drink during high-intensity stop-and-go sports, such as basketball, volleyball, and sprint cycling, can delay fatigue and maintain hydration.[23] Athletes of all ages who consume only water as a fluid replacement, even for short-term exercise, risk diluting the blood (plasma sodium, in specific) and increasing their urine output, thus shutting off the drive to drink and becoming dehydrated.

When exercise extends beyond 60 minutes, a sports drink becomes even more important. The use of sports drinks during these longer bouts of exercise—even more so in hot weather—can offer several advantages over water alone (Fig. 11-14):

- The carbohydrates in sports drinks supply glucose to muscles as they become depleted of glycogen, thus enhancing performance.
- The electrolytes in sports drinks help maintain blood volume, enhance the absorption of water and carbohydrates from the intestines, and stimulate thirst.

Beverages containing alcohol should be avoided because they increase urine output and reduce fluid retention. In addition, high intakes of caffeine (greater than 500 mg per day, or the amount in 4 to 5 cups of brewed coffee) can increase urine output. Carbonated beverages also should be avoided, as they reduce the desire to consume fluids because the carbonation leads to feelings of stomach fullness. Drinks with a sugar content above 10%, such as soft drinks or fruit juices, take longer to absorb, less efficiently contribute to hydration, and are not recommended.

Overall, the American College of Sports Medicine suggests that the consumption of beverages containing electrolytes and carbohydrates (sports drinks) can provide benefits to athletes over water alone, especially when athletes have not consumed a pre-exercise meal or are participating in intense exercise, 2-a-day training, tournament play, or back-to-back competition.[12, 24] If athletes have not consumed a sports drink and want to try one, they can experiment with them during practice before using them during competition.

Figure 11-14 Sports drinks for fluid and electrolyte replacement typically contain simple carbohydrates plus sodium and potassium. The various sugars in this product total 14 g per 1-cup (240 ml) serving. In percentage terms based on weight, the sugar content is about 6% ([14 g sugar per serving / 240 g per serving] × 100 = 5.8%). (*Note:* 1 ml of water weighs 1 g.) Sports drinks typically contain about 6 to 8% sugar. This provides ample glucose and other monosaccharides to aid in fueling working muscles, and it is well tolerated. Sports drinks containing 0.5 to 0.7 g/L of sodium and 0.8 to 2.0 g/L of potassium are recommended for athletes.[12]

Knowledge Check

1. What are the symptoms of heat exhaustion?
2. What are the symptoms of heatstroke?
3. How much fluid should an athlete drink after exercise?
4. How should athletes determine if they are dehydrated?
5. When would you recommend a sports drink over water?

11.7 Food and Fluid Intake before, during, and after Exercise

The composition of food and fluids consumed before, during, and after athletic events or exercise training sessions can affect performance and the speed with which the athlete recovers from the exercise bout. Careful planning is needed to ensure that food intake meets the athlete's needs.

Pre-Exercise Meal

The pre-event or pre-exercise training meal keeps the athlete from feeling hungry before and during the exercise bout, and it maintains optimal levels of blood glucose for the exercising muscles. A pre-exercise meal has been shown to improve performance, compared with exercising in a fasted state. Athletes who train early in the morning before eating or drinking risk developing low liver glycogen stores, which can impair performance, particularly if the exercise regimen involves endurance training.

Allowing for personal preferences and psychological factors, the pre-exercise meal should be high in carbohydrate, nongreasy, non-gas producing, and readily digested. Recall that eating carbohydrate before exercise can help restore suboptimal liver glycogen stores, which may be called on during prolonged training and high-intensity competition. Fat in pre-exercise meals should be limited because it delays stomach-emptying time and takes longer to digest.

A meal eaten 3.5 to 4 hours before exercising can have as much as 4 g of carbohydrate per kg of body weight and 26% of the calories from fat. To avoid indigestion, nausea, vomiting, and gastrointestinal distress, the carbohydrate and fat content of the meal should be reduced the closer the meal is to the exercise time (Table 11-8). For example, 1 hour before exercising, the athlete should consume only 1 g carbohydrate/kg body weight.[1] Likewise, fat in meals eaten closer to exercise start time should provide less than 26% of calories. Allowing time for partial digestion and absorption provides for a final addition to muscle glycogen, additional blood sugar, and relatively complete emptying of the stomach.

Commercial liquid formulas providing a high-carbohydrate meal are popular with athletes because they leave the stomach rapidly. Other appropriate pregame meals are toast with jelly, a baked potato, spaghetti with tomato sauce, cereal with skim milk, and low-fat yogurt with fruit-sugar flavorings (Table 11-9).

In addition to food, recall that, within 10 to 15 minutes of a long event, athletes should drink 8 to 12 oz of water or other fluid. This prehydration allows for maximal absorption of fluid without urination. After exercise begins, the kidney slows down urine production to compensate for water losses.

Table 11-8 Rule of Thumb for Approximate Pre-Event Carbohydrate Intake

Hours Before	Grams per Kilogram Body Weight	For a 70 kg Person
1	1	70
2	2	140
3	3	210
4	4	280

Table 11-9 Convenient Pre-Event Meals

Breakfast Options

Cornflakes, ¾ cup Reduced-fat milk, 1 cup Blueberry muffin, 1 Orange juice, 4 oz		450 kcal 82% carbohydrate (92 g)
Low-fat fruit yogurt, 1 cup Plain bagel, ½ Apple juice, 4 oz Peanut butter (for bagel), 1 tbsp		482 kcal 68% carbohydrate (84 g)
Whole-wheat toast, 1 slice Jam, 1 tsp Apple, 1 large Reduced-fat milk, 1 cup Oatmeal, ½ cup (with reduced-fat milk, ½ cup)		507 kcal 73% carbohydrate (98 g)

Lunch or Dinner Options

Chili with beans, 8 oz Baked potato with sour cream and chives Chocolate milk shake, 9 oz		900 kcal 65% carbohydrate (150 g)
Spaghetti noodles, 2 cups Spaghetti sauce, 1 cup Reduced-fat milk, 1½ cups Green beans, 1 cup		761 kcal 66% carbohydrate (129 g)
Orange, 1 large Reduced-fat milk, 1½ cups Chicken noodle soup, 1 cup Saltine crackers, 12 Buttered beans, 1 cup Corn, 1 cup Angelfood cake, 1 slice		829 kcal 70% carbohydrate (160 g)

The rule of thumb when timing preactivity meals is to allow 4 hours for a big meal (about 1200 kcal), 3 hours for a moderate meal (about 800 to 900 kcal), 2 hours for a light meal (about 400 to 600 kcal), and an hour or less for a snack (about 300 kcal).

392 **PART 3** Metabolism and Energy Balance

Elite athletes, such as Olympic beach volleyball gold medal winner Kerri Walsh, know that modifying their diet and training regimens to match the specific needs of their sports is key to optimum performance. Replenishing carbohydrates and fluids is especially important when training.

Fueling during Exercise

For sporting events that are longer than 60 minutes, consuming carbohydrate during activity can improve athletic performance because prolonged exercise depletes muscle glycogen stores, and low levels of blood glucose lead to both physical and mental fatigue.[10, 25] Recall that, when the supply of energy from carbohydrates runs low, athletes often complain of "hitting the wall," the point at which maintaining a competitive pace seems impossible. To avoid this situation, a general guideline for endurance events is to consume 30 to 60 g of carbohydrate per hour; however, an athlete should experiment during training sessions to establish the level that leads to optimal performance.[10]

Sports drinks that are 6 to 8% carbohydrate can provide fuel for endurance events. They supply the necessary fluid, electrolytes, and carbohydrate to keep athletes performing at their best. An alternative to sports drinks are carbohydrate gels (e.g., PowerGel™, Prime™, and Clif Shot®) and energy bars (e.g., PowerBar®). Gels contain about 25 g of carbohydrate per serving, and popular energy bars range from 2 to 45 g of carbohydrate per serving. Sports drinks, by comparison, contain about 14 g of carbohydrate per 8 oz serving. Overall, choose a bar with about 40 g of carbohydrate and no more than 10 g of protein, 4 g of fat, and 5 g of fiber. The bars also are typically fortified with vitamins and minerals, often to 100% of the Daily Values. As such, these bars can be seen as a convenient, although somewhat expensive, source of nutrients. If the athlete prefers solid sources of carbohydrate, fig cookies, gummy bears, and jellybeans yield a quick source of glucose at a much lower cost. However, any carbohydrate-containing food, including energy bars and gels, must be accompanied by fluid to ensure adequate hydration.[1]

Recovery Meals

After strenuous exercise, recovery meals promote protein synthesis and reloading of muscles with glycogen. Optimal recovery depends on the quantity and timing of nutrient intake.[12] Glycogen resynthesis is greatest immediately after exercise because the muscles are very insulin sensitive.[1] Thus, consuming 1 to 1.5 g of carbohydrate per kg of body weight within 30 minutes after exercise and at 2-hour intervals for up to 6 hours helps reload muscles with glycogen for the next day's exercise (Table 11-10). High-glycemic-load carbohydrates

Table 11-10 Sample Postexercise Meals for Rapid Muscle Glycogen Replacement

Option 1

Bagel, 1 regular
Peanut butter, smooth, 2 tbsp
Fat-free milk, 8 oz
Banana, 1 medium
Chocolate beverage powder, 1 tbsp
600 kcal, 87 g carbohydrate, 23 g protein, 18 g fat

Option 2

Carnation® Instant Breakfast, 1 packet
Fat-free milk, 8 oz
Banana, 1 medium
Peanut butter, 1 tbsp
Blend until smooth.
438 kcal, 70 g carbohydrate, 17 g protein, 10 g fat

Option 3

Gatorade® Recovery drink (16.9 oz)
130 kcal, 14 g carbohydrate, 16 g protein

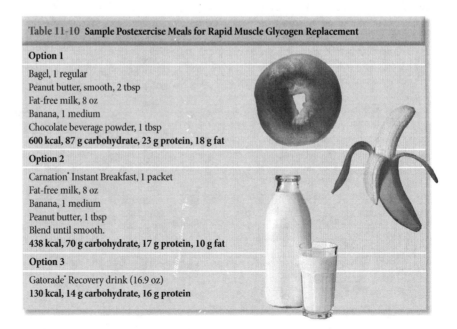

GL🌐BAL PERSPECTIVE

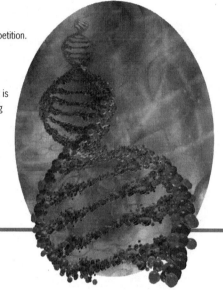

Gene Doping and the Wide World of Sports

In their quest for excellence, athletes are constantly looking for ways to gain an edge over the competition. Some of the methods used, such as healthy eating and rigorous training programs, are acceptable methods for becoming the best athlete possible. However, other substances and methods, such as using anabolic steroids or blood doping, are neither appropriate nor permitted by the International Olympic Committee or the national governing bodies. One of the newest inappropriate methods that is considered an impending threat to the world of sports is called "gene doping"—the practice of using gene therapy to artificially enhance athletic performance.

Gene therapy can be used to alter a person's DNA to fight deadly diseases, such as cancer, and counteract genetic disorders and hereditary diseases. The same techniques used to fight diseases could be used to boost an athlete's competitive capabilities.[29] Thus, scientists have developed tests that use blood samples to detect whether an athlete's DNA has been altered using gene doping techniques.[30] The tests are undergoing scientific validation and could be ready for widespread use by the next Olympic games.

especially contribute to glycogen synthesis (see Table 5-7 in Chapter 5). Athletes can consume a simple sugar candy, a sugared soft drink, fruit or fruit juice, or a sports or recovery drink right after training. Later, bread, mashed potatoes, and rice can contribute additional carbohydrates during a meal. Eating a small amount of protein (10 to 20 g) along with carbohydrate can stimulate muscle repair and protein synthesis during recovery from exercise. For a 154 lb (70 kg) athlete, the amount of carbohydrate and protein needed for recovery corresponds to about 70 g of carbohydrate and 15 g of protein, the amount found in 1 bagel and 16 ounces of Gatorade® Recovery beverage or a turkey sandwich with 1 cup of fruit-flavored yogurt.

In summary, the following are key factors for achieving the most rapid recovery of muscle glycogen after exercise.

- The availability of adequate carbohydrate
- The ingestion of carbohydrate as soon as possible after the completion of exercise
- The selection of high-glycemic-load carbohydrates

Fluid and electrolyte intake is also an essential component of an athlete's recovery diet.[12, 24] Recall that replenishing body fluids as quickly as possible is especially important if more than one workout a day is performed or if the environment is hot and humid. If food and fluid intake is sufficient to restore weight loss, it generally also will supply enough electrolytes to meet needs during recovery from endurance activities.

▶ Why hasn't fat been mentioned as a way to improve athletic performance during an endurance event? Although it is true that fat is used along with carbohydrate as fuel during prolonged aerobic activity, the processes of digestion, absorption, and metabolism of fat are relatively slow. Therefore, the consumption of fat during activity is not likely to translate into better athletic performance.

▶ For more information on sports nutrition, visit the Gatorade Sport Science Institute web page (www.gssiweb.com). For more information on sports medicine, visit www.physsportsmed .com. This home page of the *Physician and Sports Medicine* journal details current issues in sports medicine, including injury prevention, nutrition, and exercise. Also helpful are the web pages of the American College of Sports Medicine (www.acsm.org), Centers for Disease Control and Prevention (www.cdc.gov/nccdphp/ dnpa), and American Council on Exercise (www.acefitness.org).

Knowledge Check

1. What is the purpose of the pre-exercise meal?
2. What is the primary nutrient that should be consumed in the pre-exercise meal?
3. How important is timing in pre-exercise and recovery meals?
4. What effect does glycemic index have on the recovery meal?

11.8 Ergogenic Aids to Enhance Athletic Performance

Today's athletes are as likely as their predecessors to seek ways to improve performance. Most don't want to miss out on any advantage, whether real or perceived, that might give them the winning edge. As a result, many experiment with diet composition, supplements, and other aids in hopes of gaining an ergogenic (work-producing) benefit. An **ergogenic aid** is a nutritional, psychological, pharmacological, mechanical, or physiological substance or treatment intended to improve exercise performance. Most of these aids, such as artichoke hearts, bee pollen, dried adrenal glands from cattle, seaweed, freeze-dried liver flakes, gelatin, and ginseng, are ineffective. In fact, scientific support for ergogenic effectiveness exists for only a few dietary substances: sufficient water and electrolytes; abundant carbohydrates; a healthy, varied diet; and caffeine.[1, 26] Protein and amino acid supplements are not among those aids because athletes can easily meet protein needs from foods, as Table 11-6 demonstrates. Nutrient supplements should be used only to meet specific dietary shortcomings, such as inadequate iron intake.

As summarized in Table 11-11, no scientific evidence supports the effectiveness of many substances touted as performance-enhancing aids. Many are useless; some are dangerous. The risk-benefit ratio of any ergogenic aid merits careful evaluation before use.[1] Athletes should be skeptical of any substance until its ergogenic effect is scientifically verified. The FDA has a limited ability to regulate dietary supplements (see Chapter 1), and the manufacturing processes for dietary supplements are not as tightly regulated as they are for medications. As a result, some supplements do not contain the substance and/or the amount listed on the label and may contain substances that will cause athletes to test positive for various banned substances. Even substances that have been supported by systematic scientific studies should be used with caution because the conditions under which they were tested may not match those of the intended use. Finally, rather than waiting for a magic bullet to enhance performance, athletes should concentrate their efforts on improving their training routines and sport techniques while consuming healthy diets.

ergogenic aid Substance or treatment intended to directly improve exercise performance.

Table 11-11   Evaluation of Popular Ergogenic Aids

Substance/Practice	Rationale for Use	Reality
Useful in Some Circumstances		
Creatine	Increase phosphocreatine (PCr) in muscles to keep ATP concentration high	Use of 20 g per day for 5 to 6 days and then a maintenance dose of 2 g per day may improve performance in athletes who undertake repeated bursts of activity, such as in sprinting and weight lifting. Vegetarian athletes may especially show benefits because creatine is low or nonexistent in their diets. Some of the muscle weight gain noted with use results from water contained in muscles. Endurance athletes do not benefit from use. Little is known about the safety of long-term creatine use. Continual use of high doses has led to kidney damage in a few cases. Cost: $25 to $65 per month.
Sodium bicarbonate (baking soda)	Counter lactic acid buildup	Partially effective in some circumstances in which lactate is rapidly produced, such as wrestling, but induces nausea and diarrhea. The dose used is 300 mg/kg, given 1 to 3 hours before exercise. Cost: nil.
Caffeine	Stimulate nervous system, heighten sense of awareness, and may enhance nerve conduction	Drinking 2 to 3 5-ounce cups of coffee (3–9 milligrams of caffeine per kg of body weight) about 1 hour before events lasting about 5 minutes or longer is useful for some athletes; benefits are less apparent in those who habitually consume caffeine. Intakes of more than about 600 milligrams (6 to 8 cups of coffee) elicits a urine concentration illegal under NCAA rules (greater than 15 mg per ml). Possible side effects are increased blood pressure, increased heart rate, intestinal distress, and insomnia. Cost: $0.08 per 300 mg.

Table 11-11 Continued

Substance/Practice	Rationale for Use	Reality
Possibly Useful, Still under Study		
Beta-hydroxy-beta methylbutyric acid (HMB)	Decrease protein catabolism, causing a net growth-promoting effect	Research in livestock and humans suggests that supplementation with this substance may increase muscle mass. Still, safety and effectiveness of long-term HMB use in humans are unknown. Cost: $100 per month.
Glutamine (an amino acid)	Enhance immune function, preserve lean body mass	Study results are mixed and difficult to draw a conclusion at this time. Long-term studies are lacking. Protein foods are a rich source of glutamine. Cost: $10 to $20 per month for 1 to 2 g per day.
Branched-chain amino acids (BCAA) (leucine, isoleucine, valine)	Important energy source, especially when carbohydrate stores are depleted	Supplementation of BCAA (10 to 30 g/day) during exercise can increase BCAA in the blood when levels are low due to exercise. However, supplemental BCAA have not been shown to delay fatigue or improve endurance performance. Carbohydrate feeding, by delaying use of BCAA as fuel, may negate the need for BCAA supplementation. Protein-rich foods (especially dairy proteins) are rich in BCAA. Cost: $20 per month.
Glucosamine	Aid in repair of joint damage	Most of the positive evidence is for repair of knee damage in older people, but a large study showed no clear benefit for such use. May be of use to athletes experiencing knee damage, but reliable evidence is lacking. Cost: $30 per month.
Dangerous or Illegal Substances/Practices		
Anabolic steroids (and related substances, such as androstenedione and tetrahydrogestrinone [THG])	Increase muscle mass and strength	Although effective for increasing protein synthesis, anabolic steroids are illegal in in U.S. unless prescribed by a physician. They have numerous potential side effects, such as premature closure of growth plates in bones (possibly limiting potential height of a teenage athlete), bloody cysts in the liver, increased risk of cardiovascular disease, increased blood pressure, and reproductive dysfunction. Possible psychological consequences include increased aggressiveness, drug dependence (addiction), withdrawal symptoms (e.g., depression), sleep disturbances, and mood swings (known as "roid rage"). Use of needles for injectable forms adds further health risk. They are banned by the International Olympic Committee, National Football League, Major League Baseball, and other sports organizations.
Growth hormone	Increase muscle mass	It may increase height; at critical ages, it also may cause uncontrolled growth of the heart and other internal organs and even death; it is potentially dangerous and requires careful monitoring by a physician. The use of needles for injections adds further health risk. It is banned by the International Olympic Committee.
Blood doping	Enhance aerobic capacity by injecting red blood cells harvested previously from the athlete, or alternately the athlete may use the hormone erythropoietin (Epogen˚) to increase red blood cell number	It may offer aerobic benefit, but very serious health consequences are possible, including thickening of the blood, which puts extra strain on the heart. It is an illegal practice under Olympic guidelines.
Gamma hydroxybutyric acid (GHB)	Promoted as a steroid alternative for body building	The FDA has never approved it for sale as a medical product; it is illegal to produce or sell GHB in the U.S. GHB-related symptoms include vomiting, dizziness, tremors, and seizures. Many victims require hospitalization, and some have died. Clandestine laboratories produce virtually all the chemical accounting for GHB abuse. The FDA is working with the U.S. Attorney's office to arrest, indict, and convict individuals responsible for the illegal operations.

Substances that are promoted to athletes but have yet to show any clear ergogenic effects include pyruvic acid (pyruvate), glycerol, ribose, chromium, coenzyme Q-10, medium-chain triglycerides, L-carnitine, conjugated linoleic acid (CLA), bovine colostrum, insulin, and amino acids not already mentioned in this section. Any use of these products is not recommended at this time. Some of these substances are defined in the glossary.

The National Collegiate Athletic Association's Committee on Competitive Safeguards and Medical Aspects of Sports has developed lists of supplements that are permissible and nonpermissible for athletic departments to dispense. The following are some key examples.

Permissible	*Nonpermissible*
Vitamins and minerals	Amino acids
Energy bars (if no more than 30% protein)	Creatine
	Glycerol
Sports drinks	Beta-hydroxy-beta methylbutyric acid (HMB)
Meal replacement drinks (Ensure Plus®, Boost®)	L-carnitine
	Protein powders

Knowledge Check

1. What is an ergogenic aid?
2. When should supplements be used?
3. Should all athletes take a supplement?

CASE STUDY FOLLOW-UP

Jake decided to see the sports dietitian at his college. She asked him to keep a 3-day food record, so that she could analyze his diet. When they met to go over his diet, she told him that he was overconsuming protein and underconsuming carbohydrate. Jake told her he needed more protein due to his lifting, but the dietitian pointed out that he was consuming almost 300 g/day of protein. When the dietitian calculated his protein requirement using the recommended protein requirements for athletes, he actually needed 120 g/day. He was eating so much protein that he was not getting enough carbohydrate to fuel his workouts. To increase carbohydrate intake, they worked out a plan to add more whole-grain cereals for breakfast instead of the protein shake. He added rice, potatoes, or pasta and vegetables with his chicken for the evening meal and cut back his protein shake to once a day. A couple of weeks later, Jake's energy returned, he was lasting longer in the weight room, and he was lifting more weight.

Summary

11.1 The benefits of regular physical activity include enhanced heart function, improved balance, reduced risk of falling, better sleep habits, healthier body composition, and reduced injury to muscles, tendons, and joints. A gradual increase in regular physical activity is recommended for all healthy persons. A minimum plan includes 30 minutes of physical activity on most (or all) days; 60 to 90 minutes per day provides even more benefit, especially if weight control is an issue.

11.2 A good fitness program is one that meets a person's needs. To reach goals, fitness program planning should consider the mode, duration, frequency, intensity, and progression of exercise, as well as consistency and variety. Before starting a new fitness program, discuss program goals with a health-care provider. Also, assess and record baseline fitness scores. Most new exercise programs should start with short intervals of exercise at the lower end of the maximum heart rate

target zone and work up to a total of 30 minutes of activity incorporated into each day. To prepare and recover safely from an exercise session, warm-up and cooldown periods should be included.

11.3 At rest, muscle cells use mainly fat for fuel. For intense exercise of short duration, muscles use mostly phosphocreatine (PCr) for energy. During more sustained intense activity, muscle glycogen breaks down to lactic acid, providing a small amount of ATP. For endurance exercise, both fat and carbohydrate are used as fuels; carbohydrate is used increasingly as activity intensifies. Little protein is used to fuel muscles. Fuel sources for muscle cells can be estimated based on percent of VO_{2max}.

11.4 Physical activity has many effects on the body. The most pronounced effects are typically seen in the muscular, circulatory, and skeletal systems. The body contains 3 major types of muscle tissue: skeletal muscle, smooth muscle, and cardiac muscle. Skeletal muscle is composed of 3 main types of muscle fibers, which have distinct characteristics. Prolonged low-intensity exercise, such as a slow jog, uses mainly type I muscle fibers, so the predominant fuel is fat. As exercise intensity increases, type IIA and type IIX fibers are gradually recruited; in turn, the contribution of glucose as a fuel increases. Type IIA and type IIX fibers also are important for rapid movements, such as a jump shot in basketball. The relative proportions of the 3 fiber types throughout the muscles of the body vary from person to person and are constant throughout each person's life. With training, muscle strength becomes matched to the muscles' work demands. Muscles enlarge after being made to work repeatedly. Repeated aerobic exercise strengthens the heart and increases the number of capillaries in muscle tissue; as a result, oxygen can be delivered more easily to muscle cells. Another adaptation that occurs with exercise is increased bone density.

11.5 Athletic training and genetic makeup are very important determinants of athletic performance. Monitoring body weight is an easy way to assess the adequacy of calorie intake. Athletes should strive to maintain weight during competition and training. Athletes should obtain at least 60% of total energy needs from carbohydrates. Carbohydrate-loading regimens usually increase muscle glycogen stores 50 to 85% over typical conditions. Carbohydrate loading is for athletes who compete in continuous, intense aerobic events lasting more than 60 to 90 minutes. A fat intake of 15 to 25% of energy is generally recommended for athletes. Typical recommendations for protein intake for most athletes range from 1.2 to 1.7 g of protein/kg of body weight. The extra protein is needed for the repair of tissue and the synthesis of new muscle that results from training. Vitamin and mineral

needs are the same or slightly higher for athletes, compared with those of sedentary adults. The female athlete triad consists of 3 conditions: menstrual disorders, low energy availability, and low bone mineral density.

11.6 To maintain the body's ability to regulate internal temperature, athletes must consume sufficient fluids because dehydration leads to a decline in endurance, strength, and overall performance and sets the stage for heat exhaustion, heat cramps, and potentially fatal heatstroke. During exercise, the recommended fluid status goal is a loss of no more than 2% of body weight. To prevent water intoxication, athletes should drink beverages containing sodium and should consume enough fluid during exercise to minimize the loss of body weight. Most experts recommend drinking sports drinks with electrolytes instead of water.

11.7 The composition of food eaten before, during, and after athletic events or exercise training sessions can affect performance and the speed with which the athlete recovers from the exercise bout. Pre-exercise training meals keep the athlete from feeling hungry before and during the exercise bout and maintain optimal levels of blood glucose for the exercising muscles. The pre-exercise meal should be high in carbohydrate, low in fat, and readily digested. For sporting events lasting more than 60 minutes, consuming carbohydrate during activity can improve athletic performance. Carbohydrate-rich foods and a small amount of protein should be consumed 30 minutes after exercise and again at 2-hour intervals for up to 6 hours.

11.8 An ergogenic aid is a nutritional, psychological, pharmacological, mechanical, or physiological substance or treatment intended to improve exercise performance. Most of these aids are ineffective.

Study Questions

1. The benefits of regular physical activity include _____.

   a. a reduced risk of falling
   b. better sleep habits
   c. healthier body composition
   d. all of the above

2. Which mode of exercise is defined as any activity that uses large muscle groups, can be maintained continuously, and is rhythmic in nature?

   a. aerobic
   b. resistance
   c. flexibility
   d. none of the above

3. The predominant fuels for the 50-meter sprint are _____.

   a. fat and protein
   b. carbohydrate and protein
   c. protein and phosphocreatine
   d. ATP and phosphocreatine

4. The predominant fuel for a 2-hour marathon is _____.

   a. protein
   b. fat
   c. carbohydrate
   d. water

398 **PART 3** Metabolism and Energy Balance

5. The amount of ATP stored in a muscle cell can keep a muscle active for about _____.

   a. 2 to 4 seconds
   b. 10 to 30 seconds
   c. 1 to 3 minutes
   d. 1 to 3 hours

6. There are 4 main types of muscle fibers.

   a. true
   b. false

7. Although genetics largely determines the proportion of muscle fiber type, training can develop muscle fibers within some limits.

   a. true
   b. false

8. Which of the following athletes would *not* benefit from carbohydrate loading?

   a. marathon runner
   b. long-distance cyclist
   c. triathlete
   d. football player

9. Athletes who are involved in endurance activities may need to consume _____ grams of carbohydrates per kilogram of body weight.

   a. 5 to 7
   b. 7 to 8
   c. up to 10
   d. 3 to 4

10. All athletes should consume at least 2.0 grams of protein/kg of body weight.

    a. true
    b. false

11. Iron deficiency can impair athletic performance.

    a. true
    b. false

12. What 3 factors are included in the female athlete triad?

    a. _____
    b. _____
    c. _____

13. Water intoxication is a condition that can occur when athletes drink too much _____.

    a. alcohol
    b. water
    c. sports drinks
    d. milk

14. Thirst is an accurate indicator of fluid needs.

    a. true
    b. false

15. Most ergogenic aids are effective and enhance athletic performance.

    a. true
    b. false

16. How does greater physical fitness contribute to greater overall health?

17. What is the difference between anaerobic and aerobic exercise? Explain why aerobic respiration is increased by regular exercise.

18. Describe how ATP is resupplied after initiation of exercise and at various times thereafter.

19. Describe the types of muscle fibers and the predominant fuel used by each.

20. List 5 nutrients of special interest to athletes and appropriate food sources of each.

21. What are some measures athletes can take to determine if fluid intake is adequate?

22. What advice would you give a friend planning to run a 5-kilometer race about food intake before, during, and after the event?

23. What advice would you give a friend about the general effectiveness of amino acid supplements?

Answer Key: 1-d; 2-a; 3-d; 4-b; 5-a; 6-b; 7-a; 8-d; 9-c; 10-b; 11-a; 12-menstrual disturbances/amenorrhea, energy deficit/disordered eating, bone loss/osteoporosis; 13-b; 14-b; 15-b; 16-refer to Section 11.1; 17-refer to Section 11.2; 18-refer to Section 11.3; 19-refer to Section 11.4; 20-refer to Section 11.5; 21-refer to Section 11.6; 22-refer to Section 11.7; 23-refer to Section 11.8

Websites

To learn more about the topics covered in this chapter, visit these websites.

American College of Sports Medicine

www.acsm.org

Sports and Cardiovascular and Wellness Nutritionists, a Practice Group of the Academy of Nutrition and Dietetics

www.scandpg.org

NIH Office of Dietary Supplements

ods.od.nih.gov

American Alliance for Health, Physical Education, Recreation, and Dance

www.aahperd.org

Gatorade Sport Science Institute

www.gssiweb.com

The Physician and Sports Medicine **Journal**

www.physsportsmed.com

Centers for Disease Control and Prevention

www.cdc.gov/nccdphp/dnpa

American Council on Exercise

www.acefitness.org

Physical Activity Guidelines for Americans

www.health.gov/paguidelines

References

1. Williams M. *Nutrition for health, fitness, and sport.* 9th ed. Boston: McGraw-Hill; 2010.

2. Bacon S and others. Effects of exercise, diet and weight loss on high blood pressure. *Sports Med.* 2004;34:307.

3. Dunsten D. Exercise and T2DM—move muscles more often. *Nature Rev Endocrin.* 2011;7:189.

4. Ross R and others. Exercise induced reduction in obesity and insulin resistance in women: A randomized control trial. *Obesity Res.* 2004;12:789.

5. Metkus TS and others. Exercise prescription and primary prevention of cardiovascular disease. *Circ.* 2010;121:2601.

6. Bailey CA, Brooke-Wavell K. Optimum frequency of exercise for bone health: Randomised controlled trial of a high-impact unilateral intervention. *Bone.* 2010;46:1043.

7. Chan B and others. Incident fall risk and physical activity and physical performance among older men: The osteoporotic fractures in men study. *Am J Epidemiol.* 2007;165:696.

8. Haskell W and others. Physical activity and public health: Update recommendation for adults from the American College of Sports Medicine and the American Heart Association. *Circ.* 2007;39:1081.

9. Hunter G. Physical activity, fitness, and health. In: Shils M and others, eds. *Modern nutrition in health and disease.* 10th ed. Philadelphia: Lippincott Williams & Wilkins; 2006.

10. Maughan RJ and Shirreffs SM. Nutrition for sports performance: issues and opportunities. *Proc Nutr Soc.* 2012;71:112.

11. Moore DR and others. Ingested protein dose response of muscle and albumin protein synthesis after resistance exercise in young men. *Am J Clin Nutr.* 2009;89:161.

12. Rodriguez NR and others. Position of the American Dietetic Association, Dietitians of Canada, and the American College of Sports Medicine: Nutrition and athletic performance. *J Am Diet Assoc.* 2009;109:509.

13. Sedlock DA. The latest on carbohydrate loading: A practical approach. *Curr Sports Med Rep.* 2008;7:209.

14. Betts J and others. Recovery of endurance running capacity effect of carbohydrate-protein mixtures. *Int J Sport Nutr Exerc Metab.* 2005;15:590.

15. Lukaski H. Vitamin and mineral status: Effects on physical performance. *Nutrition.* 2004;20:632.

16. Rodenberg RE, Gustafson S. Iron as an ergogenic aid: Ironclad evidence? *Curr Sports Med Rep.* 2007;6:258.

17. Deimel JF and Dunlap BJ. The female athlete triad. *Clin Sports Med.* 2012;31: 247.

18. Mendelsohn FA, Warren MP. Anorexia, bulimia, and the female athlete triad: Evaluation and management. *Endocrinol Metab Clin North Am.* 2010;39:155.

19. DeFranco MJ and others. Environmental issues for team physicians. *Am J Sports Med.* 2008;36:2226.

20. Burdon CA and others. Influence of beverage temperature on exercise performance in the heat: A systematic review. *Int J Sport Nutr Exerc Metab.* 2010;20:166.

21. AAP. Climatic heat stress and the exercising child and adolescent. *Pediatrics.* 2007;120:683.

22. Sterns RH and others. Treatment of hyponatremia. *Semin Nephrol.* 2009;29:282.

23. Davis J and others. Carbohydrate drinks delay fatigue during intermittent, high-intensity cycling in active men and women. *Int J Sport Nutr Exerc Metab.* 1997;7:261.

24. Shirreffs SM and Sawka MN. Fluid and electrolyte needs for training, competition and recovery. *J Sports Sci.* 2011; 29 suppl 1:S39.

25. Nybo L. CNS fatigue provoked by prolonged exercise in the heat. *Front Biosci.* 2010;2:779.

26. Foskett A and others. Caffeine enhances cognitive function and skill performance during simulated soccer activity. *Int J Sport Nutr Exerc Metab.* 2009;19:410.

27. Phillips SM and others. Body composition and strength changes in women with milk and resistance exercise. *Med Sci Sport Exerc.* 2010;42:1122.

28. Baer DJ and others. Whey protein but not soy protein supplementation alters body weight and composition in free-living overweight and obese adults. *J Nutr.* 2012;141:1489.

29. Beiter T and others. Direct and long-term detection of gene doping in conventional blood samples. *Gene Ther Advance Online.* 2010;Sept 2:1.

30. Lasne F and others. Genetic doping with erythropoietin cDNA in primate muscle is detectable. *Mol Ther.* 2004;10:409.